SOIL MECHANICS

UNIVERSITY SERIES IN CIVIL ENGINEERING
AND APPLIED MECHANICS

Edited by

S. F. BORG, Dr. Eng.
Professor and Head of Civil Engineering
Stevens Institute of Technology

ADVANCED STRUCTURAL ANALYSIS
By S. F. Borg and J. J. Gennaro

FUNDAMENTALS OF ENGINEERING ELASTICITY
By S. F. Borg

SOIL MECHANICS
By Alfreds R. Jumikis

Additional titles will be listed and announced as published.

SOIL MECHANICS

ALFREDS R. JUMIKIS, Dr. Eng. Sc.
Professor of Civil Engineering
Rutgers—The State University
New Brunswick, New Jersey

D. VAN NOSTRAND COMPANY, INC.
PRINCETON, NEW JERSEY

TORONTO   LONDON

NEW YORK

D. VAN NOSTRAND COMPANY, INC.
120 Alexander St., Princeton, New Jersey (*Principal office*)
24 West 40 Street, New York 18, New York

D. VAN NOSTRAND COMPANY, LTD.
358, Kensington High Street, London, W.14, England

D. VAN NOSTRAND COMPANY (Canada), LTD.
25 Hollinger Road, Toronto 16, Canada

———

———

Published simultaneously in Canada by
D. VAN NOSTRAND COMPANY (Canada), LTD.

———

PRINTED IN THE UNITED STATES OF AMERICA

PREFACE

The purpose of this book is to provide a clear-cut, contemporary and stimulating text in a convenient form for engineering students who are beginning the study of soil mechanics.

There are several good reasons why engineers study soils and why this subject is a requirement of the civil engineering curriculum.

1) to learn to understand and evaluate the properties of soil materials;
2) to apply the knowledge of soils in a practical way to the safe and economical design and construction of earthworks and the foundations of structures;
3) through research and experience to develop and advance the knowledge of soil mechanics, thus adding to the store of man's knowledge, and
4) to extend the knowledge to other branches of learning still to be developed.

The civil engineer, in pursuing his field of endeavor, has a two-fold responsibility: (1) the designing and building of stable structures, and (2) the safeguarding of the lives of the people using or passing by these structures. For these reasons, and also because soil is considered to be not only a foundation material (which supports structures), but a construction material as well (earth dams, highway and other fills, ingredients in mortars), engineers should have solid knowledge of the properties and behavior of soils.

From this short review one may see that there are fundamental soil engineering problems in earthworks and in highway and foundation engineering requiring solutions for safe and economical design of structures. It can also be inferred that the application of the knowledge of soil mechanics to earthworks, highway and foundation engineering is of great importance, particularly where large amounts of soil masses are to be moved, or highway fills and cuts are to be made. To illustrate the importance of soil mechanics to a civil engineer, the following parallel example can be drawn:

As in structural design the statics of a structure depend upon the knowledge of strength of materials, so does the design of foundations and earthworks depend upon the discipline of soil mechanics. Hence, it may be concluded that soil mechanics is a basic subject in the scientific education of civil engineers which forms the foundation of a civil engineering curriculum. The value and necessity of soil mechanics for training students is now generally recognized as fundamental and, therefore, has been introduced into the curricula of most institutions of higher technical learning.

Soil is made by nature. As a natural construction material, it possesses

v

a variety of physical properties, most of which are not constant. This tendency of soils to fluctuate in their physical properties is in contradistinction to the behavior of artificially manufactured materials, iron and steel, for example, the properties of which are relatively constant.

The physical properties of soil, depending upon the type of soil, can be more or less adversely affected by several factors, including the presence of moisture in it; the proximity of ground water; atmospheric water and flood waters, natural or artificial; and freezing and thawing. One of the difficulties with soil as a material is that its physical properties in the field may vary within a distance of a couple of feet, or sometimes even less. The influence of water on the performance of soil under load, or the effect of freezing temperatures on silty soil in a highway body, play paramount roles in the behavior of soil. In soil mechanics, moisture in soil is considered to be one of the principal governing factors affecting soil properties.

Water influences the bearing capacity of soil. It may transform a cohesive soil into a plastic state. A soil may swell; it may also shrink. Water is controlled in compacting highway fills; it affects the shear strength of a soil. Upon expulsion of water from the voids of a soil under a structural load, the structure may settle uniformly or differentially. Therefore, as in the manufacturing of portland cement concrete, for example, one of the most frequent operations in the program of soil testing is water control in soil, better known as the determination of the soil moisture content. Thus one can understand the popular saying that no foundation and the structure supported by it is better than the soil upon which the foundation rests. The diverse nature of soil is the most difficult problem with which a civil engineer is confronted.

No engineer, architect, builder, or owner planning to build the foundation of a structure, a highway, railway, waterway, or an airport runway can afford to ignore the problem of investigating the physical properties of soils encountered at the site and the possibility of changes in soil physical properties due to moisture during construction. Thorough investigation of soil properties is the best way to avoid failure of the "soil-structure" system and the exploitation, maintenance, legal, and financial troubles which may ensue. If the properties of soil are properly studied and the site explored, and the results of soil exploration correctly understood and intelligently applied to the design and construction of earthworks and structural foundations, failures usually can be avoided.

The material presented here was developed from the author's experience in teaching soil mechanics and subjects allied to it—highways, foundations, airports, hydraulic structures, fluid mechanics and engineering geology; from the performance, direction, and supervision of highway and soil mechanics research at several universities; and from his consulting work as well as from other sources. Also it grew out of the necessity for a simple source of information on soil mechanics for civil engineering students.

It is hoped that this volume on soil mechanics will give to the student not only the necessary knowledge, but that it will also become a source of satisfaction and enjoyment, as well as develop in the student an attitude which will enable him to attain confidence and competence in the solution of practical problems in soil mechanics.

ACKNOWLEDGMENTS

The author expresses his cordial thanks to all of those who contributed intellectually and materially, in words and in deeds, to the preparation of this manuscript for publication.

For his encouragement and heartening support and furtherance of this work the author expresses his appreciation to Dr. E. C. Easton, Dean, College of Engineering, Rutgers—The State University, New Brunswick, New Jersey.

Appreciation is also expressed to Professor J. J. Slade, Jr., Director of the Bureau of Engineering Research, Rutgers—The State University, for reviewing the mathematics as it pertains to the consolidation theory of clay.

It is also a pleasure to acknowledge the furtherance of the manuscript by Dr. M. L. Granstrom, Chairman of the Department of Civil Engineering, Rutgers—The State University, and to thank Dr. R. L. Handy, Professor of Civil Engineering, of the Engineering Experiment Station of the Iowa State University of Science and Technology, who reviewed thoroughly and in a very fair manner the entire manuscript, pointed out unclear passages, and made many valuable suggestions.

The author also takes the opportunity to express his gratitude to the Calm Foundation for Faculty Assistance at Rutgers University, which made a grant to the author to help in preparing a certain phase of the manuscript.

To the authors credited in the documentation of this book the writer owes a great deal, because some of their ideas and work helped in building up this work. It was possible to contribute to this book the chapter on frost action in soil, through the author's work in heading for several years the Joint Highway Research Project, a cooperative effort between Rutgers University and the New Jersey State Highway Department, and in studying soil moisture migration upon freezing for the past seven years (1955-1962) under two sizable grants given to the author by the National Science Foundation.

Some of the author's early studies on deformation in soil were made under Dr. O. K. Fröhlich in Vienna. These studies are now sponsored by the Bureau of Engineering Research, Rutgers—The State University.

The author is also most appreciative of the excellent library service at Rutgers University under the general direction of Dr. D. F. Cameron, University Librarian, and of the good offices of Mr. H. G. Kelly, Head of the Reference Department, and Miss Rose E. Sieber, Reference Librarian. Their efforts in procuring the many reference sources and books now out of print were valuable in preparing the historical part on soil mechanics in this book, as well as in permitting personal examination, checking and verification of facts in bona fide references of an original nature.

A separate word of thanks is directed also to my wife and son Andris for help with the organization and systematization of the manuscript, illustrations and photographs, and for assisting the author on his field trips and for taking some of the photographs, respectively.

The author also expresses his thanks to Mrs. Ruth Ahrens for her whole-hearted technical aid in reading and preparing the manuscript, and in examining the proofs.

The publisher has lived up to its best tradition, and the author's cordial thanks go to all concerned in the production of this book.

May this volume be found useful in providing the reader with necessary knowledge in the basic principles of soil mechanics.

ALFREDS R. JUMIKIS

March, 1962
New Brunswick, New Jersey

CONTENTS

PART IV   CONSOLIDATION OF SOIL AND SETTLEMENT OF
STRUCTURES

PART I

The Subject

Chapter 1

INTRODUCTION

1-1. Soil as a Construction Material. Soils can be considered as the oldest and the most complex of the construction materials used by engineers.

Unless it is built on hard rock, every structure, whether it is a building of any kind, a bridge, a fortification, a dam, a railroad, a type of pavement, an airport, or a hydraulic structure (harbors, quays, wharves, docks, bulkheads, piers, power stations, irrigation facilities) must be founded on soil. Therefore, the choice of an adequate foundation is one of the first problems to be considered in any construction project. Because most structures are supported by soil, the importance of soil as a foundation-supporting material as well as a construction material is of utmost significance. Hence it can be understood that the stability and function of a structure will largely depend upon the behavior of the soil upon which and/or of which it is built.

Because of the undeveloped state of soil mechanics as an engineering discipline several decades ago, or wrong assumptions which involved the use of soil, or even because of ignorance of the principles of soil mechanics, engineers have been faced, in the past, in various parts of the world with an increasing number of failures due to:

    1) unanticipated action of water,

    2) frost action in soils,

    3) unexpected settlements of soils,

    4) lateral displacement of soil (creeps and slides), or

    5) other unexpected performance of the soil.

Hundreds of miles of highway and airfield runway pavements have disintegrated because of the unpredicted performance of the soil due to excessive loads, or to change in soil moisture content, or to variable climatologic factors such as frost.

Many earth dams have collapsed because engineers were unable to ascertain with any accuracy the performance of remolded and compacted soil or the effect of the action of the existing water regime on the performance of soil. The collapse of tunnels, bridge piers and abutments, and the failure of many earth retaining structures and various waterfront and other hydraulic structures have been much too frequent because engineers were unable to evaluate satisfactorily how much pressure this soil would exert on these structures under various conditions, and what was the pressure distribution in soil underneath the contact areas of the bases of footings.

3

Differential settlements of the foundations under large engineering structures were directly responsible for having caused serious structural damage in some cases and, in others, have added materially to maintenance expenses. Earth slides and ruptures of slopes of cuts and fills, as well as supported banks, continually endanger the safety of buildings, bridges, highways, railroads, and canals in many regions of the world. It can be said that almost no year has passed without some great failure in foundation and earthwork engineering.

Figs. 1-1 to 1-5 illustrate the nature of failures of some engineering structures.

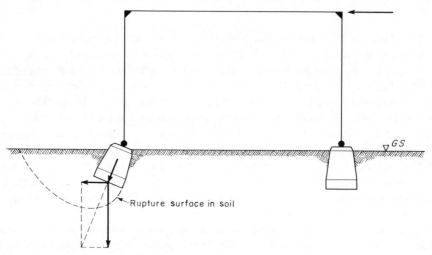

Rupture surface in soil

FIG. 1-1   A possible lateral expulsion of soil from underneath the base of footings of a two-hinged frame.

Fig. 1-1 shows a possible danger of lateral expulsion of soil from underneath the foundation of a two-hinged frame structure.

Fig. 1-2 illustrates the failure of a 1,000,000 bushel grain elevator, weighing 20,000 tons, at North Transcona, Manitoba, Canada, in 1914, due to a breaking in into the soil of "loose nature". The elevator consisted of 65 great circular silos, each 80 ft high. The silos were tied together by a reinforced mat foundation into a single unit. When the silos were first filled, they began to settle and tilt on one side, burying the low side of the structure to a depth of about 40 ft in the ground and leaning over at an angle of about 30° from the vertical. The silos were rolled back and successfully restored to an upright position. Altogether 70 piers, 6 ft in diameter, were sunk to bedrock to force the structure upright.[1,2,3,4]

When soil mechanics had provided the basis for computing the ultimate bearing capacity of soil, it was realized that the Transcona grain elevator failure afforded one of the best of the few opportunities for a full-scale check as well as a test of the validity of such computations.

A recent silo collapse was that of an 800,000 bushel grain elevator at Fargo, North Dakota,[5,6,7] on June 12, 1955. The collapse of the silo was thought to be due to a shear failure of the underlying varved clay.

FIG. 1-2 Failure of the Transcona Grain Elevator, Winnipeg, Manitoba, Canada. Courtesy of the Foundation Company, New York, N.Y.

FIG. 1-3 Rupture of slopes in the Panama Canal cuts. By permission of the National Academy of Sciences.

Extensive ruptures of slopes in the Panama Canal cuts are also often cited as examples of extensive soil failure,[8] Fig. 1-3, and the settlement of structures in Mexico City is attracting the close attention of civil engineers.[9]

Fig. 1-4 illustrates the rupture of a slope of the embankment of U.S. Route 101

FIG. 1-4   Rupture of slope of the embankment of U.S. Route 101 south of Scotia, California. Courtesy of California Division of Highways

south of Scotia, California. Note by the white center line that more than half of the roadway has slid down.

Fig. 1-5 shows a rupture of slope of the Delaware-Chesapeake Canal bank at the north pier of the Summit Bridge, Delaware. The bridge approach, made of soil, has been excavated and replaced by a light timber trestle. The pier was underpinned by H-piles. The embankment was dewatered by a permanent ground-water lowering system.

In the course of time engineers have learned that problems dealing with soils and foundations are very difficult and complex in comparison to those dealing with superstructures, which are capable of being treated mathematically. The physical and mechanical properties of the most frequently used materials of construction, such as wood, stone, brick, concrete, reinforced concrete, and steel are well known by the engineer. The allowable stresses have been determined. By means of proved theories, methods of computing the resistance of these materials have been developed. This, in turn, gives safer, more economical designs. Unexpected performance of one of these materials is quite rare.

On the contrary, soils used for supporting foundations and soils used as construction material for dams, roads, canals, etc., possess many and different properties. It is known that vibrations can transform a loose sand into a dense one; because of increasing loads soils may settle, move laterally, or slide. Soils may seem dense or loose, saturated or stiff, depending on the moisture content. Soils are permeable to air and water; they also absorb water. Some soils swell when wet, whereas other soil types give frost heaves, which are undesirable, especially in highway, railway, and canal engineering. It is more than a coincidence that most of the failures with structures as described above are caused by the unanticipated action of water, the regime of which changes as a result of the interference of the structural activity of the engineer. Water is the most important independent variable governing the subject of soil mechanics and foundation engineering.

FIG. 1-5   Rupture of slope of the Delaware-Chesapeake Canal bank at the north pier of the Summit Bridge, Delaware. Courtesy of U.S. Corps of Army Engineers, Philadelphia District.

Therefore, water control in soils is of very great importance. If there were no water on the earth, there would be no necessity for soil mechanics. Then, perhaps, we would have to deal with soil as an ideal, dry, pouring body in the case of sand (psammo-mechanics), but clays would be dry and hard. One sees that the mechanical properties of soils are far more complex and difficult to determine than those of steel, concrete, or wood. No material has greater variation of properties than soil, probably because it is not a manufactured standard product like steel. This is because the soil with which the engineer must work was placed by nature in a great variety of kinds and conditions. Thus it can be understood that soils present the most serious problem of design because they are not homogeneous.

However, as mentioned before, the foundations of every building, bridge, dam, power station, road, railroad, or other structure must be laid on soil. This indicates the importance of soil as a foundation and construction material. The solution of foundation problems, therefore, requires a proper understanding of the properties and behavior of the soil. Moreover, soil investigation must be done before the project is laid out, or before any field work is attempted.

Since the advent of the new scientific routine of engineering soil analysis, about 40 years ago, research has revealed that soils possess certain characteristic properties. These properties, though different and more complex from those of steel and concrete, are just as real and readily measurable as shearing strength and elasticity in those better understood materials. Thus, problems of design that previously could be solved only empirically, because the various factors encountered were not considered susceptible to analysis, can now be dealt with on a logical basis. The reason is that some of the laws governing them have been brought to light to assist the judgment of the experienced engineer.

Soil investigations and a knowledge of the physical and mechanical properties of soils can help to protect the owner of a building and the engineer in charge from otherwise unforeseeable conditions and the troubles which usually accompany them. These are the first steps to a proper understanding of problems in conjunction with the laying of a foundation.

1-2. Necessity for Studying Soils. Many engineers have had the experience, at least once, that the "opponent soil" has buried the results of their work; and that the "opponent water", seeping or flowing out of every pore of the soil and every hole in the soil, has flooded or washed away the results of all their efforts. It is therefore the duty of every engineer who erects structures supported on soil or uses soil as a structural material to understand clearly that water and soil are his natural opponents. Moreover, because the civil engineer in charge is the man who is responsible for the final success or failure of a structural project, it is also his duty to aquire a proper and thorough knowledge and understanding of the principles of soil mechanics. In modern times the civil engineer should rely less upon rule of thumb; rather, he should draw increasingly from the proper sciences, among which soil mechanics is of outstanding service.

From the sequence of the matter as reviewed in the previous chapter it can be understood that soil mechanics has developed from practical necessity. Since its development about 40 years ago, it has been proved that soil mechanics has saved this nation millions of dollars. If we think only of the inadequately built and frost-damaged roads and other structures which have failed, the reconstruction of which requires much money and trouble, it is obvious that soil mechanics is of national importance.

REFERENCES

1. Anon., "Righting a Twenty-Thousand-Ton Grain Elevator", *Scientific American*, December 26, 1914, vol. 111, no. 26.
2. A. Allaire, "The Failure and Righting of a Million Bushel Grain Elevator", ASCE *Transactions*, 1916, vol. 80.
3. R. B. Peck and F. G. Bryant, "The Bearing Capacity Failure of the Transcona Elevator", *Géotechnique*, 1952-1953, vol. 3.
4. L. S. White, "Transcona Elevator Failure: Eye-Witness Account", *Géotechnique*, 1952-1953, vol. 3.
5. Anon., "In Grain Elevator's Trouble 600,000 Bushels in Trouble", *Life*, June 27, 1955, vol. 38.
6. Anon., "Was it Explosion or Foundation Failure?" *Engineering News-Record*, June 23, 1955, p. 27.
7. Anon., *Engineering News-Record*, January 5, 1956, p. 27.
8. Report of the Committee of the National Academy of Sciences on Panama Canal Slides. *Memoirs of the National Academy of Sciences*, Washington, D.C., 1924, vol. 17.
9. N. Carillo, "Influence of Artesian Wells in the Sinking of Mexico City", *Proceedings*, 2d Conf. on Soil Mechanics and Foundation Engineering, Rotterdam, 1948, vol. VII, pp. 156-159.

Chapter 2

HISTORICAL REVIEW

In modern times, when every day in the field of soil mechanics and foundation engineering gives us new concepts and new knowledge, it is of interest to look back to learn how accomplishments in earthworks, foundation engineering and soil problems associated with them were solved in the old days. We have to realize that our knowledge of the present is an accumulated heritage of the past.

2-1. Soil Problems in Prehistoric Times. Although in the old days the subject of soil mechanics was not known to our predecessors in the same sense as we know it now, it can be said that since prehistoric times soils occupied people's minds. Travel and transportation, of necessity earth-bound, surely were extremely difficult, in the sense that the various types of soil (sand, mud, marshes, mountains) presented a great many obstacles. Let us remember that in very early times travel took place without roads and without modern means of transportation, and that savage tribes moved from place to place on foot, carrying their goods upon their backs.

In the more primitive civilizations, soil was used by man as a construction material for foundations of structures and for the structures themselves. The value of soil as a construction material was appreciated in building huge earth mounds for burial sites; for places of refuge during flood periods; for religious purposes; in making caves to live in, such as the ancient loess village of Su Chia Chiao, near Kalgan, and loess dwellings (caves dug into the side of a ravine) at Yang Shao Tsun; and in constructing canals, ditches, and fortifications.[1,2,3,4] It can be said that man's prehistoric progress in learning, understanding, and managing soils was very slow.

2-2. Soil Problems in Ancient Times. Soil problems in ancient times were associated with ancient roads, waterways and canals, and bridges.[5] For example, the *Dschou-Li*, i.e., a book on the customs of the Chinese Dschou dynasty, some 3000 years B.C., contains provisions and instructions for roads and bridges.[6]

The use of both timber and stone caissons for soft-ground shaft construction was known in Egypt in 2000 B.C. The shaft led to the underground burial chamber in the pyramids of Se'n Woster I, who reigned in Egypt about 2000 B.C. The cutting edge was made of a round limestone block with a vertical hole pierced through its middle. The brick caisson was sunk down through conglomerate and sand layers until it hit the limestone bedrock.[7] The outside surface of the caisson was made smooth for reasons of reducing sinking resistance caused by friction.

Soil as a construction material was also used for impounding of water and in building dikes and levees.

One of the greatest structures in ancient times was the famous "hanging garden" built by the Babylonian King Nebuchadnezzar. It towered to a great height in terraces. One above the other rose on vast and graceful arches, and was supplied with water from the river. The retaining walls to support these terraces, as well as the Babylonian defenses and fortifications, hundreds of feet in height, certainly required some knowledge of earth pressures, even if the knowledge was empirical. Hammurabi's code of laws (2250 B.C.) required that work be substantial and imposed great liability and severe penalties on builders. From this it may be inferred that the builders were required to possess certain professional skills for safe building.[8,9]

The "fabulous" wall of Babylon was found to be of double construction, with sand and gravel fill between. In our days this would pose to an engineer the problem of earth pressure on two parallel and narrowly spaced walls.

In China many bridges were built in very early times. According to Steinman and Watson,[10] the method of founding bridge piers (from 200 B.C. to approximately 220 A.D.) was as follows: part of the river was closed by a double-row cofferdam made of bamboo piles fastened together with ropes. Then bamboo mats were put on each row of piles, the intervening space being filled in with clay. The whole cofferdam was curved against water pressure. The water was pumped out by means of crude wooden tread pumps worked by pairs of men.

Quicksand conditions of soil seem to have been a really serious and troublesome topographical problem to all great warriors in moving troops and supplies through river valleys and performing tactical maneuvers. Alexander the Great, for example, was very conscious of these conditions and in military operations, was known to be skillful in avoiding terrain where quicksand conditions in soil were apt to develop.

From the professional point of view it is interesting to note that the engineer held a position of power and influence in all ancient communities.

2-3. Soil and Foundation Problems in Roman Times. In the course of time structures became larger and heavier. By the time the Roman Empire attained its peak of glory, engineers built very heavy structures, requiring solutions of earthwork and foundation designs. It is known that the Romans built notable engineering structures, for example: harbors, moles, breakwaters, aqueducts, bridges, large public buildings, sewage lines (the arch-covered Cloaca Maxima), and a vast network of durable and excellent roads.[11] Some sections of Roman roads are intact even today. The basic principles in Roman road design and construction, founded on the understanding of the performance of soil under the action of load and water, are (a) a solid foundation and (b) good drainage. These principles we still honor in our modern road design.

These large earthworks and structures, in turn, no doubt focussed the attention of the engineer on some of the soil mechanics problems still with us today. The performance of soil under load and water occupied the minds of engineers and administrators in those days. The question of the bearing capacity of soil was considered a serious one.

Probably the oldest written information and the only such evidence we have, although meager, about soil investigation for earthworks and foundation engineering purposes in Roman times is reflected by the correspondence exchanged between the Roman Emperor Trajan and Plinius.[12] In a letter to the Emperor Trajan, Plinius wrote:

"The citizens of Nicea, Sir, are building a theatre, which, though it is not yet finished, has already exhausted as I am informed (for I have not examined the account myself), about ten millions of sesterces (about $400,000), and what is worse, I fear to no purpose. For either from the foundation being laid in soft, marshy ground, or that the stone itself is light and crumbling, the walls are sinking and cracked from top to bottom. It deserves your consideration, therefore, whether it would be best to carry on this work, or entirely discontinue it, or rather, perhaps, whether it would not be most prudent absolutely to destroy it".

The history of culture indicates very little positive information or knowledge of the necessity for foundations under ancient structures. When structures settled too much, they were demolished and the rubble was used as a base for the succeeding structure.

In another letter Plinius wrote:

"To the Emperor Trajan.
The inhabitants of Sinope [a thriving Greek colony in the territory of Sinopis, on the Euxine] are ill supplied, Sir, with water, which, however, may be brought thither from about sixteen miles distance in great plenty and perfection. The ground, indeed, near the source of this spring is, for rather over a mile, of a very suspicious and marshy nature; but I have directed an examination to be made (which will be effected at a small expense) whether it is sufficiently firm to support any superstructure. I have taken care to provide a sufficient fund for this purpose, if you should approve, Sir, of a work so conducive to the health and enjoyment of this colony, greatly distressed by a scarcity of water."

Trajan to Pliny:

"I would have you proceed, my dearest Secundus, in carefully examining whether the ground you suspect is firm enough to support an aqueduct. For I have no manner of doubt that the Sinopian colony ought to be supplied with water; provided their finances will bear the expense of a work so conducive to their health and pleasure."

Unfortunately, nothing is said in these letters as to how an examination of a "suspicious and marshy" soil with respect to its being "sufficiently firm to support any superstructure" was carried out.

The technical literature of the time supplies ample evidence that the Romans paid much attention to some properties of soils, and to the stability of foundations.

The Roman engineer Vitruvius (first century B.C., during the reign of Emperor Augustus) in his *Ten Books on Architecture* described in Book II[13] that:

"Neither the same kind of soil nor the same rocks are found in all places and regions, but some are earthly, others of gravel, others pebbly, in other places sandy material; and generally there are found in the earth qualities of unlike and unequal kind with the various regions."

In Book VIII, discussing foundation problems related to water supply, Vitruvius wrote that:

"The methods of nature must be considered closely in the light of intelligence and experience because the soil contains many various elements."

Like the Babylonians, the Romans had some ideas about earth pressure. Discussing the stability of buildings, Vitruvius writes that:

"... greatest care must be taken in the substructures, because, in these, immense damage is caused by the earth piled against them. For it cannot remain of the same weight as it usually has in the summer; it swells in the winter by absorbing water from the rains. Consequently, by its weight and expansion it bursts and thrusts out the retaining walls."

On pavements Vitruvius says that:

"Paving on level ground, we must inquire whether the soil is solid throughout. But if there is a made site, in whole or in part, it must be rammed very carefully with piles."

On the foundations of walls, towns, and temples Vitruvius advises:

"Let the foundations of those works be dug from a solid site and to a solid base if it can be found. But if a solid foundation is not found, and the site is loose earth right down, or marshy, then it is to be excavated and cleared and re-made with piles of alder or of olive or charred oak, and the piles are to be driven close together by machinery, and the intervals between are to be filled with charcoal."

To this J. Gwilt[14] translated one more sentence: "The heaviest foundations may be laid on such a base."

From these letters and books by Vitruvius, the latter of which are to be considered as a real treasure chest of empirical building knowledge, it can clearly be seen that soil problems were of great concern to the Roman builders, and that they were aware, according to their state of knowledge, of the problem of the safe bearing capacity of soil and the stability of a foundation, and that they knew how to increase and to improve the bearing capacity of a soil. Also, they knew how to estimate by experience the safe load on pile groups. But the procedure of testing soils cannot be found in the technical sources by Vitruvius. However, it is clear that builders knew more than 2000 years ago at least something about soil as a material, foundation engineering, and earthworks; and that they possessed ample technical skill. It seems, however, that the scientific information they acquired in these subjects was very meager and probably very indefinite. This was in fact an empirical knowledge only, obtained and learned by slow, earlier experience and long effort. However, the Roman road builders deserve credit for pioneering the scientific art of road building.

The value of Plinius' and Vitruvius' writings is that detailed compilation served to codify what earlier generations had contributed.

2-4. Earthwork and Foundation Engineering in The Middle Ages. After the collapse of the Roman Empire, European society and activities in soil engineering and foundation engineering associated with it were very much disorganized. As a consequence, road construction and maintenance in the medieval period (about 400 to 1400 A.D.) declined to its lowest point. One gets the impression that in those days neither bridges nor roads were necessary or desirable. Warfare and religion were the universal activities in the Middle Ages. The old Roman engineering works, such as roads, bridges, dikes, and drainage facilities, were ravaged by war and neglect. Rain and frost, in their turn, broke up pavements and disintegrated the foundations.

Aside from roads and canals, the only other medieval structures associated with soil and foundation problems were

1) the heavy city walls, the bastions or flanking towers in the medieval fortifications which were of great extent and of dimensions commensurate with their importance,
2) the castles built and enclosed by heavy earthworks,
3) the great cathedrals, and
4) campaniles (bell towers) which usually were built separately from the churches.[15]

FIG. 2-1 The Archbishop's Cathedral in Riga, Latvia. Bildarchiv Foto-Marburg.

The main soil problem associated with the building of massive cathedrals is what today we would call the settlement problem and compression of soil brought about by their relatively large structural loads—relatively large loading areas of cathedrals or relatively small loading areas of the campaniles— as well as the long time elapsed since the start of construction of these monumental structures. During the past centuries the compressible soils upon which some of the cathedrals were built had enough time to consolidate under the structural loads of the cathedrals, causing, in many instances, large settlements of the structures or, in other instances, causing the mutual leaning toward each other of double church towers (for example, the Dom of Lübeck, Germany). So, for example, cathedrals known originally to have been built with many entrance steps up, now have many entrance steps down into them as a result of the 2 meters large settlement process in the past 400 years (as is the case of the Archbishop's cathedral in Riga, Fig. 2-1).

The heavy Dom of Königsberg in East Prussia (about 1330 A.D.), for example, was founded on a layer of peat. Underneath this peat there is, according to Tiedemann,[16] about a 60'-thick layer of soil consisting of clayey-limey material. Because of the consolidation of the clayey soil material the structure has never come to rest. In the course of time it has been necessary to put in new floors over the old ones five times. The settlement of the Dom of Königsberg amounts roughly to more than 5 ft. The once graceful interior spaciousness of the Dom, of course, has suffered greatly.

The campaniles of Bologna and Venice, the tower of the 14th century San Stefano Church, the campanile of San George in Zaragoza, and the tower of Pisa to name but a few, are well known as tourists' attractions for their being out of the true vertical. For example, the construction of the tower of Pisa (popularly known as the leaning tower of Pisa) was started in 1174 A.D. After the first three galleries of the eight-galleried structure were built, the tower started to tilt. After some interruption in work and slight changes in plans, the construction was continued. The tall campanile, about 15 stories, 179 ft in height, was completed in 1350. In 1910, the tower had a visible slant, and its top was 16.5 ft out of plumb. The leaning tower of Pisa is shown in Fig. 2-2.

Investigation of what caused the campanile of Pisa to lean revealed that it was due to settlement of the tower brought about by the consolidation of the clayey soil material underneath a

FIG. 2-2 The Leaning Tower of Pisa, Italy. Courtesy of Mr. H. Freese, New Brunswick, New Jersey.

layer of sand on which the tower was founded.[17] Hence, to a soil mechanics engineer, the leaning tower of Pisa and other leaning campaniles present a classic example of the settlement problems of the medieval period.

2-5. The Period from the 15th to the 17th Centuries. In the field of laying foundations for bridge piers, the builders of the Middle Ages followed in the footsteps of the Romans, i.e., they simply piled up pieces of loose rock, or drove piles upon the heads of which a timber grillage was constructed to receive the pier. The poor quality and ineffectiveness of foundations remained the most difficult and acute foundation engineering problem until the advent of modern knowledge in the 18th century. Watson and Watson[18] write thus about builders who experienced some difficulties in laying the foundations of the Wadebridge structure over the Camel (about 1425): ". . . the foundation of certain of th'arches was first sette on so quick sandy ground that Lovebone almost despaired to performe the bridge untyl such tyme as he layed pakkes of wolle for foundation."

The Watsons also tell that this story is based upon the fact that ". . . when Peter of Colechurch was building London Bridge the King contributed to the cause by means of a tax on wool. Fynes Morison seems to have started this tradition when he wrote in his Itinerary (1671) that London Bridge was built on 'packs of wool, most durable against the force of water' ". Actually, it is known that London Bridge is founded on piles. "Pakkes of wolle" actually refers to a means (tax on wool) for financing the bridge.

The Rialto single arch bridge in Venice, Italy, completed in 1591, is, like other buildings in that city, noted for its difficult foundation operations because of the soft and marshy ground and adjacent large buildings—circumstances which make pile driving operations a real and responsible problem.

Another fragment of foundation engineering of the 17th century associated with soil problems, is the famed mausoleum Taj Mahal outside the city of Agra, India. It was built by the great Indian Mogul Emperor of Dehli, Shah-Jahan, to commemorate his favorite wife Mumtaz-i-Mahal. The construction of the mausoleum began in 1632 and was completed in 1650. This tomb is of extreme delicacy and reflects a *chef-d'œuvre* of elegance in Indian art.[19]

The proximity of the river required special attention in the building of the foundations of the Taj-Mahal. It was the practice of the Mogul builders to support the structures on masonry cylindrical foundations sunk into the soil at close intervals. Apparently the terrace and the mausoleum building, as well as the minarets, rest on one firm, compact bed of masonry. The method adopted was a sound one for after three centuries ". . . its lines and angles are still as accurate as when first produced".[20] Twenty thousand people were employed on the Taj-Mahal for seventeen years, and the structure is estimated to have cost about $45,000,000.

In the 16th century, it is interesting to note, such famous artists as Michelangelo and Bramante were also known to be active in the field of building fortifications, and in executing drainage canal and water-supply problems. Leonardo da Vinci, as a civil engineer, was called in 1516 by Francis I to France to help in the latter's canal-building program.[21] Da Vinci also constructed with ease fortresses, canals, bridges, irrigation works, harbors, and locks.

The early builders were guided in their work by the knowledge and experience passed down from generation to generation, rather than by physical laws and scientific considerations. The 16th and early 17th centuries in earthwork and foundation engineering can be regarded, however, as being transitional. Other concepts of soil mechanics originating during this period are Hooke's concept of stress and strain (1676), and Newton's law of action and reaction.

The 18th century, however, can be considered as the real beginning of civil engineering when science became a basic factor in structural design.

2-6. Older Concepts on Lateral Earth Pressure. In the latter part of the 17th century French military engineers contributed some empirical and analytical data pertaining to earth pressure on retaining walls for the design of revetments of fortifications. In 1661, France undertook an extensive public works program which included the improvement of highways and the building of canals. The construction of the great fortification system along the borders of France was begun in 1667 under Marquis Sebastian le Prestre de Vauban (1633-1707), who was commissary general of fortifications and Louis the XIV's chief engineer, and who later became marshal of France. Vauban is regarded as one of the greatest military engineers of all times.

Canals which were dug in those days, and later during the times of French mercantilism, presented soil problems in connection with the terrain through which the canals were dug; but retaining walls of the fortifications presented earth pressure problems in connection with their stability. It is known that at that time Vauban gave some rules for gauging the thickness of retaining walls. However, it is not known for sure whether these were based on theoretical considerations, or whether they were merely the results of Vauban's experience. In this respect thoughts were later expressed in France that the empirical rules by Vauban appeared to be so complete that it almost seemed as if those rules were based upon an earth-pressure theory now unknown to us.

In the construction of earth dams, as well as in backfilling of masonry walls with different types of soil, the French engineers were able quite early to make observations about the equilibrium of filled earth masses, as well as about the action of earth pressure against the back of the so-called retaining walls as they were used in bridge construction, and especially in the construction of fortifications of different shapes and cross-sections. The necessity of learning in advance about the shapes and dimensions of such structures and determining them safely enough gave the observer reason to move gradually toward more rigorous theoretical investigations. Thus the first earth pressure theories developed. In 1691 Bullet[22] published a treatise entitled *Traité d'architecture pratique* in which he assumed that upon the displacement of the retaining wall all the retained soil wedge *ABC* behind the wall and above a 45° plane, *AC*, through the toe, *A*, of the retaining wall would tend to slide down as a solid mass upon this plane (Fig. 2-3).

Bullet resolved the weight of the sliding earth wedge, *ABC*, into two components, namely: normally and tangentially to the 45° sliding plane. This tangential component of the weight Bullet considered as the thrust or earth pressure on the retaining wall.

Rondelet (1734-1829) in his *Traité théorique et pratique de l'art de bâtir* (1802) deals with earth-pressure problems similarly to Bullet.

Couplet tried in 1726 to establish the earth-pressure theory scientifically, assuming the soil to be composed of small, spherical particles, i.e., he considered soil as an ideal material. His published work on this subject, entitled "*De la poussée des terres contre leurs revêtements et la force, qu'on leur doit opposer*" appeared in the *Histoire de l'Académie Royale des Sciences*, Paris, 1726-1728. The arbitrary assumption of spherical soil particles, however, prevented the theory from furnishing useful and reliable results in practice.

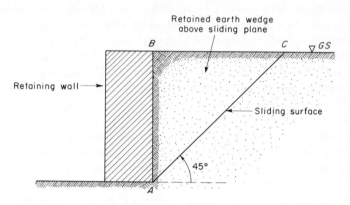

FIG. 2-3   Bullet's concept of a retained wedge of soil, △ABC, above the 45-degree sliding plane, *AC*

Later some other authors assumed the position of the sliding plane to coincide with the slope of the angle of repose of the backfill material, and still others subtracted from the tangential weight-component a certain percent for friction.

Early in the 18th century the French government recognized that, through neglect in past centuries, many bridges and roads were in a poor condition and therefore had to be rebuilt. This gave France the impetus for the establishment in 1715 of a Department of Roads and Bridges. In 1716 Colbert created a corps of military engineers to train experts in fortifications and artillery, and in 1747 the famous *École des Ponts et Chaussées* was established under the famous engineer Jean Rudolphe Perronet, where engineers were educated in sound principles of physics, mechanics, and mathematics for the construction of canals, highways, and bridges. This engineering school had a great influence upon the scientific development of civil engineering in France and abroad.

2-7. The Period of the Classical Earth-Pressure Theories. Up to about 1773 almost all theoretical considerations in calculating the lateral earth pressure of an ideal soil upon a retaining wall were based on the presupposition of a definite, arbitrarily assumed, sliding or failure plane.

Charles Augustin Coulomb (1736-1806), a famous French scientist and also a military engineer of that time, was not satisfied with such an arbitrary presupposition. On the contrary, Coulomb considered it as his principal task to determine the real or true position of the sliding surface mathematically and thus give the theory a scientific basis. Coulomb contributed much to the science of mechanics of elastic bodies, and is regarded as the founder of the so-called "Classical Earth-Pressure Theory". The period beginning with Coulomb and extending to the second half of the 19th century is usually known in the technical literature as "the period of the Classical Earth-Pressure Theories", and the theories themselves sometimes are termed "the Classical Theories of Soil Mechanics". In his widely cited essay on the application of the rules of maximum and minimum,[23] Coulomb presented an analysis of the so-called "sliding wedge theory", to bring about the calculations of the earth pressure against a retaining wall, as well as the critical height of retaining walls. In this analysis Coulomb applies the laws of friction and cohesion for solid bodies, an analysis which he assumed also valid for granular bodies such as soil; and he determines the earth pressure upon a retaining wall from the "wedge of maximum pressure".

Coulomb's ideas about the shapes of the rupture surfaces in soil are reflected in his Fig. 7, Plate I (see Fig. 2-4). Coulomb also treated the problem of surcharge on the ground surface. The laws in Coulomb's earth pressure theory, in short, are: 1) the frictional resistance on any sliding surface is equal to a fraction (constant) of the normal pressure on that surface, and 2) the cohesive resistance is equal to a constant (cohesion) times the area of the sliding surface.

One recognizes from these laws that they represent the shear strength of non-cohesive and cohesive soil material, respectively, and that the combination of the two represents the shear strength of a cohesive-frictional soil material. The shear strength in Coulomb's

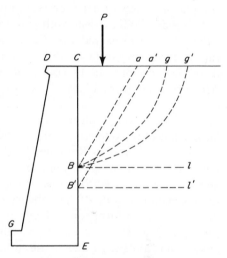

Fig. 2-4 Coulomb's ideas about the shapes of rupture surfaces in soil.

assumption is uniformly distributed over the rupture plane. However, very little effort was devoted in Coulomb's days to investigating the physical properties of soils themselves. (For more historical notes on Coulomb's earth pressure theory see Ref. 24.)

The significance of Coulomb's theoretical work may be recognized best by the fact that his ideas on earth pressure still prevail in their principal points, with a few exceptions, and are used and recognized as valid even today, particularly when dealing with the calculations of stability of retaining walls.

In the course of time Coulomb's theory underwent some alterations and new developments. However, these developments were based mostly on ideal, granular, non-cohesive soil such as dry sand or clean gravel possessing friction only between the particles.

Français,[25] Navier,[26] and possibly others investigated special cases in which the ground surface behind the retaining wall is inclined and surcharged instead of being horizontal and unloaded.

Poncelet (1788-1867),[27] a famous geometer and founder of our modern subject, projective geometry, extended Coulomb's theory giving an elegant, graphical method of finding the magnitude of the earth pressure on the wall, vertical as well as for inclined wall surfaces on the backfill side, and for arbitrarily broken polygonal ground surfaces. Also, Poncelet is to be credited as being the first to apply the direction of the earth pressure inclined to the normal of the wall under an angle of friction between the soil and wall material. Later, in 1866, Karl Culmann (1821-1881)[28] gave the Coulomb-Poncelet theory a geometrical formulation, thus supplying the method with a broad scientific basis. Culmann's theory is the most general one permitting the graphical solution of the most complicated cases of earth pressure upon a retaining wall.

Alexandre Collin[29] dealt with ruptures of slopes of canals and dams. Collin writes that he measured the slides and, upon analyzing the observed curved rupture or sliding surfaces, they were revealed to be cycloidally curved. These theoretical cycloid curves coincided well with observations made in nature. Also, from his work it may be concluded that it was probably the first time that the shear strength of soil was actually measured on a rational basis. ⋅

Darcy's law of permeability of soil has been known since 1856.[30] Also, Stokes' law of the velocity of solid particles through liquids dates back to 1856.[31]

William J. Macqorn Rankine (1820-1872), professor of Civil Engineering in the University of Glasgow, published in 1857 a notable theory on earth pressure and equilibrium of earth masses, thus offering an analytical method of dimensioning retaining walls.[32] The theory is based on an infinitesimal wedge within the mass of a uniform soil of laterally unlimited extent having a plane ground surface and subjected to its own weight only. The stress in soil at every point of the soil in a plane parallel to the surface plane is the same. The soil is assumed to be homogeneous, granular, cohesionless, and incompressible. The particles of the soil are held in position by means of friction only, the magnitude of which is proportional to the normal pressure on the rupture surface. In other words, Rankine's theory is based on the principle of the internal stress condition in soil.

O. Mohr (1835-1918) contributed in 1871 the so-called rupture theory to the subject of strength of materials, and gave a graphical representation of stress at a point, popularly known as Mohr's stress circles. Mohr also noticed and called attention to the fact that in the older theories, in case of equilibrium, the forces acting on a sliding wedge do not intersect in one common point.[33] In soil mechanics, Mohr's stress circles are extensively used in the analysis of the shear strength of soils.

Coulomb-Poncelet earth pressure theories were elaborated by graphical analyses also by Rebhann,[34] Weyrauch,[35] and others.

To test the earth pressure theories, Müller-Breslau (1906) performed some relatively extensive and elaborate experiments with a large-scale model retaining wall.[36] The results of Müller-Breslau's work showed that the earth pressure on the retaining wall may sometimes be larger than that calculated by means of Coulomb's theory. Also the manner of manipulation of the sand and the methodology of its loading and unloading may influence the magnitude of the earth pressure considerably.

The history of strength of materials[37] indicates that from the point of view of practical value one of the most important contributions to the engineering sciences was offered by Joseph Valentin Boussinesq (1842-1929).[38] This is his theory of stress distribution and deformation under loaded bearing areas in a semi-infinite, homogeneous, and isotropic medium induced by externally applied forces at the boundary plane. This theory is being applied in soil mechanics to calculate stress distribution in homogeneous soil caused by structural loads. The soil, in applying this theory, is tacitly assumed to be an ideal, non-cohesive, homogeneous, and isotropic material.

Concluding the review of the period of the classical earth-pressure theories, it can be said that the evaluation of the bearing capacity of soil and of the earth pressure was mainly a matter of practical experience supported by the simple basic classical earth-pressure theories.

The impetus for the development of early soil mechanics, it must be recognized, was given by the increased activities in bridge design and construction for highways and railways with which the following two popular names are associated: Perronet[39] and Rankine. Besides his academic activities Rankine was also known as a famous Scottish railroad engineer.

It should also be mentioned that besides Müller-Breslau, contributions to the earth pressure theory were later likewise made by O. Franzius,[40] H. Krey,[41] J. Feld,[42] K. Terzaghi,[43] the *DEGEBO* (German Society for Soil Mechanics at the *Technische Hochschule Berlin-Charlottenburg*[44]), G. P. Tschebotarioff,[45] and others with their experimental research with earth-retaining structure models on a large scale.

2-8. The Beginning of the Modern Soil Mechanics Era. The period from the beginning of the twentieth century until now may be divided into two epochs, namely: the years that preceded 1925, and the years that followed it.

The first 25 years of the 20th century should be considered as the pioneer years of the modern science of soil mechanics. Scientists and engineers gradually realized the increasing need for studying the physical properties of soils. The following description covers some highlights in the development of modern soil mechanics during the first 25-year period.

In 1911, A. Atterberg, a Swedish scientist, proposed simple test procedures for characterizing consistency characteristics of cohesive soils, namely the liquid, plastic, and shrinkage properties of soils. These tests, also known as the Atterberg limits, or else as the consistency limits of soil, are still used in engineering for soil indentification and classification purposes.[46]

The pioneering in practical soil mechanics must be credited to the Swedish Geotechnical (Soil Mechanical) Commission of the State Railways of Sweden. On December 29, 1913, after a number of serious railway, canal, and waterfront failures involving quays, docks, retaining walls, and ruptures of slopes in railroad cuts and fills, the Royal Board of State Railways appointed a committee, headed by Professor Wolmar Fellenius. It was commissioned in part to investigate the government railway lines from a geological point of view, and to state whether there might be any fear of displacements of the roadbeds in consequence of a land-slip or any similar occurrence; and in part, if such should be the case, to enter proposals for the steps which should be taken in order to secure the railway against such displacements.

This investigation resulted in 1922 in an extensive final report containing some data on modern soil sampling and testing methods applied to more than 300 places with 2400 soil profiles.[47] Also, a method (the so-called Swedish circle method) for the calculation of stability of slopes made of cohesive soils under the assumption of a circular, cylindrical sliding surface, is published in that report.[47,48]

The proponents of the circular sliding surface theory are two Swedish engineers, K. Petterson,[49] and S. Hultin.[50] The circular sliding theory with the so-called friction circle was used by Petterson and Hultin in 1916 in stability calculations in connection with the failure of the Stegberg quay in the Swedish port of Göteborg.[49,50,51]

The slide shown in Fig. 2-5 at Vita Sikudden, a railway section Nyköping-Norrköping, Sweden, occurred on October 1, 1918, at 7 p.m. Just after the slide took place, a passenger train plunged into the slide; 41 people lost their lives, and many were injured. The upper part of the slope toward the Bråviken shore consists of sand and silt, whereas the lower part consists of loose clay.

The cause of the slide appears to have been an exceptional water infiltration in the embankment fill during the unusually heavy rains before the slide took place. In Fig. 2-5, which is an aerial photograph of the slide, note the earth wedge of the slide in the Bråviken Bay, the interrupted railway line, the highway buried by the sliding earth masses, the overturned locomotive and cars in the slide, and some cars still on the tracks.

The progressive highway construction program in the United States during the years 1920 to 1925, as well as the industrial development during those years, induced intensive research on soils for engineering purposes. This research was in the hands of the U.S. Bureau of Public Roads and various other establishments such as universities and technical and professional societies (for example the American Society of Civil Engineers).

Thus, the first 25 years of modern soil mechanics can be briefly characterized as follows: research in soil mechanics expanded and was gaining impetus for its development on a scientific basis.

The period from 1925 to date may be characterized as the most fruitful in soil mechanics history. It is now fairly well agreed upon that the modern discipline of Soil Mechanics began in 1925 with the publication of the book *Erdbaumechanik* by K. Terzaghi.[52]

In this book Terzaghi gave a new philosophical view relative to soil as a material and showed how to treat the physical properties of soil, as well as how the soil material performs under various loading and moisture conditions.

He dealt with the effect of surface tension of water on the strength properties of soil and its performance, and introduced, based on the analogy of flow of heat, the consolidation theory of clays, thus enabling the engineer to determine on a scientific basis the compressibility characteristics of cohesive soils and to forecast on a more rational basis the expected magnitude of settlement of structures built on a compressible soil, and the rate of settlement.

Another important step in the new discipline was the co-authored publication by Terzaghi and Fröhlich of the settlement theory of clays.[53]

Terzaghi's publications, and the work in soil mechanics done by other authorities in this field, gave a great impetus for soil mechanics studies, and produced a considerable amount of knowledge on engineering properties of soils in the United States, as well as abroad.

FIG. 2-5 Aerial view of a railway embankment slide at Vita Sikudden, Sweden. Courtesy of the Swedish State Railways Geotechnical Commission.

The German engineer H. D. Krey published in 1918 and in the following years several editions of his famous work on earth pressures, earth resistance, and bearing capacity of soils.[54] His work is based on his experience gained mostly from the construction of one of the most important German canals, the Kiel Canal, and from laboratory and field research in the Prussian Research Establishment for Hydraulic Structures at the Schleusen Insel, Tiergarten, in Berlin.

In the course of time laboratory tests of soils became very much appreciated by the profession, and soil testing methods are continuously being refined and improved. Most of the progressive engineering colleges and universities have by now already established soil mechanics and foundation engineering laboratories and geotechnical institutes for studying soils for engineering purposes. Also, the accreditation committee for college instruction curricula of the Engineers Council for Professional Development shows a great interest in the inclusion of a soil mechanics course in the civil engineering program.

The proceedings of the many national and international conferences on soil mechanics and foundation engineering here and abroad also attest for the need, progress and importance of soil mechanics.

To summarize the progress of soil mechanics in the last 40 years, it can be said that the pioneering in the new soil mechanics discipline is completed and that today this discipline has research as its standard bearer. This historical review also points out that the subject of soil mechanics is actually not a new one in its deepest sense. It has merely been established that recently this subject has experienced development at a very intense rate, and that positive results have been attained. Today, the civil engineer has a much better knowledge of soils to enable him to encounter the two opponents—soil and water—in foundation engineering than had his colleagues only some 35 years ago.

2-9. Most Recent Development. As to the most recent development in soil mechanics, it can be observed that notable achievements have been made in soil stabilization, dynamic compaction of soil,[55] in frost action research in soil, in the field of moisture movement through soil by means of electro-osmosis, and in the techniques of airphoto interpretation for the purpose of engineering surveys and for the preparation of engineering soil maps.[56] It is interesting to note that soil mechanics has introduced a new subject, namely snow mechanics,[57] and most recently there has occurred the development of non-destructive tests to determine in place some soil properties, such as density and moisture content, by means of radioactive isotopes.

In general, modern practice continuously improves upon the methods of yesterday. Techniques of today may become inadequate tomorrow unless supplemented, completed, and changed to meet new requirements.

To sum up the review, the combined efforts of engineers and research workers from all over the world in this discipline contributed to what we may call modern soil mechanics.

REFERENCES

1. T. Beckwith, *The Indian or Mound Builder*, Cape Girardeau, Mo., Naeta Brothers Publishers, 1911.
2. A. R. Verrill, *Old Civilizations of the New World*, New York, The New York Home Library, 1942.
3. C. Thomas, *The Circular, Square and Octagonal Earthworks of Ohio*, Washington, D.C., Smithsonian Institution, 1889.
4. J. G. Anderson, *Children of the Yellow Earth*, New York, The MacMillan Co., 1934.
5. Anon., *Public Roads of the Past* (3500 B.C. to 1800 A.D.), Washington, D.C., AASHO, 1952.
6. A. Speck, *Der Kunststrassenbau*, Berlin, Wilhelm Ernst und Sohn, 1950.
7. Anon., *Eng. News-Record*, December 7, 1933, p. 675.
8. S. G. W. Benjamin, *Persia and the Persian People*, Boston, Ticknor and Co., 1887.
9. R. F. Harper, *The Code of Hammurabi, King of Babylon, About 2550 B.C.*, Chicago, University of Chicago Press, 2d ed., 1904 (§§228-233, p. 81).

10. D. B. Steinman and S. R. Watson, *Bridges and their Builders*, New York, G. P. Putnam's Sons, 1941.
11. S. B. Platner, *The Topography and Monuments of Ancient Rome*, Boston, Allyn and Bacon, 1904.
12. *Letters of Gaius Plinius Caecelius Secundus*, trans. by W. Melmoth, from the Harvard Classics, New York, P. F. Collier and Son Company, 1909.
13. Vitruvius, *Ten Books on Architecture*, trans. by Frank Granger, New York, G. P. Putnam's Sons, 1934.
14. *The Ten Books of Vitruvius*, trans. by Joseph Gwilt, London, Lockwood and Company, 1874, Book III, Chapt. III, p. 72.
15. S. Painter, *A History of the Middle Ages 284-1500 A.D.*, New York, Alfred A. Knopf, 1953.
16. B. Tiedemann, *Die Bedeutung des Bodens im Bauwesen, Handbuch der Bodenlehre* by E. Blanck, Berlin, Julius Springer, 1932, vol. 10.
17. K. Terzaghi, "Die Ursachen der Schiefstellung des Turmes von Pisa", no. 1/2, *Der Bauingenieur*, 1934.
18. W. J. Watson and S. R. Watson, *Bridges in History and Legend*, Cleveland, Ohio, J. H. Jansen.
19. J. Ferguson, *History of Indian and Eastern Architecture*, John Murray, 1876.
20. Sir Wolsley Haig, *The Cambridge History of India*, vol. 4, *The Mogul Period*, At the University Press, Cambridge, 1937.
21. R. J. Forbes, *Man the Maker, A History of Technology and Engineering*, New York, Henry Schuman, 1950.
22. G. C. Mehrtens, *Statik und Festigkeitslehre*, vol. 3, *Gewölbe und Stützmauern*, Leipzig, Wilhelm Engleman, 1912.
23. C. A. Coulomb, "Essai sur une application des règles de maximis et minimis à quelques problèmes de statique relatifs à l'architecture". *Mémoires de la mathématique et de physique*, présentés à l'Académie Royale des Sciences, par divers savans, et lûs dans sés Assemblées, vol. 7, Annee 1773. Paris, De L'Imprimerie Royale, 1776 (pp. 343-382, plus two plates of drawings).
24. A. R. Jumikis, *Active and Passive Earth Pressure Coefficient Tables*, New Brunswick, New Jersey, Rutgers University Press, (in preparation).
25. J. F. Français, *Recherches sur la poussée de terres sur la forme et dimensions des revêtments et sur la talus d'excavation. Mémorial de l'officier du génie* IV, Paris, 1820, pp. 157-206.
26. C. L. M. Navier, *Leçons sur l'application de la mécanique à l'etablissement des constructions et des machines*, 2d ed, Paris, 1839.
27. J. V. Poncelet, *Mémoire sur la stabilité des revêtments et de leurs fondations.* Note additionnelle sur les relations analytiques qui lient entre elles la poussée et la butée de la terre. *Mémorial de l'officier du génie*, vol. 13, Paris, 1840, pp. 261-270.
28. K. Culmann, "Die Graphische Statik", Section 8, *Theorie der Stütz- und Futtermauern*, Zürich, Meyer und Zeller, 1866, pp. 545-633, plus Plates 28-34.
29. A. Collin, *Recherches expérimentales sur les glissements spontanés des terrains argileux accompagnées de considérations sur quelques principes de la mécanique terrestre*, Paris, Carilian-Goeury, 1846. Collin's work is now translated by W. R. Schriever and published by the University of Toronto Press in 1956, Toronto, Canada, bearing the title *Landslides in Clays*.
30. H. Darcy, *Les fontaines publiques de la ville de Dijon*, Paris; Dijon, Victor Dalmont, Éditeur, 1856.
31. G. G. Stokes, "On the Effect of the Internal Friction of Fluids on the Motion of Pendulum", *Trans.* Cambridge Philosophical Society, 1856, vol. 9, part 2.
32. W. J. M. Rankine, "On the Stability of Loose Earth", *Philosophical Transactions*, Royal Society, London, 1857, vol. 147.
33. O. Mohr, *Technische Mechanik*, Berlin, Wilhelm Ernst und Sohn, 1906.

34. G. Rebhann, *Theorie des Erddruckes und der Futtermauern mit besonderer Rücksicht auf das Bauwesen*, Wien, Carl Gerold's Sohn, 1871.
35. J. Weyrauch, "Zur Theorie des Erddrucks", *Zeitschrift für Baukunde*, 1878, vol. 2, no. 2, p. 193.
36. H. Müller-Breslau, *Erddruck auf Stützmauern*, Stuttgart, Alfred Kröner Verlag, 1906, 1947.
37. S. Timoshenko, *History of Strength of Materials*, New York, McGraw-Hill Book Company, Inc., 1953.
38. J. V. Boussinesq, *Application des potentiels â l'étude de l'équilibre et du mouvement des solides élastiques*, Paris, Gauthier-Villars, 1885.
39. J. R. Perronet, *Description des Projets et de la Construction des Ponts de Neuilly, de Mantes, d'Orleans, de Louis XVI, etc.*, Paris, François-Ambroise Didot, 1788.
40. O. Franzius, "Erddruckversuche im natürlichen Maszstabe", *Der Bauingenier*, 1928, vol. 9, pp. 787-792; 813-815.
41. H. Krey and J. Ehrenberg, *Erddruck, Erdwiderstand und Tragfähigkeit des Baugrundes*, Berlin, Wilhelm Ernst un Sohn, 1936.
42. J. Feld, "Lateral Earth Pressure", *Trans.* ASCE, 1923, Paper no. 1529, vol. 86.
43. K. Terzaghi, "Large Retaining Wall Tests", *Eng. News-Record*, Sept. 29, 1932; Feb. 1, 22, March 8, 29, and April 19, 1934.
44. A. Hertwig, "Bemerkungen über neuere Erddruckuntersuchungen", *Veröffentlichungen* des Instituts der Deutschen Gesellschaft für Bodenmechanik, Berlin, Julius Springer, 1939, pp. 1-9.
45. G. P. Tschebotarioff, "Large-scale Model Earth Pressure Tests on Flexible Bulkheads", *Proc.* ASCE, 1948.
46. A. Atterberg, "Über die physikalische Bodenuntersuchung, und über die Plastizität der Tone", Internationale Mitteilungen für Bodenkunde, *Verlag für Fachliteratur*, G.m.b.H. Berlin, 1911, vol. 1, p. 10.
47. *Slutbetänkande*, Statens Järnvägars Geotekniska Kommission 1914-1922, Statens Järnvägar, Stockholm, 1922.
48. W. Fellenius, "Kaj- och Jordraset i Göteborg", *Teknisk Tidskrift*, no. 2, 1918.
49. K. E. Petterson, "Kajraset i Göteberg, den 5 Mars, 1916", *Teknisk Tidskrift*, 1916, no. 30, 31.
50. S. Hultin, "Grusfullningar för Kajbiggnader", *Teknisk Tidskrift*, No. 31, 1916.
51. K. E. Petterson, "The Early History of Circular Sliding Surfaces", *Géotechnique*, vol. 5, London, 1955.
52. K. Terzaghi, *Erdbaumechanik auf bodenphysikalischer Grundlage*, Leipzig und Wien, Franz Deuticke, 1925.
53. K. Terzaghi and O. K. Fröhlich, *Theorie der Setzung von Tonschichten*, Leipzig und Wien, Franz Deuticke, 1936.
54. H. Krey, *Erddruck, Erdwiderstand und Tragfähigkeit des Baugrundes*, Berlin, Wilhelm Ernst und Sohn, 1936.
55. R. K. Bernhard, *Dynamic Compaction of Soil*, Engineering Research Bulletin No. 37, New Brunswick, New Jersey, Rutgers University, 1952.
56. *Engineering Soil Survey of New Jersey*, 22 bulletins accompanied by engineering soil maps for all 21 counties of New Jersey, Rutgers University, Bureau of Engineering Research, 1950-1957.
57. R. Haefeli, *Schneemechanik, mit Hinweisen auf die Erdbaumechanik*, Der Schnee und seine Metamorphose, in Beiträge zur Geologie der Schweiz, Geotechnische Serie, Hydrologie, Bern, 1939. Trans. Jan C. Van Tienhoven for the Snow, Ice and Permafrost Research Establishment, Corps of Engineers, U.S. Army; *Snow and its Metamorphism* by H. Bader, R. Hafely, E. Bucher, J. Heher, O. Eckel and Chr. Thams, Translation 14, January, 1954, Wilmette, Illinois.

Chapter 3

SOIL MECHANICS

3-1. Definition. Soil mechanics, sometimes also called geotechnique or geotechnics, is one of the youngest disciplines of civil engineering. From the logical contents of the subject matter as discussed in the foregoing articles, one can deduce that soil mechanics is not the discipline known by the term "soil science". The latter is an agricultural and forestry science which studies soil from the angle of plant nutrition.

Soil mechanics can be defined as that discipline of engineering sciences which studies theoretically and practically soils, by means of which and upon which engineers build their structures. The essence of this definition is that the soil mechanics discipline treats soil as a construction material in any way associated with engineering. The effect of forces on the equilibrium and/or behavior of soil under static and dynamic conditions, as well as under the influence of water and temperature, is studied theoretically and experimentally. A knowledge of physics, mechanics, hydraulics, and heat transfer in soil studies is applied either to verify old or to establish new theories about the behavior of soil subjected to stress, water, and heat or cold. In other words, soil mechanics studies the mutual interaction of structure and soil.

The term "soil" as used in this book refers to the unconsolidated sediments and deposists of solid particles derived from the disintegration of rock.

Terzaghi[1] defines soil mechanics as follows:

"Soil Mechanics is the application of the laws of mechanics and hydraulics to engineering problems dealing with sediments and other unconsolidated accumulations of solid particles produced by the mechanical and chemical disintegration of rocks regardless of whether or not they contain an admixture of organic constituents."

It is probable that the English term "soil mechanics" is derived from the title of Terzaghi's book *Bodenmechanik auf bodenphysikalischer Grundlage,* published in 1925.

The term "soil mechanics" is now accepted quite generally to designate that discipline of engineering science which deals with the properties, behavior, and performance of soil as a structural material.

The practice of engineering which applies the principles of soil mechanics to the design of engineering structures is called soil engineering.

Purpose. The purpose of soil mechanics is to replace by scientific methods the empirical methods of design applied in foundation engineering in the past.

3-2. Objectives of Soil Mechanics. The objectives of soil mechanics are
1) to perform engineering soil surveys;
2) to develop rational soil sampling devices and soil sampling methods;
3) to develop suitable soil testing devices and soil testing methods;
4) to collect and classify information on soils and their physical properties in the light of fundamental knowledge of soil mechanics, earthworks, and foundation engineering;
5) to investigate the physical properties of soils and to determine co-efficients to characterize these soil properties;
6) to evaluate and interpret soil test results and their application to the use of soil in place or as a construction material;
7) to endeavor to gain more light in understanding the physical processes which actually take place in soils subjected to various factors such as static and dynamic loads, water, and temperature;
8) to apply the knowledge of soil mechanics for the solution of practical engineering problems, and
9) to replace by scientific methods the empirical ones of design used in foundation and earthwork engineering in the past, thus contributing to the advancement of this discipline.

3-3. Soil Mechanics Problems. Some of the problems listed below may indicate the kind of relationship which exists between foundations and soil and may convince one of the importance of the subject:

How deep should borings for soil exploration be made?

What is the bearing capacity of a soil on its surface and at various depths to carry various loads?

What is the load to be applied on a particular soil?

What is the intensity and what is the stress distribution in a soil induced by various kinds of loading?

How thick should a layer of a good soil over a poor one be in order to prevent the foundation from punching through it into the layer of poor soil?

Does a soil possess properties (friction and cohesion) which will assure satisfactory stability for foundations or slopes?

How much counterweight should be placed as a remedial measure against lateral motion of soil masses in order to maintain the stability of a structure?

The engineer is also interested in settlement considerations caused by applied loads: structures on soil, ground-water lowering, vibrations, tunneling, or mining, for example. Also, the rate and amount of settlement is of great importance, especially in a case where structures are built as statically indeterminate systems.

When does settlement cease?

What is the mutual interaction between soil and foundation, and what kinds and magnitudes of stresses are induced in the foundation and soil of a rigid highway or runway pavement due to various loading schemes under consideration?

To highways and airfields, besides the bearing capacities and settlement problems, the following problems also apply: frost penetration depth; frost heave and thaw with their associated problem of frost damage to pavements; remedial measures to prevent frost damage; suitability of a soil as a construction material for building highways or railway earthfills or cuts, or dams for impounding water, or water control.

Does the soil in question swell, or shrink, and how much?

What treatment should be given to such soils?

To what a degree can a waterlogged soil be drained?

From these questions one can see that "soil mechanics vs. foundation" problems are attached to the soil, and that they should be studied as problems of stability and deformation.

The scope of the contents of soil mechanics, obviously, overlaps several other disciplines of engineering and science which, in the past, were not always considered to be too closely related.

3-4. Value of Soil Mechanics. The value of soil mechanics is indisputable. No better proof is necessary than that given by the many established soil mechanics laboratories in this country and abroad, and the results obtained by various soil mechanics institutions. The value of soil mechanics study is also attested by the wealth of published technical literature in the form of books and numerous articles on this subject, as well as by the many engineering works executed by means of the application of soil mechanics principles to soil engineering. In addition, the proceedings of the five large international and many national conferences on soil mechanics and foundation engineering held during the last twenty years have proved that soil mechanics is an important and indispensable branch of civil engineering, and thus one of the most useful aids to civil engineers in their everyday professional activities. All this testifies to the enormus impetus in development soil mechanics has achieved throughout the world during the past 40 years.

REFERENCES

1. K. Terzaghi, *Theoretical Soil Mechanics*, New York, John Wiley and Sons, Inc., 1948.
2. K. Terzaghi, *Bodenmechanik auf bodenphysikalischer Grundlage*, Wien, Franz Deuticke, 1925.

PART II

Physical Properties of Soil

Chapter 4

SOIL

4-1. Definition. The noun "soil" originates from the Latin "solum" which commonly had the same meaning as our modern word. The term soil has various shades of meaning and connotation, however, depending upon the general professional field in which it is being considered.

According to Webster,[1] soil is defined as "the loose surface material of the earth in which plants grow, in most cases consisting of disintegrated rock with an admixture of organic matter."

This definition of the term soil is almost synonymous with one used in agricultural soil science where the term soil (or rather topsoil) means only the thin unconsolidated or semi-consolidated superficial stratum of the regolith or mantle-rock at, or close to, the surface of the earth—a stratum which is more or less modified biologically by the penetration of the roots of vegetation supplying the latter with water and other substances in colloidal or in true solution necessary for their growth. The regolith is the fragmental rock debris mantling the rocks of the earth's crust. The regolith may be hundreds of feet thick, or it may be wanting entirely. For example, Ries and Watson[2] say: "The soil may be considered as the superficial, unconsolidated mantle of disintegrated and decomposed rock material, which, when acted upon by organic agencies, and mixed with varying amounts of organic matter, may furnish conditions necessary for the growth of plants. In this broadest sense, the term soil has been used by geologists to include all the mantle of rock decay."

According to pedologist Joffe,[3] the term soil is defined as follows:

"The soil is a natural body, differentiated into horizons of mineral and organic constituents, usually unconsolidated, of variable depths, which differs from the parent material below in morphology, physical properties and composition, and biological characteristics."

Thus one sees that to the agronomist and pedologist the soil is limited to the surface or near-surface materials of the regolith consisting of

1) mineral matter that has originated from rocks by the action of weathering processes, i.e., which have been affected by climatic action;
2) organic matter both living and dead that has usually accumulated over a long period of time through the biologic activities and death of plants and animals;
3) soil moisture, containing mineral and organic matter in a colloidal state or in true solution, and
4) soil air.

33

From the viewpoint of soil technology, the term "soil" comprehends the entire thickness of the earth's crust which is accessible and feasible for practical utilization and exploitation in solving engineering problems. This concept comes particularly vividly to light in considering subsurface mining operations where shafts and borings are put down to considerable depths as long as such methods prove to be economical.

In foundation and earthworks engineering a great many foundations are laid in unconsolidated rock, particularly when bedrock is deep below the ground surface. This necessitates the investigation and evaluation of the physical properties and the behavior of soil subjected to structural and, where necessary, to earthquake stresses. Hence, in civil engineering, the term soil includes not only the pedologist's soil but also any unconsolidated material, including water in soil, which can be found between the ground surface and consolidated rock. In other words, the engineer's definition of the term soil includes all regolith material, or the entire soil profile down to, and sometimes even into, the underlying consolidated rock, referred to also as bedrock (borings, wells, tunneling for subsurface exploration, shelters, storage tanks). From this discussion it can be understood that "soil" in the engineering sense means deposited derivatives from the rock crust of the earth in its natural, original, undisturbed state, or that which can be excavated and placed in an earthwork (such as an earth-fill dam), or what can even be found in an earthwork already. One notes that in soil engineering, a sharp demarcation between rock and soil is no longer made. In this sense the term soil is adopted and used also in soil mechanics, and in this book only the engineer's definition of the term soil is to be understood.

From an engineer's viewpoint, soil is a material by means of which and upon which he builds his structures.

4-2. Formation of Soil. As already indicated, soil, which is a complex mixture of inorganic matter and sometimes may or may not contain decomposed organic residues and other substances, and which blankets the earth's crust, is formed by the process of weathering, that is: disintegration and decomposition of rocks and minerals at or near the earth's surface through the action of many natural physical or mechanical and chemical agents into smaller and smaller particles. The two latter kinds of weathering processes are concomitant, and occur simultaneously.

The factors of weathering in the process of soil formation may be atmospheric, such as the work of oscillations of temperature (heat, frost); wind and water (for example rain, and also ice); erosion and transportation by wind, water (rain, river, sea) and glaciers; plant and animal life; chemical action, for example the complex phenomena of solutions, crystal growth, oxidation, hydration, hydrolysis, carbonation, and leaching that are brought about by water, especially when it contains carbonic acid; man's activities, and time.

4-3. Mechanical Weathering. Mechanical weathering means the breakdown or comminution of a mass of rocks into smaller subordinate sizes of particles

without chemical changes, i.e., without destroying their identity. Examples
of mechanical weathering are cracking, crushing, and crumbling. Obviously,
the type of soil derived depends upon the type of the disintegrated *parent
rock*.

Temperature changes of sufficient magnitude, amplitude, and frequency
bring about changes in the volume of the rocks in the superficial layers of the
earth's crust in terms of expansion and contraction. Such a volume change
sets up tensile and shear stresses in the rock ultimately leading to the fracture
of even large rocks, and eventually reducing them to dust. Besides, the rock-
composing minerals possess different coefficients of heat transmission and expansion. The kind of rock weathering just described takes place in a very
pronounced manner in arid climates where free, extreme atmospheric radiation
brings about considerable variations in temperature at sunrise and sunset.
In deserts, for example, the temperature of the rock surface can rise to about
60°C in the day and fall below zero at night.

In cool, humid climates alternate freezing and thawing acting upon water
contained within rocks is considered to be one of the main factors in the physical
comminution of rocks. The expansive force of the freezing and expanding
water, 9 percent by volume, confined in the joints, bedding planes, and other
interstices of rocks exerts an enormous pressure (about $150 \, t/ft^2$) and breaks down
the structure of rocks effectively.

Rocks are disintegrated mechanically also by various *processes of movement:*
for example, abrasion of rock by moving water in swiftly flowing streams, or
mechanical effects induced by the impact of wave action, erosion by overland
flow (runoff), or the movement of one rock over or against another, moving ice
in glaciers and large ice sheets, and the abrasive effect of sand particles swept
by wind. The weathered rock material is transported and redeposited by gravity,
water, wind, ice, and, to a lesser extent, plants and organisms.

It is interesting to note that 95% of the known part of the lithosphere consists
of igneous rocks, and only 5% (4% slates, 0.75% sandstones and 0.25% lime-
stones) of sedimentary rocks.[4] Perhaps more pertinent is that on an earth surface
area basis the figures are about 4 to 1 in favor of sedimentary rocks.

The principal mineral groups that are present in the igneous rocks are

feldspars	59.5%
amphiboles and pyroxenes	16.8%
quartz	12.0%
micas	3.8%
other minerals	7.9%
Total	100.0%

4-4. Chemical Weathering. In the processes of chemical weathering rocks
are more altered than by mechanical weathering. Chemical weathering is
usually associated with liberation of heat. The action of chemical agents destroys

the identity of the mineral particles. In chemical weathering some minerals disappear partially or fully, and new chemical compounds are formed which are different from the parent minerals. The chemical weathering of rocks depends upon the presence of water and temperature and the dissolved materials in water: ammonia, oxygen, carbonic acid, chlorides, sulphates, and other materials. The most important of those materials in their effect are carbonic acid and oxygen. For example, the process of chemical weathering is at its least effective in arid climates because of lack of sufficient quantities of water, and also in arctic and alpine regions because of the low temperatures which prevail there. In humid climates, however, the intensity of the chemical weathering processes increases as the temperature of those regions increases. Accordingly, the maximum intensity of chemical weathering processes of rocks occurs in the tropical regions.

4-5. Oxidation. Oxidation is the process whereby oxygen is added to the rocks. Oxygen is the most energetic oxidizing agent in nature. The oxidation of rocks and rock-forming minerals by air is aided by the presence of moisture. Without water, oxidation is generally slow. Iron-containing minerals are the ones which are very commonly subjected to oxidation. The oxidation of pyrite, which is composed of iron and sulphur, forms sulphuric acid which attacks rocks. The products of oxidation are split off and some are washed out.

4-6. Hydration. Hydration is a common process of rock decay by which water is combined with some other soil substances thus producing certain hydrous minerals. For example, many silicates (kaolin, serpentine, talc, chlorite), oxides (iron and aluminum) and sulphates (gypsum), are in this class. The processes of hydration are more intensive in the humid than in the arid climates.

4-7. Hydrolysis. Hydrolysis is a very effective chemical process of decomposition. In such a process a mineral compound is broken up and resolved into other compounds by adding hydrogen.

4-8. Carbonation. Carbonation is the process of chemical decomposition by which carbon dioxide contained in water combines with the oxides of calcium, magnesium, potassuim, sodium, and iron. As a result of this union, carbonates or bicarbonates of these metals are produced, including dolomite and calcite. In most instances carbonates are readily soluble. Silicates, which for the most part are very resistant to solvent action, may also be changed into carbonates and removed in solution.

Carbonic acid is a weak acid, but it is an effective chemical weathering agent because it comes in large quantities (as high as 0.45%) with the rain water. Its effectiveness on the weathering of rocks shows up particularly in regions of high rainfall.

The soil contains approximately ten times as much carbon dioxide (CO_2) as the atmospheric air. It must also be noted that the moisture films adsorbed to the surfaces of the soil contain large quantities of this gas.

4-9. Leaching. Leaching is the process whereby water-soluble parts (calcium carbonate, for example) are dissolved and washed out from the soil by rainfall, percolating water, subsurface flow, or other water.

Generally soil in a humid climate is leached to a higher degree than those in arid or semi-arid climates. Also, high temperatures induce more intensive chemical processes and changes in soil directly as well as by reactions induced by living organisms.

Leaching with respect to the leach-out and leach-in zones of soil has some effect upon the formation of the horizons in a soil profile, creating some horizons with more plastic properties than other horizons.

4-10. Chemical Effects on Foundations. Chemical reactions which contribute to the disintegration of rocks may also cause dangerous effects on concrete and metal piles, and in particular on structural foundations which are made of concrete and founded in soil. Damage is more likely to become effective when there is moisture present. Particular attention should be devoted to the examination in those cases where the soil consists of artificial or man-made fill. Such fills may contain excavated soil, refuse and materials and rubbish from broken-down structures. When lixiviated by rain water, such a soil may exhibit an aggressive effect upon pile foundations or other structures made of steel and concrete.

Among the harmful chemical agents in soil found naturally or introduced artificially (for example, leakage from factories) which substantially affect concrete are: carbon dioxide, water containing carbon dioxide, sulphates, sulphides, and sulphuric acid.

In some mineral soils, the presence of the salts of $CaSO_4$, $MgSO_4$, K_2SO_4, Na_2SO_4, $(NH_4)_2SO_4$, and others are considered to have ill effects on concrete.

Sulphur-bearing coal mines and copper and zinc mines sometimes produce mineral waters which are corrosive to almost all construction materials used in foundation engineering and in drainage structures. The harm is caused by the free acid or acid-forming elements carried in the waters.

Special attention should be devoted to admixtures of iron compounds in water when pursuing operations for lowering the ground-water table. These compounds affect adversely the fine filter screens of the wells. Reaction of these chemicals in water may corrode the screens, or it may clog them by incrustation, thus stopping the yield of the wells.

Salt solutions are also dangerous to pumping installations because of the electrolytic decomposition of the filter-screen materials in case they establish a galvanic circuit. To protect steel wells covered with copper screens from electrolytic aggression and incrustation, the *Siemens Bauunion* in Germany has patented (D.R.P. No. 408799) a device whereby the steel well-casing is connected with the minus pole of a D.C.-battery source. The insulated "anode" is inserted into the pumping pipe.

Swamps which contain large amounts of fine particles of pyrites are also very aggressive to cement and concrete. Pyrites, when chemically combined with water (moisture) and oxygen, form ferric sulphates and sulphuric acid. Often swampwaters themselves disintegrate concrete if they are in contact with it.

Organic acids in swamps and marshes where vegetal matter is decaying make water aggressive. Bridge and drainage structures should be protected against aggressive waters.

Structures in salty waters—ports and maritime structures, for example— are affected mainly by chlorides which cause metal piles, sheet piling, and other metal structural elements to corrode. Certain magnesium salts are thought to deteriorate concrete. The chemical disintegration of concrete in salty waters is accelerated by the mechanical disintegration resulting from alternate wetting and drying and frost action in cold climates. Therefore the soil, the groundwater, and river, lake or sea water should be explored and tested before any construction work is started.

4-11. Time. Time has ever been recognized as an important factor in the development of distinctive soil profiles. The formation of soil from igneous and metamorphic rocks takes places within *a long period of time*. Soft shales and sandstones, however, require less time to be transformed into soil. Only limited information is available on the actual time, in years, it takes to form a soil profile in a given environment.

The geologic and climatic forces have never ceased to act; they still are at work in degrading the earth's surface. The factor time plays an important role in the consolidation process of cohesive soils.

4-12. Soil Types. One distinguishes between glacial soils, residual soils, alluvial soils, and wind-borne soils.

Glacial soils are those which have been transported and deposited by glaciers. The principal glacial deposits are of the Pleistocene Age. The glacial ice sheet filled up river valleys with the so-called *glacial drift*. Glacial drift is the glacial deposit from all types of the superficial material of rock debris of any sort, handled in any way, by the continental glacier—for example by erosion, transportation, deposition from ice, or running meltwaters emanating from the ice. The glacial deposits may be sorted, assorted, or stratified. These deposits consist of boulders, rock fragments, gravel, sand, silt, and clay in various proportions.

The position of the southern boundary of the continental glacier is distinctively recognized by the geologic feature called the terminal moraine.[5] The landform of the terminal moraine, consisting of glacial debris material, is characterized by irregular, hummocky hills. Their width varies from one to two miles, and their height can be about 100 ft.

One of the engineering aspects of terminal moraine soil materials containing lenses of silty clay and clay is the disposal of domestic wastes by means of domestic septic tanks. Septic tanks built in clayey soils, soils which by nature are of low permeability, may function improperly, thus creating unpleasant odors and becoming a nuisance to the community in question. Another engineering aspect of glacial soils relative to foundation engineering is the thickness of the glacial drift. On ridges of the bedrock the glacial drift may be thin, whereas in preglacial valleys the glacial drift may be thick. In New Jersey, the extreme known thickness of glacial drift is about 460 ft. Generally, the thickness of the glacial drift varies from zero to about 250 ft. An average thickness of the glacial drift may be said to be from about 20 to 40 ft. The practical engineering aspect of knowing the thickness of the glacial drift may be brought to the fore by a case from the construction years ago of the earth dam for the Boonton, New Jersey, water reservoir. The dam site originally selected had to be abandoned because of a loose drift material; it could not properly support the weight of the dam, nor could it meet satisfactory permeability requirements. Hence, a new dam site had to be chosen where the bedrock was encountered at a shallow depth covered with but a thin stratum of glacial drift. The thickness or depth of the glacial drift in a valley has its economic aspect since this factor governs the cost of a dam—regardless of whether it is of earth or concrete—or a highway, or railway. It also governs the cost of foundations of bridges, locks, and other engineering and hydraulic structures.

Excavation operations in glacial till (unsorted, unstratified, unconsolidated, heterogeneous material) in a dense state require a power shovel, or even explosives. Ordinarily, however, excavations in glacial till present no problem.

Unstratified drift consisting of saturated, gray rock flour, which is found in the Morristown area along the toes of the gneissic ridges, is termed by local contractors "the bull's liver". This rock flour presents to contractors great difficulties in excavation work because the rock flour has a tendency to slump, and to collapse unsupported walls of excavation pits if the ground-water table is not lowered. Also, contractors fear losing construction machinery operating on the rock flour.[6]

Some of the physiographic features of glacial drift are 1) eskers, 2) kames, 3) stratified drift, and 4) glacial clays.

1) *Esker*. An esker is a bed deposited by a sub-glacial stream confined by ice. An esker appears as a conspicuously long, narrow, low, sinusoidal ridge of crudely stratified gravel and sand. Eskers approximately parallel the direction of movement of the glacier.

2) *Kames*. Kames appear as low mounds and hills. They consist of poorly stratified gravel and sand.

3) *Stratified Drifts*. Stratified drifts are glacial deposits along the major drainage courses north of the terminal moraine. Stratified drift consists of comparatively homogeneous sand admixed with gravel and silt in various proportions. It usually provides the best road construction material and railroad ballast.

4) *Glacial Clay* (varved clay). During the course of geologic times the now extinct lakes were filled with stratified silt and clay, the so-called varved clay, Fig. 4-1. The Swedish term *varve* (turn, course, layer) means a distinctly marked annual deposit of sediment. Excavations in glacial clay reveal neat annual layers or varves. The varves indicate that the clay had once been the sediment at the bottom of a lake. The varves consist of a sequence of a thicker varve, light in color, which is the summer sediment (silt), and a thinner and darker

varve which is the winter sediment (clay), when the finer sediment settled out at low velocities of flow beneath the frozen surface of the lake. Roughly, each pair of such summer-winter varves represents one year.

This brief review on glacial soils may be summarized like this: glacial soils are important sources of soil as a construction material for earthworks, as a foundation material, and as an aggregate for concrete.

Residual Soils. Residual soils are those which have been left in place as a result of decay of the underlying parent rock, concealing the parent rock below the ground surface. Residual soils are usually encountered south of the terminal moraine. In glaciated areas residual soils are buried by glacial drift because there may be more than one terminal moraine. The parent materials for residual soils are igneous rocks such as granite or basalt, and sedimentary rocks such as limestone, sandstone, and shale.

FIG. 4-1   Varved clay.

Alluvial Soils. Alluvial soils occur in former and present flood plains and deltas, often forming very thick deposits.

Wind-borne Soils. Under this group two kinds of soil material may be comprehended, namely: the loess and dune sand. Wind-borne soils are ones which have been transported and laid down by atmospheric currents such as winds. Loess is wind-blown silt or silty clay, light in color, porous and coherent. Loess as construction material is relatively unknown to engineers. Loess often may turn out to be a very dangerous material for dams, highways, and as a support of foundations, particularly when wet. Dunes develop when and where loose sand is exposed to wind (sandy shores of lakes, rivers, seas).

4-13. Some Soil Designations. Because there are no definitions giving accurate characterizations of a soil, in practice there still are some descriptive terms of soils used for this purpose based on the soil profile, the appearance, and on some of the properties one can "touch off" from the soil. Therefore, it was found to be appropriate to give here a short description of the meanings of some soil types which are generally used in practice.

Bedrock is any layer of rock either at the surface or beneath superficial deposits of soil. Bedrock may be soft or hard.

Boulders are detached rock fragments larger than about 12 in. in diameter.

Boulder Clay is a mixture of an unstratified sedimental deposit of glacial clay, containing unsorted rock fragments of all sizes ranging from boulders, cobbles, and gravel to finely pulverized clay material.

Calcareous soil denotes a soil containing calcium carbonate. Such a soil effervesces when tested with weak hydrochloric acid.

Caliche is a soil conglomerate of gravel, sand, and clay, the particles of which are cemented by calcium carbonate.

Cobbles are rock fragments ranging in size from about 3 in. to 12 in. in diameter.

Diatomaceous earth is a fine, light gray, soft sedimentary deposit of the siliceous remains or skeletons of diatoms. Diatoms are minute unicellular marine organisms. Such a soil is very porous, and of fine structure.

Gumbo is a very fine-particled clay deposit, devoid of sand. This clay is dark, plastic, and very sticky. When moist it is sticky and spongy. It is one of the most difficult soils to handle either in excavation or as a road material.

Hardpan is a relatively hard, densely-cemented (by limonite) soil layer, like rock. It will not soften when wet. The material may be clays or silts, and cohesionless materials. Hardpans offer great resistance to the penetration of soil-drilling tools. Hardpans are difficult to excavate.

Humus is the term used to denote a dark brown organic amorphous earth of the topsoil. It consists of partly decomposed vegetal matter. As a foundation or road material, humus is undesirable because it continues to decay, shrinks, and also holds water.

Lime soils contain calcium carbonate as the predominant ingredient, the proportions of which may rise above 75%, although the usual quantity is under 50%.

Loam (an agronomic term) is a mixture combined of sand, silt, and clay, sometimes containing some organic matter, as, for example, humus. The terms sand, silt, and clay here refer to the particle size.

Loess denotes a uniform, cohesive, wind-blown, porous, but coherent deposit of very fine material. The sizes of its particles are very uniform, and usually range between about 0.01 mm to 0.05 mm, which size corresponds to silt or a silty clay fraction. The color of loess is yellowish light brown. Loess is encountered in dry continental regions. Slopes of cuts made in it are able to stand nearly vertically.

Marl is a very loose term denoting deposits which consist of mixtures of calcareous sands, or clays, or loam. The proportion of carbonate lime, however, may not fall below about 15%, nor does the quantity of clay rise above 75%.

Muck denotes a mixture of finely particled, inorganic soil and black, decomposed organic matter. This material usually is found accumulated under conditions of imperfect drainage—for example, in swamps—or is deposited by overflowing rivers.

Mud designates a mixture of silt or clay with water. The consistency of mud is an almost fluid mass.

Peat is an organic soil formed of vegetal matter under conditions of excessive moisture, as found in swamps. Peat is very compressible, and therefore unsuitable for supporting even the lightest foundations.

Pebbles are a constituent part of gravels with diameters about 50 mm to 75 mm.

Quicksand is not a special type of soil, but a condition. Any granular material through which an upward flow of water takes place may become "quick" under proper hydraulic conditions.

Till is generally understood to be that part of glacial drift which is directly deposited by ice, without transportation or sorting by water. Till consists of an unstratified, unconsolidated to moderately consolidated, heterogeneous mixture of clay, sand, gravel, and boulders. Till is also known by the term boulder-clay.

The meanings of the soil as described above reveal fully the inadequacy of the information on the properties of soils presented by the descriptive method. Soil as an engineering material is an extremely complex one. Each of the constituent parts of a soil has different physical properties, and the presence of them in varying proportions affects the different properties of the whole composite considerably.

More accurate information for the characterization of the physical and mechanical properties of soils can be obtained only from laboratory tests.

4-14. Cohesive and Non-cohesive Soils. One of the distinctive properties of the various kinds of soils is bond or cohesion between the individual soil particles. The degree of cohesion—or sticking together—can be compared by subjecting the soil sample to drying, and later attempting to rupture the sample. Observations show that in such a case sand ruptures immediately. Clayey sands can be crushed easily by means of the fingertips, but fat clays become hard. Because of their cohesive properties, soils may be classified into two main groups, namely: a) non-cohesive soils, and b) cohesive soils.

Non-cohesive soils are those formed of uncemented, finely weathered rock particles, for example gravel and sand.

Cohesive soils are those possessing cohesion. Cohesion is attributed partly to the inter-molecular attraction of the soil particles for each other throughout the soil mass—called true cohesion—and partly to binding of the soil mass together by the capillary action of the soil moisture—called the *apparent cohesion*. When submerged, the apparent cohesion of the soil mass is destroyed.

It is, of course, obvious that it is extremely difficult to make a strict delineation between a lean or light clayey sand and a fat sandy clay; hence the transition in gradation of cohesion of such soils.

Silts, for example, possess a comparatively slight cohesion. With increasing amounts of the finer-sized particles, such as clay and colloids, the cohesion of the soil increases.

4-15. Soil as a Disperse System. All surfaces of solid particles, among them also the surfaces of the finest colloidal soil particles, when moistened with a liquid such as water, adsorb part of this liquid in the form of a thin hull or moisture film. Likewise, it can be assumed that under natural conditions soil particles are in a humid or moist environment, and adsorbing moisture. The importance of this in relation to the freezing or heating of soil, and its associated soil moisture migration, is that the soil particles are already coated with adsorbed moisture films before freezing sets in.

Considering the solid particles of soil and soil moisture, soil can be considered as a disperse system: the solid particles form the disperse phase, and the water, in which the soil particles are distributed and which thereby forms the continuous phase, is the dispersion medium.

A phase is any homogeneous part of the system different from other parts of the system and separated from these by abrupt transition, as, for example, the solid soil particles dispersed in water—thus giving the concept of the solid and liquid phases of the soil.

Also, the finely-sized soil particles surrounded by the moisture films can be considered in one way as a colloidal suspension. Hence, the concepts, problems, and processes of colloid and physical chemistry are coming more to the fore in studying soil moisture transfer upon freezing. It is to be noted that, according to Wolfgang Ostwald,[7] the colloidal state is independent of the chemical composition of the dispersed solids.

REFERENCES

1. Webster's International Dictionary of the English Language, 2d ed., Springfield, Mass., G. and C. Merriam Company, Publishers, 1956.
2. H. Ries and T. L. Watson, *Engineering Geology*, 5th ed., New York, John Wiley and Sons, Inc., 1947.
3. J. S. Joffe, *Pedology*, New Brunswick, New Jersey, Rutgers University Press, 1936.
4. A. A. J. De Sigmund, *The Principles of Soil Science*, London, Thomas Murby and Co., 1938.
5. R. D. Salisbury, *The Glacial Geology of New Jersey*, vol. 5, Trenton, New Jersey, 1902.
6. A. R. Jumikis, *Engineering Aspects of Glacial Soils of the Newark Metropolitan Area of New Jersey*. Engineering Research Bulletin no. 42, College of Engineering, Rutgers—The State University, New Brunswick, New Jersey, 1959.
7. W. Ostwald, *A Handbook of Colloid Chemistry*, trans. by M. H. Fisher, Philadelphia, P. Blakiston's Son and Co., 1919, p. 2.

QUESTIONS
4-1. What is soil mechanics?
4-2. Define soil.
4-3. Describe some glacial landforms.
4-4. Why is it helpful for an engineer to recognize in nature glacial landforms?
4-5. What is varved clay?
4-6. What is soil profile?
4-7. What is soil horizon?

Chapter 5

SOME PHYSICAL PROPERTIES OF SOIL

The fundamental soil properties characterize, to a certain extent, the quality of the soil as a construction material or the degree of stability of soil under foundations of engineering structures.

Some of the fundamental physical properties of soil are color, mechanical composition, structure, particle size and shape, texture, specific gravity, unit weight, porosity, volumetric and gravimetric relationships of the various soil phases, and consistency.

5-1. Color. Color is one of the most obvious and common soil properties first to be noted as one observes the soil.

In color, soils may vary widely from almost pure white through red to black, with almost every possible color combination. The color of the soil depends mainly upon the particular type of the soil mineral matter, organic contents, the amount of coloring oxides of iron and of manganese, and the degree of oxidation.

Under favorable moisture and temperature conditions for chemical activity, the iron compounds of soil minerals become oxidized and hydrated into red, brown, or yellow compounds. Black color of soil is due to the presence of manganese compounds or highly decayed organic matter. Green and blue colors of soil are due to ferrous compounds, for example, glauconite and pyrite. Gray and white colors of soil are mainly due to absence of colored materials as grain coatings. These colors are effectuated by quartz, kaolinite and other clay minerals. Small proportions of organic matter would also impart to the soil a light gray color. As the amount of organic matter in the same soil increases, the soil becomes darker in color.

A soil changes its color with the change in its moisture content. During the drying process of a soil sample its color generally turns lighter. The impression of the color tone upon the observer depends upon the moistness of the soil, the time of the day, and the position of exposure of the soil to the sun (angle of incidence). Therefore, for identification and descriptive purposes the color of the soil should be that of the moist state and, preferably, of the undisturbed state of the soil.

5-2. Mechanical Composition of Soil. By nature soil is a very complex physical system. Soils are aggregates composed of an assemblage of the most diverse granular mineral particles, humus or organic matter, and various inorganic

44

chemical compounds. The physical make-up of a mineral soil is termed its mechanical composition.

5-3. Soil Phases. The word "phase" is derived from the Greek /φασις, meaning "appearance". By a phase of soil is understood any homogeneous part of a soil system different from other parts of the system and separated from them by abrupt transition—the soil solid particles and liquid water, for example. A system consisting of more than one phase is called heterogeneous. Each physically or chemically different, homogeneous, and mechanically separable part of a system constitutes a distinct phase. Thus ice floating in water is a two-phase *system of water* (solid and liquid phases).

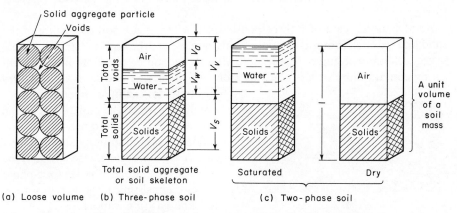

FIG. 5-1 Schematic representation of soil phases.

Because soil is a porous medium, a given volume of a *soil system* ordinarily may be regarded as a system consisting of three fundamental phases, namely:
1) the solid phase or skeleton which may be mineral, organic, or both;
2) the liquid phase or the soil water (and/or oil) filling part or all of the voids between the soil particles, and
3) the gaseous or vapor phase (e.g., soil air and/or entrapped gas) which occupies that part of the voids which is not occupied by liquid, viz. water.

In the studies of freezing or frozen soil, four phases are distinguished: 1) the solid phase, 2) the gaseous phase, 3) the liquid phase (supercooled, unfrozen water), and 4) the ice phase. The phase concept is also of great aid in designing asphalt mixes for the surfaces of road and street pavements.

The volumetric proportions of the solids and voids of a soil mass can most readily be studied by means of the so-called soil phase diagram, Fig. 5-1 b. Thus, such a phase diagram represents the relative volumetric proportions and, as it will be shown further, also the gravimetric proportions of the various soil phases. It is to be understood that there is no real means of separating the soil phases as shown in Fig. 5-1 b. The separation of solids from voids can only be imagined here. However, such a theoretical phase separation is very convenient for the visualization of the phase relationships and for the solution of such phase problems as the volumes and weights (dry densities) of solids, amounts of soil moisture, gas volumes, porosities of a soil mass, and other related problems. Therefore, the concept of the theoretical phase separation should be firmly kept in one's mind.

Depending upon the degree of filling of the voids with water (or degree of saturation) one distinguishes between a three-phase soil and a two-phase soil (Fig. 5-1). When the voids of the soil are only partially filled with water, and air occupies only that space not filled with water, such soil represents a three-phase soil. A three-phase soil is the one most often encountered in nature. When all of the voids are filled with water (saturated soil), such a soil is called a two-phase soil. It is a special case of a three-phase soil: the gaseous phase is lacking.

Also, a special case of a three-phase soil is a two-phase soil consisting of the solid and gaseous components only. This case, where the liquid phase is lacking, is very seldom met in practice because all soils encountered in foundation engineering contain more or less aqueous moisture. This case is true in a totally dry soil only, for example under laboratory conditions, when the moisture is driven out of the soil by drying or alcohol. Under certain conditions, such as freezing, a two or three-phase soil may be transformed into a complex four-phase system, consisting of solids, moisture, ice, and gas (air, vapor).

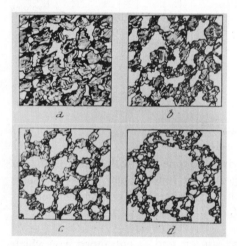

The solid phase, in which one imagines the solids compacted in a dry state in one homogeneous, void-less mass, gives us a surer basis for study rather than the quickly varying and dependent liquid and gaseous phases. Also, each of the properties of the substances comprising the solid, liquid, and gaseous phases of the soil are mutually affected not just among themselves, but also by some external physical factors such as temperature and pressure.

FIG. 5-2 Soil structures: a, b, Granular structure, c, Cellular structure, d, Flocculent structure (after K. Terzaghi, Ref. 1).

5-4. Soil Structure. Individual soil particles and combinations of them of which the soil is made up, depending upon their configuration (shape and size), commonly arrange or group themselves in the aggregate during the process of sedimentation in a suspension in various patterns of structural framework called soil structures. For classification purposes of soil texture such a definition is entirely adequate.

One distinguishes between a primary or single grain structure of soil, and a complex (compound) structure of soil. Besides the aforementioned classification system of soil structures several others have been proposed.

Terzaghi[1] grouped the most common patterns of soil structures into the following three principal groups:

1) granular or single-grained structures,
2) honeycomb or cellular structures, and
3) flocculent structures.

These structures are illustrated in Fig. 5-2.

5-5. Specific Gravity. The term specific gravity applies to the solid phase of the soil only, i.e., to the soil particle material (soil solids), and not to the composite soil as such. The latter contains, besides solids, the liquid phase (soil moisture) and the gaseous phase (e.g., air).

The specific gravity, G, of dry solids of a soil is defined as the ratio of the density, γ_s, of a given volume of the soil solids to the greatest density (at $+4°C$) of an equal volume of pure water, γ_w. The density of the substance of the soil

TABLE 5-1. SPECIFIC GRAVITIES OF SOME MINERALS

Nos.	Minerals	Specific Gravity G
1	2	3
1	Anchidrite	2.9-2.98
2	Augite	3.2-3.5-3.6
3	Biotite (black mica)	2.7-3.2
4	Calcite, $CaCO_3$	2.71-2.72-3.72
5	Chlorite	2.6-3.0
6	Dolomite	2.8-3.0
7	Feldspar	2.5-2.8
8	Glauconite	2.2-2.8
9	Gypsum	2.2-2.4
10	Hematite, Fe_2O_3	4.3-5.3
11	Hornblende	2.9-3.5
12	Illite	2.6
13	Iron oxide hydrates	3.73
14	Kaolinite	2.50-2.65
15	Limonite (iron oxide)	3.50-4.00
16	Magnesite	3.00-5.17
17	Magnetite, Fe_3O_4	5.16-5.18
18	Montmorillonite	2.00-2.40
19	Muscovite (white mica)	2.76-3.00
20	Oligoclase	2.63-2.69
21	Orthoclase	2.50-2.60
22	Plagioclase	2.67-2.74
23	Pyrite, FeS_2	4.95-5.10
24	Quartz	2.65
25	Serpentine	2.50-2.65
26	Talcum	2.60-2.70

TABLE 5-2. SPECIFIC GRAVITIES OF SOME SOILS

Nos.	Soil Types	Specific Gravity G
1	2	3
1	Bentonite clay	2.34
2	Chalk	2.63-2.73-2.81
3	Clay	2.44-2.53-2.92
4	Humus	1.37
5	Kaolin	2.47-2.50-2.58
6	Loess	2.65-2.75
7	Lime	2.70
8	Peat	1.26-1.50-1.80
9	Peat, sphagnum, 25% decomposed	0.50-0.70-0.80
10	Quartz sand	2.64-2.65
11	Quartzite	2.65
12	Silt	2.68-2.72
13	Silt with organic admixtures	2.40-2.50

TABLE 5-3. SPECIFIC GRAVITIES OF SOME NEW JERSEY AND OTHER SOILS

Nos.	Soil Types	Specific Gravity G
1	2	3
1	Beach sands: Atlantic City, N.J.	2.65
	Daytona Beach, Fla.	2.62-2.64
	Lake Champlain, N.Y.	2.64
	Sydney Beach, N.Sc., Canada	2.67
2	Bridgeton sand formation: silty-clayey sand with gravel, N.J.	2.62-2.66
3	Cape May sand formation: gravelly sand, N.J.	2.59-2.66
4	Glacial outwash material (Dunellen): sandy silt, N.J.	2.63-2.69
5	Clayey organic silt, New Haven Harbor, Connecticut	2.53-2.56
6	Montalto, silty-clayey soil, N.J.	2.77
7	Raritan sand (Nixon, N.J.), gravelly	2.64-2.65
8	Penn soil—a Triassic shale derivative	2.64
9	Raritan clay, N.J. (contains some pyrite)	2.64-2.72
10	Raritan sand, South River, N.J.	2.65-2.66
11	Gneissic rock flour, N.J.	2.62-2.65
12	Varved clay, Moonachie, N.J.	2.73

particles is their mass per unit volume of the particles. The density of water at $+4°C$ is 1.000. Therefore, specific gravity is calculated as follows:

$$G = \frac{\text{weight of soil particles in grams}}{(\text{volume of soil particles})(1.000)} = \frac{W_s}{V_s\gamma_w} = \frac{\gamma_s}{\gamma_w}, \quad (5\text{-}1)$$

where γ_s = unit weight of soil solids (absolute volume), and
γ_w = unit weight of water.

The quantity, G, is dimensionless, and it shows how many times heavier is the substance of the solid particles of soil than an equivalent amount of water. The "(volume of soil particles) times (1.000) $= V_s\gamma_w$" actually means the weight of water displaced by the soil particles.

Use of specific gravity. Specific gravity, as an auxiliary factor, is used in computing other soil properties, for example, the porosity and void ratio of a soil, its unit weight, the velocity of fall of a particle through a viscous fluid, soil particle size determination by means of the hydrometer method. It is also used in consolidation studies of clays, in calculating the degree of saturation of soil, in studies of the critical hydraulic gradient in soil when a quick condition of sand is estimated, in zero air-void calculations in the compaction theory of soils, and in other calculations. Therefore serious attention and precision should be devoted to the determination of the specific gravity of a soil.

The specific gravity of a mixture of the various minerals a soil may contain varies, on the average, from 2.50 to 2.70. The heavier the minerals composing the soil, the greater is the specific gravity of the soil. A normal, average value of specific gravity of the mineral particles made up of quartz is usually about $G = 2.65$. Table 5-1 lists specific gravities of some of the common soil minerals. Average specific gravities of various soils are listed in Tables 5-2 and 5-3.

5-6. Temperature Correction Factor. If there is a need to know the specific gravity of a soil at a temperature, say, $+4°C$ (density of water $= 1.000$), then the value of the specific gravity, G, found at $+20°C$, is to be multiplied by the following temperature correction factor:

$$\frac{G_{w4°}}{G_{w20°}}, \quad (5\text{-}2)$$

where $G_{w4°}$ and $G_{w20°}$ are the specific gravities of water at $+4°C$ and $+20°C$, respectively. Hence, the specific gravity of a soil at $+4°C$ is

$$G_{4°} = G_{20°}\frac{G_{w4°}}{G_{w20°}} \quad (5\text{-}3)$$

Of course, specific gravities of soils can be determined and reported at any other two sets of temperatures T_1 and T_2 than at $+4°C$ and $+20°C$. In such cases the proper specific gravity ratios should be calculated and used:

$$G_{T_2} = G_{T_1}\frac{G_{wT_2}}{G_{wT_1}}, \quad (5\text{-}4)$$

where T_1 = temperature at which specific gravity G_{T_1} has been determined, and
T_2 = temperature at which one is interested to know the specific gravity,
G_{T_2}, of the soil. Of course, the flasc or pycnometer has then to be
calibrated at temperature T_1.

5-7. Porosity. Depending upon the degree of soil density or packing, soil
particles are surrounded by a certain amount of voids, which are termed pores.
The total volume of all voids within a unit volume of soil, regardless of whether
fully or partially filled with liquid, is termed the *soil porosity*. Porosity, n, is
expressed by the ratio of volume of all voids, V_v, to the total volume of soil
(solids plus voids),

$$V = V_s + V_v, \tag{5-5}$$

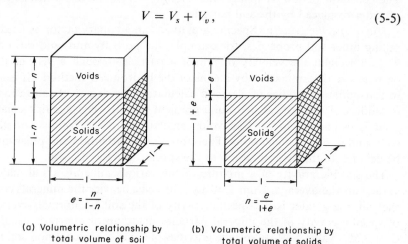

(a) Volumetric relationship by
total volume of soil

(b) Volumetric relationship by
total volume of solids

FIG. 5-3   Relationship between coefficient of porosity, n, and void ratio, e

Fig. 5-3, and is usually expressed quantitatively in percent:

$$n = \frac{\text{volume of all voids in soil}}{\text{total volume of soil}} 100 \tag{5-6}$$

or

$$n = \frac{V_v}{V} 100 = \frac{V_v}{V_s + V_v} 100, \tag{5-7}$$

where V_s = volume of solids.

Also, n can be expressed as

$$n = \frac{V - V_s}{V} = 1 - \frac{V_s}{V} = 1 - \frac{W_s}{G\gamma_w V}, \tag{5-8}$$

where W_s = weight of solids of soil, and

$$V_s = \frac{W_s}{G\gamma_w}, \tag{5-9}$$

where G = specific gravity of the soil, and
γ_w = unit weight of water.

The volume of voids in natural sands depends to some extent on their mechanical composition, degree of packing, and the natural processes of their deposition. Sands which have been deposited by rapidly receding floodwaters have a porosity of about $n = 50\%$. Sands which were deposited slowly have on the average a porosity of about $n = 25\%$.

5-8. Void Ratio. Because soil structure, depending upon various processes, may vary with time, the porosity of the soil may also vary. The change in volume of soil voids, which can take place under the action of loads, brings in its turn a change in the total volume of soil. Therefore, the total volume of soil is to be regarded as a variable quantity which causes inconveniences in calculating porosity by Eq. (5-6). For this reason, in soil mechanics practice it is customary to express porosity by a ratio of volume of total pores or voids to the total volume of solids, the latter of which can be considered as a constant quantity, and is taken as a unit of volume. The quantity expressing the ratio of the volume of voids to the volume of solids is termed the relative porosity or void ratio, e, Fig. 5-3:

$$e = \frac{\text{volume of voids in soil}}{\text{volume of solids in soil}}, \qquad (5\text{-}10)$$

or

$$e = \frac{V_v}{V_s} = \frac{V - V_s}{V_s} = \frac{V}{V_s} - 1 = \frac{VG\gamma_w}{W_s} - 1, \qquad (5\text{-}11)$$

where all symbols have the same meaning as before.

The quantity, e, is more convenient and preferred to use in mathematical calculations of practical problems than porosity, n. One sees that void ratio, e, is a figure which shows how many times more voids than solids there are in a soil.

The volume of voids includes all voids, visible as well as those invisible to the naked eye. Void ratio, e, is extensively used in calculating unit weight, critical hydraulic gradients, water transmissibility, soil consolidation tests and settlement analysis of soil, as well as in determining the relative density of soil. From the variation in pore volume or void ratio it is possible to evaluate the density of soil and thus the degree of compaction of the soil. Also, it can be said that void ratio characterizes the natural state of density of a soil.

5-9. Relationship Between Porosity and Void Ratio. The physical meaning of the soil properties porosity and void ratio can be explained by means of the soil phase diagram, Fig. 5-3. Assume that a unit volume of soil, the total height of which is one unit of length ($= 1$), contains a volume of pores the amount of which is $V_v = n$. Then, obviously, the volume of solids can be expressed as $V_s = (1 - n)$.

Now the void ratio, e, can be expressed as follows:

$$e = \frac{V_v}{V_s} = \frac{n}{1-n} \qquad (5\text{-}12)$$

From this relationship, the porosity, n, is

$$n = \frac{e}{1+e} \qquad (5\text{-}13)$$

This expression can also be obtained directly from Figure 5-3 b. Here, the volume of solids is designated as occupying one unit of volume, and the voids occupy a volume of e. Hence, the total volume of soil is

$$V = 1 + e \qquad (5\text{-}14)$$

Then, by definition, porosity is

$$n = \frac{e}{1+e} \qquad (5\text{-}13)$$

The unit volume of a soil sample is made up of the sum of the volume of solids and the volume of voids in that sample:

$$V_v + V_s = 1 \qquad (5\text{-}15)$$

By Eq. (5-11), if the void ratio of a soil is known, the volume of voids can be calculated:

$$V_v = eV_s = \frac{n}{1-n}V_s \qquad (5\text{-}16)$$

Substituting this V_v-value into Eq. (5-15), obtain the volume of solids:

$$V_s = \frac{1}{1+e} = 1 - n \qquad (5\text{-}17)$$

By a similar method of calculation the volume of voids is obtained:

$$V_v = \frac{e}{1+e} = n \qquad (5\text{-}18)$$

Dividing Eq. (5-18) by Eq. (5-17), obtain

$$\frac{V_v}{V_s} = \frac{e}{1+e} \bigg/ \frac{1}{1+e} = e = \frac{n}{1-n} \qquad (5\text{-}11)$$

The sum of these two volumes, V_s and V_v, must be equal to one unit of volume of the soil:

$$V_s + V_v = \frac{1+e}{1+e} = 1 \qquad (5\text{-}19)$$

If also the volume of air-voids, V_a, is to be considered, then the total unit volume, V, is written as

$$V = V_s + V_v = V_s + V_w + V_a, \tag{5-20}$$

where V_w = volume occupied by soil moisture. If the unit volume is a unity, then porosity, n, in fractions of the total volume, which in this instance is the total volume of voids, is as before:

$$n = \frac{V_v}{V} \tag{5-21}$$

The volume of voids occupied by soil moisture, relative to the total volume, is

$$n_w = \frac{V_w}{V} \tag{5-22}$$

The volume of voids, n_a, occupied by air:

$$n_a = \frac{V_a}{V} \tag{5-23}$$

Volume of solids:

$$n_s = \frac{V_s}{V} \tag{5-24}$$

Check: Total volume:

$$n_s + n = n_s + n_w + n_a = 1,$$

or

$$\frac{V_s}{V} + \frac{V_w}{V} + \frac{V_a}{V} = \frac{V_s + V_v}{V} = \frac{V}{V} = 1 \tag{5-25}$$

When all voids in the soil are filled full of water, then

$$V_v = n \tag{5-26}$$

In such a case the total pore volume equals the volume of the water in the pores, or $w_{sat} = n$, where w_{sat} is the saturation moisture content in per cent, and the soil is said to be fully saturated.

5-10. Soil Moisture Content. Soil moisture content is defined as that amount of water which is contained in the voids of the soil. The amount of water contained in the voids of a soil in its natural state is termed the natural moisture content of the soil. The natural moisture content characterizes in general the strength properties of that soil, as well as its performance under the action of load and temperature.

The knowledge of moisture content in soil is necessary in soil compaction control, in determining consistency limits of soil, and for the calculation of the stability of all kinds of earthworks and foundations.

The soil moisture content is determined by drying the soil sample in a drying oven at 105°C to 110°C until a constant weight of the soil sample is attained. The moisture content, w, is expressed in percent of the dry weight of the soil, and is called the absolute moisture content of the soil:

$$w = \frac{\text{weight of water}}{\text{weight of solids}} 100\% = \frac{W_w}{W_d} 100\%, \qquad (5\text{-}27)$$

where W_w = weight of water in the voids of the soil, and
$\quad\;\; W_d$ = weight of solids (weight of oven dry soil).
For example, let $W_w = 11.0$ g and $W_d = 67.0$ g. Then the moisture content, based on dry weight, is calculated as

$$w = \frac{11.0}{67.0} 100\% = 16.4\%.$$

If the soil moisture content and the wet weight, W, of the soil are known then the dry weight of the soil is calculated as

$$W_d = \frac{W_w + W_d}{1 + \dfrac{w}{100}} = \frac{W}{1 + \dfrac{w}{100}} \qquad (5\text{-}28)$$

Using the same figures as above,

$$W_d = \frac{78.0}{1 + 0.164} = 67.0\,\text{g}$$

The wet weight, dry weight, and moisture content relationship, Eq. (5-28), is applied in soil compaction operations for highway and runway fills and for the construction of earth dams.

5-11. Determination of Soil Moisture Content and Soil Density by Means of Radioactive Isotopes. Laboratory gravimetric methods of determining the soil moisture content in soils are slow and cumbersome, particularly if soil moisture content is to be determined in the field, for example under a pavement, or on soil compaction jobs of earthworks. The gravimetric methods involve the drilling of holes into the soil in order to take soil samples from certain depths, drying the soil sample to a constant weight, and calculating the soil moisture content. To facilitate a quick soil moisture content determination, attempts have been made recently to develop non-destructive testing methods by means of radioactive isotopes.[2,3]

The principle of measuring soil moisture content in the field by means of radioactive isotopes is illustrated in Fig. 5-4. A detective device containing a radioactive isotope material, for example cobalt 60, is placed in a lead shielded capsule (a), and lowered to a certain depth in a steel casing (b), placed in the bore-hole made in the soil. The casing and the capsule are provided with ray emission windows (c). Some distance apart, say 3 to 5 ft, another casing (b) is introduced into the soil. In this other casing there is lowered an electrometer tube (d), and ionization chamber connected by means of a shielded cable (e), to a radiation indicator (f). The soil moisture content can be recorded automatically.

The principle of measurement of soil moisture content in place is based on the strong effect of hydrogen atoms in scattering neutrons and causing them to lose energy. For that purpose, Dr. R. K. Bernhard[4,5] of Rutgers University used the cobalt 60 isotope. Likewise, the scattering of gamma rays by a radioactive source and the absorption of the γ-rays by an earth mass provides a quick

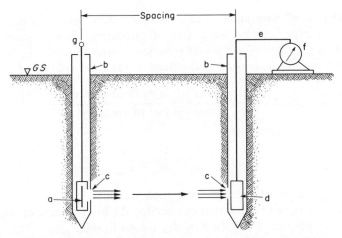

FIG. 5-4   Soil density determination by means of radioactive isotopes. a) Radioactive isotope in lead shielded capsule. b) Steel casing. c) Ray emission orifice (usually closed). d) Electrometer tube and ionization chamber. e) Shielded cable. f) Radiation indicator. g) Remotely controlled orifice opener.

and sufficiently precise method of measurement of the *density* of the soil in place without taking any soil samples. The absorption of the γ-rays is measured by a Geiger counter or by means of a special scintillometer. The radioactive preparate and the counting pipe, spaced at a certain distance, gives for the counted impulses a calibrated measure for the average density of the penetrated mass of soil for that given distance.

The non-destructive method of soil density determination in place by means of radioactive isotopes is less time-consuming and less cumbersome than that of the standard sand-cone method, and permits one to determine rapidly soil densities under field conditions, particularly when densities vary frequently due to moisture content or compaction. Thus, these two soil properties, moisture content and density, can be determined on a soil in its undisturbed state and/or in a newly constructed site, as well as on old fills. This method facilitates the quick testing of long sections of roads or many bore holes during a short period of time, as compared with the conventional soil sampling method for such tests. Besides, the new method permits making many and continuous readings with

56   PHYSICAL PROPERTIES OF SOIL

depth. The soil moisture content is detected by such a device within the standard deviation of gravimetric determinations. The new procedure has also the advantage of detecting the soil moisture content not only in its liquid state but also in its vapor and/or solid state. Also, the γ-ray method is satisfactory in gravelly soils in which the determination of densities is very cumbersome.[6,7] Radiation hazard to personnel operating the equipment is negligible if certain shielding precautions are observed.

Accurate knowledge of changes in soil moisture content and density underneath highway and runway pavements is essential in the design of these structures.

5-12. Degree of Saturation. The condition when voids are partially filled with water is expressed by the degree of saturation, S, or relative moisture content. It is the ratio of the actual volume of water in voids, V_w, to the total volume of voids, V_v, expressed in fractions of the total volume of voids:

$$S = \frac{\text{actual volume of voids filled with water}}{\text{total volume of voids}}, \qquad (5\text{-}29a)$$

or

$$S = \frac{V_w}{V_v} = \frac{W_w}{W_v} = \frac{w}{w_{sat}} \qquad (5\text{-}29)$$

where W_w = weight of water in voids present, and
$\quad\;\; W_v$ = weight of water that can occupy the total volume of voids in soil,
$\quad\;\; w$ = percent of moisture by dry weight in soil,
$\quad\;\; w_{sat}$ = percent of moisture by dry weight when all voids are totally filled with water.
Degree of saturation in terms of porosity:

$$S = \frac{n_w}{n} \qquad (5\text{-}30)$$

1) When $S < 1$, then the voids in the soil are merely partially filled with water.
2) When $S = 1$, then all voids are totally filled with water ($n_w = n$).
  a) When $S = 0$, then the soil under consideration would represent a single phase system.
  b) When $S = 1$, then the soil is a two-phase system.
  c) When $1 > S > 0$, then the soil is a three-phase system.
The expression

$$S_d = \frac{n - n_w}{n} \qquad (5\text{-}31)$$

is called the saturation deficit.

Table 5-4 illustrates the various degrees of saturation of soil for classification purposes.

TABLE 5-4. DEGREE OF SATURATION

Description	Degree of Saturation, S
1	2
Dry soil	0
Damp soil	> 0 -0.25
Moist soil	0.26-0.50
Very moist soil	0.51-0.75
Wet soil	0.76-0.99
Saturated soil	1.00

Examples

5-1. Determine the void ratio of a soil whose porosity is 32%.
By Eq. (5-12), the void ratio, e, is

$$e = \frac{n}{1-n} = \frac{0.32}{1-0.32} = 0.471$$

The result indicates that there are in the soil 0.471 times more voids than solids.

5-2. a) The porosity of a soil fully saturated with water is 57%. Calculate the corresponding void ratio.
By Eq. (5-12),

$$e = \frac{0.57}{1-0.57} = 1.318$$

There are 1.318 times more voids in the soil than solids.

b) When $n = 50\%$, then $e = 1.000$.

5-3. A laboratory test reveals that the void ratio of a certain soil is $e = 1.234$. What is the porosity of this soil?
By Eq. (5-13),

$$n = \frac{e}{1+e} = \frac{1.234}{1+1.234} = 0.553,$$

or $n = 55.3\%$.

From these examples one sees that voids furnish a means of identifying the character of the particular soil. The less the total volume of voids the denser the soil.

5-13. Packing. The amount of voids, or magnitude of porosity of a soil depends very much upon the packing of the soil particles, as well as on the shape of the particles. Packing is the spacing and mutual arrangement of soil particles within the mass of a soil. It can be inferred that upon packing such properties as the density, unit weight, bearing capacity, shear strength, amount of settlement, and permeability of a soil depends. Because the shapes of individual soil particles are varied, which makes the study of packings extremely difficult, one usually starts such studies with the simple assumption that all of the soil particles are of spherical shape, and that they are of the same size. Under such conditions it is revealed that the filling of a unit of space by solids is independent of the relative size of the spheres.

The packing concept can best be illustrated by means of certain arrangements of spheres which would represent ideally shaped particles. For example, if in a cube of unit volume a sphere of radius $r = 1$ can be placed, then at the same packing in the same unit volume cube there can be placed 8 spheres their radius of which $r = \frac{1}{2}$, or 64 spheres with $r = \frac{1}{4}$, and so on. Because the volume of a sphere is $V = \frac{4}{3}\pi r^3$, it becomes apparent that the volume occupied by these spheres or solids in all three cases is the same, and therefore independent of the relative sizes of the spheres. As was seen from the discussion on voids, it is possible to characterize a state of packing by means of the concepts of porosity, n, and void ratio, e.

The pore volume for these conditions in terms of porosity, n, is

$$n = \frac{V_v}{V} = \frac{m(2r)^3 - m\frac{4}{3}\pi r^3}{m(2r)^3} = 0.477,$$

or 47.7%,

where m = number of spheres.

These considerations indicate that porosity is a constant quality for all soils having similar shapes of particles and of similar packing.

When the uniformly sized spheres are arranged or piled immediately one upon another vertically in a rectangular arrangement as in Fig. 5-5a, then such

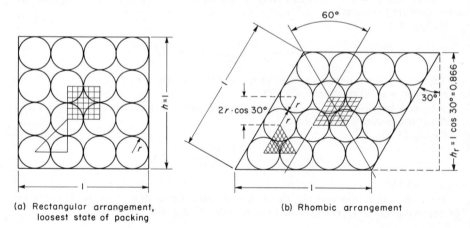

(a) Rectangular arrangement,   (b) Rhombic arrangement
    loosest state of packing

FIG. 5-5   Packing arrangement of spheres.

a packing represents with its porosity of $n = 0.477$ a soil mass of maximum porosity, or in other words, the loosest state of packing, viz., density. One sees that almost 50% of the cube is a void space. The corresponding void ratio for this condition is

$$e = \frac{n}{1 - n} = \frac{0.477}{0.523} = 0.908$$

When the spherical particles in one unit of volume are arranged one particle above the other rhombically, as in Fig. 5-5b, the porosity and the void ratio reduce to $n = 0.412$ and $e = 0.700$, respectively. Thus, if soil particles could be arranged so that the rearrangement brings about the reduction in volume of voids, then a state of denser packing is achieved. This is the principle of compaction of granular material, for example, sands consisting of uniformly sized particles. The rounded particles would roll closer together easily. However, the rounded particles cannot interlock.

The densest state of packing with uniform spheres is attained when one sphere rests upon three or four spheres. The porosity in such a packing is $n = 0.260$, and, again, is independent of the size of the spheres. Thus, all other porosity values can be between $n = 0.477$ and $n = 0.260$ (25.95%). Some fine lakebed sands possess a density which almost equals the densest theoretical packing.

Between the loosest and densest states of packing there can be an infinite number of packings of intermediate density which results in various degress of porosities.

Spherical Particles. Non-uniform Particle Sizes. Density of packing can be greatly increased by decreasing the amount of void spaces. Decrease in void

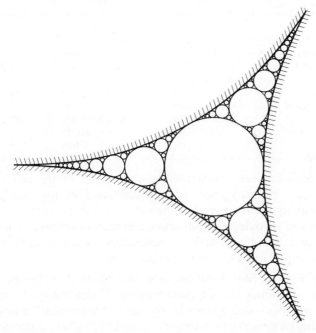

FIG. 5-6 Densest state of packing of spherical particles of various sizes.

spaces is achieved by filling the larger voids with finer particles, Fig. 5-6. However, as a rule, not all voids can be filled with finer particles. Some void spaces still remain. Hence, in dense states only average packing conditions result. Thus, a sandy soil material with so-called well graded particles from coarse to fine sizes, when compacted or vibrated, can attain high densities.

5-14. Soil Texture. Engineers recognize a soil property commonly known as *texture*. The term soil texture is used to express the percentage of the three main fractions (sand, silt, and clay) present in the soil sample passing the No. 10 mesh (2 mm) sieve. Thus, soil texture refers to the relative proportions of the various size groups of individual soil particles in a soil mass.

Table 5-5 shows the terms of the various soil fractions and their limiting sizes adopted as a standard by the U.S. Department of Agriculture, Bureau of Soils; the American Society for Testing Materials, and by the International Society of Soil Science. Note that in the International Scale the successive fractional limits are at equal decimal logarithmic intervals.

TABLE 5-5. SOIL PARTICLE FRACTIONS

Designation of Soil Fractions	Diameter of Soil Particle, in mm		
	U.S. Department of Agriculture, Bureau of Soils 1951	American Society for Testing Materials 1958	International Society of Soil Science
1	2	3	4
Fine gravel	2 to 1	> 2.00	
Coarse sand	1 to 0.5	2.0 to 0.42	2.0 to 0.2
Medium sand	0.5 to 0.25		
Fine sand	0.25 to 0.10	0.42 to 0.074	0.2 to 0.02
Very fine sand	0.10 to 0.05		
Silt	0.05 to 0.002	0.074 to 0.005	0.02 to 0.002
Clay	< 0.002	< 0.005	< 0.002
Colloids	—	< 0.001	—

Soil texture has a very great influence on many of the soil properties—packing, density, porosity, and permeability; and in the case of cohesive soils—on plasticity, swelling, and shrinkage.

The size of soil particles is of importance in such instances as construction of earth dams or railroad and highway embankments where earth is used as a material that should satisfy definite specifications.

5-15. Soil Particle Size Analysis. The soil physical make-up, or textural composition, sometimes termed granulometry, is determined by means of its particle size analysis—also known by the term "mechanical" analysis of soil. It is a screening process in which coarser fractions of soil are separated by means of series of sieves of graded mesh. The mechanical analysis is one of the oldest test methods for soil materials, and it has been practiced for centuries.

The proportions by dry weight of each of these fractions relative to the total dry weight of the dry composite soil sample used for the analysis are established by weighing.

Soils, the particle sizes of which are larger than 0.074 mm (U.S. Standard No. 200 mesh sieve), are usually analyzed by means of sieving. Soil materials finer than 0.074 mm (-200 material) are analyzed by method of sedimentation of soil particles by gravity.

Description of details for performing particle size analyses of soils are given by various agencies in their manuals or specifications of standard test methods of soils.[8,9,10] The material retained on sieves Nos. 4, 10, 20, 40, 60, 100, 140, and 200 are designated as "plus 4" material ($+4$), $+10$, $+20$, $+40$, $+60$, $+100$, $+140$, and $+200$ material, respectively. This means soil particles which are larger than the openings in a corresponding mesh screen.

Conversely, "minus 4" material (-4), -10, -20, -40, -60, -100, -140, and -200 soil material are those passing the corresponding mesh screen

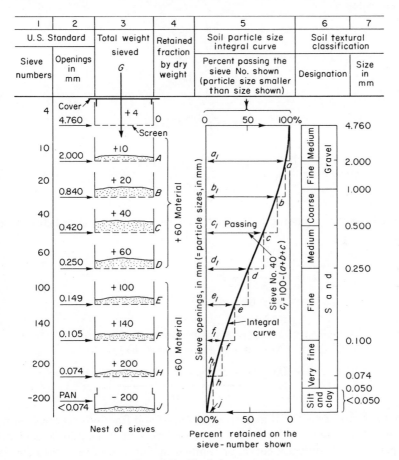

FIG. 5-7 Sieving process.

5-16. Calculations and Representations. The percent fraction, $p\%$, retained on a certain sieve in the soil particle size analysis is calculated as

$$p = \frac{g}{G} \cdot 100\%,\qquad (5\text{-}32)$$

where g = dry weight at 105°C in grams of a given fraction of soil retained on a certain sieve, and

G = dry weight at 105°C in grams of the total soil sample used in the particle size analysis.

The concept of soil particle size analysis by means of sieving is illustrated in Fig. 5-7. This figure shows a nest of sieves with the larger opening on top of the column, and with the finer sieves at the bottom. Fractions by dry weight retained on the sieves are designated by A, B, C, D, E, H, and J. The sum of these fractional weights is the total weight of a soil sample sieved, G. The fractional weights A, B . . . J, expressed in percent retained on each sieve, thus, are calculated as

$$a = \frac{A}{G} \cdot 100\%$$

$$b = \frac{B}{G} \cdot 100\%$$

$$c = \frac{C}{G} \cdot 100\%$$

(5-33)

$$\cdot \ \cdot \ \cdot \ \cdot \ \cdot \ \cdot$$

$$j = \frac{J}{G} \cdot 100\%$$

Percent fractions passing the size of sieve shown are calculated, for example, as

$$a_, = 100 - a$$

$$b_, = 100 - (a + b)$$

$$c_, = 100 - (a + b + c)$$

$$\cdot \ \cdot \ \cdot \ \cdot \ \cdot \ \cdot \ \cdot \ \cdot \ \cdot \ \cdot \ \cdot \ \cdot \ \cdot$$

(5-34)

$$h_, = 100 - (a + b + c + \cdot \cdot \cdot + h)$$

$$j_, = 100 - \underbrace{(a + b + c + \cdot \cdot \cdot + h + j)}_{100} = 0,$$

where $(a + b + c)$ is the cumulative percent of soil fractions retained on sieves Nos. 4, 10, 20, and 40. Retention on sieve No. 4 in this example is shown as zero percent. The integral curve, or summation curve, separates the cumulative percents of particle sizes smaller than the size shown from the cumulative amount in percent of all soil particles which are retained on that sieve and above it. For example, the cumulative amount of particles retained on sieve No. 40 is $(a + b + c)$ percent; the cumulative amount of particles passing No. 40 sieve (-40 material) is $c_, = 100 - (a + b + c)$ percent. The Bureau of Soils classification of the USDA is also shown on Fig. 5-7 (see Column 6, "Designation").

A sample calculation of fractionating a 200 g dry soil sample is shown in Fig. 5-8.

For gravelly and sandy soils sieving is a fundamental part of the particle size analysis to sort out the coarser grades. For clayey soils sieving is just a constituent part of, or preparatory operation in the particle size analysis. The fine particle fractions are usually separated by the method of sedimentation in water. The sedimentation method is based on the fact that the velocity of sedimentation is a function of soil particle size.

U.S. Standard sieve Nos	Total dry weight of soil sample sieved 200.0 g	Retained on sieve		Cumulative retained		Cumulative passing	
		g	%	g	%	g	%
1	2	3	4	5	6	7	8
4		0.00	0.00	0.00	0.00		
						200.00	100.00
10		2.84	1.42	2.84	1.42		
						197.16	98.58
20		5.66	2.83	8.50	4.25		
						191.50	95.75
40		46.04	23.02	54.54	27.27		
						145.46	72.72
60		44.00	22.00	98.54	49.27		
						101.46	50.73
100		23.64	11.82	122.18	61.09		
						77.82	38.91
140		11.26	5.63	133.44	66.72		
						66.56	33.28
200		63.16	31.58	196.60	98.30		
						3.40	1.70
-200 (Pan)		3.40	1.70	200.00	100.00		
		200.00 g	100.00%				

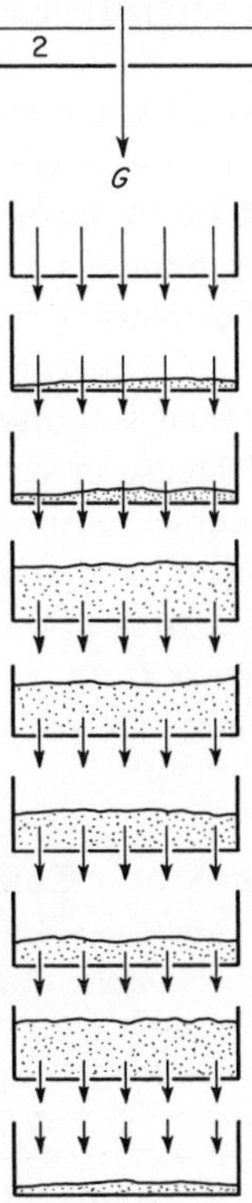

Fig. 5-8 Fractioning of a soil sample.

5-17. Specific Surface of a Soil Mass. As already indicated, many of the physico-chemical phenomena and processes in fine-particled soils, such as condensation of gases, the manifold effects of surface tension of liquids, and the majority of electrokinetic phenomena occur on the surfaces of the soil particles exposed, and their intensity increases in certain proportion with the absolute and specific surfaces of the soil particles. Likewise, many soil properties so important in soil mechanics and soil engineering depend very much upon the extent of the surfaces exposed. Because water can be held between the flat clay and colloidal particle surfaces, these surfaces are called *internal* surfaces of a soil mass. *Absolute* surface is the amount of surfaces of the various soil phases which are in contact with each other. *Specific* surface of a soil mass is the total amount of all surfaces of all particles contained (entire disperse phase) in a unit weight (or sometimes in a unit volume) of the soil mass. Of course, the chemical composition of the fine particles also influences the performance of a clayey soil.

If the internal surface is related to a unit weight (1 g, for example) of the soil, then it is called the specific surface. It is the total amount of all surfaces of all particles contained in the unit weight of the soil. Sometimes specific surface of soil particles is related to a unit volume of the soil particles; at other times to a unit volume of the soil.

Properties such as the soil moisture holding capacity, the immense increase in cohesion of a fine-particled soil with the increase in surface area, the decrease in permeability to water and air with the increase in surface area (the latter causes in soil great friction to flow through its minute voids), and electrical activities manifest clearly the importance of the internal surface. This must not be forgotten when testing soils, evaluating soil properties, designing earthworks, fills, foundation supports—and checking their stability.

The enormous increase of surface area with decrease in size of a geometrical particle is readily illustrated by imagining a cubic centimeter of a mineral material subdivided successively and decimally into smaller and smaller cubes (see Table 5-6). One notices that the total surface area upon successive subdivision of a cube of one cubic centimeter can increase from 6 square centimeters to 60 million square centimeters (6000 square meters $= 0.6$ hectares $= 2.471 \cdot 0.6 = 1.428$ acres).

TABLE 5-6. SUCCESSIVE SUBDIVISION OF A CUBE

Length of one edge of various sizes of cubes		Number of cubes	Total surface	Specific surface
1		2	3	4
1 cm	$= 10$ mm	1	6 cm^2	6×10^0
1 mm	$= 1 \times 10^{-1}$ cm	10^3	60 cm^2	6×10^1
0.1 mm	$= 1 \times 10^{-2}$ cm	10^6	600 cm^2	6×10^2
0.01 mm	$= 1 \times 10^{-3}$ cm	10^9	6000 cm^2	6×10^3
1.0 μ	$= 1 \times 10^{-4}$ cm	10^{12}	6 m^2	6×10^4
0.1 μ	$= 1 \times 10^{-5}$ cm	10^{15}	60 m^2	6×10^5
0.01 μ	$= 1 \times 10^{-6}$ cm	10^{18}	600 m^2	6×10^6
1.0 $\mu\mu$	$= 1 \times 10^{-7}$ cm	10^{21}	6000 m^2	6×10^7
0.1 $\mu\mu$	$= 1 \times 10^{-8}$ cm	10^{24}	6 ha	6×10^8
0.01 $\mu\mu$	$= 1 \times 10^{-9}$ cm	10^{27}	60 ha	6×10^9
0.001 $\mu\mu$	$= 1 \times 10^{-10}$ cm	10^{30}	6 km^2	6×10^{10}

Table 5-7 shows the internal surface areas of soil fractions. For simplicity, assume that there is only one particle size in each fraction, as indicated in column 2, Table 5-7. This means that the shape of all particles is a cube.

TABLE 5-7. INTERNAL SURFACE AREAS OF SOIL FRACTIONS

Soil Fractions	Cubical Particle Size mm	Total Internal Surface Area cm^2
1	2	3
Sand	1.0	$60 = 6.0 \times 10^1$
Silt	0.05	$1{,}200 = 1.2 \times 10^3$
Clay	0.005	$12{,}000 = 1.2 \times 10^4$
Colloids	0.0005	$120{,}000 = 1.2 \times 10^5$

So, for example, 1 cm^3 of sand, when subdivided into 1 mm^3 large cubes would give for that sand fraction 1000 such cubes. The surface area of a 1-mm large cube is $0.1 \times 0.1 \times 6 = 0.06$ cm^2. The total area exposed is $0.06 \times 1000 = 60$ cm^2. Thus, progressively smaller particle sizes create large exposed surface areas. It is interesting to note the immense difference in internal surface area between a particle of a 1 mm sand size, 0.05 mm silt size, 0.005 mm clay size and the 0.0005 mm clay size.

Baver[11] shows that in about 0.52 cm^3 of coarse silt containing spherical particles the size of which is 0.05 mm (50 μ) there is a very large surface area of 628.32 cm^2, and that in the same volume with spherical particles of 0.0002 mm (20 $\mu\mu$) in diameter (colloidal clay size) there is a surface area of 157,080 cm^2.

The great difference in specific surface area is, probably, one of the important factors in causing dissimilarities in the physical properties of clayey and sandy soils.

For spherical particles, the specific surface area per unit volume of the solids is

$$A = \frac{\pi d^2}{\dfrac{\pi d^3}{6}} = \frac{6}{d} \quad \text{(cm}^2\text{/cm}^3\text{)} \tag{5-35}$$

The experimental methods are of particular value when absolute quantities of total specific surfaces of fine particles are necessary. Among the experimental methods the permeability method and the gas adsorption method are popular.

5-18. Colloids. The term "colloid" is a translation from the Greek words *kolla* and *oidos*, meaning glue and alike, respectively. Colloid is any substance in a certain state of fine subdivision—the so-called colloidal state. According to Hauser,[12] the colloidal range of dimensions of particles of a colloid matter lies within a size interval from 1 $\mu\mu$ to 500 $\mu\mu$ or even up to 1 μ. The colloid particles are too small to be seen with a conventional microscope, but they can be observed by means of the electron microscope. In some of the soil classification systems colloids are classified as a separate soil fraction which, thus, is merely a finer subdivision of clay. Under proper conditions almost every mineral can be transformed into the colloidal state by simply grinding it fine enough. Therefore, a colloid state is just a state of matter. Soil colloids, hence, are formed in the ordinary, natural weathering process, and they may be organic as well as inorganic. In this treatment only the inorganic colloids will be considered.

The colloidal fraction of the soil, as well as the individual characteristics of the colloidal particles themselves, determine the physical behavior of the composite soil material. Colloids are the most active fraction in a soil composite. The admixture of the colloidal fraction to soil can be imagined as a colloidal coating on the surfaces of the coarser soil particles.

The divisional limits of the colloidal fraction of soil are arbitrary or conventional, because not all clay particles which are smaller in size than 1 μ are colloidal. Therefore, we deduce that not all clay particles are colloidal. Besides, there does not exist a sharp-cut division limit between non-colloids and colloids. However, because of the satisfactory control of the fine-sized particles microscopically by advanced techniques, the set size limits 1 μ and finer for the colloidal fractions can be justified.

5-19. Properties of the Colloidal Fraction of Soil. Colloidal particles contain a greater specific surface area than an equal weight of the same matter of soil consisting of larger particle sizes than the colloids. This immensely increased specific surface area of colloids is manifested in pronounced interfacial phenomena such as stability, adsorption, surface tension, shear strength of soil, and thixotropy. An especially important property of the colloidal particles is the definite electrical charge they carry. In solutions, under the influence of a direct electric current, colloidal particles migrate to the electrodes. Particles which migrate to the anode are electro-negative. Particles migrating to the cathode are electro-positive. Because of this property of carrying an electric charge, colloid particles adsorb water and gases, and ions of material in solution with opposite charge to a notable extent. They repel materials of like charge. The property of attracting and holding solvent materials, ions, gas and water on the surfaces of the particles is termed *adsorption*. Large specific surface areas can adsorb large quantities of water. Colloids also furnish cohesion, which is the binder for holding soil particles together in clods.

Absorption, in contradistinction from adsorption, is the complete intermingling of molecules of the absorbent and the absorbed substance; in reality, absorption is identical with solution. Thus, adsorption refers to surface concentration, and absorption to true solution.

When dry, colloidal particles possess practically the same physical properties as clays. When wet, however, the distinctive properties of colloidal particles become very much pronounced: they are plastic and cohesive. An increase in colloidal matter increases these soil properties.

Sand and silt particles possess a relatively small specific surface. Therefore, physically and chemically, they are rather inactive.

Colloidal particles suspended in water appear not to follow the law of gravity: they exibit the Brownian movement—an oscillatory movement of floating around. The intensity of this movement increases as the particle size decreases.

The addition of an electrolyte to a colloidal suspension (sol) causes the colloidal matter to form floccules of particles and to coagulate, i.e., settle down as a gelatinous mass. In other words, under the conditions described, a sol passes into a gel. For convenient reference, a soil is a colloidal system of very fine particles in water suspension which is not a true solution. Gel is a form of a jelly-like matter in a colloidal state formed by the coagulation of a colloidal liquid suspension upon the addition of a suitable concentration of an electrolyte. After a period of rest, the gel may break down into flocs. The gel particles are not subjected to Brownian movement. They are at a standstill. Only upon the application of a definite force to overcome the forces holding the particles together will gels exhibit flow. Therefore gels possess a measurable yield point. The process of transformation of colloidal sol into gel is termed *gelation*.

The following is a typical characteristic of a gel: when subjected to some small mechanical stress, the gel behaves as a solid, elastic body, i.e., it displays form elasticity without any flow indication. Only above a certain elastic limit—the so-called yield value—does flow of the gel begin to take place.

Colloidal fractions in soil interfere greatly with the movement of air and soil moisture by means of moisture films, capillarity, and permeability. Variations in moisture content of colloidal clay cause the material to change in volume: addition of water causes swelling; conversely, drying results in shrinkage.

The presence of the colloidal fraction in soil may limit the realm of its usefulness in certain soil engineering operations. In the construction of earth dams, however, the property of colloidal clays to adsorb to a certain degree some quantities of water and to expand attracts the interest of soil and earthworks engineers.

5-20. Clay Minerals. Most scientists now recognize three main groups of clay minerals, namely *illite*, *kaolinite*, and *montmorillonite*. Clay minerals are groups of crystalline substances of which clays are made up. This has been shown by the use of X-ray techniques.

The composition of the complex illite group (colloidal siliceous matter), according to Hauser[13] is

$$K_y Al_2[Fe_2 Mg_2 Mg_3](Si_{4-y}Al_y)O_{10}.$$

The symbols in brackets indicate that they may substitute for the symbol written to the left of the bracket. The subscript y varies between 1 and 1.5.

Illite is the general term for the mica-like clay minerals. Illites are also known by the term hydrous micas. Illite is chief constituent of many shales.

The kaolinite group, a hydrous alumino-silicate, has the general chemical composition of the formula

$$Al_2(Si_2O_5)(OH)_4.$$

Kaolinite occurs in soils of humid-temperate and humid-tropical regions.

Montmorillonite clays are most prominent in soils occurring in regions of low rainfall, for example, in deserts and prairies. Montmorillonite is the dominant clay mineral in bentonite—altered volcanic ash. The composition of the siliceous clay mineral montmorillonite is

$$Al_2[Mg](Si_4O_{10})(OH)_2xH_2O.$$

Montmorillonites are more colloidal than kaolinites, and, on wetting, the former swell considerably.[14] Because of the markedly expressed colloidal properties, montmorillonites present in themselves a very active fraction of the soil mass. The swelling is explained by water entering between the plate-like montmorillonite particles and forcing them apart; thus, the lattice structure of the clay minerals is expanded. More than one molecular layer of water can be accommodated between the scale-like particles. Montmorillonite clay is a very plastic material.

The thickness of montmorillonite (bentonite) particles is $\geq 1.10^{-3} \mu$; their length varies from 1 to $3.10^{-1} \mu$. The particle size of montmorillonite clay merely reflects the degree of dispersion and the ultimate dispersion breaks the mineral down in unit crystals or plates. Sodium-bentonite can adsorb from 600% to 700% of water. Calcium-bentonite adsorbs about 200% to 300% of water.

5-21. Bentonite. Bentonite, a geologic rock formation, is one of the well known ultra-fine clays, mainly composed of the montmorillonite group of clay minerals. Bentonite was formed from the alteration of volcanic ashes. The color of bentonite clays varies from white to light green or light blue. When a dried bentonite is immersed in water, the former increases its volume or swells more than any other dried clay. For example, 1 g of bentonite would take 7 cm³ of water to prepare it in a thixotropic paste. When moist bentonites are dried, they shrink. When in contact with water, sodium (natrium) bentonites exhibit larger volume changes than calcium bentonite. Highly colloidal bentonites swell in water just like glue or gelatin. Under ultra-microscope the dimensions of a bentonite particle can be estimated as being in ratio of (1) : (0.1) : (0.01) micron. When properly conditioned, clays are used in the construction of dams, reservoirs, ponds, or lagoons for preventing seepage of water through them. The swelling property of the clays is utilized here to advantage, namely, to seal off the voids, thus reducing seepage flow by decreased permeability.

Bentonite clays are also used for canal linings. Usually, if no special care is taken, or no special design of the sealing mixture is made, at the beginning such linings perform satisfactorily. However, when the bentonite lining starts to crack, the lining jobs have to be repeated. In irrigation canal lining jobs bentonite clay is applied in thin films. Upon swelling, the colloidal matter clogs off the voids, thus preventing water losses by percolation. Also, bentonite injections are used in sealing cracks in concrete dams and in fortifying walls of excavations for building cutoff walls (cores) for dams in weak soils.

Electron micrographs of illite, kaolinite, and bentonite are shown in Figs. 5-9, 5-10, and 5-11, respectively. Electron micrographs also show that the structure of the montmorillonite clay ranges from an amorphous type of material to clearly defined thin plates.

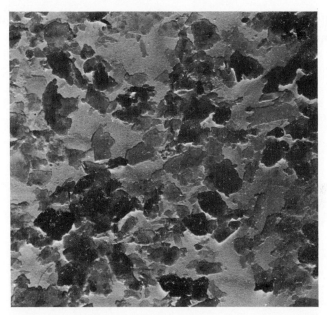

FIG. 5-9   Electron micrograph of a Juniata-Milesburg, Pa, illite, × 34,650. Courtesy of Dr. T. F. Bates, The Pennsylvania State University.

THIXOTROPY

5-22. Thixotropy. Hvorslev[15] writes that the presence of colloids in soil has a considerable effect on the properties of that soil. For example, in his doctoral thesis Hvorslev explains that some of the structural strength of a clayey material that is lost by remolding is in time slowly recovered. This strength recovery is termed by Hvorslev the thixotropic recovery. The necessary time for the recovery of the strength depends on the moisture content, and particularly on the salts in solution in the soil water. By definition, thixotropy is the property of a material to undergo an isothermal gel-to-sol-to-gel transformation upon agitation and subsequent rest. Thus, upon mechanical agitation gels liquefy, and resolidify when agitation is stopped.[13,16] This gel-sol transformation process can be repeated indefinitely without any fatigue. The gelation time under similar external conditions is the same.

Instead of mechanical agitation, a gel can also be transformed into a sol by means of warming the gel. Upon cooling, the sol again reverts to the gel. Gel-sol-gel transformation upon the application of mechanical energy can take place without the application of heat externally. If the change by warming is reversed by cooling, the gel is said to be thermally reversable. Braune and

Richter[17] report that the end value of gelation does not depend practically upon the temperature of the gelling matter itself (between 20°C and 40°C). Wolarowitsch and Tolstoi[18] have likewise shown that the flow limits of concentrated kaolin-suspensions are independent of temperatures between 10°C to 57°C.

Essentially, the sol-gel change is the change in consistency of colloidal suspensions: upon agitation gels loose their consistency and viscosity; after allowing the shaken suspension to rest, gels regain their original consistency. The loss of consistency is caused by a temporary breakdown in the structure of the thixotropic matter. Hence, the thixotropic phenomenon is the reversible, isothermal gel-sol change in state which takes place with some colloidal matter in suspension when shaken, i.e., when subjected to shear stress.

FIG. 5-10   Electron micrograph of Banda, India, kaolinite, × 44,530. Courtesy of Dr. T. F. Bates, The Pennsylvania State University.

The word thixotropy consists of two parts: thixis = the touch, the shaking, and tropo = to turn, to change. Thus, thixotropy means "to change by touch". In the mechanical agitation of a colloidal suspension it is the structure of the suspension that changes "by touch". Thus thixotropy is defined as a reversible gel-sol-gel transformation in certain materials brought about by a mechanical disturbance followed by a period of rest.

There exist many colloidal systems which have the properties of thixotropic flow, and cover a wide range in consistency. The thixotropic phenomenon is especially pronounced with sodium (natrium) bentonite suspensions, and particularly in systems where large volumes of water are adsorbed upon and held between the colloidal particles.

The following questions arise: What is the reason for the thixotropic phenomenon? What are the forces and their nature which in the thixotropic sol-gel systems keep the colloidal particles together?

FIG. 5-11   Electron micrograph of a Wyoming bentonite, × 43,000. Courtesy of Dr. T. F. Bates, The Pennsylvania State University.

Ions of the neighboring particles, together with ions which are situated within the interstices between the colloidal particles, and under the influence of the mutually attractive forces as well as the bound water to the surfaces of the particles, are arranged and oriented in a certain definite order to form an easily destroyable structure. Upon shaking, these loose bonds are destroyed. During the lapse of time when the thixotropic material is at rest, owing to their slow internal relative displacements, kations, anions, and water molecules tend to rearrange and reorient themselves, and thus the strength of the thixotropic material is again recovered.

However, this explanation does not answer the above two questions satisfactorily, particularly if one sees that the build-up forces act over a large distance —larger than the thickness of the moisture films surrounding the particles. Therefore, a more proper answer to the above questions can be formulated like this: at present, the thixotropic phenomenon is not yet very well understood, and no completely satisfactory theory on thixotropy has yet been suggested. The only thing that can be said is that the thixotropic phenomenon is a function of such a structure of the colloidal matter that, when broken down by applied energy, it can reestablish itself. Also, it can be assumed that the colloidal particles are surrounded and therefore separated from each other by moisture films. The forces which act between the relatively far-spaced particles are accordingly relatively small, a condition which can temporarily be neutralized by slightly shaking the thixotropic suspension. What is the nature of these small forces which act over such relatively large distances? Freundlich[19] estimates that these forces act across distances of many millimicrons, even up to 120 $\mu\mu$, whereas it is conventionally assumed that molecular forces between particles of matter act merely over a distance of one molecular diameter, or over a distance which is less than 1 $\mu\mu$, when their intensity then markedly decreases.

Unfortunately, there is no direct visual evidence of the breakdown of the thixotropic, colloidal structure nor can it be seen microscopically. Also, a quantitative computation with gels is very difficult.

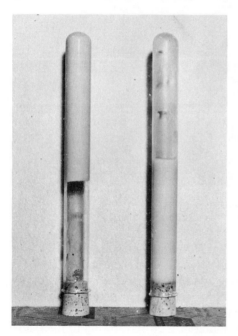

FIG. 5-12   Simple test for thixotropy.

An old, simple test for thixotropy consists of shaking vigorously a colloidal suspension in a test tube and observing the time necessary for it to gelate to such a consistency that it can no longer flow out from the test tube when inverted (Fig. 5-12). In the left tube is a bentonite suspension in the form of a gel; whereas in the tube on the right hand side in that figure the suspension is in a sol state.

After cessation of shaking, the colloidal particles supposedly are in a state of Brownian movement. This movement gradually decreases in intensity until an equilibrium between the gravitational and electrical forces is established. During the decrease of the Brownian movement the colloidal particles and the water molecules orient themselves in a certain order. This orientation takes place slowly; hence the thixotropic strength of the colloidal matter (gel) develops gradually within a certain gelation time. On the other hand, the gradually developed thixotropic strength is destroyed over a definite period of time.

Shaking or tapping the test tube containing a thixotropic gel would prevent the orientation of the colloidal particles and the water molecules, and the gel would be transformed into a sol.

The gelation time, of course, depends upon the concentration of the sol. For example, Winkler[20] gives the following gelation times in minutes for sodium montmorillonite as a function of liquid-to-solid-ratio (by volume):

Liquid/solid ratio—Gelation time, minutes

33	1
34	6
36	45

Thixotropic changes can also be brought about by ultrasonic waves. Winkler presents the following data obtained at a frequency of 175 kilohertz. In column 1, Table 5-8, is given the exposure time in seconds required to liquefy a mont-

TABLE 5-8. LIQUEFACTION BY ULTRAWAVES

Exposure Time, in sec.	Concentration V_L/V_{Sol}
1	2
0	40
5	50
10	58
15	62
30	66
45	68
60	69
120	72
180	72

morillonite suspension the concentration of which is given in column 2 of the same table as the volumetric ratio of liquid to solids (V_L/V_{Sol}).

Table 5-9 contains data by Winkler on electric energy necessary to liquefy

TABLE 5-9. ENERGY REQUIRED TO LIQUEFY VARIOUS CONCENTRATIONS OF THIXOTROPIC GELS

Concentration V_L/V_{Sol}	(Volts)$^2 \times 10^2$
1	2
12	225
16	170
20	121
24	100
28	74
30	70.5
32	68
34	64
36	64

various concentrations of thixotropic gels. As a concentration for these tests the liquid volume ratio to grams of the solid phase in that volume has been chosen.

The information presented in Tables 5-8 and 5-9, should be of considerable interest to foundation and earthwork engineers when designing and constructing earthworks and hydraulic structures in areas containing formation of thixotropic clays or when thixotropic matter, such as sodium bentonite suspensions, is used for injections under vibrating foundations, for example, machine foundations, power plants, or dams.

5-23. Thixotropy of Soil. Thixotropic properties are possessed to some degree also by many cohesive soils. Thixotropy is more pronounced the more a soil contains fine-sized thixotropic-colloidal particles. Also, thixotropy can be exhibited by sandy soils containing merely a few percents of clay. This partially explains the thixotropic regain in structural strength in time of remolded cohesive soil material. A soil possessing thixotropic properties is called a thixotropic soil.

Terzaghi and Peck[21] describe the thixotropy of soil as follows:

"If a sample of a very fine soil fraction is thoroughly kneaded and is then allowed to stand without further disturbance, it acquires cohesive strength, first at a fairly rapid rate and then more and more slowly. If the sample is again kneaded at unaltered water content, its cohesion decreases considerably, but if it is once more allowed to stand, its cohesion is completely regained. This phenomenon is known as thixotropy. The softening and subsequent recovery seem to be due to the destruction and subsequent rehabilitation of the molecular structure of the adsorbed layers."

These and other observations made upon studying clay materials indicate that a phenomenon, analogous to thixotropy, can be noticed also with deforming clays under the action of static loads. In particular this phenomenon is exhibited by deformations which cause a considerable change in the original structure of clays, for example, on shear or under considerable compression. Especially, the effect of rate of loading, viz., time effect, is here a decisive factor: upon slow changes of loading the mutual interaction of the forces within the clay system is only negligibly destroyed and restores quickly. Correspondingly, the resistance of soil to slow deformations is greater than to quick deformations.

In thixotropic soil, due to the energy transferred to the soil, pile driving operations are greatly facilitated: under the exerted blows the pile penetrates more and more easily in the softened-up soil. However, when the pile driving is interrupted for a certain period of time, during which the pile is given a rest and then the driving is resumed, it is noted that the resistance to penetration has considerably increased, approximately 4 to 8 times.

5-24. Thixotropic Fluids in Engineering Operations. As mentioned already, thixotropic suspensions are used as a means of sealing against leakage or loss of water where cement injections fail. The thixo-fluids are used in foundation operations for building an impounding as well as a sealing apron on lowering the ground-water table. The thixo-suspensions during their transport through pipes and in the voids of the soil remain liquid as long as they are in motion.

As soon as they are allowed to rest, they gelate. Another application of thixo-fluids in engineering is as a lubricant to facilitate the sinking of wells and cais-sons, as well as in driving piles, in order to reduce the resistance to penetration of a resistive soil. The bentonite slurry is injected at a concentration of 100 to 120 grams per liter of water. In winter it is advisable to warm the slurry up to about 30°C.

Thixotropic fluids are also extensively used in the drilling of oil wells, as well as in drilling bore-holes for soil exploration purposes. In these fields of endeavor such fluids are known as drilling fluids or drilling muds.

The usual drilling fluid consists of a water base, 98 to 65 percent by volume, and admixed with 2 to 30 percent by volume of clay.[22] Other ingredients may also be admitted. The proportions of those depend upon the requirements of permeability, density, and flow properties. In order that the drilling fluid be stable, the clay ingredients should be so fine in size that they will not settle out of the fluid, or at least will settle out slowly. The clay used in preparing drilling fluids is a commercial bentonite or a clay material from the bore hole.

The basic function of drilling fluid is:
1) to transport bit cuttings up to the ground surface;
2) to buoy the drill shaft;
3) to exert a hydrostatic pressure on the geologic material forming the wall of the bore-hole to prevent the entry of soil water, or oil, and gas into the borehole which might bring about the collapse of the wall of the hole if it is of unconsolidated material;
4) to aid the hydrostatic pressure through the rotary action, to form a few milli-meters thick anti-filter layer on the wall of the bore-hole made in pervious soil, thus stabilizing the hole. Due to centrifugal force the base-water of the fluid permeates into the soil, leaving on the wall a thin coating of the clay;
5) to suspend the cuttings in the hole when circulation of fluid is stopped for a while. During such a stopping time the thixotropic drilling fluid gelates, gains strength in shear and thus is able to support the bit cuttings by its mass.

These properties of a drilling fluid must be retained under various temperature conditions in the bore-hole.

To form the coating on the inside wall of the bore hole, and to prevent ground-water flowing from soil into the hole, particularly when the drilling is temporarily stopped, the pressure of the drilling fluid must be greater than the combination of the active earth pressure and the ground-water pressure. These conditions are illustrated in Fig. 5-13.

5-25. Representation of Particle Size Analyses Data. The results of soil par-ticle size analyses can be represented in various ways, for example, in tabular form or by means of various graphical methods.

Among the graphical methods, the most popular ones are by way of triangular coordinates and by the integral (summation = cumulative) curves, known also as the granulometric, or grading curves.

5-26. Triangular Coordinates. When a soil is represented by only three fractions: sand, silt, and clay, for example, then for the representation of these three fractions graphically, triangular coordinates sometimes are used in the form of an equilateral triangle, a triangle which in concrete technology is also known by the term Feret triangle.[23]

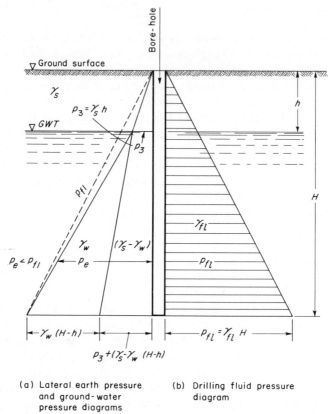

(a) Lateral earth pressure   (b) Drilling fluid pressure
    and ground-water   diagram
    pressure diagrams

FIG. 5-13   Pressure conditions in a bore hole.

The method of representing three soil fractions in triangular coordinates is based on some geometric properties of an equilateral triangle. Consider an equilateral triangle, $\triangle ABC$, Fig. 5-14, the sides of which are s units long. Select an arbitrary point, O', within this triangle; connect point O' with the vertexes of the triangle, A, B, and C, with straight lines. In doing so, the whole triangular area, $\triangle ABC$, is divided into three component triangles, the base of each of which is equal to s and the heights are h_1, h_2, and h_3. The sum of the areas of these three component triangles, $\triangle AOB$, $\triangle BOC$, and $\triangle COA$, equals the full area of the composite triangle $\triangle ABC$:

$$\frac{sh_1}{2} + \frac{sh_2}{2} + \frac{sh_3}{2} = \frac{s}{2}(h_1 + h_2 + h_3) = \frac{sH}{2}, \qquad (5\text{-}36)$$

where H = height of triangle $\triangle ABC$.

From Eq. (5-36), it follows that

$$h_1 + h_2 + h_3 = H \qquad (5\text{-}37)$$

This means that the sum of distances h_1, h_2, and h_3 from an arbitrary point O' within an equilateral triangle to its three sides is a constant quantity, and equals the height H of the triangle, $\triangle ABC$.

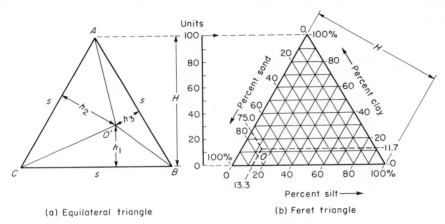

(a) Equilateral triangle   (b) Feret triangle

FIG. 5-14   Triangular coordinates.

Analogically, $h_1 + h_2 + h_3$ forms H, in the same way the three granulometric fractions of a soil always add up to 100%. This analogy is utilized for the representation of the granulometric contents of a soil. Based on the triangular properties one proceeds as follows (Figs. 5-14, a and b). Divide each of the heights, H, of the triangle, $\triangle ABC$, into 100 parts which are taken as the scale for graphical presentation of the percentile contents for the three basic soil fractions. Draw lines through the division marks on H parallel to the corresponding base of the triangle, and draw these lines in the triangle so as to obtain triangular coordinates. A triangle with triangular coordinate lines is called a Feret triangle. Each of the three heights, H, of the triangle $\triangle ABC$, correspond to the variation in one of the basic fractions from zero to 100%. Thus, plotting percentage contents of each of the three fractions on the corresponding heights, H, and passing lines through the appropriate percentage divisions parallel to the sides, s, of the triangle, $\triangle ABC$, obtain the point of intersection, O, of the three lines. Then point O represents the granulometric content of the soil. The heights, h_1, h_2, and h_3, represent each of the separate fractions of the soil. For example, assume that the three major fractions of the Dunellen soil are:

$$+ \begin{cases} \text{sand} - 75.0 \quad (= h_1) \\ \text{silt} \ \ - 13.3 \quad (= h_2) \\ \text{clay} - 11.7 \quad (= h_3) \end{cases} +$$

$$\overline{\text{Total } 100.0\% (= H)}$$

Then point O in Fig. 5-14b represents the granulometric contents of this tri-fractional soil. The soil is a silty-clayey sand.

The advantage of the triangular coordinate system is that for a tri-fraction soil its graphical representation is very simple. Besides, from the position of the "soil" point in the Feret triangle one immediately can give the soil designation according to the tri-fractional classification, for example: silty clay, clayey sand, or other designation. The disadvantage of the triangular graph is the incomplete characteristic of the total granulometric contents of the soil, because it indicates only three fractions when there may be 5, 6, 7, or 8.

5-27. Histograms. Soil particle size data in engineering practice is occasionally represented by a graph plotted to an arithmetical scale, in blocks to show the relation between the particle-size groups or fractions and their amount in percent by dry weight. Such a plot is called the frequency histogram of the distribution (Fig. 5-15). The distribution of the particle-size groups is shown by a

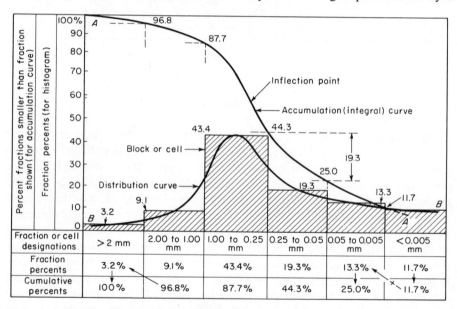

Fraction or cell designations	>2 mm	2.00 to 1.00 mm	1.00 to 0.25 mm	0.25 to 0.05 mm	0.05 to 0.005 mm	<0.005 mm
Fraction percents	3.2%	9.1%	43.4%	19.3%	13.3%	11.7%
Cumulative percents	100%	96.8%	87.7%	44.3%	25.0%	11.7%

FIG. 5-15 Histogram of fraction distribution curve for Dunellen soil $(B\text{-}B)$. $A\text{-}A$ = fraction accumulation curve.

sequence of "cells", or "blocks". In the histogram, the area enclosed by the steps represents frequency exactly, and the sides of the columns designate cell boundaries. The percentage of the different size groups or fractions is diagnostic. Connecting the tops of the various cells with a smooth curve one obtains a soil particle size, or fraction distribution curve, $B\text{-}B$. This curve indicates only the partial fractions, and it has the shape of a frequency curve. Curve $B\text{-}B$ in Figure 5-15 is the histogram of the Dunellen soil.

Although histograms represent the fractional composition of a soil very effectively, the cumulative curves of a soil are, however, more useful to the engineer.

5-28. Integral, or Cumulative, or Granulometric Curves.

General Notes. When the dry weights of each soil fraction, expressed in percent of total dry weight, are added up and these results are plotted, there results
a smooth, integral, or cumulative fraction, viz., particle size accumulation curve
(curve *A-A*, Fig. 5-15). It is called an integral or accumulation curve because
its ordinates represent not separate fractions, but the sum of fractional particles
less than a given fraction, or diameter. The curve points are plotted at cell
boundaries. Cumulative soil particle size accumulation curves are plotted either
to a decimal (arithmetical) scale or to a decimal logarithmic scale. Note that
the coordinate system into which the hitherto discussed cumulative curve is
plotted is an orthogonal one, and the abscissa and ordinate axes are drawn to
linear, arithmetical scale.

Linear Scale. A cumulative particle size curve is plotted in the following way:
the various particle diameters are plotted on the horizontal axis to an arithmetical scale, and the "percent passing" or the total percent "finer than size, or
fraction shown" is plotted on the vertical axis, also to an arithmetical scale
(decimal scale). Thus a particle size accumulation curve presents an idea of
how many percents by weight each of the fractions, viz., particle sizes represents
in a composite soil. One notes, however, that the arithmetical scale of reasonable
length for representing the particle sizes and plotting the cumulative particle
size distribution curve is very inconvenient, namely: the diameters of the fine
particles are jammed very closely together, so that it is practically impossible
to plot the position of the small diameters obtained from the hydrometer test,
or to plot the cumulative curve for the particles in the fine range even if a coarse
scale is chosen. This is usually so when the diameters of the soil particles in a
soil sample vary within wide limits, for example, from 20 mm down to 0.001 mm
and finer. In such instances the arithmetical scale becomes a very long stretched-
out one, making the representation of the fine fractions almost impossible.
Because of the impossibility of finding a convenient linear scale for plotting the
sizes of gravel and sand particles which are measured in centimeters and milli-
meters, as well as the sizes of clay particles the dimensions of which may be of
the order of thousands of millimeters, a different method for the graphical
presentation of soil particle size analysis should be used.

Logarithmic Scale. Because of the wide range in diameter between the coarsest
and finest soil particles, and in order that the contents of the fine sizes may
become more visual, the diameters of the soil particles are plotted to a decimal
logarithmic scale, thus obtaining a more compact curve. The use of the logarithmic scale simplifies the graphic presentation of the results of soil particle size
analysis considerably. Without stretching the curve along the abscissa axis
very much, the decimal logarithmic scale permits plotting the contents of the
fine fractions of soil with a satisfactory degree of accuracy. Note that the range
of the fine sizes is more recognizable in the logarithmic scale than in the linear
scale. The ordinates of the granulometric curve then represent percent by dry
weight of particles equal to or smaller than the size (equivalent diameter) shown
by the abscissa. A smooth curve is drawn through the tops of the corresponding

ordinates of the cumulative fractions (Fig. 5-16). The curve shown in Fig. 5-16 is the granulometric curve of Dunellen soil. Its histogram is also shown.

Because the abscissas are plotted to a logarithmic scale, but the ordinates to a linear, decimal scale, the plot of the granulometric curve is said to be plotted as a semi-logarithmic graph.

Experience indicates that the decimal logarithmic scale for plotting soil particle diameters is, for engineering purposes, one of the best graphical representations of particle size accumulation.

Uniformity. An important quality in regard to a non-cohesive soil material is its degree of uniformity, i.e., whether the particles are mainly of the same size, or whether there is a great range in their sizes. This can be conveniently shown by the *coefficient of uniformity*. When the largest part of the soil particles is of the same diameter, one speaks of a uniform soil (Fig. 5-17, curve 1). In contradistinction, when the soil consists of many particle sizes, it is non-uniform (curve 3). The more uniform the particle size, the steeper is the slope of the granulometric curve. For example, an ideally uniform powder represents itself graphically as an almost vertical line (curve 2). Conversely, non-uniform soils have flat slopes indicating variable particle size content.

Just as the cumulative, particle-size distribution curves indicate uniformity of the soil, so the curves are also called uniformity curves because they give us an indication of the density of a soil. For example, soils represented by non-uniform curves are of non-uniform composition, which, as a rule, will then be more dense than a soil consisting of particles of uniform size. The latter will be then less dense. Hence, the shape of the cumulative particle size distribution curve is an indication of the uniformity of the soil.

From the uniformity curves the *coefficient of non-uniformity*, U, of a soil is obtained. This coefficient, which expresses the variation in the proportions of large and small particles, and thus is a *numerical measure* of soil uniformity, and which in the technical literature is also termed the *coefficient of uniformity* of a soil, is defined as the ratio of the diameter of the particle which has 60 percent of the sample finer than the size shown to the size which has 10 percent by weight material finer than this size d_{10}:

$$U = \frac{d_{60}}{d_{10}}, \tag{5-38}$$

where U = coefficient of Uniformity,

   d_{60} = 60% diameter of soil particle, and

   d_{10} = effective size of the particle, or the effective diameter, i.e., the 10% diameter, Fig. 5-16.

The diameters d_{60} and d_{10} are scaled off directly from the uniformity graph (granulometric curve) of that soil.

Recall that the effective diameter of a soil particle is the diameter of a hypothetical sphere that is assumed to act in the same way as the particle of an irregular shape, and that data obtained from hydrometer analysis using Stokes' law lead to effective diameters, d_e of the soil particles.

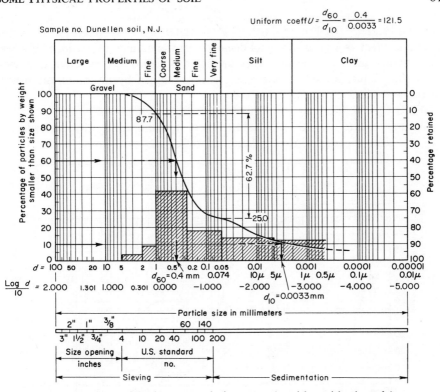

FIG. 5-16 Particle size accumulation curve (semi-logarithmic scale).

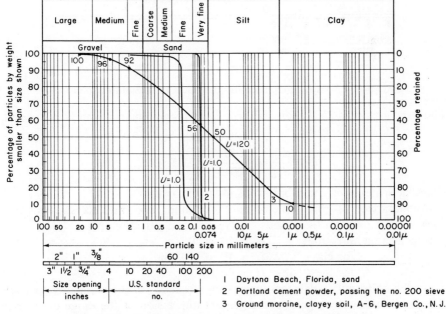

FIG. 5-17 Uniform and non-uniform granulometric curves.

Allen Hazen[24] tried to establish what diameter in actual spheres would cause the same effect as a given soil, and decided that the diameter for which 10% was finer would give this result. This diameter is called the effective diameter, $d_e = d_{10}$. Thus, the effective diameters, d_e, obtained by means of the hydrometer analysis, are the d_{10}-diameters.

When $U < 5$, the granulometry of the soil is very uniform.

With $U = 5$ to 15, the soil is said to be of medium uniformity, and when $U > 15$, the soil is very non-uniform.

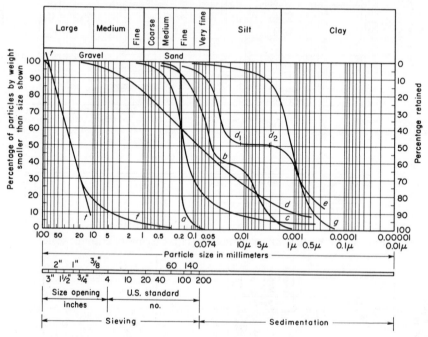

FIG. 5-18   Various shapes of soil particle size accumulation curves.

Thus, the greater is U, the less uniform is the granulometric content of the soil. For the Dunellen soil, Fig. 5-16, the uniformity coefficient is

$$U = \frac{d_{60}}{d_{10}} = \frac{0.40}{0.0033} = 121.5 > 15,$$

which indicates a very non-uniform soil.

A comparison of granulometric curves of sands, silts, and clays reveals that clays are less uniform than sands. Silty soils take a medium place.

On the average, for sands $U = 10$ to 20,

                for clays $U = 10$ to 100, and

                for loess (silts) $U = 2$ to 4.

Thus, the uniformity coefficient, expressing the shape of the cumulative particle size distribution curve, gives one a general impression of the range of the size distribution and the magnitude of natural soils.

Description of Soil Particle Size Accumulation Curves. As discussed already, a steep particle size accumulation curve indicates a uniform soil, Fig. 5-18a. Humps in the curve indicate a soil composed of a mixture of two or more uniform soils (curve *b*). A steep curve in the sand sizes that gradually flattens out into a long, flat curve in the fine sizes would characterize a soil that was formed by weathering (curve *c*) (compare also with curve 3, a glacial outwash soil, Fig. 5-19).

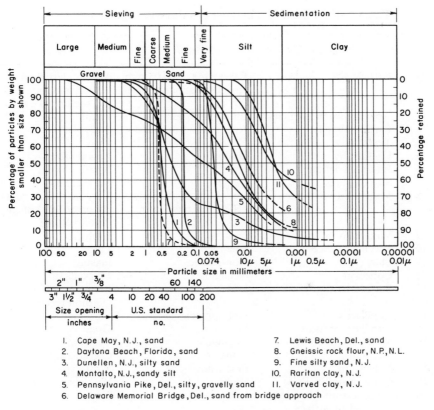

1. Cape May, N.J., sand
2. Daytona Beach, Florida, sand
3. Dunellen, N.J., silty sand
4. Montalto, N.J., sandy silt
5. Pennsylvania Pike, Del., silty, gravelly sand
6. Delaware Memorial Bridge, Del., sand from bridge approach
7. Lewis Beach, Del., sand
8. Gneissic rock flour, N.P., N.L.
9. Fine silty sand, N.J.
10. Raritan clay, N.J.
11. Varved clay, N.J.

FIG. 5-19   Various soil particle size accumulation curves.

A flat curve indicates a wide range in particle sizes. Such a soil is called well-graded (*d*). A flat section in a wavy curve indicates that the particle distribution in that soil is not normal, and that there is a deficiency of particle sizes at the flat interval ($d_1 - d_2$, Fig. 5-18) of the curve, curve *e*. This means that the soil is either made up of a mixture of two types of soil material of approximately normal particle distribution, one fine and one coarse, or it has in some way had all particles of the intermediate sizes removed.

Soils in the early stages of their development, for example in the Alpine regions, are mainly the result of physical weathering. They are generally characterized by the presence of large amounts of coarse material. Their cumulative particle size curves often show an approximation to a linear form in their upper range (Fig. 5-18, curve *f*). Soil *g* in Fig. 5-18 varies widely in its coarser range. However, the finer fractions are more uniform.

In Figure 5-19 are represented some New Jersey soils; the famous Daytona Beach sand (curve 2); some Delaware soils; a gneissic rock flour (curve 8); and a fine, silty sand—both-non-liquid and non-plastic—(curve 9) from New Jersey.

TABLE 5-10. PHYSICAL DIFFERENCES BETWEEN SAND AND CLAY

	Properties	Sand	Clay
1	Particle size	Large: 1.00 to 0.05 mm, mostly distinguishable by eye	Minute, less than 0.005 mm, not visible to the naked eye
2	Appearance of particles	Bulky and rigid	Flexible
3	Particle shape	Angular and rounded	Scaly-like
4	Texture	Coarse	Fine
5	Uniformity	Uniform	Less uniform
6	Internal friction	High	Small, or negligible
7	Size of pores	Large	Very minute
8	Volume of voids	Relatively small, about 50% at a maximum	Very high, as high as approx. 98% of the total volume
9	Void ratio	Low	High
10	Specific surface	Small	Large
11	Plasticity	Non-plastic	Plastic
12	Cohesion	Negligible	Marked
13	Surface tension	Low	Immense surface tension forces
14	Capillarity	Not appreciable	Very high
15	Capillary pressure	Low	Great
16	Shrinkage upon drying	Negligible	Very high
17	Swelling	None	Considerable
18	Expansion	Practically none	Most expansive
19	Compressibility	Slight	Very compressible
20	Compression when load applied to surface	Immediate	Slow
21	Elasticity	Low	High
22	Permeability	High degree, drains readily	Low degree, drains slowly

5-29. Differences Between Sand and Clay. Based on discussions and experience of the various physical properties of soils it is possible to summarize in Table 5-10 the physical differences between sand and clay. One notes that the main difference between sand and clay is the size and shape of their particles, and that the relationship of particles of various sizes in a composite soil is one of the principal factors which determine the physical properties of soils and their behavior under load, water, and temperature.[25]

TABLE 5-11. SUMMARY OF UNIT WEIGHT FORMULAS

Soil Condition	Degree of Saturation	Unit Weight Symbol	Unit Weight formulas	
			$\gamma = f(n)$	$\gamma = f(e)$
1	2	3	4	5
General equation	S	γ	$(1-n)G\gamma_w + nS\gamma_w$	$\dfrac{eS+G}{1+e}\gamma_w$
Dry soil	$S = 0$	γ_d	$(1-n)G\gamma_w$	$\dfrac{G}{1+e}\gamma_w$
Moist soil	$1 > S > 0$	γ	$(1-n)G\gamma_w + nS\gamma_w$	$\dfrac{(1+w)G\gamma_w}{1+e}$ $\dfrac{eS+G}{1+e}\gamma_w$
Saturated soil	$S = 1$	γ_{sat}	$(1-n)G\gamma_w + n\gamma_w$	$\dfrac{G+e}{1+e}\gamma_w$
Buoyant (submerged)	—	γ_{sub}	$(1-n)(G-1)\gamma_w$	$\dfrac{G-1}{1+e}\gamma_w$

TABLE 5-12. APPROXIMATE UNIT WEIGHTS OF SOME SOILS
$1 t/m^3 = 62.4\ lb/ft^3$

Nos.	Soil Type	Unit Weight	
		lb/ft³	t/m³
1	2	3	4
1	Gravel, wet	125	2.0
2	dry	106	1.7
3	Sand, gravelly, dense	125	2.0
4	Sand, dry	100	1.6
5	wet	100	1.6
6	10% moisture	120	1.9
7	loose	81	1.3
8	Silt	112	1.8
9	Loess	100	1.6
10	Loam	100	1.6
11	Clay	131	2.1
12	fresh, 30% moisture	125	2.0
13	dry, hard	137	2.2
14	plastic	100	1.6
15	organic	88	1.4
16	Peat	68	1.1
17	Building wreckage and debris	87	1.4

5-30. Unit Weight of Soil. As the term implies, the unit weight of soil is the weight of soil per unit of its volume. This weight comprises the whole soil mass, i.e., the solid particles plus all voids; the latter may or may not contain soil moisture. The weight of air is considered negligible, and therefore ignored.

The soil unit weight, γ, is expressed as the ratio of the weight, W, of a volume, V, of a soil mass to that volume V:

$$\gamma = \frac{W}{V} \tag{5-39}$$

The unit weight can be expressed in g/cm^3, or kg/m^3, or t/m^3, or lb/ft^3.

Unit weight of water, γ_w, is its weight, W_w, per unit of its volume, V_w:

$$\gamma_w = \frac{W_w}{V_w}. \tag{5-40}$$

For calculation purposes, unit weight of water in the British system of units is taken as $62.4 \ lb/ft^3$. In the metric system, $\gamma_w = 1 \ g/cm^3 = 1 \ kg/1000 \ cm^3 = 1000 \ kg/m^3 = 1 \ t/m^3 = 62.4 \ lb/ft^3$.

In approximative calculations, the unit weight of salt water can be taken as $64.0 \ lb/ft^3$, or $1.025 \ g/cm^3 = 1.025 \ kg/liter = 1025 \ kg/m^3 = 1.025 \ t/m^3$.

For conversion purposes the relationship of pressure $1 \ t/ft^2 \approx 1 \ kg/cm^2$ can be used.

Besides the unit weight of soil containing moisture, other unit weights are to be distinguished: for example, dry unit weight, γ_d; unit weight of solids by absolute volume, $\gamma_s = G\gamma_w$; saturated unit weight of soil, γ_{sat}, and submerged or buoyant unit weight of soil, γ_{sub}.

A summary of unit weight formulas of soil is given in Table 5-11.

Some approximate values of unit weights of some soils are compiled in Table 5-12. These values reveal that the range of the unit weights of soils may vary between quite wide limits, and that their influence upon the static effects in stability problems in soil engineering, in some instances, may be relatively large. Therefore, it is advisable in each particular engineering problem to determine the unit weight of soil by actual test.

REFERENCES

1. K. Terzaghi, *Erdbaumechanik auf bodenphysikalischer Grundlage*, Wien, Franz Deuticke, 1925.
2. D. I. Belcher, T. R. Cuykendall, and H. S. Sack, *The Measurement of Soil Moisture and Density by Neutron and Gamma-Ray Scattering*, Technical Development Report no. 127, Civil Aeronautics Administration, 1950.
3. *Radioactive Isotopes in Soil Investigations*, Symposium, ASTM, Special Technical Publication no. 134, Philadelphia, March 5, 1952.
4. R. K. Bernhard and M. Chasek, "Soil Density Determination by means of Radioactive Isotopes", *Nondestructive Testing*, vol. 11, no. 8, Nov.-Dec., 1953, and vol. 12, no. 1, Jan.-Feb., 1954.
5. R. K. Bernhard and M. Chasek, *A Statistical Analysis from Experiments with Gamma Ray Transmission Through Soils*, Second Progress Report, Bureau of Engineering Research, Rutgers University, July, 1954.

6. D. Bordan and R. K. Bernhard, "Pilot Studies of Soil Density Measurements by Means of X-Rays". Preprint no. 115, ASTM, Philadelphia, 1950.
7. R. K. Bernhard and M. Chasek, "Soil Density Determination by Direct Transmission of Gamma Rays". Preprint, no. 86, ASTM, Philadelphia, 1955.
8. "Standard Specifications for Sieves for Testing Purposes", ASTM Designation E11-39, *1949 Book of ASTM Standards*, Part 3, ASTM, Philadelphia, 1950.
9. *ASTM* "Standard Method of Mechanical Analysis of Soils", ASTM Designation D422-54, *Procedures for Testing Soils*, ASTM, Philadelphia, 1958.
10. American Association of State Highway Officials, "Standard Method of Mechanical Analysis of Soils", AASHO Designation T88-49, published in *Standard Specifications for Highway Materials and Methods of Sampling and Testing*, Part 2, Washington, D.C., 1950.
11. L. D. Baver, *Soil Physics*, New York, John Wiley and Sons, 1956, p. 12.
12. E. A. Hauser, "The Importance of Colloid Science for Highway Construction and Research", a Paper, presented at the 35th Annual Meeting of the Highway Research Board, January 17-20, 1956, Washington, D.C., p. 5.
13. E. A. Hauser, *Silicic Science*, Princeton, New Jersey, D. Van Nostrand Company, Inc., 1955, p. 8.
14. *Dana's Manual of Mineralogy*, 17th ed., revised by C. S. Hurlbut, Jr., New York, John Wiley and Sons, Inc., 1959.
15. M. J. Hvorslev, *Über die Festigkeitseigenschaften gestörter bindiger Böden*, Copenhagen, Danmarks Naturvidenskabelige Samfund, 1937.
16. E. A. Hauser and C. E. Reed, "Studies in Thixotropy. The Thixotropic Behavior and Structure of Bentonite", *The Journal of Physical Chemistry*, vol. 4, 1937.
17. H. Braune and L. Richter, "Die Thixotropie von Bentonitsuspensionen", *Kolloid-Zeitschrift*, vol. 113, no. 1, April, 1949.
18. M. Wolarowitsch and D. Tolstoi, *Kolloid-Zeitschrift*, vol. 73, no. 1, 1933.
19. H. Freundlich, "Über Thixotropie", *Kolloid-Zeitschrift*, vol. 46, no. 4, 1928.
20. H. G. F. Winkler, "Über die Thixotropie des Montmorillonits", *Kolloid-Zeitschrift*, vol. 105, no. 1, 1943.
21. K. Terzaghi and R. B. Peck, *Soil Mechanics in Engineering Practice*, New York, John Wiley and Sons, 1948, p. 16.
22. D. A. Larsen, "Colloid Features of Drilling Fluids", *Colloid Chemistry*, edited by J. Alexander, New York, Reinhold Publishing Corporation, 1946, vol. 6, pp. 509-534.
23. René Feret, "Sur la compacité des mortiers hydrauliques", *Annales des Ponts et Chaussées*, Paris, 1892, vol. 4, pp. 5-164.
24. A. Hazen, *Some Physical Properties of Sands and Gravels, with Special Reference to their Use in Filtration*, 24th Annual Report of the State Board of Health of Massachusetts, 1892, Public Document no. 34, Boston, Wright and Potter Printing Co., 1893, p. 553.
25. K. Terzaghi, "Principles of Soil Mechanics", *Engineering News Rec.*, 1925, 1 to 9, vol. 95, pp. 742, 796, 832, 874, 912, 987, 1026 and 1064.

PROBLEMS

For practice problems see Chapter 6.

Chapter 6

VOLUMETRY AND GRAVIMETRY

6-1. Functional Relationships Between Various Soil Properties. The foregoing discussions on porosity and various unit weights of soil might reveal to the reader the following: many soil quantities, for example, porosity, void ratio, proportions of volumes of solids, moisture and air, degree of saturation, dry unit weights, saturated and submerged unit weights can be calculated if the following four soil properties are determined by tests, or, in other words, if the unit weight, moisture content, and the specific gravity of soil, as well as the unit weight of water are known.

The dependence of some of the various soil constants upon γ, w, G and γ_w are summarized in the Soil Physical Constants Table 6-1. Again, it is to be remembered that in precise laboratory and research work, the actual temperature of water in specific gravity determinations of soil and water should be taken into account.

When quantities for saturated soil conditions are sought, then only three quantities actually need to be known, namely γ_w, G, and γ_d, or γ_{sat}, or w, or n, or e. The combination of primary sets of any three of the latter quantities (Col. 1, Table 6-2) permits one to calculate specific gravities, G, (Col. 2); or dry unit weight, γ_d (Col. 3); saturated unit weight of soil, γ_{sat} (Col. 4); or saturated moisture content, w_{sat} (Col. 5); or porosity n (Col. 6), or void ratio e (Col. 7).

6-2. Volumetric and Gravimetric Relationships. The calculation of the various functional relationships as illustrated in Table 6-2 can best be performed, and the relative volumetric and gravimetric proportions of soil solids, moisture, and air phases can readily and visually be illustrated, by means of the soil phase diagram, Fig. 6-1.

The phase diagram aids one considerably in understanding and solving various basic problems involving certain soil physical properties. For example, if the unit weight of water, γ_w, the specific gravity of solids, G, the moist unit weight of soil, W, its volume, V, and the dry weight, W_s, of the solids are known, then the weight of water, W_w, the volume of solids, V_s, volume of water, V_w, volume of air, V_a, dry unit weight, γ_d, and the relative values such as porosity, n, void ratio, e, moisture content, w, and the degree of saturation, S, can be calculated. For this purpose the soil phase diagram (Fig. 6-1) should be drawn, and the proper spaces in the volume and weight columns of the soil phase diagram should be filled in with the known or given quantities such as

TABLE 6-1. SOME SOIL PHYSICAL CONSTANTS

Properties to be Determined by Test	Quantities to be Calculated for a Soil in its Undisturbed State	
	Description	Equation
1	2	3
1. γ = unit weight of soil	1. Unit weight of soil skeleton or dry unit weight	(a) $\gamma_d = \dfrac{\gamma}{1 + w}$
		(b) $\gamma_d = \dfrac{G}{1 + e}\gamma_w$
2. w = moisture content by dry weight	2. Porosity	$n = 1 - \dfrac{\gamma_d}{G\gamma_w}$
	3. Void ratio	$e = \dfrac{n}{1 - n} = \dfrac{G\gamma_w - \gamma_d}{\gamma_d}$
3. G = specific gravity of soil particles	4. Relative volume of voids	$n = \dfrac{e}{1 + e}$
	5. Relative volume of solids	$n_s = \dfrac{1}{1 + e}$
4. γ_w = unit weight of water	6. Relative volume of water in soil	$n_m = nS$
	7. Soil moisture content by dry weight	$W_w = w\gamma_d$
	8. Soil moisture content by volume	$V_w = \dfrac{W_w}{\gamma_w}$
	9. Moisture content upon full saturation	$w_{sat} = \left(\dfrac{1}{\gamma_d} - \dfrac{1}{G\gamma_w}\right)\gamma_w$
	10. Degree of saturation	$S = \dfrac{w}{w_{sat}} = \dfrac{w\gamma}{n(1 + w)\gamma_w}$
	11. Void ratio upon full saturation	$e = wG$
	12. Volume of air in a unit volume of soil	$n_a = (1 - S)n$
	13. Saturated unit weight of soil	$\gamma_{sat} = \dfrac{G + e}{1 + e}\gamma_w$
	14. Submerged (buoyant) unit weight	$\gamma_{sub} = \dfrac{G - 1}{1 + e}\gamma_w$

TABLE 6-2. FUNCTIONAL RELATIONSHIPS OF VARIOUS SOIL PROPERTIES

Given Quantities γ_w and	Sought Quantities					
	Specific Gravity, G	Dry Unit Weight, γ_d	Saturated Unit Weight, γ_{sat}	Saturated Moisture Content, in %	Porosity, n	Void ratio, e
1	2	3	4	5	6	7
$G;\ \gamma_d$	—	—	$\left(1 - \dfrac{1}{G}\right)\gamma_d + \gamma_w$	$\left(\dfrac{1}{\gamma_d} - \dfrac{1}{G\gamma_w}\right)\gamma_w$	$1 - \dfrac{\gamma_d}{G\gamma_w}$	$\dfrac{G\gamma_w}{\gamma_d} - 1$
$G;\ \gamma_{sat}$	—	$\dfrac{\gamma_{sat} - \gamma_w}{G - 1}G$	—	$\dfrac{G\gamma_w - \gamma_{sat}}{(\gamma_{sat} - \gamma_w)G}$	$\dfrac{G\gamma_w - \gamma_{sat}}{(G-1)\gamma_w}$	$\dfrac{G\gamma_w - \gamma_{sat}}{\gamma_{sat} - \gamma_w}$
$G;\ w$	—	$\dfrac{G}{1 + wG}\gamma_w$	$\dfrac{1 + w}{1 + wG}G\gamma_w$	—	$\dfrac{wG}{1 + wG}$	wG
$G;\ n$	—	$G(1 - n)\gamma_w$	$[G - n(G - 1)]\gamma_w$	$\dfrac{n}{G(1 - n)}$	—	$\dfrac{n}{1 - n}$
$G;\ e$	—	$\dfrac{G}{1 + e}\gamma_w$	$\dfrac{G + e}{1 + e}\gamma_w$	$\dfrac{e}{G}$	$\dfrac{e}{1 + e}$	—
$\gamma_d;\ \gamma_{sat}$	$\dfrac{\gamma_d}{\gamma_w + \gamma_d - \gamma_{sat}}$	—	—	$\dfrac{\gamma_{sat}}{\gamma_d} - 1$	$\dfrac{\gamma_{sat} - \gamma_d}{\gamma_w}$	$\dfrac{\gamma_{sat} - \gamma_d}{\gamma_w + \gamma_d - \gamma_{sat}}$
$\gamma_d;\ w$	$\dfrac{\gamma_d}{\gamma_w - w\gamma_d}$	—	$(1 + w)\gamma_d$	—	$w\dfrac{\gamma_d}{\gamma_w}$	$\dfrac{w\gamma_d}{\gamma_w - w\gamma_d}$

$\gamma_d; n$	$\dfrac{\gamma_d}{(1-n)\gamma_w}$	—	$\gamma_d + n\gamma_w$	$\dfrac{n\gamma_w}{\gamma_d}$	—	$\dfrac{n}{1-n}$
$\gamma_d; e$	$(1+e)\dfrac{\gamma_d}{\gamma_w}$	—	$\dfrac{e\gamma_w}{1+e}+\gamma_d$	$\dfrac{e}{1+e}\dfrac{\gamma_w}{\gamma_d}$	$\dfrac{e}{1+e}$	—
$\gamma_{sat}; w$	$\dfrac{\gamma_{sat}}{\gamma_w - w(\gamma_{sat}-\gamma_w)}$	$\dfrac{\gamma_{sat}}{1+w}$	—	—	$\dfrac{w\gamma_{sat}}{(1+w)\gamma_w}$	$\dfrac{w\gamma_{sat}}{\gamma_w - w(\gamma_{sat}-\gamma_w)}$
$\gamma_{sat}; n$	$\dfrac{\gamma_{sat}-n\gamma_w}{(1-n)\gamma}$	$\gamma_{sat}-n\gamma_w$	—	$\dfrac{n\gamma_w}{\gamma_{sat}-n\gamma_w}$	—	$\dfrac{n}{1-n}$
$\gamma_{sat}; e$	$(1+e)\dfrac{\gamma_{sat}}{\gamma_w}-e$	$\gamma_{sat}-\dfrac{e}{1+e}\gamma_w$	—	$\dfrac{e\gamma_w}{\gamma_{sat}+e(\gamma_{sat}-\gamma_w)}$	$\dfrac{e}{1+e}$	—
$w; n$	$\dfrac{n}{(1-n)w}$	$\dfrac{n}{w}\gamma_w$	$n\left(\dfrac{1+w}{w}\right)\gamma_w$	—	—	$\dfrac{n}{1-n}$
$w; e$	$\dfrac{e}{w}$	$\dfrac{e}{(1-e)w}\gamma_w$	$\dfrac{e}{w}\left(\dfrac{1+w}{1+e}\right)\gamma_w$	—	$\dfrac{e}{1+e}$	—

γ_w, G (Col. 10), W_s (Col. 11), W (Col. 12), and V (Col. 7). Then calculate
a) the weight of water (Col. 11):

$$W_w = W - W_s$$

b) the volume of solids (Col. 9):

$$V_s = \frac{W_s}{G\gamma_w}$$

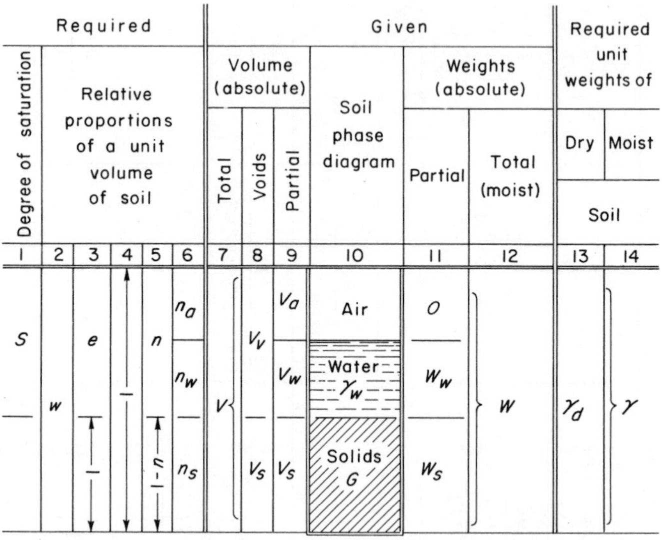

Degree of saturation	Required			Volume (absolute)			Given	Weights (absolute)		Required unit weights of	
	Relative proportions of a unit volume of soil			Total	Voids	Partial	Soil phase diagram	Partial	Total (moist)	Dry	Moist
										Soil	
1	2	3	4	5	6	7	8	9	10	11	12	13	14
S	e	n	n_a n_w n_s				V_a V_w	V_v V_w V_s V_s	Air Water γ_w Solids G	O W_w W_s	W	γ_d	γ

FIG. 6-1   Phase diagram illustrating absolute and relative volumetric and gravimetric proportions of solids, water and air in a unit of mass of soil.

c) the volume of voids (Col. 8):

$$V_v = V - V_s = V - \frac{W_s}{G\gamma_w}$$

and
d) volume of moisture (Col. 9):

$$V_w = \frac{W_w}{\gamma_w}$$

e) The absolute volume of air voids (Col. 9):

$$V_a = V_v - V_w$$

The calculations now permit one to compute the quantities required at the outset of this problem.
1) Moisture content (Col. 2):

$$w = \frac{W_w}{W_s} \tag{6-1}$$

2) Relative proportion of void spaces, or porosity (Col. 5):

$$n = \frac{V_w + V_a}{V} = \frac{V_v}{V} = \frac{V - V_s}{V} = \frac{V - \dfrac{W_s}{G\gamma_w}}{V} = 1 - \frac{W_s}{VG\gamma_w} = 1 - \frac{\gamma_d}{G\gamma_w} =$$

$$= 1 - \frac{\gamma}{G\gamma_w(1 + w)} \tag{6-2}$$

3) Relative proportion of volume of air voids (Col. 6):

$$n_a = \frac{V_a}{V} \tag{6-3}$$

4) Relative proportion of volume of water (Col. 6):

$$n_w = \frac{V_w}{V} \tag{6-4}$$

5) Relative proportion of volume of solids (Col. 6):

$$n_s = \frac{V_s}{V} \tag{6-5}$$

6) Void ratio (Col. 3):

$$e = \frac{V_v}{V_s} = \frac{n}{1 - n} \tag{6-6}$$

7) Degree of saturation (Col. 1):

$$S = \frac{V_w}{V_v} = \frac{n_w}{n} = \frac{wG}{e} = \frac{wG(1 - n)}{n} \tag{6-7}$$

The weight of the water can now also be calculated (Col. 11):

$$W_w = \frac{Se}{1 + e} \gamma_w, \tag{6-8}$$

the quantity of which should check with W_w as calculated under point a).

8) Dry unit weight of soil (Col. 13):

$$\gamma_d = \frac{W_s}{V} = \frac{V_s G \gamma_w}{V} = \frac{G}{1 + e} \gamma_w \tag{6-9}$$

9) Moist unit weight of soil (Col. 14):

$$\gamma = \frac{W}{V} = \frac{V_s G \gamma_w}{V} + V_w \gamma_w = \frac{G}{1 + e} \gamma_w + W_w = \frac{G}{1 + e} \gamma_w + \frac{eS}{1 + e} \gamma_w =$$

$$= \frac{G}{1 + e} \gamma_w + \frac{wG}{1 + e} \gamma_w = \frac{G(1 + w)}{1 + e} \gamma_w \tag{6-10}$$

TABLE 6-3. EFFECT OF MOISTURE ON BULKING OF SAND

Nos.	Designation	Symbols	Sand in dry rodded condition	Sand in dry loose condition	Sand in moist condition — Moisture content, w%, by dry weight									
1	2	3	4	5	1	2	3	5	7	10	12.5	15.0	17.5	18.0
					6	7	8	9	10	11	12	13	14	15
1	Unit weight	γ	115.75	107.8	98.1	90.7	86.4	84.7	86.6	92.0	98.8	107.4	121.3	131.6
2	Dry unit weight	γ_d	115.75	107.8	97.1	88.9	83.9	80.7	80.9	83.7	87.8	93.6	102.6	111.5
3	Volume of solids	V_s	0.70	0.65	0.59	0.54	0.51	0.49	0.49	0.51	0.53	0.57	0.62	0.68
4	Volume of voids	V_v	0.30	0.35	0.41	0.46	0.49	0.51	0.51	0.49	0.47	0.43	0.38	0.33
5	Void ratio	e	0.43	0.54	0.70	0.85	0.96	1.05	1.04	0.98	0.88	0.77	0.61	0.48
6	Porosity	n	0.30	0.35	0.41	0.46	0.49	0.51	0.51	0.49	0.47	0.43	0.38	0.33
7	Degree of saturation	$S = \dfrac{wG}{e}$	0	0	0.038	0.062	0.0827	0.1264	0.1782	0.272	0.375	0.518	0.757	0.992
8	Bulking	$\triangle V,\%$	—	7.55	18.9	29.4	36.1	43.4	42.7	38.5	31.5	23.8	12.6	3.5

6-3. Bulking of Sand. Bulking of loose, moist sand is the increase in its volume as compared to dry sand. Bulking is a well-known phenomenon, particularly in the trade of aggregates for proportioning of concrete. This phenomenon has been known since 1892 when it was investigated by Feret[1] at the French School of Bridges and Roads.

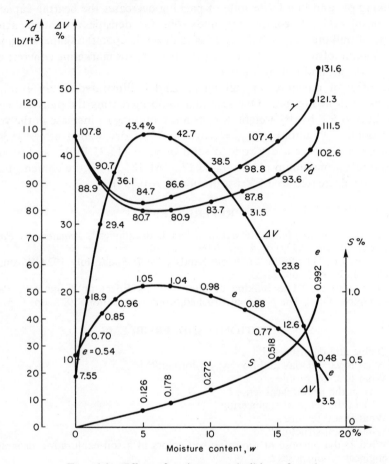

FIG. 6-2 Effect of moisture on bulking of sand.

The bulking phenomenon of sand is explained by moisture hulls or films which surround the sand particles. The contact moisture films, adsorbed to the sand particles by moisture surface tension forces, tend to cause the sand particles to occupy a larger volume as compared to their dry state. One infers that the moisture films separate the sand particles from close, direct contact. The bulking of sand, depending upon size, shape, texture and temperature of water, can amount to about 20% to 25% and more as compared with the unit weight of the material at a certain state of (dry) density.[2,3] Generally, bulking of sand increases as the particle sizes of the sand decrease. This is because of the increase in the specific surface area of the sand. Upon further subsequent increase in moisture content in sand, when a maximum increase in bulking volume is attained, bulking in its turn decreases, and upon the inundation of the sand the surface tension forces are neutralized, and most of the bulking, in such a case, vanishes. As a consequence, the sand particles now rearrange themselves into a denser packing.

Bulking of sand in a loose state of packing decreases the bearing capacity of sand considerably. In compacting sandy soils, low densities are usually achieved because of bulking. Thus, bulking of sand depends upon the shape, size and texture. Bulking of moist sand is one of the reasons for marketing concrete aggregates by weight and not by volume.

The effect of moisture on bulking of sand is illustrated by an example in Table 6-3 and in Fig. 6-2. One sees that upon increasing the moisture content in sand up to 5% by dry weight, for instance, bulking or increase in the volume of the sand, $\triangle V$, initially at $\gamma_d = 107.8$ lb/ft^3 of dry weight at $e = 0.54$ and $w = 0$ increases over a dry rodded sand of $\gamma_d = 115.75$ lb/ft^3, and attains in this example a maximum of $\triangle V = 43.4\%$. At 18% moisture content, bulking of sand has decreased to 3.5% (saturation $S = 0.992$).

REFERENCES

1. R. Feret, "Sur la compacité des mortiers hydrauliques", *Annales des Ponts et Chaussées*, Paris, 1892, vol. 4, pp. 5-164.
2. A. A. Levison, "The Bulking of Moist Sands", *Public Roads*, July, 1924, Washington, D.C., vol. 5, no. 5, pp. 21-23.
3. A. T. Goldbeck, "The Bulking of Sand and its Effect on Concrete", *Bulletin*, Washington, D.C., The National Crushed Stone Association, 1927, no. 1, p. 3.

QUESTIONS AND PROBLEMS

6-1.   Define and describe soil.
6-2.   What is varved clay and how was it formed?
6-3.   What is a soil profile
      a) in the pedological sense?
      b) in the sense of engineering?
6-4.   What is soil texture?
6-5.   What is soil structure?
6-6.   What is the purpose of reporting soil colors in a soil exploration program for engineering purposes?
6-7.   What is
      a) unit weight of soil?
      b) specific gravity of soil particles?
      c) wet density of soil?
      d) dry density of soil?
      e) porosity and
      f) void ratio of soil?
6-8.   The wet density of a glacial outwash soil is 120 lb/ft^3, the specific gravity of the solid particles of the soil is $G = 2.67$, and the moisture content of the soil is $w = 12\%$ by dry weight.
    Calculate:
      a) dry density
      b) porosity

c) void ratio
d) degree of saturation
e) percent of air voids.

Draw a phase diagram of this soil showing the absolute and relative volumetric and gravimetric relationships.

6-9. From a borrow pit in which the void ratio is $e = 1.20$, 250,000 cu yd of soil have to be excavated for building a fill with a void ratio of $e = 0.70$. How many cubic yards of fill can be constructed?

6-10. The moisture content of a saturated clay sample is 345%. The unit weight of the solids is 2.38 g per cc. Determine the unit weight of the saturated clay (in pounds per cubic foot). Draw a phase diagram.

6-11. The unit weight of the solids of a given sand is 2.60 g per cc. Its void ratio is 0.572. Calculate:
   a) the unit weight of dry sand
   b) the unit weight of the sand when saturated
   c) the submerged unit weight of the sand.

Draw phase diagrams for each of the cases mentioned.

6-12. Plot a curve expressing $e = f(n)$. Read the curve and report.

6-13. Plot the moisture content, w in $\%$, of a soil (by dry weight) on the abscissa axis and the moisture content based on total weight of the soil, w_t, in $\%$, on the ordinate axis. Complete the curve expressing the total weight of the soil as a function of its dry weight: $w_t = f(w)$. First, derive $w_t = f(w)$, then plot the soil moisture content relationship by dry and total weights.

6-14. Derive the following equation: $e = \dfrac{w}{100} G$, which expresses the relationship between the void ratio, e, the true specific gravity, G, and the moisture content, w, for full saturation of voids.

6-15. Derive a formula for soil moisture content, w, as a function of void ratio, e, degree of saturation, S, and specific gravity of soil particles, G.

6-16. The porosity, n, of a medium sand is 33%. Determine its void ratio. Sketch e and n by means of a phase diagram.

6-17. Prove that $\gamma_{dry} = \dfrac{G\gamma_w}{1 + e} = G\gamma_w(1 - n)$.

6-18. One cubic foot of wet soil weighs 124 lb. Its dry weight is 112 lb. The specific gravity of the solid particles of soil is $G = 2.67$. Determine the moisture content, porosity, void ratio, and degree of saturation, S. Draw a phase diagram, and show relative and absolute volumetric and gravimetric relationships.

6-19. A sheet of water the thickness of which is one unit of length is to be used to saturate the voids of a non-cohesive soil. The void ratio of the soil in question is e (given). How thick a soil layer is required to accommodate this amount of water?

6-20. A clay sample, containing its natural moisture content, weighs 34.62 g. The specific gravity of the solids of this soil is 2.70. After oven-drying, the soil sample weighs 20.36 g. To determine the volume of the moist clay, the sample is immersed in mercury prior to oven-drying. The displaced volume of the clay sample is found to be 24.26 cm³. Calculate:
   a) moisture content,
   b) void ratio, and
   c) degree of saturation of the soil.

6-21. A clay sample, originally 1.000 in. thick and at initial void ratio of 1.120, was subjected to a compressive load. After the clay sample was completely consolidated, the thickness of it was measured to be 0.955 in. Compute the final void ratio.

6-22. What are the commonly noted differences between sand and clay?

6-23. A soil has a unit weight of 100 lb/ft³, and a moisture content of $w = 8\%$ by dry weight. Assuming that the void ratio of the soil remains the same, calculate how much water in gallons (and in cu ft) should be added to a cu yd of soil to increase the soil moisture content to 10%. Explain each step of computation performed.

6-24. The soil natural moisture content is $w = 54.0\%$, its boid ratio $e = 2.075$, and specific gravity $G = 2.65$. Calculate the degree of saturation, S, of this soil and indicate whether this soil is moist, or saturated. ($S = (w)(G)/e = (0.54)(2.65)/(2.075) = 0.689$. The soil is characterized as very moist, see Table 5-9).

6-25. An airport runway fill needs 600,000 cu yd of soil compacted to a void ratio of 0.75. The engineering soil map shows that there are two available borrow pits designated by the geologic formations of the soil as Bridgeton and Cape May. The void ratio of the soil in each of the aforementioned pits, and the estimated transportation cost of the soil from the pits to the airport are compiled in the following tabulation.

Borrow Pit	Void Ratio	Transportation Cost
Bridgeton	0.80	40 cents per cu yd
Cape May	1.70	29 cents per cu yd

Determine the minimum expense of soil transportation, indicating which borrow pit is the most economical for the contemplated job.

6-26. For an airport runway, a base course 125 ft wide, 2 miles long and 6 in. in compacted thickness of crushed rock with a 30% achieved porosity is to be constructed. The moisture content of the crushed rock material in the stockpile is 8.2%. The specific gravity of this aggregate is 2.67. In its loosest state, the porosity of the crushed rock is 46%. The crushed-rock material is to be weighed loose in trucks as it is taken from the stockpile. Determine for both dense and loose states where this applies:

   a) the dry weight in lb/ft³ for the loosest state of the crushed rock, and for the compacted state;
   b) the thickness of the crushed rock in its loosest state necessary to compact it down to the required 6 in. thickness with $n = 30\%$;
   c) the ratio of the loose and compacted volume;
   d) the amount of water in lbs and cu ft contained in one cubic foot of moist crushed rock;
   e) degree of saturation of the crushed rock;
   f) the number of cubic feet of solids and water transported from the stockpile to the airport to build one mile of runway base course;
   g) with the moisture content given, the number of tons of crushed rock required per one mile of the runway base course;
   h) the number of 5-cu yd truck loads of crushed rock required for the construction of one mile of runway base course.

Draw phase diagrams and other pertinent sketches. Assume other engineering properties and values where necessary.

6-27. A highway fill is to be compacted to 95% standard compaction. The dry density of soil from a proposed borrow pit at its optimum moisture content (100% compaction) is 120 lb/ft³. The void ratio of the borrow material in the pit is 0.50, and the specific gravity of the solids of the soil particles is 2.67.

   a) How many cubic feet of borrow material are needed to compact 1 cu ft of highway fill?

b) How much water in lb/ft^3 and in ft^3/ft^3 is needed to achieve 100% and 95% compaction, respectively?

c) What is the optimum moisture content?

d) At what moisture content does the borrow material become saturated when tested? At what moisture content does the borrow material become saturated when compacted?

Assume all other necessary quantities.

Present all necessary and appropriate sketches. Draw neat phase diagrams.

Assume a compaction curve.

6-28. Prepare a diagram which would illustrate for classification purposes the degree of saturation of soil as a function of moisture content. Given: $w = 54\%$ at $G = 2.65$ and $e = 2.075$. Classify degree of saturation of this soil.

Hint. Designate the corresponding moisture content with w_s at any degree of saturation, S. By Eq. (6-7), the degree of saturation is

$$S = \frac{w_s G}{e},\tag{6-7}$$

or

$$S = \frac{(0.54)(2.65)}{2.075} = 0.69.$$

The general expression of the soil moisture content at any degree of saturation is, by Eq. (6-7)

$$w_s = \frac{eS}{G}\tag{6-7a}$$

Let us designate the moisture contents corresponding to 0%, 25%, 50%, 75%, and 100% saturation as w_0, $w_{0.25}$, $w_{0.50}$, $w_{0.75}$ and $w_{1.00}$, respectively. Then

$$w_{0.25} = \frac{S_{0.25}e}{G} \, 100\%,$$

and upon saturation, with $S = 1.00$, or $S = 100\%$,

$$w_{1.00} = \frac{e}{G} \, 100\%.$$

By Eq. (6-7a) find and plot the scale of moisture contents, w_s, on the abscissa axis using for S the classification boundary values of $S = 0, 0.25, 0.50, 0.75,$ and 1.00. The points with coordinates w_s/S can now be connected with a line, giving the required graph. Thus, the soil classification by degree of saturation can now be represented graphically by a diagram. At $w = 54\%$, or at $w = 0.54$, $S = 0.69$ (very moist soil).

6-29. What is a soil particle size accumulation curve?
What is a soil particle size distribution curve?
What is a grading curve of a soil?

6-30. What is the effective size (effective diameter) of soil particles? What is the coefficient of uniformity of soil particles?

6-31. Calculate the coefficients of uniformity of soils, the particle size accumulation curves of which are shown in Figs. 5-17, 5-18 and 5-19.

6-32. The effective diameter of a soil is 0.1 mm, and the coefficient of uniformity of this soil is $U = 10$. Sketch the soil particle size accumulation curve and report the uniformity classification of this soil.

6-33. What soil characteristics are revealed by the slope of the soil particle size accumulation curve?

6-34. Distinguish between the concept of uniform soil material and uniform (even) gradation.

6-35. Why is semi-logarithmic plotting of soil particle size accumulation curves preferable to the arithmetical scale?

6-36. What are the principal soil textural groups?

6-37. Explain Feret triangle.

6-38. What is sedimentation? What is flocculation? What is deflocculation?

6-39. The combined mechanical analysis of a soil yielded the following results:

Sieve Number	Soil Particle Size in mm	Percent Passing
1	2	3
10	2.00	100
20	0.84	96
40	0.42	85
60	0.25	69
140	0.105	41
200	0.074	38
	0.034	30
	0.025	27
	0.160	23
	0.009	22
	0.006	18
	0.005	15
	0.002	12
	0.0009	9

Plot the soil particle size accumulation curve. Is the soil frost-susceptible? Also, prepare a histogram and particle size distribution curve.

Describe this soil by means of the Feret triangle.

What is the coefficient of uniformity of this soil?

6-40. According to certain specifications, the soil for a highway fill is to be compacted to 95% of standard Proctor compaction test density. The dry density of a sandy borrow material immediately adjacent to the earthworks project is found to be 115 lb per cu ft at 100% compaction. The borrow material in place in its natural condition has a void ratio of 0.65. The specific gravity of the solid matter of the soil is 2.65. How large a volume in cubic feet of the sandy borrow material is necessary to make 1 cu ft of highway fill?

6-41. Explain the concept of specific surface. At about what magnitude of specific surface do soil materials start to show their colloidal nature in a pronounced manner?

6-42. Calculate the magnitude of the total surface area in cm^2/cm^3 and in $acres/ft^3$, and also in cm^2/g and in acres/pound of the soils as shown in Fig. 5-19. Assume that the soil particles are ideal spheres. The specific gravity of the soil particles of all soils in question is $G = 2.65$ and the unit weight $\gamma_d = 100$ lb/ft^3.

6-43. What is the reason for bulking of sand?

6-44. Verify the figures given in Table 6-3, line 8, Bulking, $\triangle V\%$.

6-45. Check the correctness of the ordinates of the γ_d, γ, $\triangle V$, e, and S curves shown in Fig. 6-2 as a function of moisture content relative to bulking of sand.

Chapter 7

MOISTURE-DENSITY RELATIONS OF SOILS

SOIL COMPACTION

7-1. Introduction. The stability of an earth embankment, Fig. 7-1, depends upon the shear strength of the soil of the embankment. The shear strength, τ, in tons/ft^2 $\approx$ kg/cm^2 is expressed analytically as

$$\tau = \sigma_{n_{eff}} \tan \phi + c, \tag{7-1}$$

where $\sigma_{n_{eff}}$ = effective normal stress, in tons/ft^2 $\approx$ kg/cm^2, acting normal to the rupture surface, Fig. 7-1,

$\tan \phi$ = coefficient of internal friction of soil,

ϕ = angle of internal friction of soil, and

c = cohesion of soil, in tons/ft^2 $\approx$ in kg/cm^2.

This equation shows that the shear strength of a frictional-cohesive soil consists of two properties: the internal friction, $\sigma_{n_{eff}} \tan \phi$, and cohesion, c.

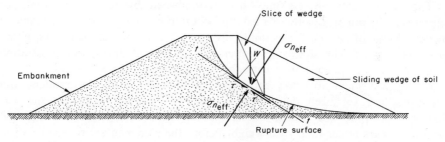

FIG. 7-1 Illustrating the concept of shear in an earth embankment.

Obviously, the normal stress depends upon the unit weight of the soil or its density; the amount of voids in the soil; the soil moisture content in these voids; or, in other words, on the degree of saturation of the soil, and the amount of cohesion. When $c = 0$, the soil represents a non-cohesive soil. Also, it can be understood that a mass of soil may become unstable if the soil contains a large amount of voids, and the stability against slope failure decreases as the degree of saturation of the soil with water increases. Conversely, the fill is more stable in proportion as there are finer voids present in the soil: less saturation and greater dry density. This statement, however, is true only up to a certain point, the engineer then being faced with the problem of moisture-density relations in soil. To increase the shear strength of a soil in a fill, therefore, the dry density of the soil in the fill must be increased. The dry density of a soil may be increased by compaction, for example.

7-2. Definition. In general, the term "compaction" is understood to mean the increase in the dry density of soil by a dynamic load. This concept should not be confused with that of consolidation. "Consolidation" is the gradual decrease in volume of voids, and thus the increase in density of a cohesive soil brought about under the action of continuously acting *static* load over a period of time (for example, fill under its own weight, or soil under the pressure of a structure). In cohesive, saturated soils the process of consolidation is accompanied by the gradual expulsion of some of the saturation water and air/or gas out of the voids of the soil with a consequent decrease in volume of the soil.

7-3. Maximum Dry Density. This is the greatest weight in pounds per cubic foot of a soil obtained by a soil compaction device at a certain moisture content and on the application of a certain compactive effort. The "optimum moisture" content is that moisture content in percent of a soil by dry weight at the maximum dry density of that soil.

7-4. Compaction Fundamentals. In soil engineering, compaction is any process by which the soil particles are artificially rearranged and packed together into a closer state of contact by mechanical means in order to decrease the porosity of the soil and thus increase the dry density of the soil, or unit weight of the solid particles. The compaction process is accompanied by the expulsion of air only.

The compaction process may be accomplished by rolling, tamping, or vibration. In practice, soils of medium cohesion are compacted by means of various kinds of rollers, for example, by smooth and sheepsfoot rollers, or by pneumatic tires. The sheepsfoot roller is a cylindrical drum with protruding pegs. Non-cohesive soils are most effectively compacted by vibration.

In the past when no heavy earthwork equipment like tampers, rollers, and vibrators had yet been developed, compaction by mechanical means was naturally not practiced. Earth fills were usually allowed to settle over a period of 3 to 5 years under their own weight before the pavement or railroad ballast and tracks were put down.

Compaction
  1) increases the density of the soil, thus increasing its shear strength and bearing capacity;
  2) decreases the tendency of the soil to settle under repeated loads, and
  3) brings about a low permeability of the soil.

The degree of compaction of a soil is characterized by its dry density. The degree of compaction of a soil depends upon its moisture content, the amount of compactive effort or energy expended on it, and the nature of the soil. A change in either moisture content or compactive effort brings about a change in density. Temperature affects the surface tension of water, viscosity, and density of water; and the amount of manipulation likewise influences density of soil.

7-5. Compaction Phenomenon. As applied to compaction of a soil in the field, it can be said that for any given soil that is intended to be rolled into a fill, two things are necessary for its greatest compaction: a certain amount of water and a certain predetermined amount of rolling with a particular piece of rolling equipment. This particular moisture content is known by the term the "optimum moisture content" of the rolled soil material. To learn the soil moisture-density relationship, and to evaluate a soil as to its suitability for making highway, runway, and other fills, the soil is subjected to a compaction test.

In 1933, Proctor[1,2] showed that

1) there exists a definite relationship between the soil moisture content and the degree of dry density to which a soil may be compacted, and

2) that for a specific amount of compaction energy applied on the soil there is one moisture content termed the "optimum moisture content" at which a particular soil attains its maximum dry density.

Such a maximum dry density-optimum moisture content relationship gives a practical and satisfactory method of construction control of earthworks.

7-6. Compaction Test of Soil. To determine the soil moisture-density relationship of a soil intended for making a fill, and to check and compute the achieved moisture-density relationship in a rolled fill of the same soil as tested before in the laboratory, two types of tests are needed: a standard laboratory compaction test, and a field density test. The ratio of the field density to the standard laboratory density of a soil is termed the "relative compaction". In practice, a compaction between 90% and 97% is often specified.

Fig. 7-2 Devices for performing standard compaction test of soil.

Standard methods of tests for the compaction and density of soils, according to the American Association of State Highway Officials (AASHO) Designation T99-49[3], or the test for moisture-density relations of soils by the American Society for Testing Materials, Designation D698-57T,[4] generally known as the standard Proctor soil compaction test, prescribe special procedures for performing the dry density-optimum moisture relationship test. According to these procedures, a 6 lb sample of the soil to be used for a fill taken from a portion of the soil material passing the No. 4 sieve shall be air-dried, thoroughly mixed, and then compacted in a standard compaction cylinder, 4.6 in. high, 4.0 in. in diameter and 1/30 cu ft in volume. The compaction of the soil in the cylinder is performed in three soil layers by means of a metal rammer, 2 in. in diameter, weighing 5.5 lb. Each of the three layers of soil should receive 25 blows from the rammer falling freely from a height of 12 in. above the elevation of each finally compacted layer. The soil compaction devices are illustrated in Fig. 7-2. The net dry weight of the compacted soil should be determined, as well as the compacted moisture content. These two quantities, moisture content and dry density, form a pair of coordinates, or a point "1" on a dry density graph, Fig. 7-3.

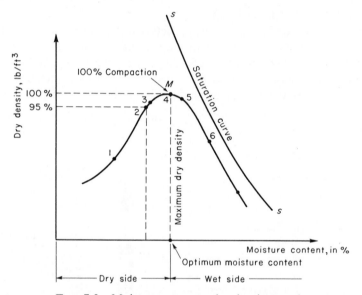

FIG. 7-3   Moisture content—dry density graph.

The standards say that the compacted soil be used over again; that it should be broken up until it will pass a No. 4 sieve; that the moisture content of the soil sample be increased by about 1%, the compaction procedure repeated, and the moisture-dry density relation be determined as before. This, and repeated procedures give, for example, points 2, 3, 4, 5, and 6 on the graph, Fig. 7-3. This series of determinations shall be continued until the soil becomes very wet (or "spongy") or there is a substantial decrease in the wet weight of the compacted soil. Highly micaceous soils, however, should be used only once, for they suffer appreciable degradation in the compaction test, changing test results.

7-7. The Moisture Content-Dry Density Curve. The relation between moisture content and dry density of a soil at a particular compaction energy is illustrated in Fig. 7-3. Two quantities are needed for the calculation of the dry density of soil: wet density and moisture content. The calculation of the dry density of the compacted soil in terms of its wet density and moisture content is calculated for each test made as follows:

$$w = \frac{A - B}{B - C} \, 100\%, \tag{7-2}$$

$$W_d = \frac{W_w}{1 + \dfrac{w}{100}}, \tag{7-3}$$

where w = percent of moisture by oven-dry weight in the specimen of the soil,
   A = weight of dish and wet soil,
   B = weight of dish and oven-dried soil,
   C = weight of dish,
   W_d = dry weight per cubic foot of compacted soil,
   W_w = wet weight per cubic foot of compacted soil.
The soil moisture contents are plotted on the graph, Fig. 7-3 as abscissas, and the dry densities as ordinates. Connecting the plotted points with a smooth line, a curve is obtained the shape of which is, generally, of a hyperbolic form. In order to determine better the course of the curve, it is advisable to obtain before, at, and past the peak test points. The curve thus obtained would also indicate better what happens to the rapidly dropping dry density with the increase in soil moisture content.

The moisture content corresponding to the peak, or maximum ordinate of the curve, is termed the "optimum moisture content" of the compacted soil sample at a specified amount of energy applied on that soil.

The oven-dried soil weight in pounds per cubic foot of the soil tested at "optimum moisture content" is termed the "maximum dry density" for the compaction as specified by the test procedures under discussion. The maximum dry density point, M, obtained at the optimum moisture content, is commonly adopted as the 100% compaction when determinations of relative compactions are made.

The maximum weight per cubic foot of dry soil as determined by the compaction test is indicative of the suitability of the material for use in embankments and subgrades.

Just above the compaction curve (points 1-2-3-4-5-6, Fig. 7-3), there is a complete saturation curve, s-s, showing for various moisture contents the densities if the voids are entirely occupied with water.

7-8. Moisture-Dry Density Relationships of Some Soils. Depending upon the type of soil and the specified compaction method, the numerical values of the optimum moisture contents range from about 9% to about 35%. Dry weights per cu ft of soil as determined by the standard compaction test vary from about 75 to 130 lb. The dry densities and optimum moisture contents of some soils are illustrated in Table 7-1. Granular soils, such as A-1, A-2, A-2-4 soils, for example, have greater values of dry weights than plastic materials and mucks.

7-9. Saturation Line (or Line of Zero Air Voids). If a soil is compacted to such a degree that all voids are full with water (100% saturation), i.e., there

TABLE 7-1. MOISTURE-DRY DENSITY RELATIONSHIPS OF SOME NEW JERSEY SOILS

Nos.	Soil Type	Standard Maximum Dry Density, lb/ft³	Optimum Moisture Content, in %	Highway Research Board Soil Classification System
1	2	3	4	5
1	Dunellen, glacial outwash	118	11	A-2-4
		122	12	A-1-b
2	Glacial lake bed	97-114	14-23	A-7-6
3	Glacial stratified drift	103-124	10-17	A-2-4 to A-4
4	Glacial terminal moraine	105-121	10-18	A-2-4 to A-4
5	Merchantville clay	91-104	20-28	A-6; A-7-5
6	Penn soil, shale derivative	105-115	13-18	A-4
		90-115	13-27	A-6 to A-7-6
7	Raritan clay	110-120	10-16	A-4; A-6

are no air voids present, and no soil moisture is expelled from the voids, then the soil is said to be saturated, and its dry density is then the maximum possible. The dry density, W_{d0}, of soil at saturation for any given moisture content is calculated as follows:

$$W_{d0} = \frac{G\gamma_w}{1 + \dfrac{Gw}{100}}, \tag{7-4}$$

where W_{d0} = dry density of soil at saturation.

   G = specific gravity of soil particles, and

   w = moisture content in percent.

7-10. Derivation of Dry Density Equation at Various Percent Air Voids. The volume of voids, occupied by air, V_a:

$$V_a = 1 - V_s - V_w, \tag{7-5}$$

where

$$V_s = \frac{W_d}{G\gamma_w} \tag{7-6}$$

is the volume of soil solid particles in a unit volume of soil, and

$$V_w = \frac{wW_d}{100\gamma_w} \tag{7-7}$$

is the volume of voids occupied by water in the soil. Then the volume of air voids is

$$V_a = 1 - \frac{W_d}{\gamma_w}\left(\frac{1}{G} + \frac{w}{100}\right). \tag{7-8}$$

If the volume of air voids is expressed in terms of percent of the total volume of voids, then

$$V_a = \frac{n_a}{100} V_v = \frac{n_a}{100}(1 - V_s) = \frac{n_a}{100}\left(1 - \frac{W_d}{G\gamma_w}\right) \tag{7-9}$$

and

$$\frac{n_a}{100}\left(1 - \frac{W_d}{G\gamma_w}\right) = 1 - \frac{W_d}{\gamma_w}\left(\frac{1}{G} + \frac{w}{100}\right), \tag{7-10}$$

and the dry density of soil in terms of percent air voids, viz., degree of saturation, is

$$W_d = \frac{G\gamma_w\left(1 - \frac{n_a}{100}\right)}{1 + \frac{Gw}{100} - \frac{n_a}{100}} \tag{7-11}$$

This equation permits one to plot the dry density curve, viz., lines of percent of constant air-voids curve (or at various constant degrees of saturation), as a function of soil moisture content. The specific gravity, G, of the soil particles must be known.

When all of the air voids of the soil are fully saturated, then $V_a = V_w = V_v$, $n_a = 0$, and $S = 1$ (100% saturation). In such a case Equation (7-11) transforms into Equation (7-4).

$$W_{do} = \frac{G\gamma_w}{1 + \frac{Gw}{100}} = \frac{G\gamma_w}{1 + e}, \qquad \text{not known} \atop = calc. \, e \, \frac{(s)}{100} \tag{7-4}$$

an equation which is known as the zero air void equation, or the saturation line (100% saturation, when $S = 1$). Here $e =$ void ratio.

The dry density equation, Eq. (7-11) for a constant percent of air voids, n_a, can also be expressed in terms of degree of saturation, S, as follows:

$$\frac{n_a}{100} = 1 - \frac{V_a}{V_v} = 1 - S \tag{7-12}$$

and

$$W_d = \frac{G\gamma_w S}{S + \frac{Gw}{100}}, \tag{7-13}$$

or

$$W_d = \frac{G\gamma_w}{1 + \frac{Gw}{100S}} \tag{7-14}$$

For full (100%) saturation $S = 1$, and Eq. (7-14) transforms into

$$W_{do} = \frac{G\gamma_w}{1 + \dfrac{Gw}{100}} = \frac{G\gamma_w}{1 + e},$$

(7-15)

where e = void ratio.

This is the same equation as Eq. (7-4).

Example. Derive the dry density equation, Eq. (7-14), for any constant degree of saturation as a function of moisture content, specific gravity of the soil, and unit weight of the water.

Solution.

1) Degree of saturation, S, in decimal fractions:

$$S = \frac{V_w}{V_v} = \frac{V_v - V_a}{V_v} = 1 - n_a$$

(7-16)

2) Volume of water in soil, V_w:

$$V_w = \frac{wW_d}{\gamma_w}$$

(7-17)

3) Total volume of voids occupied by air and water in each cubic foot of soil, V_v:

$$V_v = 1 - V_s = 1 - \frac{W_d}{G\gamma_w}$$

(7-18)

4) Substitute Eqs. (7-17) and (7-18) into Equation (7-16):

$$S = \frac{wW_d}{\gamma_w\left(1 - \dfrac{W_d}{G\gamma_w}\right)}$$

(7-19)

5) Rearrangement of Eq. (7-19) yields:

$$S\gamma_w - \frac{SW_d}{G} - wW_d = 0,$$

(7-20)

and

6) the dry density of soil, W_d, at any moisture content, w, and any constant degree of saturation, S, is:

$$W_d = \frac{G\gamma_w}{1 + \dfrac{Gw}{S}}, \qquad \text{Q.E.D.}$$

(7-21)

The moisture content, w, is here expressed in decimal fractions. For example, if the moisture content were 9%, then w here is: $w = 0.09$.

Example. In Table 7-2 are given standard compaction test results on Dunellen soil.
1) Plot the wet density, and the dry density curves of this soil.
2) Determine the maximum dry density and the optimum moisture content of this soil. Also, calculate the relative compaction if the field density of the same soil has been attained at 118.6 lb/ft³.
3) Plot the zero air void (100% saturation) curve.
4) Draw the percent air void curves for 4%, 8%, 12%, and 16% air voids.

Solution.
1) The required wet and dry density curves are plotted in Fig. 7-4.

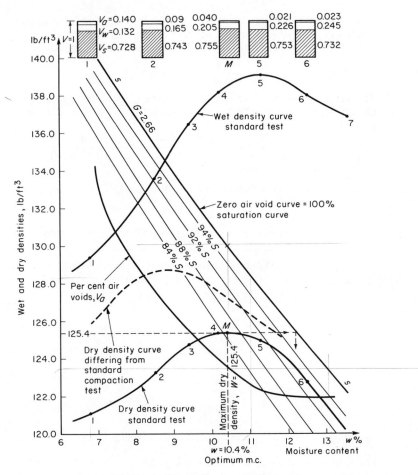

FIG. 7-4   Compaction test graphs.

TABLE 7-2. COMPACTION TEST RESULTS

Point No. on Curve	Moisture Content w%	Wet Density lb/ft³	Dry Density lb/ft³	Remarks
1	2	3	4	5
1	6.8	129.2	121.0	Specific
2	8.5	133.5	123.2	gravity
3	9.4	136.5	124.8	of soil
4	10.2	138.1	125.3	particles:
5	11.3	139.1	125.0	$G = 2.66$
6	12.5	138.0	122.7	
7	13.6	136.9	120.5	

2) The maximum dry density of the soil is 125.4 lb/ft³ at an optimum moisture content of $w = 10.4\%$ for that method of compaction.

If the field density if 118.6 lb/ft³, then the relative compaction is

$$\frac{118.6}{125.4} \, 100\% = 94.5\%.$$

3) The zero air void curve (100% saturation, $S = 1$), s-s, is calculated by Eq. (7-14), viz., Eq. (7-15), for each even percent of moisture, from $w = 7\%$ to $w = 14\%$:

$$W_d = \frac{G\gamma_w}{1 + \dfrac{Gw}{100S}} = \frac{(2.66)(62.4)}{1 + \dfrac{(2.66)(w)}{(100)(1)}} = \frac{165.98}{1 + (0.0266)(w)}$$

The W_d-values as a function of moisture content, w, are compiled in Table 7-3 (slide rule calculation):

TABLE 7-3. MOISTURE CONTENT-DRY DENSITY RELATIONSHIPS

Moisture Content $w\%$	Dry Density lb/ft³
1	2
7	140.5
8	136.8
9	134.0
10	131.0
11	128.4
12	125.9
13	123.5
14	121.0

The zero air void curve is plotted on Fig. 7-4.

4) The percent of air voids, n_a, can be expressed in terms of degree of saturation, S. By Eq. (7-16),

$$S = 1 - n_a \qquad\qquad (7\text{-}16)$$

The constant degree saturation curves are calculated by Eq. (7-14):

$$W_d = \frac{G\gamma_w}{1 + \dfrac{Gw}{100S}} = \frac{165.98}{1 + \dfrac{(0.0266)(w)}{S}}$$

If the standard method of compaction is modified by, say, increasing the amount of compaction, by increasing the weight of the rammer, increasing the height of fall of the rammer, or increasing the number of blows on the soil specimen to be compacted, singly or combined, then the moisture-dry density curve appears above the standard compaction curve and somewhat shifted to the left relative to the standard curve. Such a modified compaction curve, differing from the standard one, is shown by a dotted curve on Fig. 7-4. Thus, the dotted curve represents a high compactive effort as compared with the standard compaction curve, which represents a low compactive effort. The modified standard compaction test specification prescribes the use of a 10 lb rammer falling from a height of 18 in.

The modified compaction test was not invented out of curiosity, but because the U.S. Corps of Army Engineers needed a specification test for use with soils under heavy-duty aircraft pavements. It should be noted that there is a great difference in foot-pounds between the standard and modified compaction test methods for the relatively small gain in density. In other words, density costs money.

TABLE 7-4. DRY DENSITY AS A FUNCTION OF AIR VOIDS, n_a, AND DEGREE OF SATURATION

Moisture Content, $w\%$		Dry Density, W_d, in lb/ft³				
	$n_a \rightarrow$	0	4	8	12	16
	$S \rightarrow$	1.00	0.96	0.92	0.88	0.84
1	2	3	4	5	6	7
7	–	140.5	139.0	138.1	137.1	136.0
8	–	136.8	136.0	134.8	133.5	132.5
9	–	134.0	133.2	132.0	130.5	129.5
10	–	131.0	130.1	129.0	127.5	126.3
11	–	128.4	127.2	126.0	124.5	123.2
12	–	125.9	124.5	123.5	122.0	120.5
13	–	123.5	121.8	120.5	119.0	117.6
14	–	121.0	119.7	118.0	116.5	115.0

The modified compaction curve shows that with more compaction energy applied on the soil, the optimum moisture content is decreased, but the maximum dry density of the compacted soil is increased. The practical aspect of this phenomenon is this: if a soil material in the field is drier than its optimum moisture content as determined by the standard compaction test, then 1) the soil in the field to be compacted may be wetted prior to compaction to increase the moisture content to its optimum one, or 2) the soil may be compacted at its field moisture content (drier than optimum) by applying more energy on the soil, viz., heavier rollers, and/or more rolling passages.

As seen on the moisture-dry density graph, Fig. 7-4, the standard compaction test reveals two basic relationships of compacted soil samples, namely: 1) for each soil there is an optimum moisture content at which maximum density can be achieved for a specified compaction; 2) the dry density, viz., shear strength, viz., stability of a soil mass, decreases rapidly with an increase in the moisture content past the optimum. Simultaneously, and indirectly this test indicates also the least volume of voids arrived at a specified compaction.

The soil phase diagrams show an interesting picture of the changing relationships in density, volume of air and moisture with varying moisture content in soil. The phase diagram is here calculated for point "1" on the dry-density curve. For other points the calculations are not shown. Only the final calculations in Table 7-5, and the phase diagrams, Fig. 7-4, are shown.

Phase Calculations. Point No. 1.
Volume of solids:

$$V_s = \frac{W_d}{G\gamma_w} = \frac{121.0}{(2.66)(62.4)} = \frac{121.0}{165.98} = 0.728\,(\text{ft}^3)$$

Volume of water:

$$V_w = \frac{W_w - W_d}{\gamma_w} = \frac{129.2 - 121.0}{62.4} = \frac{8.2}{62.4} = 0.132\,(\text{ft}^3)$$

Volume of air:

$$V_a = 1 - V_s - V_w = 1 - 0.728 - 0.132 = 0.14\,(\text{ft}^3).$$

The soil phase diagrams are shown on Fig. 7-4.

TABLE 7-5. CHANGE IN VOLUMETRIC RELATIONSHIPS WITH
VARYING MOISTURE CONTENT

Point Nos. on Curve	Moisture Cont. $w\%$	Relative Volume of Solids V_s	Relative Volume of Water V_w	Relative Volume of Air V_a	Total Volume of Voids V_v
1	2	3	4	5	6
1	6.8	0.728	0.132	0.140	0.272
2	8.5	0.743	0.165	0.091	0.251
3	9.4	0.752	0.187	0.061	0.248
4	10.2	0.755	0.205	0.040	0.245
M	10.4	0.755	0.205	0.040	0.245
5	11.3	0.753	0.226	0.021	0.247
6	12.5	0.732	0.246	0.020	0.268

The volumetric relationships with increase in moisture content in soil, Table 7-5, show that the relative volume of solids increases up to a certain point corresponding to maximum dry density at optimum moisture content (point M whose coordinates are $w = 10.4\%$ and $W_d = 125.4$ lb/ft^3). Beyond this point, with the increase in moisture content, w, the dry density, W_d, decreases. As the moisture content increases, the relative volume of water in soil, V_w, naturally increases, but the relative volume of the air voids, V_a, decreases (air is expelled!). As the relative volume of solids, V_s, increases and then decreases, simultaneously the total volume of voids, $V = V_w = V_a$, first decreases, and then concurrently increases (see columns 3, 4, 5, and 6 in Table 7-5).

In soil engineering, the soil optimum moisture content in making fills and earth dams is of important significance. Soil *moisture control*, or water control, as it is also practiced in fabricating concrete, affords a measuring stick for the guidance of soil compaction. At the optimum moisture content the fine particles of the soil, within the range of compaction energy, permit themselves to be densified best mechanically. As in the technology of concrete, where water with its physical and chemical properties (capillary pressure and hydration, respectively) has an effect on the hardened concrete—and thus a decisive influence upon density and strength—so in compacting the various types of soil the optimum moisture content, in order to bring about the greatest density at a specified compaction, is different. As the plasticity values, corresponding to the various amounts of specific surfaces of soil particles and surface tension, depend so much upon the granulometry of the soil, so also the granulometry has an effect upon the density of the soil: soil moisture films affect the densities to which soils may be compacted. The density of soil moisture varies with temperature, and so does the viscosity and the surface tension of water. With decrease in temperature these properties of water increase; hence a greater amount of compaction energy must be applied to the soil at lower temperatures (compaction operations in fall and winter, for example) than at higher temperatures. Thus changes in soil moisture film characteristics furnish a reasonable explanation of the observed phenomenon that compacting soil in cold weather is more difficult than in warm weather.

7-11. Needle Penetration Test. The degree of compaction of soil attained in the field and that attained in the laboratory can be compared by using the so-called Proctor's plasticity needle. The needle, or penetrometer, is a rod with an enlarged, exchangeable tip, Fig. 7-5. The penetrometer is a hand-operated instrument with a calibrated spring to measure the force of penetration. The penetrometer with a known bearing area of the tip is forced with a gradual, uniform push at a rate of about $\frac{1}{2}$ in. per second to a depth of 3 in. into the soil (field or laboratory), and the resistance in pounds per square inch to penetration is read off the calibrated shaft of the penetrometer. The resistance to penetration of a soil is the

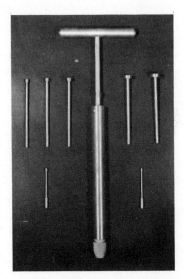

FIG. 7-5 Proctor's penetrometer.

firmness of the soil in lb/in². The interchangeable tips have bearing areas of 0.05, 0.1, 0.25, 0.50, and 1.0 sq in. The penetration readings in the laboratory are made on the compacted soil sample in the compaction mold. The penetration tests made in the field are compared with the laboratory readings of penetration. Both readings, theoretically, should coincide.

The resistance to penetration depends upon the gradation of soil, the density of the soil, its moisture content, frictional resistance between the soil particles and the needle, applied pressure for penetration, upon the true and apparent cohesion, and possibly other factors. Hence, the penetrometer measures a complex of soil conditions. Moisture content and structure being the same, sandy soils are more easily penetrable than clayey soils. In fine-textured soils penetration gets easier as the moisture content increases. Resistance to penetration also increases with increasing depth below the surface of the soil sample, viz., compacted soil in the field.

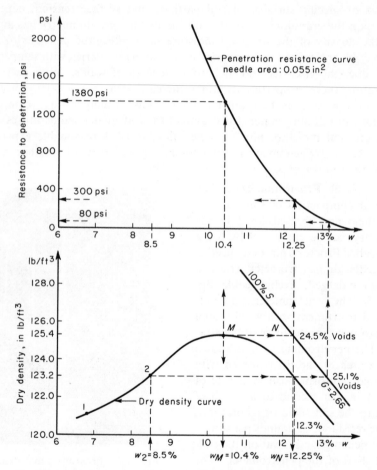

FIG. 7-6   Moisture-dry density and penetration resistance curves.

The penetrometer is used by the field inspector to test the adequacy of rolling, i.e., density as compaction operations proceed. This method is simple but not always positive. When coarse-particled material interferes with the uniform penetration of the needle, the penetrometer test cannot be made.

The penetrometer readings, in lb/in² as ordinates, may be plotted as a function of the soil moisture content on the moisture-dry density graph. For a consistent penetration curve, always use one and the same needle tip. Proctor suggests that a minimum needle penetration resistance of 300 lb/in^2 should be attained for any soil compaction project at the optimum moisture content. In practice satisfactory readings vary from 200 to 300 psi, and sometimes even higher.

A penetration resistance curve is illustrated in Fig. 7-6. Note on the graph that a maximum dry density of a soil has been attained at an optimum moisture content of 10.4%. At this optimum moisture content and density the resistance to penetration shown by the penetration resistance curve is 1380 lb/in^2. At this density the soil contains approximately 24.5% voids (see point N). If the voids were entirely filled with water instead of the amount of the optimum moisture content, the soil would contain 12.25% moisture by dry weight. At this moisture content the resistance to penetration of the needle into the soil for the same maximum dry density would be reduced to approx. 300 lb/in^2. At 8.5% and 12.3% moisture, it can be noted from Fig. 7-6, the dry densities are equal (123.2 lb/ft^3) and less than the maximum; and the void contents are also equal, namely: $V_v = 25.1\%$. At 8.5% moisture content, the penetration resistance is high (out of paper range), but at $w = 12.3\%$, the resistance is very low (less than 300) at the same densities of 123.2 lb/ft^3 in both cases. If the 25.1% voids now were fully saturated with water, the resistance to penetration in water-saturated soil would attain a value of 80 lb/in^2 and approach zero.

Although true readings on the penetrometer are difficult to obtain, both in the laboratory and in the field, the concept of resistance to penetration, nevertheless, serves well to explain the phenomenon of the increase in shear strength of soil by way of compaction. Laboratory tests show that the maximum shear strength is attained at a moisture content which is somewhat less than the optimum moisture content (refer to section on Unconfined Compression Test).

7-12. Summary.

1) The soil optimum moisture-dry density relationship test is a test, established by agreement, or convention, and has no absolute limiting value, but represents merely the degree of compaction.

2) The degree of compaction achieved in the standard compaction test of soil varies with the soil moisture content.

3) The moisture-dry density curve gives an insight into the variation in soil dry density with varying soil moisture content.

4) The standard compaction test results are used in controlling the amount of water to be added to the soil, and the density of the rolled fill material. The test is extensively applied in earth dam, highway, and airfield construction.

5) In the standard compaction test of soil, the falling rammer is considered to be equivalent to a roller on the soil in the field.

6) The principal application of the compaction test is to indicate how the soil will react to compaction, and what proportion of the maximum compaction can be achieved by field equipment on the construction site.

7) The shear strength of the soil increases with the amount of compactive effort applied, but up to a certain percent of moisture content only.

8) Also, the compaction test results are used for writing compaction specifications for field compaction of soils. So, for instance, some agencies prescribe that the subgrade should be compacted in the field to such a degree that the dry density of the soil should not be less than 95% of the maximum compaction (100%). Here 95% density (dry) is specified on the "dry side" of the optimum moisture content.

QUESTIONS

7-1. Which is the most economical and feasible method of improving the bearing capacity of subgrade soils and fills?
(Densification by compaction and vibration).

7-2. Upon what depends the stability of a subgrade soil or embankment?
(Upon the shear resistance of the soils of which they are composed).

7-3. Of what properties does the shear resistance of soils consist?
(The combined properties of internal friction and cohesion of soil).

7-4. By what factors are internal friction and cohesion affected?
(By the amount of voids in the soil and the amount of water within these voids).

7-5. What will happen to a soil containing a high percentage of voids when exposed to high moisture content?
(It will become very unstable. Conversely, a soil with low porosity will resist the entrance of water into the voids and thus be much more stable than a soil having a high porosity).

7-6. What is densification?
(Any process which reduces the amount of voids in a soil mass is termed densification).

7-7. Upon what depends the density to which any soil can be compacted?
(Upon its moisture content and the amount of compactive energy applied on the soil).

7-8. Of what value is the needle penetration test in soil?
(Soil compaction operations in the field can be checked continuously. The check permits comparing easily whether the soil material is worked in too moist or too dry).

PROBLEMS

7-1. Given soil compaction test results as follows:

Trial Nos.	Moisture Content $w\%$ by dry weight	Wet weight of Compacted Soil lb/ft^3
1	8.3	126.2
2	9.6	131.9
3	10.5	135.3
4	11.3	137.4
5	12.2	136.6
6	13.4	135.8
7	13.8	134.7

The specific gravity of this silty soil is $G = 2.65$. The test is standard test.

Required:
1) Plot the moisture-dry density curve.
2) Plot the saturation (zero air voids) curve.
3) Plot the percent air-voids curve.
4) Determine the optimum moisture content and the achieved maximum dry density of this soil.
5) Discuss the three curves.

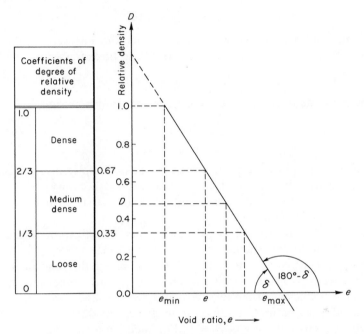

FIG. 7-7 $D = f(e)$.

RELATIVE DENSITY

7-13. The Concept. The concept of "relative density" is a criterion for the density of a sand deposit. This criterion is of an arbitrary character; it is not based on any plausible physical concept of density of any one physical body. Relative density applies only to sand, not silt and/or clay.

Assume that the sand soil is in its loosest state:

$$e_{max} = \frac{V_{vmax}}{V_{smin}} \qquad (7\text{-}22)$$

for which there is a corresponding coefficient of relative density, $D = 0$. For the same sand in its densest state

$$e_{min} = \frac{V_{vmin}}{V_{smax}}, \qquad (7\text{-}23)$$

and its relative density is $D = 1$.

One sees that relative density is a function of void ratio, viz., porosity:

$$D = f(e) \qquad (7\text{-}24)$$

7-14. Derivation of Equation for Relative Density. The foregoing e/D-relationship can be represented by a graph (Fig. 7-7), from which the following mathematical expression can be established:

$$\frac{D_{(=1)}}{e_{max} - e_{min}} = \tan \delta \qquad (7\text{-}25)$$

or

$$e_{max} - e_{min} = \cot \delta \qquad (7\text{-}26)$$

For any intermediate pair of e/D-values within the interval from $D = 0$ to $D = 1$ on the D-axis the maximum void ratio can be expressed as

$$e_{max} = e + D \cot \delta = e + D(e_{max} - e_{min}), \qquad (7\text{-}27)$$

which permits one to solve for the coefficient of relative density:

$$D = \frac{e_{max} - e}{e_{max} - e_{min}}, \qquad (7\text{-}28)$$

where e = void ratio of sand at its natural density under investigation, viz., density in its natural state in the field or laboratory;

e_{max} = void ratio of the same sand in its loosest state (to be established in the laboratory), and

e_{min} = void ratio of the same sand under investigation in its densest state (to be established in the laboratory).

Analyzing the D-equation one notes the following. If the sand in its natural condition already is in its loosest state ($e = e_{max}$), then, according to the D-equation, the coefficient of the relative density of the sand is $D = 0$.

If the sand in its natural condition is in its densest state ($e = e_{min}$), then its coefficient of relative density is $D = 1$. For indeterminate values of e the D-values are between 0 and 1.

Sometimes the D-equation is expressed in terms of porosities. Because $e = n/(1 - n)$,

$$D = \frac{e_{max} - e}{e_{max} - e_{min}} = \frac{(n_{max} - n)(1 - n_{min})}{(n_{max} - n_{min})(1 - n)}, \qquad (7\text{-}29)$$

where n_{max} = maximum possible porosity of the given sand soil (loosest state),

n_{min} = minimum possible porosity of the given sand soil (densest state), and

n = natural porosity of the given sand soil (natural state in the field, or prepared in the laboratory). The most effective means of densifying sand fills is the method by vibration of the soil.

7-15. Definition. Physically, relative density expresses the ratio of actual decrease in volume of voids in a soil to the maximum possible decrease in volume of voids. In other words, relative density indicates how far a sand under investigation is capable of further densification beyond its natural state of density under externally applied loads or energy.

7-16. Degree of Relative Density. Attempts have been made to characterize the various degrees or states of densities by means of numerical coefficients. The analysis of the D-equation indicates the possibility of doing so. According to Terzaghi, the conventional coefficients are:

For loose sand	$0 < D < \frac{1}{3}$
Medium-dense sand	$\frac{1}{3} < D < \frac{2}{3}$
Dense or well-compacted sand	$\frac{2}{3} < D < 1$

(see Fig. 7-7).

As already noticed, a sand in its loosest state of compaction has a relative density of $D = 0$, and in its densest state a value of unity, i.e., $D = 1$.

The loosest state of packing of a sand seems to be a quite clearly defined concept. However, it is to be emphasized that this is not so with the packing of sand in the densest state. Let this be illustrated by the following example. Imagine a cubic foot of quartz rock. Obviously this is the densest state of packing with porosity $n = 0$. If this cubic foot of quartz were subdivided by grinding to a sand size (artificial aggregate), and reshoveled, it is obvious that it is no longer possible to restore this sand in its densest state of packing. There will always result some volume of voids regardless of attempts to densify the sand by tamping, rolling, or vibration. From this reasoning one arrives at the idea that the densest state of packing is one which the mass of sand permits attaining. Above such a density it is then always possible to imagine a more dense state of packing.

For very dense *gravelly sand* it sometimes can happen that $D > 1$. This would mean that the natural packing does not permit itself to be repeated in the laboratory. The application of the relative density test to sand is to check the achieved density and the compactness of fills made of granular material. Loose sand can best be densified by vibration[6,7,8]. In evaluating sandy soils, their natural and relative densities are of paramount importance for the evaluation of their properties as a material upon which to found structures.

From the change in the volume of voids in a soil, for example on compaction, it is possible to evaluate the changes in density of a soil medium, and thus to judge the achieved degree of compaction.

Depending upon the properties of the particles of the sand and the texture of the latter, two kinds of sands of the same volume of voids (porosity) may possess totally different abilities of densification (compaction). Hence, the coefficient of relative density of a given sand usually gives us a clearer idea of the density than the value of the void ratio itself.

Example. Calculate the relative density of a sand soil whose void ratios are as follows:

$$e_{max} = 0.55; \qquad e = 0.30, \text{ and} \qquad e_{min} = 0.20.$$

Also, evaluate whether the sand deposit is in a loose state, medium dense or dense state.

$$D = \frac{e_{max} - e}{e_{max} - e_{min}} = \frac{0.55 - 0.30}{0.55 - 0.20} = 0.71$$

Because $1.00 > 0.71 > 0.66$, the result, $D = 0.71$, indicates that the sand is in a dense state of compaction.

DETERMINATION OF RELATIVE DENSITY

7-17. Equipment. In its natural state of density, a sand soil is characterized by its void ratio, e. However, it is very difficult to determine soil densities, viz., degree of compaction, visually. Therefore, engineers resort to certain methods of testing. For the determination of relative density of sand, relatively simple equipment is used. The apparatus consists essentially of two brass cylinders, I and II, Fig. 7-8. One of the metal cylinders, cylinder I, of known volume, say

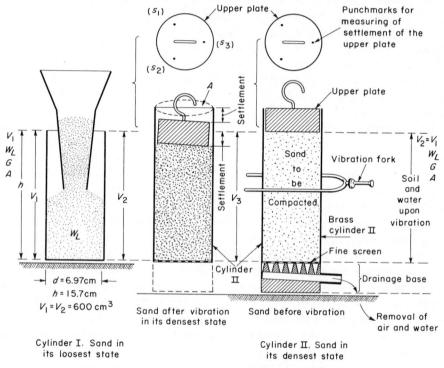

Fig. 7-8   Sketch of relative density test equipment.

$V_1 = 600$ cm^3, has a closed bottom; the other cylinder, cylinder II, of same volume as the first one ($V_2 = V_1 = 600$ cm^3), has a drainage base. The cross-sectional area, A, of both cylinders is the same. The brass drainage base is connected to an aspirator attached to a spigot to provide a vacuum for removing water and air from the voids of the sand in cylinder II. Also, a large funnel, a straightedge, a scoop, a vibration fork, a cm-scale, depth gage, weighing balance, and a vacuum source (pump or aspirator) belong to the necessary set of equipment. The sand to be tested must be oven-dried.

7-18. Procedure.

1) First of all, determine the specific gravity, G, of the sand to be tested.

2) For the determination of porosity, n, of a sand in its *natural state*, proceed as described under the topic "Porosity":

$$n = 1 - n_s = 1 - \frac{W_d}{VG\gamma_w} \qquad (5\text{-}34)$$

where n_s = relative volume of solid particles of dry soil,
$\quad\quad W_d$ = dry weight of the soil sample obtained in its natural state,
$\quad\quad V$ = volume of the soil sampler (volume of soil sampled in its natural state),
$\quad\quad G$ = specific gravity of sand particles, and
$\quad\quad \gamma_w$ = unit weight of water.
Now the void ratio of the sand in its natural state is calculated as

$$e = \frac{n}{1 - n}.$$

3) To determine the density of sand in its loosest state, viz., n_{max}, or e_{max}, the oven-dried sand is poured loosely through a funnel into the bottomed metal cylinder. By means of a straightedge, level off the sand on the top of the cylinder (I). Determine the loose weight of sand in this cylinder, W_L, and calculate n_{max}:

$$n_{max} = 1 - \frac{W_L}{V_1 G\gamma_w} \qquad (7\text{-}30)$$

where V_1 = volume of the bottomed cylinder (I) = volume of loose sand. Accordingly,

$$e_{max} = \frac{n_{max}}{1 - n_{max}}.$$

4) To determine the porosity of the same sand in its densest state, n_{min}, viz., e_{min}, gradually muddle the weighed sand from the first cylinder into the second one (the one with the drainage base), the volume of which between the screen and the upper plate is $V_2 = V_1$. First fill the cylinder with sand to $\frac{1}{5}$th of its height. Then pour water into this cylinder, and vibrate this cylinder by means of the vibration fork, exerting 30 pairs of blows on the outside walls of the cylinder. Apply vacuum to remove air and water from the soil while vibrating. Then vibrate in the second fifth of the volume, and so on until all of the sand from cylinder I is vibrated into cylinder II. Remember, the weight of the transferred sand is known. Apply vacuum to remove moisture from the voids of the sand and cylinder. Then place the upper plate on top of the vibrated sand in cylinder II, and by means of the depth gage determine the average vibration settlement, viz., decrease in volume of the sand from its loosest state to its densest state at the three punch marks in the upper plate:

$$s = \frac{s_1 + s_2 + s_3}{3} \qquad (7\text{-}31)$$

Then calculate the vibrated volume of sand, V_3, (the densest state of the vibrated sand):

$$V_3 = V_2 - As,$$

where A is the cross-sectional area of the drainage-based cylinder. Of course, the two cylinders can also be of different dimensions. In the latter case, these have to be observed in calculating V_3 and n_{min}. The minimum porosity is now calculated as

$$n_{min} = 1 - \frac{W_L}{V_3 G \gamma_w}, \tag{7-32}$$

and the minimum void ratio

$$e_{min} = \frac{n_{min}}{1 - n_{min}}.$$

5) Now we are ready to calculate the coefficient of relative density D of the sand tested:

$$D = \frac{e_{max} - e}{e_{max} - e_{min}} \tag{7-29}$$

Example. Determine D from the data as follows.
1), 2) The specific gravity of a sand was found to be $G = 2.65$. The unit weight of water, in the metric system of units, is $\gamma_w = 1$ g/cm³. The porosity of sand in its natural state is $n = 0.329$, or its corresponding void ratio $e = 0.487$. The cross-sectional area of both cylinders: $A = 38.0$ cm².
3) Porosity in the loosest state, n_{max}.
Volume of the bottomed cylinder: $V_1 = 600.0$ cm³.
Weight of dry, loose sand: $W_L = 1030.4$ g.

$$n_{max} = 1 - \frac{1030.4}{(600)(2.65)(1)} = 0.352$$

$$e_{max} = 0.542$$

4) Porosity in the densest state, n_{min}.
Vibration settlement of sand in cylinder II from three measurements:

$$s = \frac{0.99 + 1.02 + 1.05}{3} = 1.02 \text{ (cm)}.$$

Volume of second cylinder: $V_2 = V_1 = 600$ cm³.
Volume of settlement after vibration:

$$V_{se} = As = (38.0)(1.02) = 38.8 \text{ (cm}^3).$$

Volume of vibrated sand:

$$V_3 = V_2 - As = 600.0 - 38.8 = 561.2 \text{ (cm}^3).$$

Minimum porosity:

$$n_{min} = 1 - \frac{1030.4}{(561.2)(2.65)(1)} = 0.307$$

Minimum void ratio:

$$e_{min} = \frac{n_{min}}{1 - n_{min}} = 0.443.$$

5) Coefficient of relative density:

$$D = \frac{e_{max} - e}{e_{max} - e_{min}} = \frac{0.542 - 0.487}{0.542 - 0.443} = 0.555,$$

or

$$D = \frac{(n_{max} - n)(1 - n_{min})}{(n_{max} - n_{min})(1 - n)} =$$

$$= \frac{(0.352 - 0.329)(1 - 0.307)}{(0.352 - 0.307)(1 - 0.329)} = 0.554.$$

Because the calculated $D = 0.555$ is

$$0.33 < 0.555 < 0.670,$$

the result indicates that the sand is in a medium-dense state. The conditions involved in this example are illustrated graphically in Fig. 7-9.

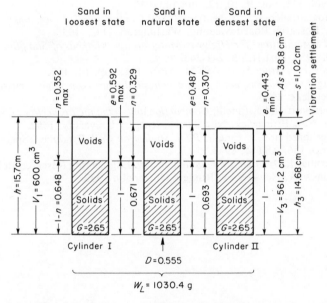

FIG. 7-9   Porosity conditions on determining relative density of sand.

7-19. Discussion. This test is definitely limited to sands. Fine sands should be protected from flowing out of the second cylinder through the drainage base by placing a layer of filter paper on the top of the screen.

Some errors in the test results can easily be introduced when determining porosity in the loosest state: the slightest bit of vibration of cylinder I while pouring the sand would cause the sand to become denser than the loosest state possible. Another important error arises from erratically determined porosity of sand in its natural state. The difficulty here is in correctly obtaining the sand sample in its natural, undisturbed state. Therefore all the necessary experiments must be exercised with great care.

7-20. Applications. The relative density theory finds its application in compaction of granular material; in various soil vibration problems associated with engineering operations in earthworks, foundations of structures (pile driving), foundations of machinery, vibrations transmitted to sandy soil from trains and automobiles, and a number of other applications. In such instances the relative density values of sand give us an indication whether or not unpleasant consequences can be expected from engineering operations which might affect structures or foundations due to *vibration settlement.*

Relative density tests for various points on a lot may show variety in *D*-values and may indicate the necessity of densifying the whole area. Repeated relative density tests then serve as criteria for the achieved degree of density.

REFERENCES

1. R. R. Proctor, "Fundamental Principles of Soil Compaction", *Engineering News-Record*, vol. 111, nos. 9, 10, 12, and 13, 1933.
2. C. A., Hogentogler, Jr., "Essentials of Soil Compaction", *Proceedings*, 16th Annual Highway Research Board Meeting, Washington, D.C., 1936.
3. *Standard Specifications for Highway Materials and Methods of Sampling and Testing*, AASHO, 1950, Part II, pp. 241-243.
4. *Procedures for Testing Soils*, ASTM, April, 1958, pp. 102-107.
5. K. Terzaghi, *Erdbaumechanik uf bodenphysikalischer Grundlage*, Leipzig und Wien, Franz Deuticke, 1925.
6. R. K. Bernhard and J. Finelli, *Compaction and Dynamic Properties of Soils* (mimeographed), New Brunswick, New Jersey, Rutgers University, 1952.
7. R. K. Bernhard and J. Finelli, *Pilot Studies on Soil Dynamics*, Special Technical Bulletin no. 156, ASTM, 1953.
8. R. K. Bernhard, *Dynamic Compaction of Soil*, Engineering Research Bulletin no. 37, New Brunswick, New Jersey, Rutgers University, 1952.

Chapter 8

SOIL CONSISTENCY

8-1. Definition. For the purpose of structural characterization and evaluation of cohesive soils as construction materials, it is necessary to determine their consistency properties. It is known that the physical properties of cohesive soils vary with the degree or state of "consistency".

Consistency, in general, is that property of material which is manifested by its resistance to flow. The term "soil consistency" conveys the idea of the degree of cohesion (adhesion) between the soil particles. Also, consistency can be regarded as the outward result of the forces of cohesion and adhesion acting at various stages of moisture contents. In this sense, "consistency" refers to the resistance of soil offered against forces that tend to deform or rupture the soil aggregate.

Physically, *cohesion* is the binding together of like substances by intermolecular forces and frequently, as in soils, through the medium of moisture films. In popular terms cohesion means the tendency that the soil particles exhibit in sticking together and holding the soil mass intact. In effect, the cohesion of soil is that part of its shear strength which does not depend upon inter-particle friction. There is a greater cohesion in the moist, fine-textured materials due to the combined effect of water films (surface tension) and the physical forces that are associated with colloidal matter. The surface tension effects are produced by the moisture films distributed throughout the soil mass. The surface tension of an annular neck between the contact of two soil particles tends to pull the two soil particles together.

Consistency pertains to cohesive soils only. Consistency is commonly described by such terms as cemented, solid, hard, brittle, stiff, sticky, plastic, mellow, or soft. These gradations of soil consistency, as mentioned already several times before, are greatly influenced by the soil moisture content.

8-2. Plasticity. In the arts and industries plasticity is an important property of materials. The most generally accepted definitions of plasticity in the arts and industry are:

"That property which enables a material to be deformed continuously and permanently without rupture", or

"Plasticity is the ability of a body to undergo dislocation of its smallest structural particles, a consequence of the application of external forces, at ordinary temperature, without disturbance by their coherence."

In soil mechanics: The problem of plasticity does not concern the "plasticity" in itself, but it is considered merely from the standpoint of the *degree of plasticity*.

This simply means the capacity of a soil to undergo certain important changes of shape which may involve a complete rearrangement of particles, without a noticeable change in volume. Plasticity is probably the most conspicuous property of clay.

Also, a soil is said to be in a *plastic state* when the water content is such that it can change its shape *without* producing surface cracks.

Depending upon the water content soils can change their state from a solid to a liquid.

Cohesive soils may also have a consistency between both states mentioned above, i.e., *cohesive soils may also be in a plastic state.* Therefore, for purposes of classification, degrees or *limits of plasticity* have been set up.

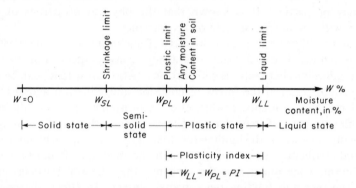

FIG. 8-1   States of consistency, consistency limits, and plasticity index.

8-3. States of Consistency and Their Limits. Consistency limits indicate conventionally the soil moisture content limits for various states of consistency. The consistency limits are: the liquid limit, $w_{L.L.}$ or *L.L.*, the plastic limit, $w_{P.L.}$ or *P.L.*, and the shrinkage limit, $w_{S.L.}$ or *S.L.* With the increase in soil moisture, the thickness of the moisture films which surround the clay particles increases until at a certain state—liquid state—the cohesion is reduced so low the soil behaves as a liquid. Suppose that this soil-water mixture is now subjected to drying. Drying of soil means a decrease in its moisture content. At the beginning of the drying process the soil mass represents a more-or-less uniform dense liquid. It is said to be in the *liquid state.* During the drying process the thickness of the moisture films between the soil particles decreases. Upon further drying, the cohesive soil mass becomes dryer and somewhat stiffer, and at a certain moisture content, the so-called *liquid limit*, $w_{L.L.}$, the soil transforms from the liquid into the *plastic state*, thereby losing its ability to flow as a liquid. In this plastic state the soil can be readily molded, holding its shape, or can change shape without the appearance of cracks in it. Any material which allows a change of form without rupture and which will retain this form when the pressure is removed, is said to be plastic. Upon a further decrease in moisture, the plastic properties of the cohesive soil are lost, and at a certain moisture content, termed the *plastic limit*, $w_{P.L.}$, the clayey soil transforms from the plastic state into the *semi-solid state*. At the plastic limit the change in consistency, viz., the change in shape of a cohesive soil, is accompanied by visible cracks; when worked upon, the soil crumbles.

The next stage of the drying-out process below the $w_{P.L.}$-point gradually approaches from the semi-solid to the *solid state*. The moisture content of the soil at which the soil transforms from the semi-solid state to the solid state is termed the *shrinkage limit*, $w_{S.L.}$. The shrinkage limit is attained at that moisture content at which the cohesive soil, regardless of drying, remains volume-constant. Also, the change in color, upon drying, from dark to light approximately indicates the shrinkage limit. The moisture contents characterizing consistency limits are based on dry weight of the soil.

The previously discussed consistency limits of soils may be conveniently represented graphically as illustrated in Fig. 8-1. Consistency limits of soil, $w_{L.L.}$ and $w_{P.L.}$, give one an idea about the plastic properties and volume-constancy or stability and also about the internal friction of soil.

The consistency limits, liquid limit, plastic limit, and shrinkage limit, at which the transition from one state of soil consistency to another one takes place, were suggested by the Swedish soil scientist Atterberg.[1] These Atterberg consistency limits are the most convenient characteristics of the consistency of cohesive soils, which give one a clearer concept of the range of water content of a soil in the plastic state. The consistency concepts are extensively used in soil engineering for identification, classification, and characterization purposes of soil as construction material.

8-4. Plasticity Index. With reference to the Atterberg consistency limits cohesive soils, through their change in moisture content, can assume the following states of consistency: 1) liquid, 2) plastic, 3) semi-solid, and 4) solid.

Each of these states of consistency of soils is characterized by definite physical properties which are determined by their corresponding moisture contents. As seen in Fig. 8-1, the liquid limit separates the liquid state from the plastic one; the plastic limit separates the plastic state from the semi-solid one; and the shrinkage limit separates the semi-solid state from the solid one.

At the liquid limit the soil particles separate by water just widely enough to deprive the soil mass of its shear strength, and the fine soil particles tend to flow out under the influence of gravity. At the plastic limit the soil moisture does not separate the soil particles. Here the moisture has enough surface tension to effect contact between soil particles, causing the soil mass to behave as a semi-solid.

The difference in moisture content or interval between liquid and plastic limits is termed the *plasticity index*, $P.I. = w_{P.I.}$:

$$P.I. = w_{L.L.} - w_{P.L.} \quad (\%) \qquad (8\text{-}1)$$

The plasticity index, $P.I.$, indicates the moisture range through which a cohesive soil has the properties of a plastic material.

As can be inferred from Fig. 8-1, the plasticity index characterizes the plastic behavior of a soil, and indicates the degree of cohesiveness of the soil. For example, the narrower the *P.I.* interval (the smaller the *P.I.*) is, the less plastic is the soil.

According to Atterberg[2,3] when *P.I.* < 7, the soil is said to be of low plasticity. When $7 \leq P.I. \leq 17$, the soil is of medium plasticity. When *P.I.* > 17, the soil is of high plasticity. These relationships are shown in Table 8-1.

TABLE 8-1. PLASTICITY INDEXES

Plasticity Index	Soil Characteristics By Plasticity	Soil Type	Cohesiveness
1	2	3	4
0	Non-plastic	Sand	Non cohesive
<7	Low-plastic	Silt	Partly cohesive
7-17	Medium plastic	Silty clay (Clayey silt)	Cohesive
>17	High plastic	Clay	Cohesive

All of the cohesive soils can be at three different consistencies depending upon the moisture content present. When the moisture content of a soil is greater than the liquid limit, i.e., when $w > w_{L.L.}$, the soil is in a liquid state. When $w = w_{L.L.}$, the moisture content is at the liquid limit of the soil. When $w_{P.L.} < w < w_{L.L.}$, the soil is in a plastic state of consistency. When $w_{S.L.} < w < w_{P.L.}$, the soil is in a semi-solid state of consistency. When $w < w_{S.L.}$, the soil is in the solid state of consistency.

Burmister[4] classifies plastic properties of soils according to their plastic index as follows:

Plasticity Index	Plasticity
0	Nonplastic
1 to 5	Slight
5 to 10	Low
10 to 20	Medium
20 to 40	High
>40	Very high

Table 8-2 illustrates soil classification by its plasticity index.

An inspection of Table 8-2 reveals that with a decrease in the plastic properties of soil the liquid limit decreases faster than the plastic limit (compare Columns 3 and 4). This would indicate why fine sands and silts in cuts are very sensitive with respect to saturation and flow pressure (quicksand condition phenomenon). These soils in earthwork engineering are the most difficult to cope with.

Many construction companies in highway engineering use the plasticity index not to exceed 6 as a criterion for specifying soil material used close under the pavement, whereas others specify a *P.I.* ≤ 3.

TABLE 8-2. EXAMPLE OF SOIL CLASSIFICATION BY ITS PLASTICITY INDEX

Type of Soil	Degree of Plasticity	Consistency Limits			
		Liquid Limit $w_{L.L.}$	Plastic Limit $w_{P.L.}$	Plasticity Index P.I.	Limits of Plasticity Indexes
1	2	3	4	5	6
Sand	Non-plastic	20	20	0	0
Silt	Low-plastic	25	20	5	<7
Silty Clay Clayey silt }	Medium-plastic	40	25	15	{ >7 <17
Clay	High-plastic	70	40	30	>17

There is a very pronounced difference in the plasticity of some soil materials which are composed of very fine particles. Rock flour, for example, will exhibit practically no plasticity, whereas a clay composed of equally fine material will exhibit a marked plasticity. A similar comparison may be made between bentonite and kaolinite clays.

Some sands and rock flour free of cohesive material cannot be subjected to the consistency test. Such soils are indicated as non-liquid (N.L.) and non-plastic (N.P.). Such soils may follow the same general process in volumetric change caused by drying out as the cohesive soils. The difference, however, is that upon drying the sandy soils do not pass through the $w_{P.L.}$-point from the liquid state into the solid state of solid, coherent, hard structure as do clays. Contrary to clays, sands change states from the liquid to the semi-solid abruptly, resulting in non-coherent material. Non-cohesive soils do not possess plasticity, the limit of which, therefore, cannot be determined by test. Such soils are indicated as non-plastic (N.P.). In short, cohesionless soils have no plastic state, and the liquid and plastic limits can be imagined to coincide. Thus, their plastic limit, theoretically, is zero.

Consistency limits of some New Jersey soils are compiled in Table 8-3.

8-5. Index of Relative Plasticity. The natural moisture content of a soil, w, depending upon the moisture condition in soil, may be located anywhere on the moisture scale (Fig. 8-1). The natural moisture content by itself tells one actually very little about the consistency conditions of a soil. However, its position relative to the position of liquid and plastic limits is very significant, and indicates whether a cohesive soil is in the solid state, plastic or in the liquid state.

The ratio of difference between the moisture content and P.L. to the P.I. is called the *consistency index*, or *relative plasticity index*, R:

$$R = \frac{w - w_{P.L.}}{w_{P.I.}} \qquad (8-2)$$

Sometimes this quantity is called the *liquidity index*.

This expression can be derived by geometry as in Fig. 8-2, from similar triangles $\triangle(w_{P.L.})(R_w)(w)$ and $\triangle(w_{P.L.})(R)(w_{L.L.})$.

TABLE 8-3. CONSISTENCY LIMITS OF SOME NEW JERSEY SOILS

Nos.	Soil Description	Agronomic Series	Symbols used in the Engineering Soil Survey of New Jersey, Ref. (5)	Liquid Limit (L.L) $w_{L.L.}$ %	Plasticity Index (P.I.) $w_{P.I.}$ %
1	2	3	4	5	6
1	Silt, silty and clayey sand with thick layers of silty clay and clay	Collington	MV-47	NL to 77	NP to 23
2	Silt, silty clay	Croton	Sa-4	19 to 43	2 to 15
3	Silt, sandy silt, silty sand	Dunellen	GS-24	NL to 46	NP to 17
4	Clay	Elkton	M-67	20 to 44	3 to 16
5	Silty sand, gravelly sand	Lakewood	ML-23	NL	NP
6	Silt and silty clay	Montalto	Is-46	23 to 34	2 to 7
7	Silt and some clayey silt	Penn	Sh-4	20 to 46	2 to 22
8	Silty clay	Raritan	M-46	20 to 40	5 to 20
9	Sand, silty sand and some clay	Sassafras	ML-23	NL to 40	NP to 10
10	Silt, silty sand with thick layers of silty clay and clay	Shrewsbury	MV-47	28 to 53	4 to 22
11	Silt and silty clay	Whippany	GM-46	22 to 51	1 to 20
12	Clay with silt	Woodstown	M-67	22 to 74	3 to 40
13	Inorganic silt (gneissic rock flour)	—	—	20 to 22	NP to 6

The limits of relative plasticity vary between 0 and 1 at $w_{P.L.}$ and $w_{L.L.}$, respectively.

When $R < 0$, the soil is in a semi-solid or solid state.

When $0 \le R \le 1$, the soil is in a plastic state.

When $R > 1$, the soil is in a liquid state.

For the purpose of convenience, the interval of the plastic state, as shown in Fig. 8-2, can further be subdivided into the following four subdivisions:

stiff consistency,	R varies from 0 to 0.25
medium-soft consistency,	R varies from 0.25 to 0.50
soft consistency,	R varies from 0.50 to 0.75
very soft consistency,	R varies from 0.75 to 1.00

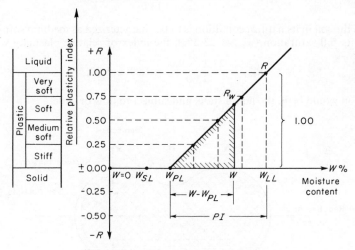

FIG. 8-2 Relative plasticity index.

The consistency or relative plasticity index, R, permits one to recognize the possibility of a flow or slide of slopes of embankments. In places where the soil moisture approaches nearest to the liquid limit, R would approach a value of unity. Therefore, R can be considered as a slide or flow coefficient. Hence, the relative plasticity index, R, indicates in which part of its plastic range a given soil sample lies, and helps one to assess its natural moisture content.

Example. Determine the plasticity index, $P.I.$, and the relative plasticity index, R, for a cohesive soil the properties of which are given as follows:

$$\text{specific gravity } G = 2.65$$
$$\text{porosity } n = 38\%$$
$$\text{natural moisture content } w = 13\%$$
$$\text{liquid limit } w_{L.L.} = 22\%$$
$$\text{plastic limit } w_{P.L.} = 9\%.$$

Solution. *The plasticity index, $P.I.$, is calculated as* $P.I. = w_{L.L.} - w_{P.L.} = 22\% - 9\% = 13\%.$
Saturation Moisture Content

$$w_{sat} = \frac{n}{G(1-n)} = \frac{0.38}{2.65(1-0.38)} = 0.232, \text{ or } \underline{23.2\%}$$

Degree of Saturation

$$S = \frac{w}{w_{sat}} = \frac{13.0}{23.2} = 0.56 < 1.00$$

State of Consistency
  a) Because $9 < w < 22$, where $w = 13\%$, the soil in its natural condition is in the plastic state
  b) Because $w_{sat} > 22$, where $w_{sat} = 23.3$, the soil, when saturated, would be in the liquid state.

Index of Relative Plasticity

$$R = \frac{w - w_{P.L.}}{w_{P.I.}} = \frac{13.0 - 9.0}{13.0} = 0.307;$$

therefore the soil in its natural condition is to be characterized as medium soft.

Upon its full saturation ($w_{sat} = 23.2\%$), the index of relative plasticity would be

$$R_{sat} = \frac{23.2 - 9.0}{13.0} = 1.09 > 1.00,$$

i.e., the soil would be in the liquid state, and subject to flow or slide.

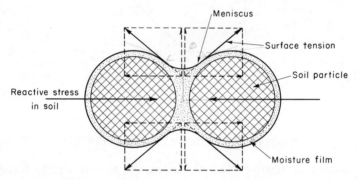

FIG. 8-3   Illustrating the concept of compressive surface tension forces and induced reactive stress in soil.

8-6. Shrinkage Limit. When a moist, cohesive soil is subjected to drying out, it loses moisture and shrinks. During the drying process the compressive surface tension forces of the pore water compress the particles of the skeleton of the cohesive soil together into a compact, coherent mass and thus densify it (Fig. 8-3). Hence, the void ratio of the soil decreases. The moisture loss continues down to a certain moisture content. When this moisture content is attained, any further decrease in moisture content ceases, and no further decrease in volume, viz., shrinkage, takes place. This is the time when the induced reactive stresses in the soil skeleton attain the magnitude of the capillary pressure; at this instant the menisci of the capillary moisture are tearing off and the pore moisture retires into the interior of the soil mass. At this point it can be noted that the soil changes its color from dark to light, and the soil ceases to shrink. The moisture content at this condition is termed the *shrinkage limit*. At the shrinkage limit the soil passes from the semi-solid to the solid state. The relative position of the shrinkage limit ($w_{S.L.}$) on the consistency scale is shown in Figs. 8-1, 8-2, and 8-4. On the average, soil shrinkage limits vary from about 10 to 15 percent by dry weight of soil.

The process of drying out a moist cohesive soil containing no air voids may be characterized by two stages (Fig. 8-4). In the first stage, as the moisture evaporates, it translocates from the interior of the soil to the exterior, and linear decrease in volume or linear shrinkage takes place. Diagrammatically, the relation between volumetric change and decrease in moisture content from an original moisture content w_{orig} is a straight line (AB), i.e., the volume change equals the volume of moisture lost.

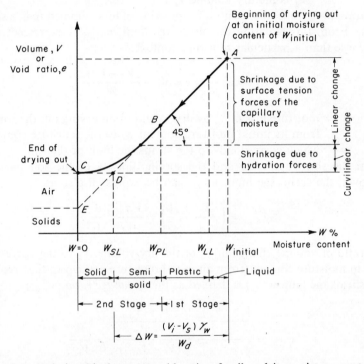

FIG. 8-4   Relationship between void ratio of soil and its moisture content.

Upon further evaporation, in the second stage, air starts to enter into the voids of the soil, and the decrease in volume no longer corresponds to the decrease in moisture content; the decrease in volume is less than the volume of water lost. Thus, this relationship is not a linear one but rather a curved one. Point D, corresponding to the shrinkage limit, $w_{S.L.}$, can in practice be found graphically as the point of intersection of tangents, EA and CD. Segment, OE, characterizes the volume of solids of the soil, and segment, EC, corresponds to the air volume. Thus, from Fig. 8-4 it can be inferred that $w_{S.L.}$ is that moisture content of soil at which no appreciable decrease in the external volume of the soil takes place although the drying still continues.

The shrinkage limit is expressed as follows:

$$w_i W_d - w_{S.L.} W_d = (V_i - V_f)\gamma_w, \tag{8-3}$$

134   PHYSICAL PROPERTIES OF SOIL

where $w_i W_d$ = initial amount of soil moisture, in grams, before drying-out;
w_i = initial moisture content, in %;
W_d = dry weight of a soil sample, in grams;
$w_{S.L.} W_d$ = amount of moisture, in grams, at shrinkage limit;
$\gamma_w = 1$ = unit weight of water = 1 g/cm³;
V_i = initial volume of a soil sample before drying;
V_f = final volume of a soil sample after drying. The final volume V_f is the dry volume V_s.

Equation (8-3), thus, represents an expression of loss in moisture in a shrinking process. From this equation the shrinkage limit, $w_{S.L.}$, is expressed, which is nothing else than a particular moisture content:

$$w_{S.L.} = w_i - \triangle w = w_i - \frac{(V_i - V_s)\gamma_w}{W_d}, \tag{8-4}$$

where $\triangle w$ = moisture loss in % by dry weight upon drying out the soil sample from its initial moisture content w_i to the moisture content $w_{S.L.}$ which corresponds to the shrinkage limit of the soil.

When the shrinkage ratio and the specific gravity of the soil particles, G, are known, the shrinkage limit, $w_{S.L.}$, can be expressed also as

$$w_{S.L.} = \left(\frac{1}{w_{S.R.}} - \frac{1}{G}\right) = \frac{V_s\gamma_w}{W_d} - \frac{1}{G}. \tag{8-5}$$

The ratio of volume change in % of the dry volume V_s to the corresponding change in moisture content (from an initial moisture content to that represented by the shrinkage limit $w_{S.L.}$) is defined as the *shrinkage ratio*, $w_{S.R.}$:

$$w_{S.R.} = \frac{\dfrac{V_i - V_{S.L.}}{V_s}}{w_i - w_{S.L.}} = \frac{\dfrac{V_i - V_{S.L.}}{V_s}}{\dfrac{(V_i - V_{S.L.})\gamma_w}{W_d}} = \frac{W_d}{V_s\gamma_w}. \tag{8-6}$$

By means of the shrinkage limit and shrinkage ratio, the specific gravity of the soil can be calculated. By definition, the specific gravity is

$$G = \frac{\gamma_s}{\gamma_w} = \frac{W_d}{V_s\gamma_w} = \frac{W_d}{\gamma_w(V_i - V_w)} = \frac{W_d}{\gamma_w[V_i - (W_w)/(\gamma_w)]} =$$
$$= \frac{W_d}{\gamma_w\left(V_i - \dfrac{w_i W_d}{\gamma_w} + V_s - V_s\right)} = \frac{1}{\dfrac{V_s\gamma_w}{W_d} - \left[w_i - \dfrac{(V_i - V_s)\gamma_w}{W_d}\right]} \tag{8-7}$$

or

$$G = \frac{1}{\dfrac{1}{w_{S.R.}} - w_{S.L.}}. \tag{8-8}$$

The degree of shrinkage, S_r, is expressed as the ratio of the difference between initial volume, V_i, and final volume, V_f, of a soil sample to its initial volume, V_i:

$$S_r = \frac{V_i - V_f}{V_i}. \tag{8-9}$$

Scheidig classifies the soil from a qualitative viewpoint based on its degree of shrinkage in the following manner[6]:

when $\quad\quad\quad S_r < 5\%$, the soil is "good";
when $\quad 5\% < S_r < 10\%$, the soil is "medium good";
when $10\% < S_r < 15\%$, the soil is "poor";
when $\quad\quad\quad S_r > 15\%$, the soil is "very poor".

Thus the concept shrinkage limit of cohesive soil is useful in evaluating the behavior of slopes of dams and cuts, particularly relative to the possibility of development of cracks in earthworks. In rainy seasons shrinkage cracks may be filled with water and saturate the soil, thus increasing the weight of the earth mass, which in its turn may slide down. The effects of shrinkage are more pronounced in cohesive, colloidal soils, which have high liquid limit values.

Shrinkage of cohesive soil is often accompanied by surface cracks before the moisture content is exhausted. These cracks may extend to a great depth. When such a dry, cracked soil is sufficiently wetted the soil swells. Swelling means an increase in volume of soil and disappearance of cracks. Swelling action is attributed to the colloidal content of the soil mass, and also to its content of organic matter.

Swelling of certain types of clays may bring about structural damage to light structures founded on montmorillonite clay. Tschebotarioff[7] describes a study of a one-story house built in eastern Cuba where the central part of the house had heaved. This phenomenon is explained by the concentration of soil moisture in the upper layers of the montmorillonite clay caused by the natural process of thermo-osmosis, and by defective drains bringing about local swelling of the clay. The damage by swelling clays to structures is pronounced, leading to heaving floors and cracking walls. Dawson[8] describes movement of small houses erected on an expansive clay in the United States. The cause of the movement Dawson attributes to similar reasons as those described by Tschebotarioff.

8-7. Consistency Diagram of Thixotropic Soils. If the moisture content of a thixotropic clay is higher than the liquid limit, then the clay is not in a permanently liquid state but it is quasi-solid, that is, it can become liquid temporarily. The liquid state, brought about by vibrations or stirring, can transfer after a certain gelation time into a quasi-solid state; the clay, thus, behaves thixotropically. Hence, between the permanent plastic and permanent liquid conditions of Atterberg's forms of consistencies, there exists for thixotropic clays a *thixotropic form of consistency* (Fig. 8-5). To separate the thixotropic form of consistency from the liquid state, Ackermann[9] proposed the so-called "gelation limit".

The gelation limit indicates that moisture content with which a well-stirred fine thixotropic soil in an 8 mm diameter test tube after one minute of gelation time just barely still flows under its own weight.

Low gelation limits (30% to 60%) indicate weak thixotropy. High values, above 100%, indicate a high degree of thixotropy.

Soils with thixotropic consistency can, in an illusory manner, stand up in slopes of embankments for a fairly long time until the entire soil mass, induced by vibrations, overloading, excess pore-water pressure, or other disturbances, suddenly transforms temporarily into the liquid state.

Middlebrooks[10] describes the failure of a large, hydraulically filled earth dam—the Fort Peck Dam in Montana—and tries to find the reasons for this slide. It is said that the foundation conditions of this dam were quite complicated. A thick layer of plastic clay existed about 60 ft below the ground surface.

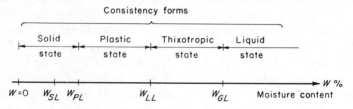

FIG. 8-5   Consistency diagram of thixotropic soils; $w_{G.L.}$ = moisture content at gelation limit.

Tests revealed principally that, among other things, the bentonite and the weathered shale were the weakest materials in the whole foundation. Besides, the bentonite seams showed considerable movement. This, then, is considered the cause of the dam to slide and fail. The water squeezed out by the weight of the soil was trapped along the seams of the bentonite. This hydrostatic water is considered another cause for failure. Investigations also revealed that originally the soil foundation explorations were not complete enough to show the extent of the weathering of the shale and the bentonite.

DETERMINATION OF CONSISTENCY LIMITS OF SOILS

8-8. General Notes. For the determination of the various states of consistency of soils, special tests are devised. The purpose of the consistency limit tests is to determine and to indicate the moisture conditions in a soil at the time when the consistency of the soil is defined.

The routine procedures and devices used for testing consistency limits (or Atterberg limits) of soils are standardized and provided in standard specifications for testing soils by the various materials testing agencies, as for example, the American Association of State Highway Officials (AASHO), by the American Society for Testing Materials (ASTM), or other agencies. From the descriptions of the particular consistency limit tests note that the soil consistency tests, as well as many other soil tests, are conventional tests.

In the laboratory, two characteristic quantities relative to consistency are usually determined:

1) the moisture content at which a cohesive soil transforms from the plastic into liquid state (liquid limit), and
2) the moisture content at which a cohesive soil transforms from the plastic into the solid, viz., semi-solid state (plastic limit).

These tests are sometimes called *the physical tests*.

8-9. Liquid Limit Test. The liquid limit test of soils can be performed, for example, according to ASTM Standard Specification D423-54T.[11]

Hand Method. According to these standards, the liquid limit is that moisture content, expressed as a percentage of the weight of the oven-dried soil (passing the No. 40 mesh sieve), at which the soil will just begin to flow to close a $\frac{5}{64}$ of an inch-wide groove when lightly jarred ten times. This definition holds strictly true only when applied to the "hand method".

To perform a liquid limit test on a soil, about 30 grams of air-dried soil is thoroughly mixed with water until the soil mass becomes pasty. Then, about a $\frac{3}{8}$-in. thick layer or pat of the soil mass thus prepared is formed at the center of the porcelain dish, and, by means of a grooving tool, the soil pat is divided into two parts, see Fig. 8-6.

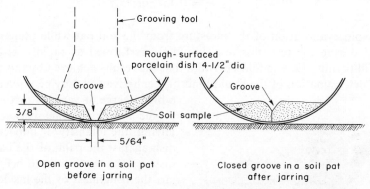

FIG. 8-6   Open and closed grooves.

The porcelain dish, held firmly in one hand, is then lightly jarred ten times against the palm of the other hand. That moisture content at which the groove closes upon jarring ten times, is the liquid limit.

If the lower edges of the two parts of the soil pat do not flow together after ten blows have been struck, the moisture content of the soil is below the liquid limit. More water is to be added, and the procedure repeated.

If the lower edges of the soil pat meet before ten blows have been struck, the moisture content of the soil is above the liquid limit. More dry soil is to be added, and the procedure repeated.

One sees that this method of determining the liquid limit of a soil is very cumbersome, because it is very difficult to prepare the right consistency of the soil to close the groove exactly at ten blows. In this method of test, one must resort to trial and error.

When the groove has properly closed, two soil samples from the closed gap area are taken, oven-dried at 110°C until constant weight is attained, and the liquid limit determined. The average of these two determinations may be considered as a constant characterizing the soil consistency, viz., liquid limit, of the given soil tested.

The ratio of the weight of moisture lost to the weight of the oven-dried soil is then by convention the liquid limit, $w_{L.L.}$:

$$w_{L.L.} = \frac{\text{weight of moisture lost}}{\text{weight of oven-dried soil}}.$$

When $w_{L.L.} = 100\%$, this means that the amount of water in the soil by weight equals the dry weight of that soil sample; or, in other words, there are in that soil 50% moisture and 50% solids. At $w_{L.L.} = 50\%$, there are of $\frac{2}{3}$ solids by dry weight and $\frac{1}{3}$ of water by dry weight in that particular soil sample.

If, for example, the weight of moisture at ten blows is 8.16 grams, and the weight of the oven-dried soil is 17.83 grams, then the liquid limit of the soil tested would be

$$w_{L.L.} = \frac{8.16}{17.83} = 0.457, \text{ or } 45.7\%.$$

To avoid evaporation of the moisture from the soil pat while preparing the pat and during the test, this test should be performed as rapidly as the test itself will permit. One should be aware that the results achieved by this method for the determination of the liquid limit of a cohesive soil may be influenced by

a high degree of variable factors, such as the length of time between each jarring, the intensity of impact of the dish against the palm of the hand, the distance the cup is moved before each jar, the roughness of the inside of the porcelain dish, and other factors.

A. Casagrande's Method. To eliminate the variable factors or the so-called personal effects, A. Casagrande[12] devised a mechanical device as illustrated in Fig. 8-7. This device for the determination of the liquid limit of soil in accordance with Atterberg's definition consists essentially

FIG. 8-7 A Casagrande's device for determining liquid limits of soils.

1) of a specified size cup made of brass and weighing 200 g $\pm$ 10 g,
2) a cam and crank mounted on a hard rubber block, and
3) a grooving tool.

The cranking of the cam lifts the brass cup up to a specified height of 1 cm from which height the cup drops upon the block exerting a blow on the latter. The cranking is to be performed at a specified rate of two rotations per second.

In this mechanical method, the number of blows required to close the groove in the soil at its bottom along a distance of about one half of an inch is recorded, and the corresponding moisture content of the soil taken from around the closed groove determined. This operation is to be repeated three more times at different consistencies or moisture contents. The soil samples should be prepared at such consistencies that the number of blows or shocks required to close the groove will be below and above 25 blows. The relationships between the number of blows and their corresponding moisture contents thus attained are plotted on a one cycle, semi-logarithmic graph paper. The best fit to the plots results in the so-called flow graph of the soil tested. The moisture content, $w_{L.L.}$, corresponding to the intersection of the flow graph with the 25-blow ordinate is taken as the liquid limit of the soil (Fig. 8-8).

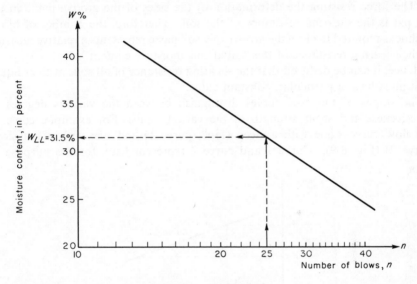

FIG. 8-8   Flow graph.

According to Atterberg and A. Casagrande, liquid limit tests performed at temperatures of 7°C and 24°C, and between 35°C and 40°C, respectively showed no difference from the values obtained at 20°C.

Example. Given the following liquid limit test data.

Trial Nos.	Number of blows	Moisture content, %
1	14	40.0
2	21	34.4
3	31	28.0
4	39	25.0

Determine the liquid limit of this soil.

The liquid limit test data are plotted in Fig. 8-8. The liquid limit of the soil tested is scaled off from the flow graph at 25 blows as $w_{L.L.} = 31.5\%$.

Discussion. The magnitudes of liquid limits of non-cohesive soils such as sands range in the order of about 20%. The liquid limits of silty and clayey soils may reach up to 100%. An average value of liquid limits of cohesive soils is about 60%.

Because cohesion retards flow, the liquid limit test serves as an indicator of the soil cohesion. For example, from high values of liquid limits it can be deduced that the soil tested contains a large percent of clay and even particles of colloidal sizes. In turn, this can be interpreted that the soil possesses a poor foundation or traffic load-bearing capacity.

In describing his research on Atterberg limits of soils, A. Casagrande explains the nature of the liquid limit test and the physical significance of the flow curve as follows:

"The force resisting the deformation of the sides of the groove made in the soil pat is the shearing resistance of the soil. Therefore, the number of blows or shocks required to close the groove of a soil paste represents a relative measure of the shearing resistance of this soil at this moisture content".

Hence, it can be deduced that the shearing resistance of all soils at their liquid limit must have a particular, constant value.

The slopes of the flow curves distinguish between the various degrees of cohesiveness and shear strength of the various soils. For example, consider two flow curves, one with a steep slope (curve 1) and one with a flat slope (curve 2) (Fig. 8-9). Curve 1 and curve 2 represent here, for the purpose of

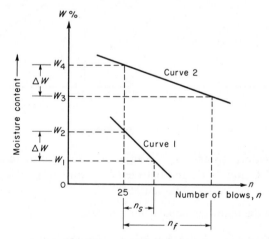

FIG. 8-9   Flow curves.

elucidating the point, two different soils but with the same *P.I.*-values. In this method of presentation it can be seen that in order to decrease the moisture content, $\triangle w$, in both soils by the same amount, the soil with a flat flow curve (2) takes a greater number of blows; here $n_f > n_s$. The comparison of the slopes of the flow curves, thus, gives us an indication that the soil with a flow curve (1) possessed a lesser shear strength than the soil with a flow curve (2).

8-10. Plastic Limit Test. The plastic limit of a soil can be determined, for example, according to the ASTM Standard D424-54T. It is performed by trial and error. According to this standard, the plastic limit is defined as follows:

"The plastic limit of a soil is the lowest moisture content, expressed as percentage of the weight of the oven-dried soil, at the boundary between the plastic and semi-solid states. The water content at this boundary is arbitrarily defined as the lowest water content at which the soil can be rolled into threads $\frac{1}{8}$ in. in diameter without the threads breaking into pieces":

$$w_{P.L.} = \frac{\text{weight of water lost}}{\text{weight of oven-dried soil}} 100\%.$$

Test Procedure. A plastic soil sample passing the No. 40 mesh sieve is shaped into a ball. This ball is rolled between the palm of the hand and the ground glass plate covered with a piece of rough-textured paper. Just enough pressure is used to roll the soil into threads approximately $\frac{1}{8}$ in. in diameter without the threads breaking into pieces or crumbling. Rolling brings about the reduction in moisture content, until the rolled thread crumbles. Then the moisture content of the crumbled threads is determined. The moisture content at which the soil thread crumbles is defined by convention as the plastic limit. According to this definition the plastic limit merely means the moisture content at which a soil ceases to be plastic, where the word "plastic" means the capacity of a soil to be rolled out into threads of a definite diameter. This means that, in cohesive soils, during the process of rolling in the test, considerable pressure is exerted on the thread of soil by the hands—water is forced out of the pores of the soil mass. Thus, the plastic limit test, like the liquid limit test, is a conventional test. Besides, in both of these tests the natural structure of soil is disturbed or destroyed; the tests are performed on remolded soil samples.

Discussion. Sands do not have a plastic limit. Soils which cannot be subjected to plastic limit tests are called non-plastic.

Soils containing silts, clays, and colloids have plastic limits, and vice versa: soils which have plastic limits are cohesive, containing silts, clays, and particles of colloidal sizes. Thus the moisture content of the plastic limit depends in a way on the amount and nature of the colloids admixed. High clay contents usually give high moisture values.

As the moisture content of a cohesive soil passes from the plastic state through the plastic limit into the semi-solid state, the load-bearing capacity of such a soil increases considerably (because of the decrease in moisture content below the plastic limit). It can be inferred that in the field the soil load-bearing capacity, viz., soil strength, varies with the seasonal moisture conditions in the soil (rainy seasons or thawing periods of frozen ground). Therefore, earthworks and pavement design should be based on the weaker soil strength rather than upon some drier soil condition with greater strength.

Example. Upon performing the plastic limit test, the moisture lost by drying the collected crumbled soil threads is 3.48 g. The dry weight of the soil threads is 15.38 g. The plastic limit is calculated as

$$w_{P.L.} = \frac{3.48}{15.38} = 0.2262, \text{ or } \underline{22.62\%}.$$

Plasticity Index. The plasticity index is the difference between the liquid and plastic limits:

$$w_{P.I.} = w_{L.L.} - w_{P.L.} = 36.8\% - 22.6\% = \underline{14.2\% = P.I.}$$

Because $7 < w_{P.I.} < 17$, the soil tested has a degree of medium plasticity. The soil is classed as silty clay or clayey silt.

From the description of determination of Atterberg consistency limit tests it can be inferred that these tests are somewhat subjective. Therefore, this observation permits one to consider the Atterberg consistency limits of soils merely as approximative soil characteristics.

8-11. Shrinkage Limit Test. According to the ASTM standard method of test for shrinkage factors of soils, D427-39 of 1958, the shrinkage limit of a soil is defined as that moisture content, expressed as a percentage of the weight of the oven-dried soil, at which a reduction in moisture content will not cause a decrease in the volume of the soil mass, but at which an increase in moisture content will cause an increase in the volume of the soil mass.

FIG. 8-10   Illustrating shrinkage of soil.

The shrinkage test of soil is essentially performed following a predescribed method on a soil material passing the No. 40 mesh sieve. This material is thoroughly mixed with distilled water to such a consistency as to fill all of the voids of the soil completely, and to permit the soil thus prepared to work into the shrinkage dishes without inclusion of air bubbles. The best consistency of the soil for preparing the shrinkage cakes is a few percent above the liquid limit of that soil. To prevent the cake from adhering to the shrinkage dish, and consequent cracking of the cake upon drying, the inside of the shrinkage dish must be greased with vaseline prior to filling it with the pasty soil. The top of the shrinkage dish is then cleared of excess soil by means of a straightedge. The dish containing the soil is then weighed, dried to constant weight at $+110°C$, and weighed again. Then the amount of moisture loss by weight, and the dry weight, W_d, of the soil sample, as well as the volumes of the shrinkage cake in its wet condition prior to drying, and in its dry condition after drying, are determined, and the shrinkage limit of the soil calculated by Eq. 8-4.

Some shrinkage cakes of soil are shown in Fig. 8-10.

The amount of moisture lost by weight, as in Eq. 8-4, is

$$(V_i - V_s)\gamma_w. \tag{8-10}$$

The volume of the moisture lost, $(V_i - V_s)$, is determined as follows. The volume of the shrinkage dish, which is the initial volume, V_i, of the freshly prepared shrinkage cake, is determined by measuring the volume of mercury filling the shrinkage dish. The volume of the dried shrinkage cake, V_s, is determined by the mercury displacement method. The difference in these volumes $(V_i - V_s)$ is the volume of moisture lost upon drying from an initial moisture content, w_i, to the shrinkage limit, $w_{S.L.}$. With $\gamma_w = 1$ g/cm^3, the shrinkage limit, by Eq. 8-4, is

$$w_{S.L.} = w_i - \frac{(V_i - V_s)(1)}{W_d} 100\%. \tag{8-4}$$

To obtain comparative results and to avoid errors in tests, two shrinkage limit tests should be performed on one type of soil, and the average of the two results reported and taken as the average shrinkage limit of the soil.

Shrinkage limit tests can be performed on undisturbed as well as on remolded (disturbed) soils.

Example. Given: $w_i = 51.78\%$; $V_i = 15.10$ cm^3; $V_s = 9.95$ cm^3; $\gamma_w = 1$ g/cm^3; $W_d = 16.84$ g; $G = 2.66$.
Determine: a) shrinkage limit, b) shrinkage ratio, c) check specific gravity, and d) calculate degree of shrinkage.

a) *Shrinkage Limit.* By Eq. (8-4):

$$w_{S.L.} = w_i - \frac{(V_i - V_s)\gamma_w}{W_d} \cdot 100\% =$$

$$= 51.78 - \frac{(15.10 - 9.95)(1)}{16.84} 100\% = \underline{21.2\%}$$

By Eq. (8-5), if the specific gravity of the soil is known:

$$w_{S.L.} = \frac{V_s\gamma_w}{W_d} - \frac{1}{G} = \frac{(9.95)(1)}{16.84} - \frac{1}{2.66} = 0.214 \approx \underline{0.212.}$$

b) *Shrinkage Ratio:* By Eq. (8-6):

$$R = \frac{W_d}{V_s\gamma_w} = \frac{16.84}{(9.95)(1)} = 1.695 \approx 1.70.$$

c) *Specific Gravity:* By Eq. (8-8):

$$G = \frac{1}{\dfrac{1}{R} - \dfrac{w_{S.L.}}{100}} = \frac{1}{\dfrac{1}{1.70} - \dfrac{21.20}{100}} = 2.659 \approx 2.66$$

d) *Degree of Shrinkage:* By Eq. (8-9):

$$S_r = \frac{V_i - V_f}{V_i} = \frac{15.10 - 9.95}{15.10} \, 100\% = 34.1\% > 15\%.$$

i.e., qualitatively the soil tested is "very poor".

FIG. 8-11 Repetitional loading device.

THE EFFECT OF PLASTIC SUBGRADE MATERIAL
UPON THE STABILITY OF FLEXIBLE PAVEMENTS

The detrimental effect of plastic soil material on the performance of flexible pavements built directly on such a soil, and the beneficial effect of a subbase course placed between the plastic material and the base course of the pavement can best be demonstrated by the following laboratory experiment using a repetitional loading device as illustrated in Fig. 8-11.

The repetitional loading device consists of a plastic cylinder in which highway base, subbase, and subgrade soil materials are placed to be tested under repetitional loading conditions. The load is transmitted to the test sample by a piston and plunger forced down by a bearing point on a lever arm. The mechanical advantage of the lever arm is found to be equal to 3.0.

The effect of repetitional loading is brought about by a wheel attached eccentrically to a shaft that rotates by an electric motor. Thus the lever arm is raised and lowered each time the eccentric wheel makes one revolution. The number of repetitions of loading is automatically counted by a counter that is activated by a rod connected to the eccentric wheel.

Fig. 8-12a illustrates a "flexible pavement" before repeating loads (simulating the weights of rolling stock over a flexible pavement) are applied. The cross section of the soil-pavement system consists of plastic soil, crushed stone, and pavement.

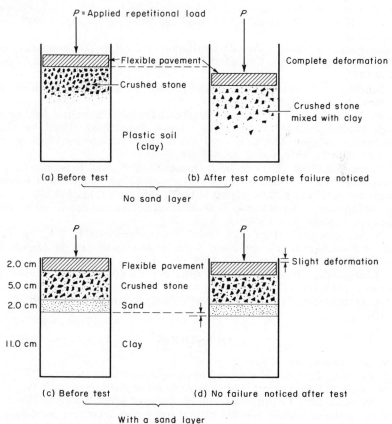

FIG. 8-12 Repetitional loading test.

Fig. 8-12b illustrates the same pavement after about 250 repetitions of load. The plastic clay intrudes into the voids of the crushed stone base and the crushed stone has intruded into the plastic clay, both materials being intermixed. The "flexible pavement", lacking a proper support, disintegrates. The moisture content of the plastic subgrade was 18%.

Fig. 8-12c illustrates the same system as in Fig. 8-12a, except that between the plastic soil and the crushed stone base course a 2.5 cm thick layer of sand was placed. This system did not fail after 16,373 repetitions of loading were applied.

REFERENCES

1. A. Atterberg, "Die Konsistenz und die Bindigkeit der Böden", *Internationale Mitteilungen für Bodenkunde*, Vol. II, Heft 2/3, 1912. Verlag für Fachliteratur G.M.B.H., Berlin, pp. 149-189.
2. A. Atterberg, "Die Plastizität der Tone". *Internationale Mitteilungen für Bodenkunde*, vol. I, no. 1, 1911, Verlag für Fachliteratur G.M.B.H., Berlin, p. 10.
3. A. Atterberg, *Die Plastizität und Bindigkeit liefernden Bestandteile der Tone*, vol. 3, no. 4, 1913, Verlag für Fachliteratur G.M.B.H., Berlin, pp. 291-330.
4. D. M. Burmister, "Principles and Techniques of Soil Identification", *Proceedings*, Annual Highway Research Board Meeting, Washington, D.C., 1949, vol. 29, pp. 402-433.
5. *Engineering Soil Survey of New Jersey*, Reports 1 through 22 (all counties), Bureau of Engineering Research, College of Engineering, Rutgers—The State University, 1950-1957.
6. A. Scheidig, in F. Kögler and A. Scheidig, *Baugrund und Bauwerk*, 5th ed., Berlin, Wilhelm Ernst und Sohn, 1948, p. 56.
7. G. P. Tschebotarioff, "A Case of Structural Damages Sustained by One-Storey High Houses Founded on Swelling Clays", *Proceedings*, Third International Conference on Soil Mechanics and Foundation Engineering, held in Zürich, August 16 to 27, 1953, vol. 1, pp. 473-476.
8. R. F. Dawson, "Movement of Small Houses Erected on an Expansive Clay Soil", *Proceedings*, Third International Conference on Soil Mechanics and Foundation Engineering, held in Zürich, August 16 to 27, 1953, vol. 1, pp. 346-350.
9. E. Ackermann, "Thixotropie und Fliesseigenschaften feinkörniger Böden", *Geologische Rundschau*, 1948, vol. 36, p. 17.
10. T. A. Middlebrooks, "Fort Peck Slide", *Transactions*, ASCE, 1942, pp. 723-764.
11. *ASTM Procedures for Testing Soils, Tentative Method of Test for Liquid Limit of Soils*, ASTM, Philadelphia, April, 1958, pp. 94-98.
12. A. Casagrande, "Research on the Atterberg Limits of Soils", *Public Roads*, October, 1932, vol. 13, no. 8, pp. 121-130.
13. C. A. Hogentogler, "The Subgrade Soil", *Public Roads*, July, 1931, vol. 12, no. 5, p. 126.

QUESTIONS

8-1. What is consistency of soil?
8-2. Is the liquid limit of soil a natural or conventional soil index?
8-3. Is the liquid limit a constant or variable factor of one sort of soil? Why?
8-4. Is the liquid limit a constant or variable factor of different sorts of soils? Why?
8-5. What is the distinction between natural soil moisture content and liquid limit?
8-6. Could the content of natural soil moisture be equal to liquid limit?
8-7. What is understood by "lower liquid limit" of a soil?

8- 8. What is understood by "upper limit of plasticity" of a soil?

8- 9. Why is the index "liquid limit" valuable in connection with highway subgrading?

8-10. What is plasticity of soil?

8-11. Is plastic limit a natural or conventional soil constant?

8-12. Has sand plasticity?

8-13. To what property of the soil particles is the plasticity of clays due?

8-14. In what state (disturbed or undisturbed) should soil samples be sampled for testing the liquid limit? Plastic limit? For determining the plasticity index?

8-15. Of which consistency are soils, if

a) $w > w_{L.L.}$?

b) $w_{L.L.} > w > w_{P.L.}$?

c) $w_{P.L.} > w$?

Here w means the natural moisture content of a soil.

8-16. Does a dry soil change its bearing capacity at the plastic limit?

8-17. What is the numerical value of the plasticity index if the soil is not plastic?

8-18. What happens to a soil whose $P.I. = 0$, if it is submerged in water?

8-19. Are soils in the solid and plastic states suitable for laying of foundations?

8-20. What is the purpose of classifying soils according to their plasticity index?

8-21. What is the technical meaning of the expression "soft clay"? Of what value is such a term?

8-22. What is the nature of shrinkage of soil?

8-23. Is shrinkage limit a natural or conventional soil constant?

8-24. Does the shrinkage phenomenon occur in sand? In clayey soils? Why?

8-25. When and why may one expect a greater capillary pressure and greater shrinkage in clays than in sands?

8-26. Upon what does the height of capillary rise in tubes depend?

8-27. Under what nature of stress is water in a capillary tube during evaporation?

8-28. Which of the two components of the surface tension take part in shrinkage?

8-29. Why do soils shrink?

8-30. When is the maximum value of surface tension reached?

8-31. Does the shrinkage limit depend also upon the shape of the soil particles? The uniformity of the soil? How?

8-32. In what kind of soils do you expect greater capillary height and pressure—in uniform or less uniform soil?

8-33. What conclusions can be drawn in connection with highway and railway construction on uniform and non-uniform soils as to their performance under load and water?

8-34. What could happen during heavy rains with slopes erected in or with clay soil if the slope surfaces are shrunk?

8-35. Are shrinkage limits different for undisturbed and disturbed soil samples?

8-36. Of what value are shrinkage limits of soils anyway?

8-37. What are the physical differences between sand and clay?

8-38. Given the following data obtained from a liquid limit test of a soil:

Number of Shocks	Moisture Content, %
38	16.2
34	18.0
20	19.9
12	19.4

Determine the value of the liquid limit for this soil.

8-39. A soil the liquid limit of which is 60% and the plastic limit of which is 27% is excavated from a borrow pit for use in an earthwork. The natural moisture content of the excavated soil is 32%.
Determine:
a) the plasticity index of the soil.
b) Is this soil "stiff" or "soft" when compacted at its existing natural moisture content in an earthwork?
c) What would be the effect of a light rain on the consistency of the soil?

8-40. The plastic limit test on a soil sample rendered the following moisture contents:

Trial Nos.	$w_{P.L.}$
1	12.9
2	11.2
3	12.5
4	14.6

Determine the plastic limit of this soil, calculate the plasticity index, and characterize this soil.

8-41. The plasticity index of the soil in Problem 6-39 is equal to 8%, and the liquid limit is 20%. Characterize this soil.

Chapter 9

CLASSIFICATION OF SOILS

9-1. Classification. Soils can be studied most effectively if they are classed according to certain principles into a definite system. A *system* is generally understood to be an ordered grouping of certain elements and/or facts in a field of knowledge according to certain principles.

By its very nature, classification is usually the very first and most important step of activities in the organization of any branch of a scientific discipline. Naturally, therefore, this applies also to soil mechanics in general, as well as to soil classification into certain systems in particular.

According to Burmister[1] "... a soil classification should be recognized for what it really is, namely, a *rating of soils* with regard to a certain limited number of qualities and potential behavior characteristics only, significant and important for subgrade or base course work in highway and airfield engineering." Soil classification, therefore, should be considered to be one of the necessary prerequisites in highway, street and runway pavement design and construction.

Subgrade material is understood to be the material in cuts, fills, and embankment foundations immediately below the subbase course, or base course, or pavement.

A *subbase course* consists of a specified or selected material of designed thickness placed as a foundation for a base course.

A *base course* consists of a specified or selected soil material of designed thickness placed as a foundation for a pavement.

In soil mechanics, a soil classification system may be defined as a specially coordinated body consisting of a fundamental division of the various types of soil into groups according to certain principles, for example: certain common physical properties; soil component parts or texture; or field performance under load, water, and upon freezing.

There exist several different soil classification systems. Each of them is accepted by various branches of the engineering profession as represented by their respective organizations as being the system best suited for their expressed need and use. For instance, the Public Roads Administration and the American Association of State Highway Officials (AASHO) soil classification systems are honored by the Bureau of Public Roads and by many state, county, municipal, and township highway departments. The so-called "Unified Soil Classification System" is accepted by the U.S. Army Corps of Engineers, and is most commonly used, with a few minor modifications, by the Bureau of Reclamation

149

and several other organizations. The Civil Aeronautics Administration's soil classification system is used in airfield work. In fact, there is no such thing as a soil classification system accepted by all soil engineers and pavement technologists. Therefore it can be concluded that an "accepted" soil classification system would simply be nothing else than a system which satisfies best the engineering profession in its particular endeavor.

Generally, the *purpose* of a soil classification system is to present for rating purposes a systematic and satisfactory method of groups of units of soil which have certain similar, distinct physical properties. It is expected that such groupings in units would describe the various soil types encountered, for instance, in soil exploration; or to indicate certain drainage characteristics of a soil; or indicate the suitability of a soil for use as a base course; or its performance under static and dynamic loads, water, or frost action and its associated consequences such as thawing; or the system should convey any other essential information to satisfy the needs in the design and construction of earthworks and in the solution of special engineering problems.

9-2. Some Historical Notes. The rapid development of soil mechanics some 35 years ago gave an impetus to the civil engineer to realize the need for a soil classification system for engineering purposes. In those days there were very few methodologic and useful systems available to engineers from the various other fields of knowledge. This fact gave reason for engineers to devise an engineering soil classification system of their own. Unfortunately, it must be generally said that at the present time there is not yet available a satisfactory classification system which would satisfy all engineers.

At this point, it is felt that an historical note of cultural value is in order. J. Thorp[2] writes that one of the oldest known soil classification systems was created not by an agronomist, as is commonly believed, but by a Chinese engineer by the name of Yu, some 4000 years ago, who classified soils according to color and structure. Unfortunately, his soil classification system is lost to later generations.

About 3000 years ago, the Chinese were renowned in road construction. So, for example, the Book of Customs of the Chinese King You Dynasty contains provisions, regulations, and instructions for roads and streets. King You also ordered a network of roads to connect his extensive waterway system.[3]

It is also interesting to note that in antiquity, about 3000 years B.C., bitumen and asphalt were used as prominent road and pavement building materials. The best-known example of roads where the foundation bricks were jointed with a bituminous mortar is the Processional Road in the Temple of Ishtar and Assur, and at Babylon.[4,5] Of course, because of the nature of traffic, the arteries were not asphalt-surfaced, but were primitive.

9-3. General Requirements of a Soil Classification System. An ideal, effective soil classification system should meet the following requirements:

a) The system should be based on a scientific method.

b) It should be simple.

c) It should eliminate the subjective element in rating the soil.

d) To characterize the classified soil in commonly well-understood and well-conversant terms, the system should be based on a generally accepted uniform soil terminology.

e) It should permit classifying the soil by simple visual and manual tests, or at least it should be based on a few simple tests easily performed.

f) The soil group boundaries within a soil classification system should be drawn as closely as possible at the point where soil engineering practice has demonstrated the transition of significant changes in soil properties and performance under certain sets of conditions.

g) It should describe and emphasize adequately the specific engineering properties of a soil.

h) The system should have fair accuracy in indicating the probable performance of a soil under certain field conditions.

i) It should warn against the use of inferior soil material in certain earthworks.

j) It should be acceptable to all engineers.

These, obviously, are very ambitious requirements for a soil classification system. These requirements, although desirable, unfortunately are not met 100% by any of the existing systems, because soil is a complex material made by nature, and does not lend itself to a simple classification. The more numerous and the more rigid the requirements imposed upon a soil classification system, the more complicated it turns out to be—whether in the structure itself, or requiring much time to study and understand it, or cumbersome to use.

As mentioned before, soil classification systems are usually established according to the needs and viewpoints of their applicants. Therefore, an engineering soil classification system is probably satisfactory only for that field of engineering endeavor for which this system is hopefully developed. However, what is now available is better than nothing for the guidance of the engineer in the pursuance of his everyday important and responsible work.

One of the reasons for the existence of the many soil classification systems is, perhaps, the fact that the geologist, the agronomist, and the engineer have slightly different concepts about the matter of soil. In engineering, soil is defined as the material by means of which (earthworks) and upon which engineers build their structures (foundations on soil). As to their performance under load, water, and temperature, soils are anything but simple. The properties of the materials the soil engineers have to work with are very complex indeed.

9-4. Various Soil Classification Systems. For the purpose of this discussion, the various soil classification systems can be listed as follows:

1) Geologic soil classification systems
2) Agronomic soil classification systems
3) Various soil mechanics soil classification systems
4) Systems for classifying soils in engineering soil survey work
5) Textural soil classification systems
6) Highway subgrade soil classifications

    7) The Unified soil classification system
    8) The Civil Aeronautics Administration's (CAA) soil classification system
    9) The Engineering Soil Survey of New Jersey soil classification system
    10) Other systems.

    1) *Geologic Soil Classification System.* In the geologic soil classification system, natural soil formations are classified according to their origin, mode of formation, geologic time, and other geologic factors. Nowadays there exists a trend toward including in engineering soil surveys geologic information also, which helps the engineer to understand better some of the physical properties of soils and their probable behavior as an engineering material.

    2) *Agronomic Soil Classification System.* Among several agricultural soil classification systems which are geared to the fertility and productivity of soils (or from the point of view of plant nutrition), the pedological soil classification system is of interest to civil engineers. The basis for the pedological soil classification is the discipline of soil science. Pedology groups soils which were formed in a similar manner from the same parent rock and under the similar climatic conditions. This idea is the reason for the assumption that such soils have similar engineering properties and, hence, would perform similarly under load, water, and temperature. The pedological classification system is a very useful constituent part in every engineering soil survey, serving as a check for soil tests taken from the various soil horizons. The pedological system by itself, however, seems at the present time not to be well-enough developed to serve in civil engineering as a basic tool for design. It is not fully appreciated by the profession as yet, although the illuviated and elluviated soil horizons may possess a considerable degree of difference in the plastic properties of the soil.

    The pedologic principles were broadly used in the Engineering Soil Survey of New Jersey.[6]

    3) *Various Soil Mechanics Soil Classification Systems.* Each of the various soil mechanics soil classification systems characterizes a degree of a certain soil property—for example, degree of density, degree of saturation, or other property—and each such property classification by itself would not predict the probable performance under field conditions. The various classified properties, though, are very helpful in classifying soils and in predicting their performance when manipulated and handled in earthwork construction as a whole.

    4) *Systems for Classifying Soils in Engineering Soil Survey Work.* This kind of classification system, actually, is a system which takes its place between systems for classifying soils in their undisturbed and disturbed conditions. In its undisturbed condition soil is grouped and mapped by delineating soil and non-soil areas as these soils are found in the field; but to characterize these soils, their properties are determined on disturbed soil samples taken from the various delineated soil areas. In such soil survey work the soil classification proper is performed by using soil classification systems as described under "Systems for Classifying Soils in their Disturbed Condition".

    The Engineering Soil Survey of New Jersey is described in greater detail in Chapter 26 dealing with soil exploration.

5) *Textural Soil Classification Systems*

a) *General Notes.* Although the textural soil classification is not too satisfactory for the prediction of the performance of soil for many engineering purposes, it is felt that its review here would be necessary to form the basis for the understanding of the more extended highway and airfield subgrade soil classification systems.

In soil mechanics, soil texture is understood to be the combination of the size or granulometry of individual soil particles and the proportions by dry weight of the material of certain groups of particle sizes present.

The size of a soil particle is one of the most apparent physical properties of a soil. It is, therefore, no wonder that most of the older soil classification systems used in soil technology are based on soil particle size or diameter. Accordingly, such systems are termed textural soil classification systems.

As for natural soils themselves, they are, by nature, composite materials consisting of various proportions of the predominant soil fractions such as gravel, sand, silt, and clay. Probably the most significant fractional divisions in the textural soil classification system in a granulometric analysis of a soil are usually between fine gravel and fine sand, then fine sand and silt, and finally between silt and clay. Clay particles finer than 0.002 mm are often termed colloid particles.

b) *Bureau of Soils Soil Classification System.* In the United States of America, one of the earliest soil classification systems was put forward before 1896 by the Bureau of Soils, United States Department of Agriculture (USDA). The divisional soil fractions and particle sizes in mm in this system are shown in Table 9-1.

TABLE 9–1. U.S.D.A. BUREAU OF SOILS CLASSIFICATION

Fractions	Size (*in* mm)	
Gravel		> 2
Sand	2	- 0.05
Silt	0.05	- 0.005*
Clay	0.005*	- 0.0005
Colloids		< 0.0005

* In 1938 the U.S.D.A. Bureau of Soils changed the 0.005 mm size limit to 0.002 mm. However, by tradition probably, engineers still favor and continue to use the original 0.005 millimeter limit.

The Bureau of Soils soil classification shows that, in this system, the basic components of a soil, or the limits of the principal soil fractions, are broadly and arbitrarily separated on a particle-size basis, viz., their predominance in the composite soil. This textural soil classification system is still used by many soil technologists.

It should be noted that in different countries in the world, as well as in the United States of America, the limits of divisions between the sand and silt fractions and those between the silt and clay fractions were fixed arbitrarily.

Although arbitrary in a broad sense, the fundamental divisions between various fractions are, however, based on certain practical considerations in soil technology. The upper limit of the gravel fraction of 3 in. is based on common soil compaction practice. The fractional limit between gravel and sand at the standard U.S. No. 10 sieve (or 2 mm mesh size as in the ASTM or the MIT soil classification systems, for example) is chosen because this size soil particle is easy to see; it can be picked out from the mass of the composite soil, examined, and identified. The sand-silt division at the No. 200 mesh sieve is based on textural and visual distinction, because the material passing the No. 200 sieve is not visible as discrete grains to the naked eye. Besides, physically, as the particle sizes decrease, permeability of the soil generally decreases, capillarity increases and so does the frost susceptibility of the silt, clayey silt, and silty clay soils.

The silt-clay division line was based on the fact that the shape and configuration of clay particles are very different from that of silt; that clays, when wet, exhibit plasticity, and that the fine-particled clay has a colloidal nature.

The gravel and sand fractions, in their turn, are subdivided into coarse, medium and fine subgroups. Using various combinations of the five main textural terms, such as gravelly sand, or sandy clay, the possible number of soil classification groups is increased. Note that the adjective form of that type name of the soil textural group which affects the soil composite mixture most is placed first. For example,

80% clay + 20% sand = sandy clay
55% sand + 40% gravel + 5% clay = clayey sand-gravel.

Another way to indicate a mixture of different soil fractions is as follows: if two or more soil types are mixed in approximately equal amounts, then the predominant fractional designation is placed first:

60% gravel + 40% sand = gravel-sand
60% sand + 40% gravel = sand-gravel
40% sand + 30% gravel + 30% silt = sand-gravel-silt.

It is almost safe to say that a soil is never composed of only one fractional group, except, probably, with fine-sized particle soils where the clay-colloid fraction can be considered as being one single clay fraction because mineral colloids can be considered as an extremely fine clay. Also, depending upon the uniformity of the soil particle sizes, the soil can be designated as a pure sand, a pure silt, or a pure clay. Unfortunately, very little effort has been devoted in recent years to the textural classification of soil material the size of which is larger than 2 mm in diameter. It is quite obvious that a material containing pebbles, stones, and boulders may be encountered in certain areas in great abundance, and that such a material may or may not be of importance for use in certain earthworks.

In 1947, Committee VII on Foundations and Soil Mechanics of the American Society for Engineering Education recommended that the fraction "boulders"

TABLE 9-2. SOME TEXTURAL SOIL CLASSIFICATION SYSTEMS

1. Bureau of Soils USDA

Boundaries (mm): 2.0 | 1.0 | 0.5 | 0.25 | 0.1 | 0.05 | 0.002

2.0 – 0.5	0.5 – 0.25	0.25 – 0.1	0.1 – 0.05	0.05 – 0.002	< 0.002
Coarse	Medium	Fine	Very Fine	Silt	Clay
Sand	Sand	Sand	Sand		

2. ASTM

Boundaries (mm): 2.0 | 0.25 | 0.074 | 0.005 | 0.002 | (0.001 mm = 1 Micron) | 0.0002

2.0 – 0.25	0.25 – 0.074	0.074 – 0.005	0.005 – 0.001	< 0.001
Coarse sand	Fine sand	Silt	Clay	Colloidal clay

3. MIT nomenclature

Boundaries (mm): 2.0 | 0.6 | 0.2 | 0.06 | 0.02 | 0.006 | 0.002 | 0.0006 | 0.0002

2.0 – 0.6	0.6 – 0.2	0.2 – 0.06	0.06 – 0.02	0.02 – 0.006	0.006 – 0.002	0.002 – 0.0006	0.0006 – 0.0002	< 0.0002
Coarse	Medium	Fine	Coarse	Medium	Fine	Coarse	Medium	Fine (colloidal)
Sand	Sand	Sand	Silt	Silt	Silt	Clay	Clay	Clay

4. International nomenclature

Boundaries (mm): 2.0 | 1.0 | 0.2 | 0.02 | 0.002 | 0.0006 | 0.0002

2.0 – 1.0	1.0 – 0.5	0.5 – 0.2	0.2 – 0.1	0.1 – 0.05	0.05 – 0.02	0.02 – 0.006	0.006 – 0.002	0.002 – 0.0006	0.0006 – 0.0002	< 0.0002
Very Coarse	Coarse	Medium	Fine	Coarse	Fine	Coarse	Fine	Coarse	Fine	Ultra fine
Sand	Sand	Sand	Sand	Mo*	Mo*	Silt	Silt	Clay	Clay	Clay

* Mo is a Swedish term used for glacial silts or rock flour having little plasticity.

and "rock" be classed as that material which remains on the 3-in. (76.2 mm) sieve.

Separation of a soil sample into fractions coarser than 0.074 mm is accomplished by sieving. The finest sieve affording an effective sieving is recognized as being the U.S. standard No. 200 mesh sieve, the size of the opening of which is 0.074 mm. Soils finer in texture than 0.074 mm in size are separated into fractions by various sedimentation methods. The sieving can be performed with relative ease, whereas accurate sedimentation requires some knowledge, considerable skill, time and patience.

c) Other Textural Soil Classification Systems. The textural soil classification systems adopted for their use by other organizations have other particle sizes for the division points. A comparison between the Bureau of Soils soil classification system and some others is shown in Table 9-2.

The systems shown are:

1) Bureau of Soils, USDA[7]
2) American Society for Testing Materials (ASTM)[8]
3) Massachusetts Institute of Technology (MIT)[9]
4) The International Soil Classification System, established by the International Society of Soil Science [10] upon suggestion by A. Atterberg in 1908.

Besides these soil textural classification systems, there are also other systems which are based on particle size fractions, for instance: the British classification system (in agreement with the MIT soil classification system), and the German Industrial Norms (DIN), and others.

All these textural soil classification systems have in common the decimal logarithmic scale for plotting of the soil particle size accumulation curve.

It can also be said that regardless of differences in the division points in the various textural soil classification systems, they all have a common intention, namely, to present a criterion for relating soil particle size to the performance of that soil.

Like the Bureau of Soils soil classification system, so in the MIT soil classification system fractional divisions are set up to correspond with changes in engineering properties of the soil. Also, like the International system, so the MIT system is simple, and the limits of division for soil fractions are easy to remember.

The soil classification system of the American Association of the State Highway Officials (AASHO) by soil particle size is shown in Table 9-3.[11]

TABLE 9-3. AASHO SOIL CLASSIFICATION SYSTEM

Fractions	Particle Size in mm
Gravel	76.2 mm to 2.00 mm
Sand, coarse	2.00 mm to 0.42 mm
Sand, fine	0.42 mm to 0.074 mm
Silt	0.074 mm to 0.005 mm
Clay	< 0.005 mm

d) Evaluation of Textural Soil Classification Systems. Because of its simplicity the textural soil classification system does not require great skill to use, and is still one of the most popularly accepted systems used in American engineering practice. The various textural soil classification systems, which are based on soil particle size only, are suitable for classifying non-cohesive, coarse-particled soils for many purposes and, among other things, are also used in highway engineering. A certain size soil fraction, or a mixture of fractions or soils from several borrow pits is used to give a road a stable base and subbase course. Unfortunately, classification by particle size alone does not characterize the other properties of soil, such as the fine sizes, shapes, specific surfaces (more moisture films adsorbed in a unit of weight of soil upon the surfaces of particles, hence more frost-susceptible), plasticity, compressibility, nor the mineralogic properties of the soil particles, which influence considerably the performance of a soil.

For example, a fine rock flour, a non-plastic silt material derived from the gneisses by a grinding action (glacier), and locally (in Morristown, New Jersey) known by the unscientific term "bull's liver",[12] may have a particle-size summation curve similar to a clayey silt or silty clay, containing some clay minerals and thus having some plastic properties. The performance, though, of these two materials under load, water, and freezing temperatures may be entirely different. Even with coarser materials the behavior may be different. For instance, two sands consisting of uniform size particles may have similar particle size accumulation curves, but would have different frictional properties, depending upon whether their particles are smooth, rounded, or sharp and angular, providing for better interlock between particles. For these reasons engineers tried to devise new and more satisfactory soil classification systems than those based on texture.

EXTENDED SOIL CLASSIFICATION SYSTEMS

9-5.—6. Highway Subgrade Soil Classification.

a) The forerunner of the present American Association of State Highway Officials (AASHO) soil classification system was the Bureau of Public Roads (BPR) soil classification system. The BPR system, based on extensive research, was developed in about 1928[13,14] and adopted in 1931.[15] It classifies *subgrade soils* according to some engineering points of view, namely: stability under vehicular loads, and the performance of soils under freezing and thawing conditions.[16] The Bureau of Public Roads soil classification system applies only to soil material passing the U.S. Standard No. 10 sieve.

Originally, this system divided all soils into two groups: group *A* and group *B*. The *A* group comprehended subgrade soils which distinguished themselves as giving a uniform pavement support. Here the soils were grouped according to those characteristics which are most conspicuous in their performance. The *B* group comprehended soils giving non-uniform pavement support. These soils would cause concrete pavements to crack or fault excessively and flexible types of pavements to fail or to develop rough riding surfaces. The *B* soils, natural and fill, were characterized by abrupt variation in soil properties under field conditions.

The *B* group of soils, however, was abandoned, so that only the group *A* remained. The letter symbol "*A*-", thus, has no other significance. The *A* soils are classified into eight subgrade soil groups designated by the symbols from *A*-1 to *A*-8, each of these soil groups containing similar characteristics, as listed in Table 9-4. The group numbers 1 through 8 are merely used for convenience, and, like the symbols *A* and/or *B*, have no other significance. Although in the course of time this system has undergone some changes and modifications, the literal description of the main soil groups as in Table 9-4 is approximately still valid.

Some of the soil constituents of the eight soil groups suggest some important physical properties. So, for example, from Table 9-4, it can be observed that soil groups designated as *A*-1, *A*-2 and *A*-3 possess high internal friction between soil particles. When properly selected and prepared, these soils would provide a good pavement support.

Group *A*-1 subgrades, in general, are characterized by high stability in fills and would give insignificant settlement.

Group *A*-2 subgrades are more affected by moisture than those of group *A*-1, because *A*-2 soils contain some binder and are of inferior quality as compared with *A*-1 soils.

Group A-3 soils, lacking in fine fractions of particles < 0.005 mm, consequently are lacking in cohesion. These soils would not shrink, nor possess any plasticity.

Soils grouped under *A*-4 are the silts. They have little friction and cohesion. Generally, silts are considered as being frost-susceptible, and they are likely to fail under flexible pavements.

The *A*-5 soils have variable internal friction, and no appreciable cohesion. These soils are characterized by their porosity, deformation and rebound, and are also considered frost-susceptible.

Soils classed as *A*-5 and *A*-6 somewhat overlap as to their properties and performance. The *A*-6 group consists of clay, and is greatly affected by field conditions.

The *A*-7 group comprehends clays, is similar to *A*-6 soils in characteristics, and possesses some elasticity and expansive properties. Also, clays from different regions classified as *A*-6 or *A*-7 soils may possess a considerable range of plastic properties.

The *A*-8 soils include peat, muck, and similar organic material. These soils have low internal friction and low cohesion. They are very soft and compressible and therefore can afford very little pavement support without stabilization.

One notes that the distinction between the various soil groups is based on particle size analysis and some simple physical tests of soils, such as the consistency limits of soils. The classification itself of a given type of subgrade soil with which an engineer is working is made by the aid of various tables, for

TABLE 9-4. CLASSIFICATION OF UNIFORM SUBGRADE SOILS
BY U.S. PUBLIC ROADS ADMINISTRATION

Group	Soil Constituents	Soil Characteristics	Subgrade Performance
1	2	3	4
A-1	Well-graded materials; sand, silt, and clay; excellent binder	High internal friction, high cohesion; no detrimental shrinkage, expansion, capillarity, or elasticity	Highly stable under wheel loads, irrespective of moisture conditions; functions satisfactorily when surface-treated or when used as a base for relatively thin wearing courses
A-2	Coarse and fine materials; improper grading or inferior binder	High internal friction and high cohesion only under certain conditions; may have detrimental shrinkage, expansion, capillarity, or elasticity	Highly stable when fairly dry; likely to soften at high water content caused either by rains or by capillary rise from saturated lower strata when an impervious cover prevents evaporation from the top layer, or to become loose and dusty in long-continued dry weather
A-3	Sand, no binder	High internal friction, no detrimental capillarity or elasticity	Lacks stability under wheel loads but is unaffected by moisture conditions; not likely to heave because of frost or to shrink or expand in appreciable amount; furnishes excellent support for flexible pavements at moderate thickness and for relatively thin rigid pavements
A-4	Cohesionless silts; friable clays; no appreciable amount of sticky colloidal clay	Internal friction variable, no appreciable cohesion, no elasticity, capillarity important	Has tendency to absorb water very readily in quantities sufficient to cause rapid loss of stability even when not manipulated; when dry or damp, presents a firm riding surface which rebounds but very little upon the removal of load; likely to cause cracking in rigid pavements as a result of frost heaving, and failure in flexible pavements because of low supporting value

TABLE 9-4—*continued*

Group	Soil Constituents	Soil Characteristics	Subgrade Performance
1	2	3	4
A-5	Micaceous and diatomaceous silts and sands	Similar to A-4 and in addition possesses elasticity in appreciable amount	Similar to Group A-4 but furnishes highly elastic supporting surfaces with appreciable rebound upon removal of load even when dry; elastic properties interfere with proper compaction of macadams during construction and with retention of good bond afterwards
A-6	Cohesive clays; dispersed state	Low internal friction, cohesion high under low moisture content, no elasticity, likely to expand and shrink in detrimental amount	In stiff or soft plastic state absorbs additional water only if manipulated; may then change to liquid state and work up into the interstices of macadams or cause failure due to sliding in high fills; furnishes firm support essential in properly compacting macadams only at stiff consistency; deformations occur slowly, and removal of load causes very little rebound; shrinkage properties combined with alternate wetting and drying under field conditions are likely to cause cracking of rigid pavements
A-7	Micaceous, diatomaceous, and flocculated clays; may contain lime or associated chemicals productive of flocculation in soils	Similar to A-6 but possess elasticity also	Similar to Group A-6, but at certain moisture contents deforms quickly under load and rebounds appreciably upon removal of load, as do subgrades of Group A-5; alternate wetting and drying under field conditions lead to even more detrimental volume changes than in Group A-6 subgrades; may cause concrete pavements to crack before setting and to crack and fault afterwards

TABLE 9-4—*continued*

Group	Soil Constituents	Soil Characteristics	Subgrade Performance
1	2	3	4
A-8	Peats and mucks	Low internal friction, low cohesion, apt to possess capillarity and elasticity in detrimental amounts	Very soft; incapable of supporting a road surface without being previously compacted

From *Highway Engineering*, by John Bateman.
Courtesy John Wiley & Sons, Inc.

example, Table 9-4, and various graphs. Once the soil group has been determined, this Bureau of Public Roads soil classification system would predict the probable performance of the subgrade soil under load and climatic conditions.

The BPR soil classification system has been extensively used by many highway engineering organizations. However, in the course of time engineers realized that each soil group within the scope of the BPR soil classification system comprehends a great many physical properties, and that dissimilar types of soils could be included under one and the same soil group under one and the same symbol, or, too, that some soils may have some of the characteristics of two groups. Thus, there is a possibility of overlapping in soil properties between certain neighboring soil types or groups. The BPR soil classification system for classifying soils by their field performance as a subgrade material does not disclose any information as to the mechanical properties of soils, nor does it consider the effect of vibrations caused by dynamic load of the rolling stock over the pavement. Also, it is quite possible that soils which perform similarly under one set of conditions may perform entirely differently under different sets of conditions. Because of the many possible variations in soil physical properties, highway organizations modified the basic BPR soil classification system of June and July, 1931—which has been considered a tentative one—to fit their particular needs, and several other engineering agencies dealing with soils as a construction material tried to devise their own soil classification systems. In 1942, the BPR system was revised to become what is now known as the Public Roads Administration's Soil Classification System[16] (see Table 9-5). Some of the major changes in the classification system are reflected in the simplified charts[17] as follows:

1) The limits of the A-6 soils are defined by a band instead of a line.
2) The maximum value of the liquid limit of the A-1 group was changed from 25% to 35% so as to include stabilized road surface materials covered by the Standard AASHO and ASTM Specifications.
3) The symbol, NP, was introduced for those materials for which the plastic and liquid limits cannot be obtained due to a lack of plasticity in the soil.

TABLE 9-5. SUMMARY OF SOIL CHARACTERISTICS AND CLASSIFICATION

Group	A-1	A-2 Friable	A-2 Plastic	A-3	A-4	A-5	A-6	A-7	A-8
1	2	3	4	5	6	7	8	9	10
General stability properties	Highly stable at all times	Stable when dry; may ravel	Good stable material	Ideal support when confined	Satisfactory when dry; loss of stability when wet or by frost action	Difficult to compact; stability doubtful	Good stability when properly compacted	Good stability when properly compacted	Incapable of support
Physical constants:									
Internal friction	High	High	High	High	Variable	Variable	Low	Low	Low
Cohesion	do.	Low	do.	None	do.	Low	High	High	do.
Shrinkage	Not detrimental	Not significant	Detrimental when poorly graded	Not significant	Detrimental	Detrimental	Detrimental	Detrimental	Detrimental
Expansion	None	None	Some	Slight	do.	High	High	do.	do.
Capillarity	do.	do.	do.	do.	Detrimental	do.	do.	High	do.
Elasticity	do.	do.	do.	None	Variable	Detrimental	None	do.	do.
Textural classification:									
General grading	Uniformly graded; coarse-fine excellent binder	Poor grading; poor binder	Poor grading; inferior binder	Coarse material only; no binder	Fine sand cohesionless silt and friable clay	Micaceous and diatomaceous	Deflocculated cohesive clays	Drainable flocculated clays	Peat and muck
Approximate limits:									
Sand percent	70-85	55-80	55-80	75-100	55 (max)	55 (max)	55 (max)	55 (max)	55 (max)
Silt do.	10-20	0-45	0-45	*	High	Medium	Medium	Medium	Not significant
Clay do.	5-10	0-45	0-45	*	Low	Low	30 (min)	30 (min)	do.

Physical characteristics:									
Liquid limit	14-35†	35 (max)	35 (max)	NP‡	20-40	35 (min)	35 (min)	35 (min)	35-400
Plasticity index	4-9†	NP-3‡	3-15	NP‡	0-15	0-60	18 (min)	12 (min)	0-60
Field moisture equivalent	Not essential	Not essential	Not essential	Not essential	30 (max)	30-120	50 (max)	30-100	30-400
Centrifuge moisture equivalent	15 (max)	12-25	25 (max)	12 (max)	Not essential	Not essential	Not essential	Not essential	Not essential
Shrinkage limit	14-20	15-25	25 (max)	Not essential	20-30	30-120	6-14	10-30	30-120
Shrinkage ratio	1.7-1.9	1.7-1.9	1.7-1.9	do.	1.5-1.7	0.7-1.5	1.7-2.0	1.7-2.0	0.3-1.4
Volume change	0-10	0-6	0-16	None	0-16	0-16	17 (min)	17 (min)	4-200
Lineal shrinkage	0-3	0-2	0-4	do.	0-4	0-4	5 (min)	5 (min)	1-30
Compaction characteristics:									
Max. dry weight, pounds per cubic foot	130 (min)	120-130	120-130	120-130	110-120	80-100	80-110	80-110	90 (max)
Optimum moisture, percentage of dry weight (approximate)	9	9-12	9-12	9-12	12-17	22-30	17-28	17-28	
Max. field compaction required, percentage of maximum dry weight, pounds per cubic foot	90	90	90	90	95	100	100	100	
Rating for fills 50 feet or less in height	Excellent	Good	Good	Good	Good to poor	Poor to very poor	Fair to poor	Fair to poor	Waste.
Rating for fills more than 50 feet in height	Good	Good to fair	Good to fair	Good to fair	Fair to poor	Very poor	Very poor	Very poor	Unsatisfactory.
Required total thickness for subbase, base and surfacing, inches	0-6	0-6	2-8	0-6	9-18	9-24	12-24	12-24	do.

*Percentage passing No. 200 sieve, 0 to 10.
†When used as a base course for thin flexible surfaces the plasticity index and liquid limit should not exceed 6 and 25, respectively.
‡NP-nonplastic.

From H. Allen, "Classification of Soils and Control Procedures Used in Construction of Embankments". Courtesy of *Public Roads Magazine*.

TABLE 9-6. CLASSIFICATION OF SOILS AND SOIL-AGGREGATE MIXTURES

General Classification	Granular Materials (35% or less passing No. 200)			Silt-Clay Materials (More than 35% passing No. 200)			
Group Classification	A-1	A-3*	A-2	A-4	A-5	A-6	A-7
Sieve analysis:							
Percent passing:							
No. 10	—	—	—				
No. 40	50 max	51 min	—				
No. 200	25 max	10 max	35 max	36 min	36 min	36 min	36 min
Characteristics of fraction passing No. 40:							
Liquid limit	—	—	†	40 max	41 min	40 max	41 min
Plasticity index	6 max	NP	—	10 max	10 max	11 min	11 min
Group index	0	0	4 max	8 max	12 max	16 max	20 max
General Rating as subgrade	Excellent to good			Fair to poor			

*The placing of A-3 before A-2 is necessary in the "left to right elimination process" and does not indicate superiority of A-3 over A-2.

†See Table 9-8 for values.

From "Standard Specifications for Highway Materials and Methods of Sampling and Testing". Courtesy American Association of State Highway Officials.

TABLE 9-7. CLASSIFICATION OF SOILS AND SOIL-AGGREGATE MIXTURES (WITH SUGGESTED SUBGROUPS)

General Classification	Granular Materials (35% or less passing No. 200)							Silt-Clay Materials (More than 35% passing No. 200)			
	A-1		A-3	A-2				A-4	A-5	A-6	A-7
Group Classification	A-1-a	A-1-b		A-2-4	A-2-5	A-2-6	A-2-7				A-7-5; A-7-6
Sieve analysis: Percent passing:											
No. 10	50 max										
No. 40	30 max	50 max	51 min								
No. 200	15 max	25 max	10 max	35 max	35 max	35 max	35 max	36 min	36 min	36 min	36 min
Characteristics of fraction passing No. 40:											
Liquid limit			—	40 max	41 min	40 max	41 min	40 max	41 min	40 max	41 min
Plasticity index	6 max		NP	10 max	10 max	11 min	11 min	10 max	10 max	11 min	11 min*
Group index	0		0	0	0	4 max		8 max	12 max	16 max	20 max
Usual types of significant constituent materials	Stone fragments gravel and sand		Fine sand	Silty or clayey gravel and sand				Silty soils		Clayey soils	
General Rating as subgrade	Excellent to good							Fair to poor			

*Plasticity index of A-7-5 subgroup is equal to or less than LL minus 30. Plasticity index of A-7-6 subgroup is greater than LL minus 30.
From "Standard Specifications for Highway Materials and Methods of Sampling and Testing". Courtesy American Association of State Highway Officials.

4) The liquid limit values for the A-3 group have been dropped because the standard test procedure cannot be used on purely granular materials.

The A-4 group (silts) is characterized as subject to frost heave. Soils of the fifth and sixth groups are not suitable as subgrades for thin flexible-type base courses. Table 9-5 summarizes the soil characteristics and the PRA soil classification system.[18]

At the 25th Annual Meeting of the Highway Research Board a committee, appointed in 1943 to review the status of the subgrade soil classification, presented in 1945 a report on three different systems in order to establish a useful classification of subgrade materials that may be made by simple, routine tests performed by practically all highway departments.[19] The three systems are:

1) that prepared by a group representing highway organizations,
2) that in use by the Corps of Engineers, U.S. Army, and
3) the Civil Aeronautics Administration (CAA) soil classification system.

b) *The AASHO Soil Classification System.* The soil classification system presented by the highway representatives is a modification of the PRA soil classification system. This modified system is summarized in Tables 9-6 and 9-7†,[20] from which it can be noted that all soils are classed in *seven* groups, from A-1 to A-7. This system classifies soils based on their texture, physical properties (such as liquid limit and plasticity index), and on their expected field performance as subgrade materials for supporting pavements. The highway representatives' system has been adopted as one of the AASHO standards for subgrade soil classification. The AASHO system appears now in the 1950 and 1955 Specifications for Highway Materials as AASHO Designation M145-49.[21] The AASHO system divides the A-1, A-2 and A-7 groups into subgroups (Table 9-7) to avoid duplication, which was possible in the PRA system, and to permit making distinctions which were not possible in the PRA system. Also, the AASHO system permits making a relative evaluation of the effect of both coarse and fine soil particles within a given group. Recall that the PRA soil classification system was applicable only to the -10 material. The distinction of the fines is accomplished by gradation of the soil material over the No. 200 sieve.

The A-1 group represents a well-graded mixture of stone fragments or gravel, coarse sand, and a non-plastic or feebly plastic soil binder, as well as soil with no binder. The A-1-a subgroup comprehends materials consisting predominantly of stone fragments or gravel, either with or without a well-graded soil binder of fine material. The A-1-b subgroup comprehends materials consisting predominantly of coarse sand, either with or without a well-graded soil binder. The A-2 groups are borderline materials between soil groups A-1 and A-3. They show the effect of the fine particles on the composite soil material. The old A-2 group was granular soil of which less than 35% passed the No. 200 sieve. The new system with the subgroups, for example A-2-4, indicates a silt content, or A-2-7 shows that plastic clay, with a maximum of 35% passing the No. 200

†Tables 9-6 and 9-7 can also be found in AASHO *Specifications*, 1955, on pp. 48 and 49, respectively, in Ref. (21).

sieve, is present in the granular material, and cannot be classed as A-1 or A-3 material.

The subgroup A-7-5 indicates elastic soil with moderate plasticity indexes, which is subject to considerable volume change. The A-7-6 subgroup comprehends soils with high plasticity indexes and subject to large volume changes. The literal description of the soil groups in the AASHO soil classification system is approximately the same as in the original BPR subgrade soil classification system of June and July, 1931 (see Ref. 15).

Group Index. A new factor in the AASHO soil classification system is the so-called group index, defined by the empirical equation:

$$\text{Group Index} = 0.2a + 0.005ac + 0.01bd,$$

where a = that portion of percentage passing No. 200 sieve greater than 35% and not exceeding 75%, expressed as a positive whole number (1 to 40);

b = that portion of percentage passing No. 200 sieve greater than 15% and not exceeding 55%, expressed as a positive whole number (1 to 40);

c = that portion of the numerical liquid limit greater than 40 and not exceeding 60, expressed as a positive whole number (1 to 20);

d = that portion of the numerical plasticity index greater than 10 and not exceeding 30, expressed as a positive whole number (1 to 20).

Under average field and construction conditions, drainage and compaction, for instance, the good qualities of a subgrade material are rated as being in inverse ratio to its group index. For example, a group index the value of which is zero generally indicates a good subgrade material. A group index the value of which is 20 indicates a poor subgrade material.

The group index, based on actual soil performance, permits a closer determination of the probable performance of the soil in question than by the soil classification alone. The group index is used for determining empirically the combined thickness of flexible bituminous or Portland cement concrete pavement, base and subbase courses to be placed on a given subgrade. An empirical group index design diagram is shown in Fig. 9-1.[22] The original of this group index thickness diagram was published by D. J. Steele in 1946 (see Ref. 20).

The following are examples of calculation of the group index:

1) An A-6 material has 65% passing No. 200 sieve, a liquid limit of 32, and a plasticity index of 13. The calculation is as follows:

$a = 65 - 35 = 30$

$b = 55 - 15 = 40$ (55 is substituted for 65, as critical range is 15 to 55)

c = zero, because liquid limit is below 40

$d = 13 - 10 = 3$

$$\text{Group index} = (0.2 \times 30) + (0.01 \times 40 \times 3) = 7.2$$

(should be recorded to nearest whole number, which is 7).

2) An A-7 material has 54% passing No. 200 sieve, a liquid limit of 62, and a plasticity index of 33. The calculation is as follows:

$a = 54 - 35 = 19$
$b = 54 - 15 = 39$
$c = 60 - 40 = 20$ (60 is substituted for 62, as critical range is 40 to 60)
$d = 30 - 10 = 20$ (30 is substituted for 33, as critical range is 10 to 30)

Group index $= (0.2 \times 19) + (0.005 \times 19 \times 20) + (0.01 \times 39 \times 20) = 13.5$ (13).

If, for example, the daily volume of truck and bus traffic is heavy—about 625 —and the group index of the subgrade soil is 13, then the total thickness of a bituminous or Portland cement concrete pavement, according to Fig. 9-1, is

top (pavement + base):	7″
subbase:	14″
a total of	21″

The AASHO soil classification system is now also the Bureau of Public Roads soil classification system.

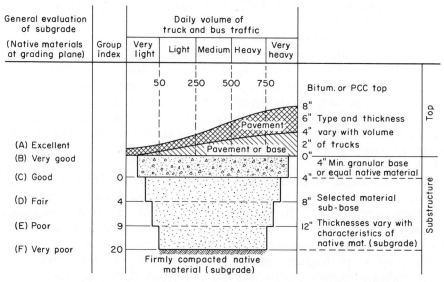

FIG. 9-1   Group index design chart (after D. J. Steele) John Wiley and Sons, Inc., and the Highway Research Board.

9-6.—7. Unified Soil Classification System. The soil classification system in use by the Corps of Engineers and prepared and submitted to the Highway Research Board in 1946 by Middlebrooks,[23] was known as the Airfield classification (AC) system. This system was developed by A. Casagrande and was tentatively adopted in 1942 by the Corps of Engineers as the "Airfield Classification".[24]

In June, 1947, A. Casagrande reviewed the existing soil classification used in civil engineering and presented a new soil grouping tentatively adopted by the United States Engineers Department in 1942.[25,26] The Airfield classification system reported by Middlebrooks at the 25th Annual Highway Research Board Meeting is the same system devised by Casagrande and adopted by the Corps of Engineers, U.S. Army, in 1942, and published in References 23 and 24.

Since 1942 the original classification has been expanded and revised in co-operation with the Bureau of Reclamation, so that it applies not only to airfields but also to embankments, foundations, and other engineering features. The revised Casagrande's Airfield classification system is now known as the Unified soil classification system. This system, in its turn, had its latest revision in 1957.[27]

In the Unified soil classification system soils are primarily classed into coarse-particled soils (50% or less -200 material), fine particled soils (75% -200 material), and highly organic soils. The first two groups are distinguished by the degree of their plasticity. The gravelly soils are designated by the symbol, G, sandy soils by S. Well-graded gravel and sand is designated by the symbols, GW and SW. Poorly-graded material is indicated by symbols, GP and SP.

Fine-particled soils are subgrouped based on their liquid limit (LL):

if the LL is < 50, the symbol is L;

if the LL is > 50, the symbol is H.

Organic soils are symbolized by Pt. Other symbols and features of the Unified soil classification system can be seen and inferred, respectively, from Table 9-8†.

Columns 5, 6, and 7; Table 9-8, describe the suitability of the soil groups for use as subgrades, subbase courses, and base courses, respectively, when not subjected to frost action. The suitability of soil groups for the same purposes under freezing conditions is tabulated in column 8. Drainage characteristics of this soil classification system are indicated in column 9. The special reference to frost action is an important feature of the Unified soil classification system.

According to A. Casagrande,[28] "Under natural freezing conditions and with sufficient water supply (from groundwater) one should expect considerable ice segregation in non-uniform soils containing more than three percent of grains smaller than 0.02 mm, and in very uniform soils containing more than 10 per-cent smaller than 0.02 mm. No ice segregation was observed in soils containing less than one percent of grains smaller than 0.02 mm."

For a discussion of other frost criteria see Reference 29. For a discussion of the upward migration of soil moisture upon freezing, see References 30, 31, and 32. On frost susceptible glacial soils of the Newark, N.J., metropolitan area, see Ref. 12.

Table 9-9 is an approximate comparison, according to Casagrande's idea (see Ref. 26), of the symbols used in the Unified soil classification system and in the Public Roads Administration's soil classification system. The value of these soil materials when subjected to frost action is also indicated.

---

†This Table 9-8 is an abstract from the Vicksburg Experiment Station's Table B 1, in Ref. 27, 1957, omitting their columns 4, 5, 11, 13, 14, 15 and 16.

TABLE 9-8. THE UNIFIED SOIL CLASSIFICATION SYSTEM*

CHARACTERISTICS PERTINENT TO ROADS AND AIRFIELDS

Major Divisions (1)	(2)	Symbol Letter (3)		Name (4)	Value as Subgrade when Not Subject to Frost Action (5)	Value as Subbase when Not Subject to Frost Action (6)	Value as Base when Not Subject to Frost Action (7)	Potential Frost Action (8)	Drainage Characteristics (9)
Coarse-grained soils	Gravel and gravelly soils	GW		Well-graded gravels or gravel-sand mixtures, little or no fines	Excellent	Excellent	Good	None to very slight	Excellent
		GP		Poorly graded gravels or gravel-sand mixtures, little or no fines	Good to excellent	Good	Fair to good	None to very slight	Excellent
		GM	D	Silty gravels, gravel-sand-silt mixtures	Good to excellent	Good	Fair to good	Slight to medium	Fair to poor
			U		Good	Fair	Poor to not suitable	Slight to medium	Poor to practically impervious
		GC		Clayey gravels, gravel-sand-clay mixtures	Good	Fair	Poor to not suitable	Slight to medium	Poor to practically impervious
	Sand and sandy soils	SW		Well-graded sands or gravelly sands, little or no fines	Good	Fair to good	Poor	None to very slight	Excellent
		SP		Poorly graded sands or gravelly sands, little or no fines	Fair to good	Fair	Poor to not suitable	None to very slight	Excellent
		SM	D	Silty sands, sand-silt mixtures	Fair to good	Fair to good	Poor	Slight to high	Fair to poor
			U		Fair	Poor to fair	Not suitable	Slight to high	Poor to practically impervious
		SC		Clayey sands, sand-clay mixtures	Poor to fair	Poor	Not suitable	Slight to high	Poor to practically impervious

Major Divisions (1)	(2)	Symbol Letter (3)	Name (4)	Value as Subgrade when Not Subject to Frost Action (5)	Value as Subbase when Not Subject to Frost Action (6)	Value as Base when Not Subject to Frost Action (7)	Potential Frost Action (8)	Drainage Characteristics (9)
Fine grained soils	Silts and clays LL is less than 50	ML	Inorganic silts and very fine sands, rock flour, silty or clayey fine sands or clayey silts with slight plasticity	Poor to fair	Not suitable	Not suitable	Medium to very high	Fair to poor
		CL	Inorganic clays of low to medium plasticity, gravelly clays, sandy clays, silty clays and lean clays	Poor to fair	Not suitable	Not suitable	Medium to high	Practically impervious
		OL	Organic silts and organic silt clays of low plasticity	Poor	Not suitable	Not suitable	Medium to high	Poor
	Silts and clays LL is greater than 50	MH	Inorganic silts, micaceous or diatomaceous fine sandy or silty soils, elastic silts	Poor	Not suitable	Not suitable	Medium to very high	Fair to poor
		CH	Inorganic clays of high plasticity, fat clays	Poor to fair	Not suitable	Not suitable	Medium	Practically impervious
		OH	Organic clays of medium to high plasticity, organic silts	Poor to very poor	Not suitable	Not suitable	Medium	Practically impervious
Highly organic soils		Pt	Peat and other highly organic soils	Not suitable	Not suitable	Not suitable	Slight	Fair to poor

*By Permission Abstracted from "The Unified Soil Classification System", Appendix B, Characteristics of Soil Groups Pertaining to Roads and Airfields, U.S. Army Engineer, Waterways Experiment Station.

The Unified soil classification system is a quick visual system for the evaluation of the probable soil performance for highway and airfield design and construction.

One notes that the Unified system employs simple symbols easy to use, thus disclosing the type and nature of the soil. The tests required to group a given soil are not many, and they are simple to perform. The main basis for the classification of the soils is the soil texture for the coarse fractions and plasticity for the fine fractions. This system comprehends 15 soil groups instead of seven as in the AASHO system. The USC system correlates soil performance under frost conditions, drainage conditions, compaction characteristics, and the California Bearing Ratio (CBR) of the soils.

TABLE 9-9. COMPARISON OF THE UNIFIED AND PUBLIC ROADS
ADMINISTRATION'S SOIL CLASSIFICATION SYSTEMS

Soil Symbols in the Unified System	Potential Frost Action	Soil Symbols in the PRA System
1	2	3
GW	None to very slight	A-3
GP	None to very slight	A-3
GM	Slight to medium	A-2
GC	Slight to medium	A-1
SW	None to very slight	A-3
SP	None to very slight	A-3
SM	Slight to high	A-2
SC	Slight to high	A-1
ML	Medium to very high	A-4
CL	Medium to high	A-4, A-6, A-7
OL	Medium to high	A-4, A-7
MH	Medium to very high	A-5
CH	Medium	A-6, A-7
OH	Medium	A-7, A-8
Pt	Slight	A-8

9-7.—8. The Civil Aeronautics Administration's (CAA) Soil Classification System. The CAA soil classification system[33] lists 13 groups of subgrade soils, tabled by symbols E-1 to E-13. This table could be applied directly to the problem of determining the thickness of flexible (F) and rigid (R) airfield pavements under various climatic conditions, including freezing, in the United States and Alaska. The subgrade soil classification is based on texture, soil plasticity and the California Bearing Ratio (CBR).

In the CAA system, soils E-1 through E-4 are granular materials (50% or more sand). Soils E-5 to E-10 are non-granular (containing less than 55% sand), which means non-plastic or moderately plastic A-4 silt. Soils designated E-7, E-8, and E-9 are clay soils, and E-10 (A-5) very elastic soil.

The CAA system also classifies the granular soil into non-frost heaving (E-1, E-2) and frost-susceptible soils (E-3, E-4).

9-8. Conclusions.

1) Soil classification is considered to be one of the necessary prerequisites in highway, street, and pavement design and construction.

2) Seldom has any single soil classification system ever provided the engineer with complete information on soil and its performance.

3) Although the available soil classification systems are better than nothing, the status of soil classification for engineering purposes is, unfortunately, still far from satisfactory.

4) The classification of all types of soils into a few groups for satisfying the many soil mechanics problems is, at the present time, a very difficult task.

5) In applying a certain soil classification system, judgment must be used, the system rationally evaluated and applied by each individual engineer in the light of his own personal experience.

6) The textural soil classification system is not quite satisfactory because it does not reflect the plastic properties of the soil, and it does not classify soil performance under load, water, and freezing conditions.

7) The main advantage of the AASHO soil classification system is that it has provided information on subgrade materials between highway organizations.

8) It is felt that the Unified soil classification system is, probably, the most satisfactory to civil engineers. In highway work the AASHO system receives considerable acceptance. The CAA soil classification system has about the same merits as the AASHO system.

9) Important progress in developing new engineering soil classification systems has been made in recognizing the drainage characteristics of the soil and the frost problem in highway and airfield soil engineering. The destruction of pavements by frost, together with desintegration of road surfaces, frost heaves, frost boils, spring break-up, and various other effects of seasonal freezing, make the technical frost action problem in highway engineering economically significant, and it is increasingly receiving the attention of highway engineers. The frost penetration problem in highway engineering is of national importance.

10) The relationship between each type of soil and its environment should be sought out in an engineering soil classification system.

REFERENCES

1. D. M. Burmister, *Identification and Classification of Soils—An Appraisal and Statement of Principles*, Symposium on the Identification and Classification of Soils, presented at the 53rd Annual Meeting of the ASTM, June 29, 1950. Special Technical Publication no. 113, ASTM, 1951.

2. J. Thorp, *Geography of the Soils of China*, Nanking, 1936.
3. A. Speck, *Der Kunststrassenbau*, Berlin, Wilhelm Ernst und Sohn, 1950, p. 1.
4. Ibid., p. 3.
5. R. J. Forbes, *Studies in Ancient Technology*, Leiden, E. J. Brill, 1955, Vol. 1.
6. *Engineering Soil Survey of New Jersey*, consisting of 21 county soil bulletins, two key reports and engineering soil maps. New Brunswick, New Jersey, Rutgers University Press, 1952-1957.
7. M. Whitney, *Methods of the Mechanical Analysis of Soils*, U.S. Department of Agriculture, Division of Agricultural Soils. Bulletin no. 4, Washington, D.C., Government Printing Office, 1896.
8. ASTM, *Procedures for Testing Soils*, April, 1958, p. 93, ASTM, Philadelphia.
9. D. W. Taylor, *Fundamentals of Soil Mechanics*, New York, John Wiley and Sons, Inc., 1948.
10. A. Atterberg, "Die mechanische Bodenanalyse und die Klassifikation der Mineral-böden Schwedens", *Internationale Mitteilungen für Bodenkunde*, Verlag für Fachliteratur, G.m.b.H., Wien-Berlin-London, 1912, vol. 2, no. 4, pp. 312-342.
11. AASHO, *Definition of Gravel, Sand and Silt-Clay, Standard Specifications for Highway Materials and Methods of Sampling and Testing*, Part I, AASHO, Washington, D.C., 1955.
12. A. R. Jumikis, *Engineering Aspects of Glacial Soils of the Newark Metropolitan Area of New Jersey*, Engineering Research Bulletin no. 42, Bureau of Engineering Research, Rutgers—The State University, New Brunswick, New Jersey, 1959.
13. C. A. Hogentogler, "Present Status of Subgrade Soil Testing", *Public Roads*, March, 1928 (Tentative classification). Bureau of Public Roads, Washington, D.C., vol. 9, no. 1, pp. 1-8.
14. C. A. Hogentogler, "Interrelationship of Load, Road and Subgrade", *Public Roads*, May, 1929, vol. 10, no. 3, pp. 37-64.
15. C. A. Hogentogler, "Subgrade Soil Constants, Their Significance and Their Application in Practice", *Public Roads*. Bureau of Public Roads, Washington, D.C., vol. 12, no. 4, June, 1931, Part I. Parts II and III, vol. 12, no. 5, July, 1931.
16. H. Allen, "Classification of Soils and Control Procedures Used in Construction of Embankments", *Public Roads*, February, 1952, vol. 22, no. 12.
17. Ibid., Figs. 9, 10, and 11, p. 267.
18. Ibid., p. 273.
19. "Report of Committee on Classification of Materials for Subgrades and Granular Type Roads" (Chairman, H. Allen), *Proceedings*, 25th Annual Meeting of the Highway Research Board, Washington, D.C., 1946, pp. 375-392.
20. D. J. Steele, "Classification of Highway Subgrade Materials", *Proceedings*, 25th Annual Meeting of the Highway Research Board, Washington, D.C., January, 1946, pp. 376-384.
21. "Standard Recommended Practice for the Classification of Soils and Soil-Aggregate Mixtures for Highway Construction Purposes", pub. in *Standard Specifications for Highway Materials and Methods of Sampling and Testing*, Part I, AASHO, Washington, D.C., 1950, pp. 29-35; 1955, pp. 45-51.
22. D. J. Steele, "Application of the Classifications and Group Index in Estimating Desirable Subbase and Total Pavement Thickness", *Proceedings*, 25th Annual Highway Research Board Meeting, Washington, D.C., January, 1946, pp. 388-392.
23. T. A. Middlebrooks, "Classification of Materials for Subgrades for Airfields and Granular Type Roads", *Proceedings*, 25th Annual Meeting of the Highway Research Board, Washington, D.C., January, 1946, pp. 384-386.
24. *The Unified Soil Classification System*, Technical Memorandum no. 3-357, prepared for the Office of the Chief of Engineers by Waterways Experiment Station, Vicksburg, Mississippi, March, 1953, vol. 1.

25. A. Casagrande, "Classification and Identification of Soils", *Proceedings*, ASCE, New York, June, 1947, vol. 73, no. 6, Part I, pp. 783-810.
26. A. Casagrande, "Classification and Identification of Soils", *Transactions*, ASCE, New York, 1948. Paper no. 2351, vol. 113, pp. 901-930. Discussions start on p. 931.
27. *The Unified Soil Classification System*, Appendix B, Technical Memorandum no. 3-357, March, 1953, revised June, 1957. U.S. Army Engineer Waterways Experiment Station, Corps of Engineers, Vicksburg, Mississippi.
28. A. Casagrande, "Discussion on Frost Heaving", *Proceedings*, Highway Research Board, Washington, D.C., 1932, Part I, p. 169.
29. A. R. Jumikis, *The Frost Penetration Problem in Highway Engineering*, New Brunswick, New Jersey, Rutgers University Press, 1955, pp. 139-144.
30. A. R. Jumikis, "The Soil Freezing Experiment", published in *Factors Influencing Ground Freezing*, Highway Research Board, Washington, D.C., 1956, pp. 150-165.
31. A. R. Jumikis, "Some Concepts Pertaining to the Freezing Soil System", published in the Highway Research Board International Water Symposium, *Special Report no. 40*, HRB, Washington, D.C., 1958.
32. A. R. Jumikis, "Concerning a Mechanism for the Soil Moisture Translocation in the Film Phase Upon Freezing", paper presented before the Highway Research Board's Annual Meeting, in January, 1960, Washington, D.C.
33. A. H. Hadfield, "Soil Classification and Evaluation of Subgrade Supporting Power for Airfields", *Proceedings*, 25th Annual Highway Research Board Meeting, Washington, D.C., January, 1946, pp. 386-388.

QUESTIONS

9-1. What are the various soil classification systems?
9-2. What are the fractional limits of gravel, sand, silt, and clay in the USDA Bureau of Soils soil classification system?
In the AASHO system?
In the International system?
9-3. Explain the concept of "group index".
9-4. Upon which soil test properties is based the AASHO soil classification system? The Unified soil classification system?
The Civil Aeronautics Administration's soil classification system?

PROBLEMS

9-1. Laboratory soil tests gave the following results on soil No. *S-86-2*:
Liquid limit = 20%. Plastic limit = 12%.
Sieving analysis: percent of soil material passing sieve No. 10—100%
No. 40— 85%
No. 200— 38%
Determine the plasticity index and the group index of this soil. Classify the soil according to the Highway Research Board's soil classification system and according to the Unified soil classification system.
9-2. If the daily number of buses and trucks on a road on this soil is 700, determine by means of Steele's diagram the thickness of the flexible pavement to use, and report also the thickness of the base and subbase courses if the latter ones are necessary.
9-3. The following table contains the results of particle size analysis and liquid limits and plastic limits of seven soils. Which of these soils would be considered frost susceptible? Explain.

Sieve Nos. Size	Percent Passing						
	Soil Sample Numbers						
	1	2	3	4	5	6	7
No. 10	80.0	35.2	84.0	37.3	98.3	100.0	78.2
20	78.4	25.1	79.7	26.0	97.6	98.7	75.1
40	75.0	19.8	72.8	19.0	87.6	97.2	71.6
60	69.0	17.8	67.5	15.9	58.2	95.5	68.7
140	50.1	15.5	60.3	12.5	9.2	90.2	64.5
200	43.2	14.8	60.0	12.3	9.0	85.3	63.2
0.05 mm	33.0	11.5	53.0	10.5	5.0	70.0	59.5
0.01 mm	10.5	5.0	24.0	6.0	2.0	40.0	32.0
0.005 mm	6.3	3.0	17.0	4.0	1.0	10.0	21.0
L.L. in %	23.2	28.0	30.8	27.5	NL	41.6	48.0
P.L. in %	15.7	19.5	19.9	21.5	NP	36.4	30.8
P.I. in %							

PART III

Water in Soil

Chapter 10

THE LIQUID PHASE OF SOIL—WATER

10-1. The "Opponent" Water. The "opponent" water in many cases appears especially troublesome in connection with the construction of foundations and earthworks when it is necessary to carry their footings below the ground-water table. The water head, causing an upward flow into the open excavation, may loosen the soil. In such cases where the hydraulic gradient exceeds the critical one, the so-called "quicksand" phenomenon occurs. Here water really presents the most difficult of the foundation engineering problems to be solved. It then means the adoption of a more elaborate and expensive method of construction.

From what has just been said, one can understand that water plays an important role in all construction work concerning foundation engineering and earthworks. Therefore, no planning or foundation engineering operations of any importance that must be carried out below the ground surface level should be started before accurate information about the "opponent" at the site is obtained. In foundation and highway engineering the "opponent" water is justly termed "public enemy No. 1".

10-2. Modes of Occurrence of Water in Soil. Water in soil can occur in the form of aqueous vapor, in the form of films adsorbed to the surfaces of the soil particles, as free water (gravitational water), or water in bulk, and as water in the solid state of aggregation, as for example, ice. There are no sharp breaks in this classification between the different forms of water in soil.

Having weight, soil moisture content increases the unit weight of a dry soil. In soil engineering that part of the subsurface water which occupies the voids in the soil above the groundwater table is called the *soil moisture.*

Adsorbed Water. This category of water comprises the hygroscopic soil moisture and the soil moisture films.

Hygroscopic Soil Moisture. All mineral matter is covered with a very thin film of moisture. Soils which appear quite dry nevertheless contain an amount of water—the so-called hygroscopic moisture. In the technical literature hygroscopic moisture is also termed adsorbed moisture, contact moisture, or surface-bound moisture. This form of soil moisture is in a dense state, and surrounds the surfaces of the individual soil particles as a very thin hull of film of water.

The soil particles obtain the hygroscopic moisture not only from water but also from the atmosphere (air) by the physical force of attraction, and is held by the force of adhesion; or they obtain it from the aqueous vapor present around them, by condensation. For example, if an oven-dried soil sample is placed in moist air, the weight of the sample increases, i.e., its moisture content increases. The increase of the moisture content continues until it reaches some constant value corresponding to its maximum hygroscopicity. The quantity of the hygroscopic moisture for a given soil varies with the temperature and the relative humidity of the air, and the characteristics of the soil particles themselves.

Hygroscopic moisture is not in union with the groundwater. Therefore, it does not take part in the fluctuation of the ground-water table, nor does it transmit hydrostatic pressure. Whether the hygroscopic moisture film consists of a single molecular, layer of water or of a polymolecular layer is not clearly known. However, the hygroscopic moisture film is known to be bound or attached rigidly to the soil particles with an immense physical force—up to about 10,000 atmospheres. Under the action of these forces, the hygroscopic soil moisture film is densified. The nearer the hygroscopic soil moisture is attracted to the surface of the solid soil particle, the more it is densified. The latest research explains these physical forces as being of an electro-chemical nature.

Hygroscopic moisture, being bound to the soil particle, is not affected by gravity. It would not move in the liquid form also under the influence of capillary forces, nor can it be evaporated under ordinary conditions. However, when transformed into vapor, the latter would move. Hygroscopic moisture can be removed by drying the soil particles at $+105°C$. The difference between the weight of the air-dried soil sample and its weight after oven-drying at $+105°C$ determines the amount of hygroscopic moisture present in a soil.

If the soil under consideration is coarse (sand or silt), the amount of hygroscopic moisture is relatively small due to its limited amount of specific surface. In fine-sized soils with large specific surface area, such as clays, the hygroscopic moisture can amount up to about 20% or more, by dry weight. Here the moisture film may be equal to or larger in volume than the soil particles themselves.

The maximum hygroscopicity for various soils has approximately the following average values: sands 1 percent, silts 7%, and clays 17% of their dry weight. However, the amount of hygroscopic moisture does not depend solely upon the texture of the soil, but also upon the degree of saturation of humidity—or water vapor of the atmosphere, i.e., on the vapor pressure of the water in the air.

The change in the thickness of the hygroscopic moisture film can take place by means of

    1) an electrolyte;
    2) a change in temperature, as already mentioned;
    3) a change in the air moisture content;
    4) a change in pore water pressure, and
    5) a change in mechanical pressure on the soil particles.

The cause or reason for covering the surfaces of the soil particles with a hygroscopic moisture film is found in the attractive forces of unsatisfied ionic bonds in the surfaces of soil particles. This results in a bonding and densification of the moisture within the range of action of these attractive forces. The moistening of the soil particles to their full hygroscopic capacity, at which the water molecules fully envelop the soil particles, is accompanied by heat release—the heat of wetting.

Soil moisture in hygroscopic form possesses properties which differ considerably from those of ordinary water. The density of hygroscopic moisture is > 1.0; it has a higher boiling point, greater viscosity, and greater surface tension than ordinary water. Therefore, hygroscopic moisture cannot be removed either by air-drying at ordinary temperatures or by the force of gravitation. Centrifugation, for example, fails to remove the adsorbed hygroscopic moisture film. The heat capacity of hygroscopic soil moisture is about 0.9, and its dielectric constant is approximately 2.2.

Hygroscopic moisture ordinarily would not freeze. However, when densified, hygroscopic soil moisture freezes at $-78°C$.

On the average, the heat of wetting of hygroscopic soil moisture is 3 to 10 gram calories. For 1 g till full hygroscopic saturation of adsorbed moisture the heat of wetting is 50 gram-calories.[1]

Hygroscopic moisture has a very definite effect on the cohesion and plasticity of a clayey soil. The thickness of the hygroscopic moisture hull, according to figures given in the literature, varies greatly. So, for example, according to Zunker's[2] figures in Table 10-1, one can see that hygroscopic moisture is present in considerable amount in fine-particled soils. This is because of the large internal surface area in such soils. The greater the internal surface, the greater the content of the hygroscopic moisture which can be adsorbed from the atmosphere by that soil.

Briggs[3] estimated the thickness of the water·film on powdered quartz in an atmosphere of 99% humidity to be 4.5 $\mu\mu$. Odén[4] found that the thickness of water film in a saturated atmosphere was about 2×10^{-5} to 3×10^{-5} mm, whereas at a very low vapor pressure the thickness was of the order of 1×10^{-6} mm.

TABLE 10-1. HYGROSCOPIC SOIL MOISTURE FILMS†

Soil type	Particle size, in mm	Hygroscopically bound soil moisture in percent of dry weight of the soil	Thickness of hygroscopic soil moisture film, in $\mu\mu$	Number of the densified layers of the molecules of the hygroscopic moisture
1	2	3	4	5
Silt	0.006	1	23.1	110
Clay	0.002	3	22.4	107
Colloids	0.0004	8	13.2	63
Colloids	0.00005	16	3.3	16
1 $\mu\mu = 10^{-6}$ mm				

The hygroscopic moisture film surrounding the soil particle affects the test results of specific gravity of the soil. This takes place even though the soil

† After F. Zunker, Ref. 2.

sample is weighed totally dry (without hygroscopic moisture), because its soil particles, at the time of determination of the volume of the water displaced by them, attract and thereby densify the hygroscopic moisture. Thus the determination of the volume of the displaced water is too low by the amount of the hygroscopic moisture. This, in turn, furnishes higher values of the specific gravities of soils than the actual one should be. According to Zunker, instead of the true specific gravities of the order of 2.65, with bound hygroscopic soil moisture of the amount of 8% to 16% (as frequently occurs with clays), specific gravities of the order of 2.75 and 2.84, respectively, are obtained.

Film Moisture. Film moisture forms in soil upon the condensation of aqueous vapor, or remains there after the removal of the bulk of the free water. The film moisture is attached to the surfaces of the soil particles as a hull or film upon the layer of the hygroscopic moisture film. The film moisture is held by molecular forces of considerable intensity but not as large as in the case of the hygroscopic moisture film.

Film moisture is connected to the groundwater table if one is present, but is not affected by gravity. The film moisture is set in motion or migration by the application to the soil system of an external energy potential, called primary potential—a thermal or electrical potential for example. The moisture in soil then will migrate from places of higher temperatures (or higher electric potential, whichever the case is) to places of lower temperatures. Film moisture does not transmit externally applied hydrostatic pressure, but in case of upward migration it is stressed, however, in the sense of soil moisture tension. This kind of moisture translocates very slowly. It moves in the form of a liquid film from points of higher potentials (heat, electric) to lower ones, from greater concentrations to smaller ones, and from points of thicker films to thinner films. The film water freezes below $0°C$, depending upon the thickness of the film, degree of stressed condition and upon the duration of freezing.

Considering the mode of film-water, it can thus be concluded that the greater is the specific surface area of soil the more film-water the soil particles can contain. The adsorption conditions depend upon the presence of ferrous and aluminum colloids, or silica colloids. Clay particles possess the property to adsorb upon their surfaces only a certain number of various salts of ferrum, of calcium, and others. It suffices already to have adsorbed on the clay particle surfaces just small traces of these "contaminators" to cause the fundamental change in adsorption conditions of the water and, thereby, the thickness of the film, viz., the film moisture content in the soil. Ferrum and aluminum colloidal contaminations usually result in thin films, but silica colloids lead to thick films.

The amount of soil moisture which corresponds to the maximum thickness of the moisture film (liquid phase), and which is attracted on the surfaces of the soil particles (the solid phase) by molecular forces, is termed the maximum molecular moisture capacity of soil. At this moisture content the soil possesses its maximum cohesion and stability.

10-3. Gravitational Water. Gravitational water can further be subdivided into a) free water (or bulk water), and b) capillary water.

Free water, in its turn, is distinguished as follows: i) Free surface water and ii) Groundwater.

Gravitational water is the water which is in excess of the amount of moisture the soil can retain. It translocates as a liquid and it can be drained away by the forces of gravity. It transmits hydraulic pressure.

a) *Free water* (bulk water) possesses the usual properties of liquid water. It translocates at all times under the influence of gravity forces, or because of a difference in hydrostatic pressure head, or b) it can be in a suspended condition held by the surface tension forces of the liquid, when it is called *capillary water*.

i) *Free Surface Water.* Free surface water conditions (precipitation, runoff, melting snow, flood-water, water flowing from broken mains or from certain hydraulic operations) should be investigated when a structure comes in direct or indirect contact, or when it influences the groundwater in one way or another. For the construction work as well as for the exploitation of the structure it is of importance to determine the *amount* and the *fluctuation* of the free water.

Rainfall and *runoff* are erosive agents that are very destructive because they detach soil and transport it away.

1) The erosive action of water is the effect of the energy developed by its movement as it falls onto the land in the form of rainfall or runs over the land as runoff.

2) Erosion may result from a sheet flow or confined flow. The magnitude of erosion depends upon the erodibility of soil; the slope of the ground surface and its length; the intensity, duration, frequency of rainfall, as well as the velocity of flow and turbulence.

3) The tremendous force of the uncontrolled, downslope running water carves deep gullies and channels in unprotected soil. Hence, uncontrolled water can wash out road, railroad, and canal embankments; dams and levees; bridge piers; foundations of structures. It can destroy cofferdams for foundation work and equipment and construction material. Or, the eroded and transported material may be deposited in reservoirs, thus filling them up with silt and taking the volume needed to store water for irrigation, flood control, domestic water supply, power, and recreation.

From the viewpoint of soil mechanics, the influence of large quantities of precipitation may become unpleasantly apparent

1) in the increase of the hydrostatic uplift in the soil layers near the ground surface,

2) in the creation in slopes in permeable soil layers—which are sandwiched between impermeable clay layers—of an artesian pressure caused by water seeping through the surface cracks of the soil on the ground surface. The stability of the slope in such an instance is greatly impaired; and

3) in the so-called lubricating action between clayey soil layers.

The freezing point, the boiling point, the surface tension, and the viscosity of the free surface water correspond to those of ordinary water.

ii) *Groundwater.* Groundwater is that kind of gravity water which fills up the voids and other open spaces in the soil up to the groundwater table and translocates through them. It obeys the laws of hydraulics. Groundwater fills coherently and completely all the voids of the soil. In such a case it is said that the soil is saturated, and the water content by volume is equal to the volume of the voids.

The movement of the groundwater along a slope is downward, because it is subjected to the gravitational force only. The movement itself, however, is slow and restrained. Restraint is caused by the resistance offered to flow by the soil through which the water flows. Free gravitational water may be removed from soils by drainage, or by lowering of the groundwater table, or by pumping it out from foundation pits. The upper surface of the zone of the full saturation of the soil, at which the groundwater is subjected to atmospheric pressure, is called the *groundwater table*. On construction sites, or, generally, in the field, the groundwater table is the locus of the water levels to which it rises and levels itself out in observation wells, bore holes, test pits, and open basins in free communication through the voids of the soil. If the soil is of poor permeability or is practically impermeable, establishment of the levels often takes a very long period of time, or sometimes it does not even take place at all.

The groundwater table is not a fixed surface plane, but is undulating, tending to parallel the undulations or contours of the surface topography. However, the parallelism is imperfect. Also, the groundwater table fluctuates in different places—and even in the same place—according to the amount of precipitation and to the season of the year; because of withdrawals for water supply, other industrial purposes, or lowering of the groundwater table.

In winter or in wet seasons, the groundwater table is generally higher than in dry or summer seasons. The depth to which the groundwater table fluctuates below the ground surface usually varies from zero to several feet. The groundwater table is determined by the general drainage level at which the surface drainage streams flow in that region. The elevation of the groundwater table at a given point is called the *groundwater level*.

The depth of the fluctuating groundwater table can be determined in each particular case by measuring the elevation to which water rises in a well sunk below the ground surface at any point.

Sometimes the main zone of saturation, containing the main or true groundwater, is overlain in places by unsaturated material that contains an impervious geologic formation above which a local zone of saturation may occur. Groundwater in such a zone is called "perched groundwater". Its upper surface is called the perched groundwater table.

Perched Groundwater. Runoff water, seeping into the soil, may also be trapped in depressions in pockets of moraine clay located below ground surface in permeable sand, thus forming a perched groundwater. The amount of groundwater accumulated depends upon the season, rate of evaporation from the depression in the direction of ground surface, and freezing (if this occurs). If there prevails a certain freezing temperature gradient between the ground surface and the perched groundwater table, and if the freezing period lasts long enough, and all other physical conditions are favorable, the perched water may migrate from the warmer, perched water zone towards the colder, downward-penetrating cold front, and the whole amount of the perched groundwater may be transferred upwards. Thus it can be understood that freezing, in a way, is a drying process.

From this discussion it can be understood that in most locations there does not exist such a thing as the "permanent" groundwater level to which reference is often made.

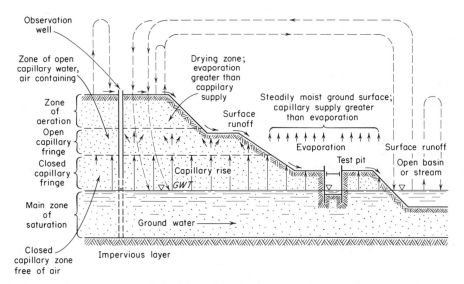

FIG. 10-1   Groundwater zones.

The groundwater temperature in the New York - Wilmington (Del.) area varies, according to observations by the author, from about 6°C to 10°C year round. Generally, the daily temperatures do not affect the temperature of the groundwater at a depth of 3 to 5 ft below the ground surface.

Artesian Water. Artesian water is confined groundwater under hydrostatic or pressure head (a permeable water-bearing soil layer or aquifer sandwiched between impermeable zones above and below it).

10-4. Capillary Moisture. Capillary water is that soil moisture which is located within the interstices and voids of capillary size of the soil.

Capillarity, in general, is a phenomenon of the rise or depression of liquids in tubes having a bore so fine as to be comparable in diameter with a hair (capillus). The rise takes place and the liquid is held by means of a force called the surface tension force of the menisci at the top of the water column in a capillary tube, or by surface tension forces plus the effect of gravity.

Capillary movement in soil is the movement of the soil moisture through the minute pores between the soil particles. The minute pores serve as capillary tubes through which the soil moisture rises above the groundwater table. Movement results whenever the soil moisture "surface tension pull" is increased by loss of water through evaporation from the ground surface. Thus, capillary water is hydraulically and *continuously connected* to the groundwater table or to a perched groundwater table, and can be raised against the force of gravity.

For capillarity of rise in soil to exist, all the voids should be completely and *uninterruptedly* filled with capillary water. The capillary-saturated zone between the groundwater table and the plane of the menisci is called the *closed capillary fringe*. This contains no air (Fig. 10-1). The thickness of this closed capillary fringe depends mainly on the fineness of the soil particles. The larger the pore size (diameter of the capillary), the less the height of rise, or the less the capillary fringe.

The transition from free capillary water to film water in soil is gradual. There fore, in the capillary fringe capillary water as well as film water can be encountered.

Above the closed capillary fringe there is the so-called *open capillary fringe*, i.e., the air-containing capillary zone which reaches to the height of the menisci in the finest pores of the soil. Here the larger pores are not filled with capillary moisture.

Capillary water cannot be drained away by means of drainage systems installed within the capillary fringe, but it can be controlled by lowering the groundwater table. The drainage system must be installed in the groundwater to pull it down together with the capillary fringe, thus controlling the capillary height to which the capillary water can rise.

Capillary water can be removed from soils by drainage only when the quantity of water present in the soil is in excess of that retained by surface tension forces. Capillary water can also be removed by heating or by its evaporation at ordinary temperatures. It freezes at about $-1°C$.

Capillary moisture may translocate in soil in any direction, not just vertically upward. The presence of capillary moisture in cohesive soil decreases considerably its cohesion and stability: the soil transforms into a sticky-plastic condition which makes it difficult to work with, to compact, or even to mix.

The freezing of a capillary-saturated soil results in an accumulation of a considerable amount of moisture at the cold isothermal boundary where the water freezes, causing heaves and other damage to roads.

By definition as well as physically, the boundary between capillary and gravitational water is a very broad one and cannot be determined accurately.

The moisture content interval corresponding to the transition from maximum molecular moisture capacity to the capillary moisture characterizes the *critical moisture*. At this transition to the higher moisture content, the soil begins sharply to decrease in its stability under load (refer to optimum moisture content, Chapter 7), decreases in cohesion and assumes plastic properties. At the critical moisture content the soil in a compaction procedure is subjected to the maximum densification for the least amount of energy spent. The critical soil moisture content is more popularly known as the optimum moisture content of soil—a favorable property from the viewpoint of building firm fills of roads, runways for aircraft, earth dams, and other earthworks.

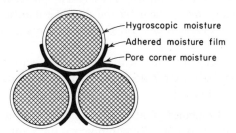

FIG. 10-2   Pore corner moisture.

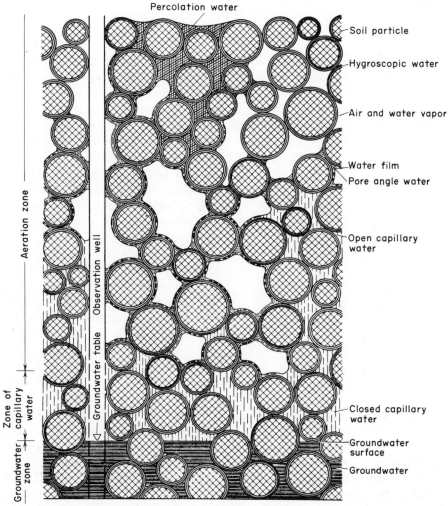

FIG. 10-3   Modes of occurrance of water in soil, after F. Zunker, Ref. (1).

Pore corner or *neck moisture*, known in German by the term *Porenwinkelwasser*, is the annular moisture wedge held by the concave menisci, or rather surface tension forces, in the angularities formed by the points of contact of the soil particles (Fig. 10-2).

Each of the principal kinds of soil moisture, viz., water, is represented diagrammatically in Fig. 10-3 after Zunker[1] so that fundamental differences can be distinguished easily and clearly.

10-5. Chemically Combined Water. Besides the aforementioned kinds of water in soil, there exists chemically combined water contained within mineral particles. This water can be freed only by chemical processes of the substance. The chemically bound water does not influence the physical-chemical properties of soil. As a matter of interest, clay, for example, contains up to about 14% of combined water.

SURFACE TENSION

10-6. Nature and Magnitude of Surface Tension. Surface tension of water is that property which exists in the surface film of water tending to contract the contained volume into a form having a minimum superficial area possible. In the case of molecules in a drop of water the drops tend to assume a spherical shape. Surface tension is also defined as the force per unit length required to extend the surface of the film in its own plane. Surface tension is, in one way or another, considered in soil mechanics, thermal soil mechanics, moisture migration in porous medium, frost action problems, and in soil mechanics research.

The magnitude of the surface tension is usually determined by balancing it along a certain boundary or interface line with a force which can be measured. For this purpose, a liquid film is formed in a loop (Fig. 10-4). The three sides of the loop, *l-a-b-b-a-l*, are rigid, whereas the fourth side, *a-a*, which is a cross wire, is movable. The water film is stretched from position *a'-a'* to position *a-a* by moving outward the movable side *a-a* of the loop. Upon stretching, the film resists expansion.

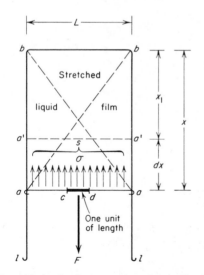

FIG. 10-4 Surface tension in a liquid film.

The tendency of the liquid film to resist expansion is a manifestation of the tangential force (surface tension) in the film surface. Upon stretching it, the film is said to be stressed, and the liquid film surface is said to be under tension. The maximum amount of the force, *F*, necessary to bring about a very slow stretching of the film is proportional to the length, L, of the movable side, a-a, of the loop. The magnitude of this force perpendicular to a-a and per unit length of it is called the coefficient of surface tension, S, of the liquid. In the cgs system of units, the force, F, is expressed in dynes, and the surface tension in dynes per centimeter. In the loop shown in Fig. 10-4, as the frame, viz., wire a-a, is dragged out, the total force, F, applied to the total length, L, in cm, of the movable wire, a-a, is

$$F = 2S = 2\sigma L \quad \text{(dynes)}, \tag{10-1}$$

where σ = surface tension in dynes/cm.

The coefficient 2 here means that the film has two faces. Thus, the incremental area of the film, including both sides is $A = 2L(x - x_1)$. Note again that the discussion thus far pertains to surface forces which are limited to air-liquid interfaces, and that it is the maximum value of the tension in the film which is being measured to detach the cross wire from the surface of the liquid. According to Bain *et al.*,[5] the least possible thickness of water surface films is 2 to 3Å.

Work done by stretching the film through a distance of $(x - x_1)$ is

$$W = F(x - x_1) \tag{10-2}$$

This work is equal to the increase in the potential energy of the film. Hence, the increase in the potential energy of the film is equal to

$$F(x - x_1) = 2\sigma L(x - x_1)$$

$$= \sigma(\text{increase in area of film}),$$

i.e., to surface tension times increase in area of film.

The surface tension from experiment illustrated in Fig. 10-4 can then be expressed as

$$\sigma = \frac{W}{A} = \frac{F(x - x_1)}{2L(x - x_1)} = \frac{F}{2L} \quad \text{(dynes/cm)} \tag{10-3}$$

The units of σ are (dynes/cm), or $\left(\dfrac{\text{dynes cm}}{\text{cm}^2}\right)$, or (ergs/cm^2).

10-7. Effect of Temperature on Surface Tension. The surface tension of liquids at room temperatures are of the order of 0.03 g/cm. For water, the surface tension is more than double this figure and is equal to about 0.08 g/cm.

The values of the coefficients of surface tension of some common liquids are given in Table 10-2 from Smithsonian Physical Tables.[6]

It can be seen that the coefficients of surface tension depend upon the chemical nature of the liquid. The symbol σ^* in this Table means force grams per cm.

The surface tension of all liquids decreases with increase in temperature and is practically unaffected by changes in total area, pressure, or volume. The change is approximately proportional to the rise in temperature and about 0.15 dynes/cm per degree. The surface tension of all liquids decreases linearly as the temperature rises. Analytically, the surface tension σ_T at $T°C$ can be expressed over moderate ranges by a linear equation

$$\sigma_T = \sigma_0[1 - \alpha(T - T_0)],\qquad(10\text{-}4)$$

where σ_0 = surface tension at 0°C, or rather at melting point,
   T = temperature,
   T_0 = temperature at melting point, and
   α = a constant, or the temperature coefficient.

TABLE 10-2. SURFACE TENSION OF SOME COMMON LIQUIDS
AT 20°C AT AIR-LIQUID INTERFACE.

Compiled from Smithsonian Physical Tables.

Substance	Surface Tension	
	σ dynes/cm	σ^* g/cm
1	2	3
Acetone	23.7	24.2×10^{-3}
Alcohol, ethyl	22.03	22.46×10^{-3}
Benzene	28.9	29.5×10^{-3}
Benzene, at 0°C	27.0	27.5×10^{-3}
Benzol	27.7	28.25×10^{-3}
Carbon tetrachloride	26.8	27.3×10^{-3}
Ether	27.01	17.35×10^{-3}
Glycerine, at 18°C	63.0	64.2×10^{-3}
Mercury	513.0	521.1×10^{-3}
Olive oil	33.1	33.8×10^{-3}
Petroleum	26.0	26.5×10^{-3}
Turpentine	28.4	29.0×10^{-3}
Water	72.75	74.18×10^{-3}

The minus sign at α accounts for the fact that the surface tension decreases as the temperature rises.[7] A decrease in surface tension would mean a decrease of the cohesive forces between the liquid molecules in the surface. For most liquids, the decrease can be represented by a straight line which intersects the temperature axis at about 6°C.

The values of the coefficients of surface tensions of water in dynes/cm at various temperatures are interpolated and compiled from the International Critical Tables,[8] calculated in g/cm, and tabulated in Table 10-3.

Equation (10-4) remains valid even below the melting point in accordance with the general rule that the properties of undercooled liquids change in the same manner as the corresponding properties above the melting point. This was proved for water down to $-8°C$.[9]

TABLE 10-3. SURFACE TENSION OF WATER TO AIR
AT ORDINARY TEMPERATURES

Temperature °C	Surface Tension		Capillary Constant $a^2 = \dfrac{2\sigma^*}{\gamma_w}$
	σ dynes/cm	σ^* g/cm	(cm²)
1	2	3	4
−8	76.96	78.48×10^{-3}	0.1574
−5	76.42	77.91×10^{-3}	0.1562
−4	76.26	77.76×10^{-3}	0.1559
−3	76.11	77.61×10^{-3}	0.1556
−2	75.95	77.45×10^{-3}	0.1552
−1	75.80	77.29×10^{-3}	0.1549
0	75.64	77.13×10^{-3}	0.1545 (average)
1	75.50	76.99×10^{-3}	0.1543
2	75.3	76.83×10^{-3}	0.1540
3	75.21	76.69×10^{-3}	0.1536
4	75.06	76.54×10^{-3}	0.1533
5	74.92	76.40×10^{-3}	0.1529
6	74.78	76.25×10^{-3}	0.1527
7	74.64	76.12×10^{-3}	0.1525
8	74.50	75.97×10^{-3}	p.1522
9	74.36	75.82×10^{-3}	0.1519
10	74.22	75.67×10^{-3}	0.1516
11	74.07	75.53×10^{-3}	0.1513
12	73.93	75.39×10^{-3}	0.1510
13	73.78	75.23×10^{-3}	0.1508
14	73.64	75.06×10^{-3}	0.1505
15	73.49	74.94×10^{-3}	0.1502
16	73.34	74.78×10^{-3}	0.1499
17	73.19	74.63×10^{-3}	0.1496
18	73.05	74.49×10^{-3}	0.1494
19	72.90	74.34×10^{-3}	0.1491
20	72.75	74.18×10^{-3}	0.1488
25	71.97	73.39×10^{-3}	0.1474
30	71.18	72.58×10^{-3}	0.1460
35	70.38	71.77×10^{-3}	0.1446
40	69.56	70.93×10^{-3}	0.1431
100	58.85	60.01×10^{-3}	0.1253

The value of α can be evaluated from the condition that at the critical temperature, T_c, the surface tension is zero:

$$\alpha = \frac{1}{T_c - T_0} \quad (\deg^{-1}) \qquad (10\text{-}5)$$

Thus, for example, the temperature coefficient, α, for water at its critical temperature of $+374°C$ is $\alpha = 0.0027 \ (\deg^{-1})$.

Generally, electrolytes increase the surface tension of water, but the effect is usually small. Soaps, alcohols, and acids, when added to water in small amounts, will give solutions the surface tensions of which will be far below that of water. This explains the relative ease of stretching of the water film in the formation of a soap bubble.

10-8. Capillary Rise. The capillary rise takes place by means of a force called the surface tension force of the menisci, acting at the top of the water column in a capillary tube between water and the wall surface of the tube, and distributed around the circular, wetted perimeter of the tube (Fig. 10-5). The

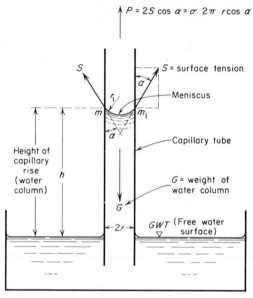

$$P = 2S \cos \alpha = \sigma \, 2\pi \, r \cos \alpha$$

Fig. 10-5 Capillary rise. Equilibrium condition in a capillary system.

force which brings about the capillarity is also called the capillary force. The curved, upper crescent-shaped surface of the liquid column in the capillary tube is termed *meniscus*. This meniscus is concave relative to its top when the liquid wets the wall of the capillary, as in the case of water. It is convex relative to its top as in the case of mercury.

When a capillary tube is placed in a liquid that wets the walls of its surface, the liquid will rise in the capillary above the free water surface of the liquid into which the capillary is dipped, provided that the liquid wets the tube. Adhesive forces induce a thin film of moisture over the inner and outer cylindrical surface of the capillary tube, producing a large surface area. However, the surface tension of the liquid acts to decrease or contract the magnitude of that surface to a certain minimum. The surface contraction is brought about by the adhering moisture film being pulled down into the main body of the liquid, or by the liquid being pulled up into the capillary. But because, by observation, the adhesive forces between the liquid and the wall of the capillary tube are large enough to prevent the former case, then capillary ascent or rise of water inside the tube to a certain height, h, above the water level where the tube is immersed takes place. This height, h, is termed the *height of the capillary rise*.

The height of the capillary rise in the tube depends upon the magnitude of the force of the surface tension pulling the liquid upward, as compared to the force of gravity pulling the liquid column downward. When the two forces are balanced, further rise is prevented and a condition of equilibrium results. This equilibrium condition is represented in Fig. 10-5. The liquid is held up in the tube by the action of the surface tension at the circular line of contact between the liquid column and the adsorbed film on the capillary wall.

The magnitude of the surface tension force acting around the circular line of contact or wetted perimeter is $\sigma 2\pi r$, where r is the inside radius of the capillary tube. The curved surface of the liquid in the tube, however, makes a contact with the film on the wall of the tube at an angle, α. This angle is called the *contact angle*. More precisely, a certain angle is formed between a plane tangent to the surface of the liquid and a plane tangent to the surface of the solid wall at a point on the curve of contact. Therefore, the upward component of the surface tension force is the force which is counterbalanced by the force of gravity. The magnitude of the upward force is (Fig. 10-5):

$$\text{Upward force} = P = 2S \cos \alpha = \sigma 2\pi r \cos \alpha \qquad \text{(dynes)}. \qquad (10\text{-}6)$$

The horizontal component is taken up and counterbalanced by the reaction of the wall of the tube.

The downward acting force, G, is due to gravity, and is the weight of the liquid column, h, in the capillary tube above the plane, free water surface. The magnitude of the downward acting force is

$$G = \rho_L gah = \rho_L g\pi r^2 h \qquad \text{(dynes)} = (\text{g cm sec}^{-2}) \quad (10\text{-}7)$$

or

$$G = \gamma_w \pi r^2 h \qquad \text{(weight grams)}, \qquad (10\text{-}8)$$

where ρ_L = density of liquid, in g/cm³,
$\quad\quad g$ = 981 cm/sec² = acceleration of gravity,
$\quad\quad a$ = cross-sectional area of the capillary tube, in cm²,
$\quad\quad r$ = radius of tube,
$\quad\quad \gamma_w$ = 1 g/cm³ = unit weight of water in capillary tube,
$\quad$ 1 dyne = 1.0197 × 10⁻³ grams (weight) = 1 gram (mass) × 1 cm/sec²,
1 force gram = 981 dynes.

At force equilibrium, the magnitude of the upward force equals the downward force:

$$\uparrow P = \downarrow G,$$

or

$$\sigma 2\pi r \cos \alpha = \rho_L g\pi r^2 h, \qquad (10\text{-}9)$$

when σ is expressed in dynes/cm,

or

$$\sigma^* 2\pi r \cos \alpha = \gamma_w \pi r^2 h, \tag{10-9a}$$

when σ^* is expressed in force grams per cm.

On wetting of the walls of a capillary tube when the angle of contact, α, and $\cos \alpha$, have values of

$$0 < \alpha < 90°$$

$$1 > \cos \alpha > 0,$$

the capillary rise, h, is calculated, neglecting the density of saturated vapor above the meniscus, as

$$h = \frac{2\sigma \cos \alpha}{\rho_L g r} \quad (\text{cm}), \tag{10-10}$$

or, expressed in terms of the diameter of the tube,

$$h = \frac{4\sigma \cos \alpha}{\rho_L g d} \quad (\text{cm}), \tag{10-10a}$$

or

$$h = \frac{2\sigma^* \cos \alpha}{\gamma_w r} \quad (\text{cm}). \tag{10-11}$$

This means that in a capillary tube a liquid will rise to such a height that the gravitational force will just balance the force of surface tension.

The value $(2\sigma^*)/\gamma_w = a^2$ in Eq. (10-11) is called the *capillary constant* (see Table 10-3).

At 0°C, the surface tension is $\sigma_0 = 77.13 \times 10^{-3}$ g/cm. At such a temperature, the capillary rise or height is

$$h_0 = \frac{2(0.07713)\cos \alpha}{\underbrace{(0.99986)}_{\approx 1} r} = \frac{(0.15426)\cos \alpha}{r} = \frac{0.30852}{d} \cos \alpha, \tag{10-12}$$

where $d = 2r = $ the diameter of the capillary tube.

It can be seen that the capillary height is proportional to the surface tension and the angle of contact, and inversely proportional to the unit weight of water and to the diameter of the capillary tube. Practically, the capillary height increases with the decrease in diameter of the tube.

Besides, the value of capillary height reaches a maximum when $\cos \alpha = 1$. This, in its turn, means that the contact angle α is zero. In such a case

$$h_{max} = \frac{2\sigma^*}{\gamma_w r} \tag{10-13}$$

or, with $\gamma_w = 1$ g/cm³,

$$h_{0_{max}} = \frac{0.30852}{d}. \tag{10-13a}$$

The value of the contact angle, α, can be assumed to be zero for liquids which wet the tube, for example, water and alcohol.

The angle of contact, α, between the surface of a liquid and that of a solid is dependent upon the nature of the surfaces, and differs for contaminated surfaces from that for clean surfaces.

The angle of contact, α, between liquid and glass covered with a film of the liquid at room temperatures for water, ethyl alcohol, benzene, carbon tetrachloride, and aqueous solutions of various salts is zero.

For maximum capillary rise the tube should be clean and pre-wetted. Dry tubes and dusty tubes decrease h. Oil and paraffin on the walls of a tube retard the capillary rise. When there is an air or gas plug in the capillary water column, the water will not rise. There should be an uninterrupted column of capillary water in the capillary tube above the free, plane water surface; then there will by a capillary rise of water in the tube as a function of its diameter.

When $\alpha = 0$, then the radius of curvature, r_1, of the meniscus, m-m, equals the radius of the tube, r.

When $\alpha = 90°$, and $\cos \alpha = 0$, the capillary height and capillary pressure are zero.

In general, the capillary height depends upon many physical and chemical properties of the liquid and tube material, viz., soil particles. Unfortunately, there are not yet available undisputable experimental data to elucidate and verify the influence of the many active factors involved.

The height of the capillary rise does not depend upon the inclination of the capillary tube, nor does it depend upon the shape of the tube and the diameter of the tube below the meniscus of the liquid in the tube. The height depends, however, upon the diameter of the meniscus (Fig. 10-6). When the upper part of

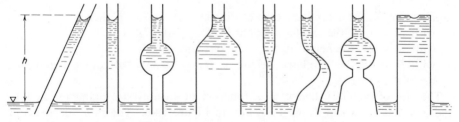

FIG. 10-6 The capillary height is the same with various shapes of capillary tubes if the diameter of their menisci is the same.

variously shaped capillary tubes is finished off by capillary orifices of one and the same diameter, the water in the capillaries reaches the same height above the plane free water table no matter whether the tubes are broadened below it or not.

Owing to the variation in surface tension with variation in temperature, capillary height decreases with the increase in temperature. Analogous to Eq. (10-4), the capillary height, h, at any temperature, T, can be expressed as

$$h_T = h_0 \left[1 - 0.0027(T - T_0) \right] \quad \text{(cm)}, \quad\quad (10\text{-}14)$$

or, with reference to Eq. (10-13a),

$$h_T = \frac{0.30852}{d}[1 - 0.0027(T - T_0)], \tag{10-14a}$$

where h_0 = capillary height at temperature $T = 0°C$.

This equation shows clearly that with the increase in temperature, T, the height, h_T, of the capillary water in the tube drops. This also happens to the height of the capillary fringe in the soil. However, an increase in temperature in the soil may not necessarily lower the position of the groundwater table, which depends for the most part on the hydrologic regime.

The relative variation in capillary height with temperature can be very well followed in Table 10-3.

The relative effect of capillary diameter on capillary height and the inversely proportional relationship are demonstrated in Figure 10-7. For example, if the

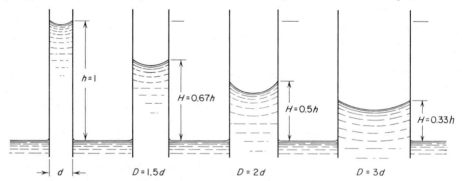

FIG. 10-7   Effect of diameter on capillary height.

capillary height for a capillary tube of diameter, d, is $h = 1$, then

with $D = 1.5d$, the capillary height is $H_{1.5} = (0.67)h$;

with $D = 2d$, the height is $H_2 = (0.5)h$; and

with $D = 3d$, the capillary height is $H_3 = (0.33)h$, all other conditions being the same.

The rise of capillary height as a function of various size diameters at 0°C and $\alpha = 0$ is shown in Table 10-4, and in Figure 10-8. The rapid decrease in capillary height with increase in diameter is very conspicuous.

In the discussion of the capillary rise in a tube, the vapor density, ρ_v, in comparison with ρ_L is neglected.

Taking into account the density of saturated vapor above the meniscus, the expression of the height of capillary rise is (see also Eq. (10-10)):

$$h = \frac{2\sigma \cos \alpha}{r(\rho_L - \rho_v)g} \quad \text{(cm)}, \tag{10-15}$$

where ρ_L = density of water, in g/cm^3,

ρ_v = density of saturated vapor, in g/cm^3.

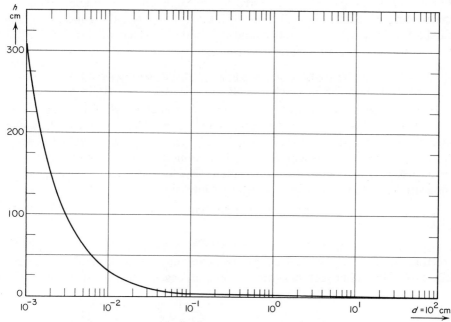

FIG. 10-8   Capillary rise as a function of diameter at 0°C.

TABLE 10-4. CAPILLARY HEIGHT
AS A FUNCTION OF DIAMETER OF CAPILLARY TUBE AT 0°C

Diameter of Capillary Tube			Capillary Height	
mm	cm	cm	cm	cm
1	2	3	4	5
100	10	10^1	0.030852	3.0852×10^{-2}
10	1	10^0	0.30852	3.0852×10^{-1}
1	0.1	10^{-1}	3.08520	3.0852×10^0
0.1	0.01	10^{-2}	30.852	3.0852×10^1
0.01	0.001	10^{-3}	308.52	3.0852×10^2
0.001	0.0001	10^{-4}	3085.2	3.0852×10^3
0.0001	0.00001	10^{-5}	30852.0	3.0852×10^4
0.00001	0.000001	10^{-6}	308520.0	3.0852×10^5

Note, that in soils there are no geometrical capillary tubes such as were here discussed from the physical point of view. Rather, the voids, interstices, and passages in the soil are of irregular shape and various sizes, which might be filled partially or fully with water, or air, or gas, or in combination of these substances. Besides, these passages are not necessarily vertical. However, the capillary concepts help us to understand certain phenomena occurring in soil.

For example, soil particles are wetted by soil moisture in a manner similar to the wetting of the inside wall of a capillary tube. Also, the concepts of the capillary theory help us to understand the mode by which water is retained in the soil by surface tension forces.

RELATIONSHIPS BETWEEN CURVATURE-PRESSURE, SURFACE TENSION, AND CURVATURE OF LIQUID SURFACE

10-9. Pressure Due to Surface Tension. Consider a cylindrical surface as shown in Fig. 10-9a. Let $S = \sigma 1$ dynes be the surface tension force of the upper lamina of the boundary surface of the liquid. The cylindrically curved surface, c-c-c'-c', is 1 cm wide; its length is dL. The radius of curvature of the cylindrical surface is r_1 from point, C, as a center. The surface tension stress, acting tangentially to the curved surface, is of an intensity of

$$S = \sigma 1 \qquad \text{(dynes/cm)(cm)} = \text{(dynes)}, \qquad (10\text{-}17)$$

or

$$S = \sigma^* 1 \qquad \text{(force grams)}. \qquad (10\text{-}17a)$$

Vectors, S, may each be resolved into two components: horizontally and vertically. The horizontal components compensate each other (Fig. 10-9b). The

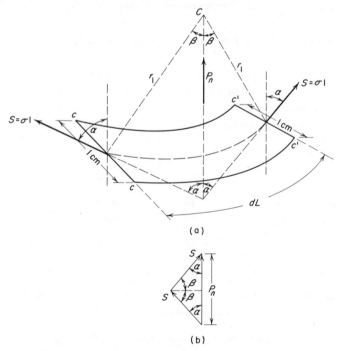

(a)

(b)

FIG. 10-9 Cylindrical surface.

two vertical components caused by the surface tension forces, which in turn are caused by a pressure (unbalanced vertical attraction) pulling inward the boundary surface or air-liquid interface, represent in magnitude the pressure within the liquid. From the vector diagram, in Fig. 10-9 b, the magnitude of the normal (vertical) vector, P_n upon the curved elementary area, $dA = (1)(dL)$, is

$$P_n = 2S \sin \beta = 2S \cos \alpha = 2\sigma 1 \cos \alpha = 2\sigma \cos \alpha, \qquad (10\text{-}18)$$

the units being in dynes, or gram force, depending upon the units in which σ is expressed. For comparison, the normal pressure, P, for a circular capillary tube is

$$P = \sigma 2\pi r \cos \alpha. \qquad (10\text{-}19)$$

Assuming that β is small, set that

$$\sin \beta \approx \widehat{\beta},$$

and

$$\widehat{\beta}r_1 = \frac{dL}{2},$$

where r_1 is the radius of curvature.
Then

$$\widehat{\beta} = \frac{dL}{2r_1}.$$

It follows that the total normal pressure, P_n from Equation (10-18) is

$$P_n = \frac{2S\, dL}{2r_1} = \frac{2\sigma 1\, dL}{2r_1} = \frac{\sigma\, dA}{r_1} \qquad \text{(dynes) or (grams).} \qquad (10\text{-}20)$$

The pressure intensity per unit area, or the compressive stress s_c is:

$$s_c = \frac{P_n}{dA} = \frac{\sigma\, dA}{r_1\, dA} = \frac{\sigma}{r_1} \qquad \text{(dynes/cm}^2\text{), or (g/cm}^2\text{).} \qquad (10\text{-}21)$$

If the surface is curved in two directions perpendicular to each other, then the total compressive stress is the sum of the pressures resulting from the surface tension forces in two directions:

$$s_c = \sigma\left(\frac{1}{r_1} + \frac{1}{r_2}\right), \qquad \text{(dynes/cm}^2\text{) or (g/cm}^2\text{)} \qquad (10\text{-}22)$$

where r_2 is the radius of curvature of the interfacial surface in the other direction. Eq. (10-22) gives the pressure in terms of the principal radii of curvature.
For an interfacial meniscus of the shape of a hemisphere, $r_1 = r_2 = r$, where r is radius of the capillary tube, and simultaneously also the radius of the hemispherical meniscus (contact angle $\alpha = 0$). Then the compressive stress is

$$s_c = \frac{2\sigma}{r}. \qquad (10\text{-}23)$$

This is an excess pressure on one side of the curved surface directed from the convex to the concave side across the curved surface (see. Fig. 10-9 for direction of P_n). Radius of curvature is considered positive when the curvature is convex towards the vapor, and negative when it is concave relative to vapor.

10-10. Capillary Stresses

Capillary Pressure. Equation $s_c = (2\sigma^*)/r$ can also be derived from Equation (10-11) when $\alpha = 0$:

$$h = \frac{2\sigma^*}{\gamma_w r} \quad \text{(cm)}. \tag{10-11a}$$

Multiplying both sides of this equation by γ_w, obtain

$$\gamma_w h = \frac{2\sigma^*}{r} = \frac{4\sigma^*}{d} = s_c = p_c \quad \text{(g/cm}^2 \text{ in force units)}. \tag{10-23a}$$

The quantity $h\gamma_w = p_c$ expresses a hydrostatic pressure. This pressure is caused by the curvature of the boundary surface, viz., surface tension, and is known as the curvature pressure, called here the *capillary pressure*. The surface meniscus transfers its supporting surface tension force from the liquid circumferentially around to the wall of the capillary causing the capillary pressure (↓). This pressure induces in the solid phase (walls of capillary tube, soil particles, or skeleton) a compressive stress equal to the weight of the column of the water. The surface tension causes the water to spread around the idealized, round soil particles, thus inducing a pressure on the solid phase which compresses the particles together. This capillary pressure on the solid phase is also called the *capillary force*.

Capillary Tension. Upon studying the physical phenomenon of capillarity one observes and gets the impression that the column of the capillary water is hanging or suspended at the curved meniscus by means of the surface tension forces. Through such a suspension of the column of the capillary water there is a tensile stress induced upon the liquid phase (water). This tensile stess is called the *capillary tension*, suggesting that the pressure in the capillary water is below atmospheric (subpressure). The magnitude of the tensile stress is equal to $p_t = \gamma_w h$. Thus the principle of force equilibrium, *Actia = Reactia*, i.e., where an active force calls for a reaction, equal and opposite, is here satisfied.

The plane free water surface is considered as the reference plane or datum of zero pressure (atmospheric pressure). Pressures below the free surface of the water are larger than atmospheric, and are designated as positive pressures. Pressures existing in the capillary water between the free surface and the meniscus are less than atmospheric, and are designated as negative pressures, negative hydrostatic pressures, or subpressures. Vice versa, capillary water subjected to a negative hydrostatic pressure is said to be under tension. The word "tension" in this case indicates a pressure deficiency relative to atmospheric pressure. Above the plane free water table the hydrostatic pressure in the capillary water is negative, i.e. $p_t = -\gamma_w h$.

Hence, in water in a capillary tube, as a consequence of the capillary rise of water in the capillary (which in turn is caused by surface tension forces), the pressure is less than atmospheric—the magnitude varying with the height above the plane free water surface. If all voids in the soil were uninterruptedly

filled with capillary water, then, in soil, capillary water could transmit hydrostatic pressure.

Figure 10-10 illustrates graphically stress diagrams in water in a capillary tube
system. The upper end of the capillary tube is open. The liquid-air interface
as well as the free plane water surface are subjected to atmospheric pressure,
p_a. The hydrostatic pressure diagram, representing the state of stress in water

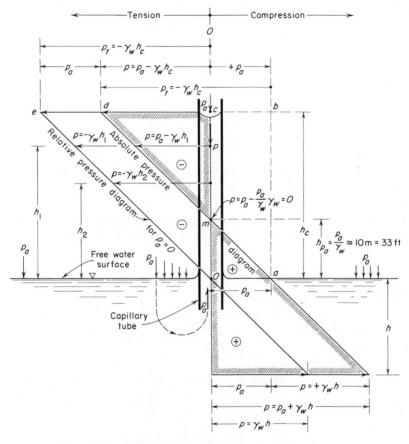

FIG. 10-10 Stress diagrams for water.

in the tube and below the free plane surface, can be plotted in two ways. One
method of plotting a stress diagram is to show absolute pressures, taking into
account atmospheric pressure (diagram o-m-d). The atmospheric pressure
outside the tube can practically be considered as constant (diagram O-a-b-c).
Just below the meniscus in the tube the state of stress is negative, or reduced
below atmospheric, by the amount of $p_t = -\gamma_w h_c$. Thus the absolute stress,
p, in water along the capillary tube above the free, plane water surface can be
expressed at any elevation as

$$p + \gamma_w h - p_a = 0,$$

or

$$p = p_a - \gamma_w h = p_a - p_t \qquad \text{(dynes/cm}^2) \text{ or (g/cm}^2) \qquad (10\text{-}24)$$

Eq. (10-24) tells the following: as long as the capillary height, h, does not exceed 10.33 m = 32.18 ft = p_a = 1 atm = 14.7 lb/in.[2] the stress, p, in the capillary water, viz., pore water in soil, cannot be negative. When the capillary height is $h > 10.33$ m (32.81 ft), there must be tensile stresses in the liquid.

Just below the meniscus, the pressure is

$$p = p_a - \gamma_w h_c = p_a - \frac{2\sigma^*}{r} \qquad (10\text{-}24a)$$

The absolute stess ordinates characterizing hydrostatic pressure conditions in water below the free, plane water surface are calculated as

$$p = p_a + p_t = p_a + \gamma_w h. \qquad (10\text{-}25)$$

This indicates that the hydrostatic pressure ($\gamma_w h$) is here increased by the atmospheric pressure, p_a.

Another method is to plot the stress diagram assuming that the atmospheric pressure is a relative zero pressure, see diagram O-c-e, Fig. 10-10. Then the pressure ordinates for the capillary tube in this diagram are expressed as $p_t = -\gamma_w h$, indicating reduced pressure, or pressure deficiency relative to atmospheric pressure. The magnitude of the hydrostatic pressure in this system of presentation is $p = \gamma_w h$.

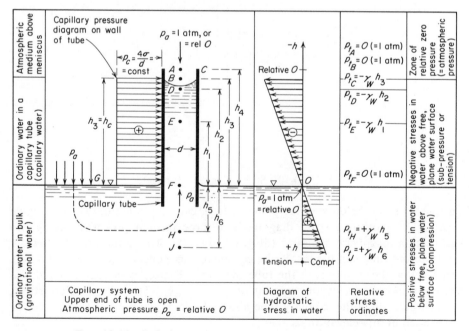

FIG. 10-11   Relative stress conditions in a capillary system.

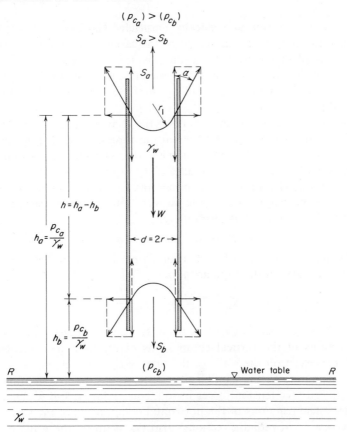

$$(p_{c_a}) > (p_{c_b})$$

$$S_a > S_b$$

FIG. 10-12   A vertically suspended capillary.

Detailed relative pressure conditions in a capillary system, assuming atmospheric pressure as relative zero pressure, or zero pressure reference, are illustrated in Fig. 10-11. In this figure it can be seen that atmospheric pressure exists at points A, B, F and G. Points F and G are at the same level and under atmospheric pressure, or relative zero pressure. Because points E, D, and C are in the medium of the capillary water, and are higher than point F, by the capillary heads h_1, h_2, and h_3, respectively, the hydrostatic pressures at E, D, and C are less than atmospheric by the amount of $\gamma_w h_1$, $\gamma_w h_2$, and $\gamma_w h_3$, respectively. Thus, for points located above the free plane surface of water the hydrostatic pressure in the capillary tube becomes negative, which has a conventional meaning only. The negative sign of this negative hydrostatic pressure indicates only that pressure within the capillary fringe is less than that at the ground-water table. The pressures below the free, plane water surface are above atmospheric by the amounts of $\gamma_w h_5$ at point H, and $\gamma_w h_6$ at point J, respectively.

The capillary pressure, $p_c = (4\sigma)/d$, transmitted to the wall of the tube, as seen from this equation, is constant throughout the height of capillary rise.

10-11. Surface Tension in Vertically Suspended Capillaries. If the free plane surface of water is removed, as would be the case in lowering the ground-water table, for example, then the water in the tube may translocate downward under the influence of gravity force; or it may remain suspended in the capillary tube, viz., soil, as a liquid column with both its ends free, and endowed with a meniscus at each end (Fig. 10-12).

The suspended condition depends upon the relative value of gravity; the diameter of the capillary orifice; surface tension forces, which are, in their turn, a function of temperature; the contact angle α; the concentration of soluble matter in the liquid and, of course, the nature of the liquid itself.

The curvatures, viz., radii, of the upper and lower menisci are here different, and therefore the magnitude of the surface tension forces (sometimes called the moisture lifting forces), is also different:

$$S_a \neq S_b, \quad \text{or} \quad \sigma_a \neq \sigma_b.$$

The difference in these surface tension forces is equal to the weight, W, of the column of water in the capillary tube:

$$S_a - S_b = W = \gamma_w \frac{\pi d^2}{4} h, \tag{10-26}$$

a weight which can be imagined as being suspended at the upper meniscus.

The reactions of the vertical components of the obliquely directed surface tension forces exert on the walls of the tube, viz., soil skeleton, a compression equal in magnitude to the capillary pressure. Thus, as a consequence of the action of the surface tension forces in soil, consolidation and settlement of soil takes place. The reactions of the horizontal components of the surface tension forces are (acting in radial directions) also taken up by the walls of the tube. Physically, relative to soil, these latter force components exert on a soil mass a shrinkage effect upon drying.

The position of the free plane reference surface below the upper end of the capillary tube is

$$h_a = \frac{4S_a}{\pi d^2 \gamma_w}, \quad \text{(cm)} \tag{10-27}$$

or, expressed in terms of capillary pressure, p_{c_a}

$$h_a = \frac{p_{c_a}}{\gamma_w} = \frac{2\sigma_a}{r\gamma_w} \quad \text{(cm)} \tag{10-28}$$

The distance of the lower end of the tube from the free plane reference surface is

$$h_b = \frac{4S_b}{\pi d^2 \gamma_w} \quad \text{(cm)} \tag{10-29}$$

or

$$h_b = \frac{p_{c_b}}{\gamma_w} = \frac{2\sigma_b}{r\gamma_w} \quad \text{(cm)} \tag{10-30}$$

All force units are expressed here in weight grams.

The height of the capillary column of water, h, by Eqs. (10-28) and (10-30), or the difference in subpressure heads is

$$h = h_a - h_b = \frac{2}{r\gamma_w}(\sigma_a - \sigma_b). \qquad (10\text{-}31)$$

If $h_b = 0$, Eq. (10-31) transforms into Eq. (10-28).

10-12. Suspended Water in Soil. Suspended water in soil is observed in nature in the rapid draw-down of a water table, for example, on emptying a reservoir quickly, or on lowering the ground-water table. If upon such a lowering the continuity of the capillary fringe is disrupted, or torn off, the former capillary fringe can be imagined as hanging, or suspended.

Also, suspended water in soil can be encountered under the following conditions (see Fig. 10-13). If the upper layer of silt or peat possesses capillary properties and its capillaries are saturated, then the soil water in the sand layer

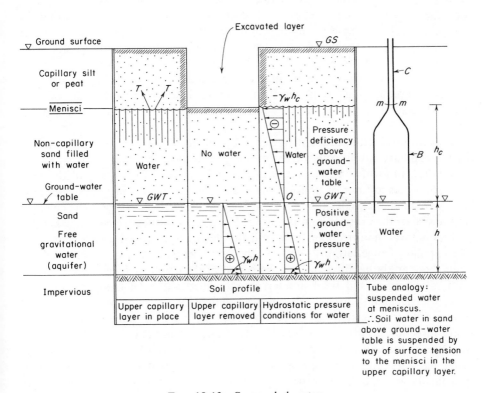

FIG. 10-13 Suspended water.

(assume the latter as having non-capillary properties) may be hanging from the menisci of the peat. This phenomenon is analogous to that where a glass bell, B, with a capillary tube, C, at its top is immersed into water and pulled out again as shown in Figs. 10-13 and 10-6. The water is imagined as suspended at the meniscus, *m-m*. The suspension of water from the upper layer of soil possessing capillary properties can take place during lowering of the gravitational water after high tides or floods. In foundation work or highway construction, upon the removal of the upper capillary silt or peat layer (removal of upper menisci), water will drain out from the sand layer into the aquifer below the ground-water table. The hydrostatic pressure conditions for suspended and free water are also shown in Fig. 10-13.

SURFACE TENSION IN SOIL

10-13. Capillary Height in Soil. The term capillarity has been initially referred to as the action of liquids in tubes of fine bore. However, the term has since come to be used to indicate a wide variety of phenomena in connection with the translocation of liquids through a porous medium such as soil, for example. But in soil the conditions relative to surface tension, ascent or descent, and their associated compressive and tensile stresses are more complex than in a capillary tube. Instead of circular and straight capillary tubes, there are in soil irregularly shaped voids—a network of small, irregular cellular units with widenings and constrictions. The soil voids communicate with each other through narrow necks as water rings at the contact points of the soil particles.

Discontinuous moisture in soil forms wedges of water in the corners of contact between adjacent soil particles and other points, and moisture films around the particles.

In contradistinction to the diameter of hypothetical capillary tubes, the height of the capillary rise in soils varies inversely with the size of the voids or pores. The latter, in turn, is a function of the particle size and the density of the soil. The soil pores are not of uniform diameter, but are of different sizes. Besides, these irregular "capillary tubes" in soil are not necessarily vertical. The changes in the size of the cross section of the voids control the effective capillary height.

In a natural, uniformly textured soil the height of soil moisture ascent, viz., the capillary fringe, attains relatively the same height, whereas in non-uniform soils there are large differences in the height of the capillary fringe.

If all voids in soil were uninterruptedly filled with soil moisture, the soil moisture, depending upon the direction and intensity of driving potentials, ordinarily would translocate in all directions. The moisture translocation in a downward direction is aided by gravity forces. Besides, different types of soils limit the size of the voids, viz., the height of the capillary fringe. The sizes of coarse sand particles, for example, are relatively so large that such a soil possesses practically no capillary properties. In coarse-textured soils, the voids of which are larger than capillaries, or when water enters soil cracks—both cases involving no surface tension control—then such water is rather more correctly classified as gravitational water, and not as capillary water.

The surface tension phenomenon and the ascent of soil moisture are most pronounced in soils composed mainly of fine sands, silts, or silty clays. The particle size of silt is enough smaller than that of sands to afford considerable height of moisture ascent above the groundwater table, and, at the same time, large enough to provide voids of such a size as to permit rapid translocation of soil moisture through them. This tendency of silt results in the rapid loss of the stability of such a soil under certain conditions.

Clays are made up of very fine particles exhibiting great heights of soil moisture ascents, approximately twice those of silts, but the velocity of flow is slow. This explains, in part, as well as the large specific surface areas of such soils, why the voids between the scaly particles of clay are usually filled with much moisture.

Also, the magnitudes of capillary pressures which can occur in clays are very large. For example, for a void size the diameter of which is 0.2μ, which gives at $\alpha = 0$ a radius of curvature of the meniscus of 0.1μ, the capillary pressure, with $\sigma^* = 75/981 = 76.4 \times 10^{-3}$ g/cm, can be calculated as

$$p_c = \frac{2\sigma^*}{r} = \frac{(2)(76.4)(10^{-3})}{10^{-5}} = 15280 \text{ (g/cm}^2) = 15.3 \text{ (kg/cm}^2) \approx 15.3 \text{ (t/ft}^2).$$

The dependance of the capillary height on the particle size of the soil is shown in Table 10-5. The values given are for a closed capillary fringe, i.e., active capillary heights. The values shown are average values for average conditions.

TABLE 10-5. CAPILLARY HEIGHTS OF SOILS

Soil	Fractions, mm		Capillary Height, h_c cm	Stress, p_c kg/cm² ($\sim$ t/ft²)
1	2		3	4
Fine gravel	2	to 1	2 to 10	0.002 to 0.010
Coarse sand	1	to 0.5	10 to 15	0.010 to 0.015
Medium sand	0.5	to 0.25	15 to 30	0.015 to 0.030
Fine sand	0.25	to 0.05	30 to 100	0.030 to 0.10
Silt	0.05	to 0.005	100 to 1000	0.10 to 1.00
Clay	0.005	to 0.0005	1000 to 3000	1.00 to 3.00
Colloids		<0.0005	3000 and more	3.00 and more

10-14. Determination of Capillary Height. The capillary height of soil is determined directly in the laboratory by means of a long, transparent tube, the upper end of which is open, and the lower end of which is covered with a screen to support the soil to be tested in the tube.

The lower end of the tube is immersed into water, and the maximum height of the capillary rise above the free plane surface of water outside the tube observed. This method of measuring the capillary height of soil is applicable practically only for coarse-textured soils with relatively low capillary height—say up to about 3 to 5 ft. For soils exhibiting greater capillary heights than about 5 ft or about 150 cm, this method, because of the necessary long tubes and difficult packing of soil, becomes very inconvenient. Besides, in sandy soils the maximum capillary height is attained in a relatively short time, whereas in fine-grained soils, such as silts and clays, the rise takes place during a long period of time, for example over several weeks, months, and even years. Thus, the direct method for observing capillary heights in fine soils is extremely inconvenient. Therefore different methods and devices should be used, for example, capillarimeters.

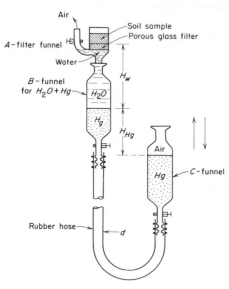

FIG. 10-14   Beskow's capillarimeter.

One of the best-known methods for the determination of capillary height of fine-textured soils is the hydrostatic (sub-pressure) method, utilized, for example, in the Beskow type capillarimeter[10] (see Fig. 10-14).

In this apparatus undisturbed as well as disturbed soil samples can be tested for capillary height. The soil sample is connected to the water column by means of surface tension forces. Upon lowering funnel C a subpressure (suction) is induced in the water-mercury system. The lowering of funnel C is continued until the contact between the water and the soil sample above the glass filter is broken, and air bubbles start to work through the soil sample. This means that at this moment the surface tension force of water to the soil sample can no longer hold from below the water-mercury column suspended at the soil sample.

The combined difference between the water level under the soil sample and the mercury level in funnel C, gives the length of that column. The capillary height at a certain temperature is then calculated as

$$h_c = H_w + (13.6)H_{Hg} \qquad (10\text{-}32)$$

centimeters of water column, and as

$$p_c = \gamma_w h_c \qquad (\text{g/cm}^2). \qquad (10\text{-}33)$$

The capillary heights as determined by this method are the minimum heights which are dependent upon the largest pore sizes in the soil sample. This means that at places where the voids are finer than those which determine the minimum capillary height, the capillary height in nature may be greater than that determined in the laboratory by means of Beskow's capillarimeter.

Beskow's capillarimeter has the following limitation: capillary heights cannot be measured higher than approx. 10 m ($\approx$ 33 ft), because at pressures close to below 1 atmosphere water releases dissolved air in the form of bubbles, so that sometimes it is difficult to tell whether the appearance of the air bubbles underneath the glass filter originates from sucking air through the soil sample, or whether the bubbles originate from the water between the soil sample and mercury. Besides, this air facilitates the tearing off of the suction water from the soil sample. Also, as mentioned before, the capillary height is measured for the largest void sizes filled with water as exhibiting the least resistance to tearing off of the capillary menisci. However, relative to frost problems, the finer voids of frost-susceptible soils permitting the ascent of soil moisture to greater heights are of considerable importance.

10-15. Effect of Surface Tension on a Soil Mass.

Intergranular Pressure. At all points where moisture menisci touch soil particles, surface tension forces act, causing a grain-to-grain pressure within the soil similar to that of the capillary tube in compression under the surface tension forces. This grain-to-grain pressure is recognized as the *capillary pressure*, and is also called in soil mechanics the *intergranular*, or *contact*, or *effective pressure*. This intergranular pressure tends to force the solid particles together with a pressure equal and opposite to the tension through the water.

These compressive stresses on the soil skeleton contribute to the strength and stability of the soil mass. This surface tension-induced strength of soil under proper conditions of particle size, temperature, salinity, and other factors permits it to bear the weight of the heaviest auto races for speed and drag, as for example, the auto races held on the famous Daytona Beach in Florida.

The surface tension forces are relatively immense in magnitude, and during the landing operations in France by the Allied Forces have proved to be able to support on beaches heavy equipment such as tanks, guns, and construction machinery.

The surface tension-induced strength, p_c, of soil, however, is only temporary in character and may be destroyed entirely upon the full saturation of soil or inundation of the soil material by, for example, high tides or during flood conditions, because inundation eliminates interface menisci, and the contact pressure, p_c, reduces to zero.

The compressive stress, p_c, of the surface tension forces-induced strength of soil is termed after Terzaghi the "*apparent cohesion*", or, as suggested by Johann Ohde, the "suction strength" (Saugfestigkeit).

Lowering of Capillary Fringe. The effect of surface tension forces on the performance of soils is, thus, very significant. Let this significance be cited by another example, Capillary moisture, contrary to free gravitational water, cannot be drained out of the soil, particularly from silt and clay, by any system of drainage (gravitational) installed within the capillary fringe. This is because capillary moisture is held within the soil by surface tension forces, and the capillary flow does not obey the law of gravity.

However, if the groundwater table is lowered (drainage facility installed in gravitational water, or pumping operations applied), the whole capillary fringe might be lowered. The clear establishment of the lowered capillary fringe takes place slowly with a great time lag, after the thermo-osmotic flow of capillary moisture has stabilized.

The fact that capillary moisture cannot be drained out of soils can be illustrated by the following experiment (Fig. 10-15).

Two transparent tubes with screened bottoms, one of which is provided with

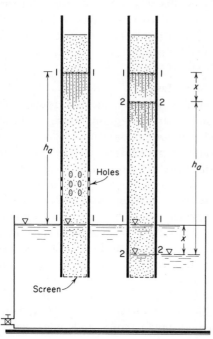

perforations in the cylindrical walls, are filled with capillary soil and immersed in water. After some time the active capillary height, h_c, can be observed in both cylinders. When the water table in the pan is lowered by an amount of x (from position 1 down to position 2), there is established after some time approximately the same capillary height, h_c, above the lowered water table. This indicates that in treating a practical case, as for example in the case of a highway, which is built on soil with a high capillary rise and where the frost penetration reaches within the so-called capillary fringe, it is useless to install drains within the zone of capillary fringe in order to remove the capillary moisture. The groundwater table has to be lowered, or the fill raised, or layers of coarse soil or artificial, tight, impermeable membranes should be introduced to break capillary ascent.

FIG. 10-15. A capillary experiment.

10-16. Capillary Siphoning Phenomenon. One of the ways by which water may be lost from a storage reservoir is by capillary siphoning over the crest of the impervious core of an earth dam, as illustrated in Fig. 10-16. Siphoning takes place if the crest is not sufficiently high.

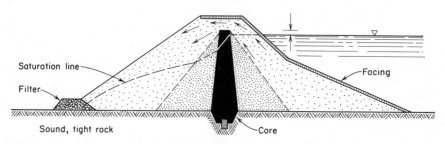

FIG. 10-16 Capillary siphoning over the crest of an impervious core of an earth dam.

Capillarity in soils is also an important factor entering into under-ground reservoir calculations and exploitations, for example, in the petroleum industry.

10-17. Stress Conditions in Soil Caused by Surface Tension Forces.

The Closed Capillary Fringe. The effect of action of surface tension forces in a porous soil mass is analogous to that of a uniformly distributed load placed on the ground surface. The magnitude of this load is determined by the height of the closed and open capillary fringes which cause the additional pressure on the soil mass. The closed capillary fringe of a height of h_c above the ground-water table exerts a compressive stress on the soil mass the magnitude of which is

$$p_c = \gamma_w h_c n \qquad (10\text{-}34)$$

where γ_w = unit weight of water, and
$\quad n$ = porosity of soil.

Also, it can be said that the soil moisture increases the unit weight of a soil so that the pressure ordinates in the soil vertical pressure diagram are now increased by a constant amount, p_c, of capillary pressure (Fig. 10-17). For

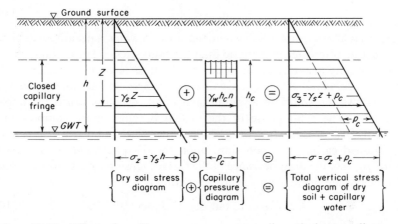

FIG. 10-17   Effect of capillary pressure, p_c, on soil vertical stress diagram.

example, the vertical stress of a soil (self-weight) and the moisture acting on a unit area can be expressed as

$$\sigma = \sigma_s + p_c = \gamma_s h + \gamma_w h_c n, \qquad (10\text{-}35)$$

where γ_s = unit weight of the soil,
$\quad h$ = thickness of the soil layer.

If the capillary water in soil causes an additional load upon the solid particles, then the effect of this penomenon on soil would be its tendency to decrease the swelling pressure of a soil.

The capillary pressure, the head of which is h_c, acts within the soil mass in all directions, and, as shown before, is in addition to the principal stresses, σ_{s1}, and $\sigma_{s2} = \sigma_{s3}$, i.e.

$$\sigma_\downarrow = \sigma_{s1} + \gamma_w h_c, \text{ and}$$

$$\sigma_\rightarrow = \sigma_{s3} + \gamma_w h_c.$$

The whole thickness of the soil layer in question, h, is affected by the additional height and weight of the closed capillary fringe by the additional load, p_c, because it can be imagined that the capillary moisture might be attached and suspended to the surfaces of the menisci.

The soil moisture in the open capillary fringe rises above the groundwater table a distance of $(h_c + h_0)$ units. However, the intergranular or effective pressures in the zone of the open capillary fringe are less when compared to those caused by the closed capillary fringe. This is because not all of the voids are filled with water.

Again, to understand stress conditions in capillary soils, remember that the surface tension forces induce a tensile stress in capillary water, and a compressive stress (effective or intergranular stress) upon the skeleton of the soil.

The total pressure or stress, σ_t, is the sum of the effective (intergranular) stress, $\sigma_e = p_c$, and the neutral stress, u, which is the stress due to water pressure:

$$\sigma_t = \sigma_e + u. \tag{10-36}$$

One sees that at all points in soil where the stress in water is negative, the effective stress must be of greater magnitude than the total stress. The amount by which it is greater is numerically equal to the tensile stress in capillary water.

Apparent Cohesion. The capillary or effective pressure, as can now be understood, endows the soil with an additional bond, which is called the apparent cohesion, c. The solid phase of the system becomes more compressed and densified by this pressure, the effect of which is consolidation of the soil material. As mentioned earlier, this cohesion, upon the disappearance of the capillary pressure, p_c, viz., the disappearance of the surface tension forces, also disappears.

The magnitude of this "apparent" strength c is

$$c = p_c \tan \phi, \quad (\text{kg/cm}^2) \tag{10-37}$$

where ϕ = angle of internal friction, and
  $\tan \phi$ = coefficient of internal friction of the soil material.

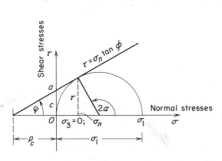

FIG. 10-18 $c = p_c \tan \phi$.

These quantities can be seen on the Mohr's stress diagram in Fig. 10-18. This figure, as well as Eq. (10-37) show that, knowing the angle of internal friction of the material, and knowing also the value of p_c, the major principal stress, σ_1, of soil, which is the unconfined compression strength of soil, can be obtained. In this figure, τ is the shear stress in soil, but σ_n is the normal stress in soil at a point on the rupture plane. The angle, α, is known as the angle of rupture, i.e., the angle between the rupture plane and the horizontal.

Apparent cohesion permits the excavation of deep cuts in soil without shoring up the excavation walls. However, with an increase in moisture in the voids of the soil the surface tension forces may become destroyed, and after the amount of excess water in the soil has reached a certain magnitude, the walls of the excavation slump out and collapse.

GENERAL CONCLUSIONS ABOUT THE
SURFACE TENSION PHENOMENON IN SOIL

10-18. Summary.

1) Surface tension forces are significant in that they affect the strength and performance of soil under load, water, and temperature.

2) Surface tension phenomenon has more practical significance in fine-particled soils, the particle size of which is $d \leqslant 0.1$ mm, rather than in coarse-textured soils.

3) In the soil, the radius of curvature of the menisci of the soil-water interfaces depends upon the amount of the moisture content present, as well as upon certain characteristics of the soil skeleton itself, for instance, the size of the soil particles, the specific surface of the particles, chemical nature of the constituent minerals, salinity of the liquid, as well as soil temperature.

4) Neutral stresses, u, in water within the capillary fringe are below atmospheric pressure (absolute pressures); or they are negative based on the gage system, if atmospheric pressure is considered as the relative pressure.

5) Tension in water can be regarded as the negative hydrostatic pressure of water.

6) The compressive, viz., tensile stresses depend upon the radius of curvature of the surface menisci.

7) The capillary pressure endows the soil with an additional bond.

8) Because of the capillary pressure, the soil receives an additional, uniformly distributed load, which in its turn contributes to the consolidation of soil by its own weight.

9) Upon drying of soil, the capillary pressure increases. It ceases at the shrinkage limit.

10) Upon inundation, surface tension forces are destroyed.

11) The soil does not consist of "bundles of capillary tubes". However, the surface tension phenomenon helps us to understand the performance of soil under the influence of load, water, and temperature.

12) In capillary translocation of moisture in capillary tubes as well as in soil, all voids should be full of water between the groundwater and surface menisci at the top of the "capillary" column.

ELECTROKINETICS OF SOIL-WATER SYSTEMS
THE STRUCTURE OF WATER MOLECULE

10-19. Polarity. According to Debye[11,12,13], a molecule of water can be represented as a system of electrical charges arranged in a *polar structure*.

The polar structure of water molecules is due to a non-symmetrical distribution of electrical charges in the individual atoms entering into the contents of the molecules. Therefore, in a certain region of the molecule there is a surplus of positive electrical charge, but in others there exists a surplus of negative electrical charge. One would expect that in the polar water molecules electrical poles would exist. Hence, water is designated as a polar substance. Fig. 10-19a shows a simplified diagrammatic representation of the geometrical arrangement of the atoms in a polar water molecule. The "plus" and the "minus" poles form a dipole. Therefore, generally, polar molecules are called dipoles.

It is interesting to note that according to Partington[14] the existence of separated positive and negative charges in molecules was assumed by Berzelius, who called this state *polarization*, comparing it with the polarity of magnets.

If indeed such "polar" molecules exist, one must expect that the action of an energy field upon the medium consisting of polar molecules will disclose electric properties in it by virtue of the directive action of the field, because it will tend to set the positive to negative axes of the molecule in the direction of its own lines of force. Thus, within the molecule of water, there must occur an orientation of the polar molecules or dipoles.

(a) Simplified representation of a polar water molecule
The $\oplus$ and $\ominus$ poles form a dipole

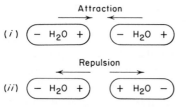

(b) Mutual orientation of polar water molecules:
    (*i*) Stability (attraction)
    (*ii*) Instability (repulsion)

FIG. 10-19 Diagrammatic illustration of polar water molecules.

The property—polarity—of water is very important in that it gives water the ability to support ionization. Ionization is a process which results in the formation of ions in a certain medium, in this case, water. The polarity of water can thus be considered a link in the mechanism of the soil moisture transfer in the moisture film phase.

10-20. Orientation of Water Molecules. Because of the presence of electrical charges the polar water molecules have among themselves a mutual electrostatic interaction and orientation, namely: the positive pole of one molecule is attracted to the negative pole of another molecule, and vice versa. For example, in Fig. 10-19bi the two molecules attract each other and are said to be stable. Fig. 10-19bii indicates a mutual repulsion between two water molecules. They are said to be instable. As a result of mutual interaction, polar molecules of one and the same substance combine among themselves and form complexes with the ions, leading to associations. Fig. 10-20 illustrates the concept of attraction of dipole water molecules by a positive ion called a cation. In the case of a negative ion, the attraction and orientation of dipole water molecules is the converse of that shown in Fig. 10-20.

Associating liquids, for example, are water, acetone, liquid ammonia, and other ionizing solvents.

10-21. Electrical Charge on Surface of Colloidal Particles. Water molecules forming moisture films or hulls around the solid soil particles are not the only factors that are adsorbed on the surfaces of solid soil particles. One of the conspicuous characteristics of a soil particle in a medium of water is that under certain conditions it carries an electrical charge, which, in contrast to heat, tends to reside on its surface.

The charge on the particle is usually the result of adsorption of ions. The soil particles acquire their electric charges from naturally occurring solutions which act as electrolytes, the molecules of which upon solution separate into electrically charged units or ions. For example, a molecule of table salt consisting of a Na-atom and a Cl-atom upon solution divides into positively charged ions of Na and negatively charged ions of Cl. The more finely the soil is dispersed, the greater is its specific surface. Consequently, more ions can be accommodated on the surfaces of the soil particles. However, it must be understood that this simple explanation

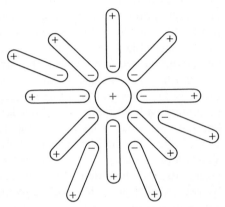

FIG. 10-20   Attraction and orientation of dipole water molecules by a positive ion.

of the manner by which soil collodial particles acquire their electric charges is far more complex in reality.

The sign of the charge is different for various substances. However, the particles carry the same kind of charge if all of the soil colloidal particles are of the same matter in a certain solution. The nature and magnitude of the charge varies greatly with the liquid used as a dispersion medium. For instance, the character of this charge on the surface of a clay colloid particle in water is usually negative[15].

10-22. The Electric Double Layer. The purpose of discussing the electric double layer is to relate this subject to an understanding of the orientation of the polar dipole water molecule and soil moisture migration when the soil system is placed in an electric field, or when subjected to a thermal gradient.

If a soil particle is considered individually and immersed in water, then from the previous description it can be deduced that the solid particle is surrounded by an *electric double layer*. One layer of this double layer is formed by the negative charge on the surface of the soil colloidal (clay) particle. The negatively charged soil particles tend to surround themselves with an ionic atmosphere, i.e., with ions of the opposite charge (cations), thus forming the second layer of the electrical double layer—the outer layer. This outer layer is formed by the excess of the oppositely charged ions in the solution (water). This means that polar molecules of water may be oriented at the interface between the solid soil particle and the dispersion medium—water.

10-23. Helmholtz's Electric Double Layer. Historically, Quincke[16] suggested that the solid particle in contact with the liquid becomes charged in some way with an electrical charge while in the immediate vicinity of the surface of the solid, but in the liquid there is a layer of electrical charges of the opposite kind, exactly equal in magnitude to the charge on the solid. This was the origin of the so-called double layer theory conceived by Quincke, usually called the Helmholtz double layer because of the fact that Helmholtz[17] formulated theoretically the concept of the existence of differently charged layers—the so-called electrical double layer—at the solid-liquid interface in a mathematical form expressing the relation between the various physical quantities involved.

According to Helmholtz, an electrical double layer of a fixed thickness—of the order of magnitude of one molecule—forms at the interface of any phase in contact with a liquid. The outer layer of oppositely charged ions is mobile, and the inner layer, which lies in the liquid, is rigid, adhering firmly to the wall of the solid. The mobile layer neutralizes the oppositely charged surface layer. This simple concept of the Quincke-Helmholtz electrical double layer is diagrammatically illustrated in Fig. 10-21. The double layer could be represented by two parallel, flat, electrical condenser plates. Such electrical double layers are supposed to exist not only at plane surfaces but also surrounding the solid colloidal soil (clay) particles suspended in a liquid medium such as water.

It is also interesting to note that Helmholtz formulated the following: The layer of water molecules in contact with the wall of the solid particles is immobile. It is fixed to the wall regardless of the physical forces imposed on the liquid. That is, there is no slip. The rest of the molecules in the double layer are mobile and subject to the ordinary laws of friction of normal liquids.

10-24. Zeta (ζ) Potential. It was seen that, in general, when two phases—solid and liquid—come in contact there is a separation of charges: one phase becomes negative in respect to the other. This separation of charges gives rise to an electric potential difference or a potential gradient at the interface between the two phases. According to Helmholtz, the gradient of this potential drop across the double layer is sharp and it varies linearly with distance (Fig. 10-21a). The electric potential across the double layer is called the *electrokinetic or zeta potential.*

The difference in cross potentials at the interface of two phases when there is no mutual relative motion is called the thermodynamic potential, or the Nernst Potential (ε). It is the potential difference created at the interface upon the mutual relative movement of two phases which is called the electrokinetic or zeta potential. This means that the electrokinetic potential can be measured only under conditions of phases in motion relative to each other, i.e., when electrokinetic processes are taking place.

Usually the electrokinetic (ζ) potential is considerably less than the thermo-dynamic potential, and under some circumstances can even have an opposite sign of ε.

It is conceived that the zeta potential has a major part in the electrical properties of colloidal (soil) systems. Also, it is most important because its value is often connected with the stability and viscosity of suspensions. The ions in the double layer attract water. The amount of water taken up will influence the viscosity. Thus the viscosity of the liquid will not only be influenced by the quantity of electrolyte present, but also by the kind of ions.

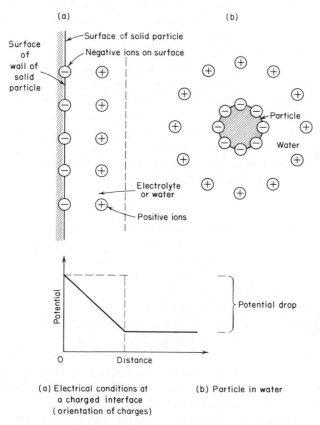

(a) Electrical conditions at
a charged interface
(orientation of charges)

(b) Particle in water

FIG. 10-21   The Quincke-Helmholtz electrical double layer.

One more word has to be said here. There exists an important difference between surface tension and viscosity of a liquid, namely: surface tension is essentially a surface phenomenon, whereas viscosity is concerned with the internal properties of a liquid. Therefore, it can be expected that viscosity will respond with great sensitiveness to changes in the molecular configuration of the liquid. This explains the importance of the zeta potential and viscosity of the dispersion medium (here, water) in research.

The concept that the colloidal soil particles carry an electrical charge might give one the mistaken impression that the soil represents an aggregate of statically charged ideal spheres, and that an electroscope, therefore, when brought close to the soil (in situ, or a laboratory sample), would show a deflection. However, this is not so. It has to be remembered from the previous discussion that the electrical charges in the system are self-compensating. This principle finds its validity in the idea of the electrical double layer.

10-25. Gouy Double Layer. In the course of time it was revealed that the Helmholtz model of the double layer is inadequate because the thermal motions of the liquid molecules could scarcely permit such a rigid array of charges at the surface of the solid particle. Scientists came to the conclusion that the electrical double layer at the interface could not be rigid, as was originally assumed, and of fixed thickness equal to the diameter of a molecule.

Gouy[18] thought that the charges of one sign in the liquid side of the Helmholtz double layer would attract charges of opposite sign. This attraction, in its turn, would cause a non-uniform distribution of the charges in the liquid near the solid-liquid interface that Helmholtz proposed. Gouy's ideas about the electrical conditions at the solid-liquid interface are principally as follows: the rigid part of the electric double layer lies in the liquid adhering firmly to the surface of the solid particle; the second part lies in the mobile part of the liquid and extends into the homogeneous interior of the liquid.

Movement of the liquid takes place against the liquid adhering firmly to the surface of the solid, and thus the charge is imbedded in it, but not against the solid surface directly. At very low temperatures ions are rigidly adsorbed on the surface, thus forming a true Helmholtz layer. With increase in temperature— the room temperature, for example—a large amount of the adsorbed ions "dissipate" from the surface. However, these ions are unable to escape entirely from the influence of the charge on the wall.

The distributions of ions in the rigid part of the double layer is governed by the mutual interaction of electrostatic forces and specific energy of adsorption, as well as by the presence of molecular heat movement. The distribution of ions in the mobile part of the double layer is governed by electrostatic forces and by thermal action. Electrostatic forces concentrate the oppositely-charged ions around the solid particle, but the forces of the molecular heat movement tend to distribute ions uniformly within the liquid phase.

Owing to these circumstances, a *diffuse* double layer results, where the negative charges are adsorbed primarily near the surface or wall of the solid particle, but the positive ions farther away from the wall. The ionic atmosphere in the immediate vicinity of the surface is fairly dense, and at greater distances from the surface the ionic density decreases until the net charge density is zero.

While not all the ions in the diffuse double layer are of the opposite sign from those at the surface of the solid, the ions of opposite sign do predominate. Thus Gouy and Chapman[19] imagined the double layer as a diffuse distribution of electrification, an "ionic atmosphere". Also, Gouy supposed that the double layer frequently extends considerably farther out from the solid surface into the liquid phase than a distance of one molecule.

Gouy termed the outer part of the double layer *diffuse* because there the ion concentration decreases with the increase in distance from the surface of the solid particle. In consequence of this, the electrical density of the ionic atmosphere drops off away from the wall into the interior of the liquid according to an exponential law, in contradistinction to Helmholtz's linear rule, which calls for a sharp drop in the ζ-potential gradient at the interface. The Gouy-Chapman diffuse double layer and the drop in zeta potential are illustrated diagrammatically in Fig. 10-22.

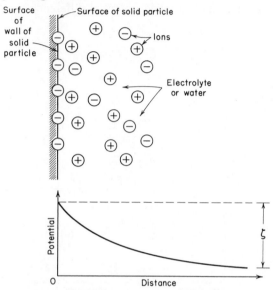

FIG. 10-22   Gouy-Chapman electric diffuse double layer.

The thickness of the double layer, according to Rutgers[20] is of the order of 10^{-6} or 10^{-7} cm.

Because the diffuse layer extends some distance into the water phase, it is necessary in soil moisture migration studies, particularly upon freezing, to take into account the dielectric constant of water. This constant may probably be assigned the value it has in pure water.

10-26. Stern Double Layer. More recently, Stern[21] showed that neither the sharp nor the diffuse double layer theory alone is adequate. He presented a view combining the essential features of both. As in the Helmholtz layer, in Stern's proposition there is a rigidly attached charge on the surface of the solid. Then, immediately adjacent to the surface, there exists a layer with a charge opposite to that which is fixed on the surface of the solid (Fig. 10-23). This layer adjacent to the surface is approximately one ion thick, and it is almost rigidly adsorbed to the surface of the solid; thus, this thin layer can be considered as practically immobile. This layer, one ion in thickness, is part of Stern's double layer. In this almost fixed layer, there is a sharp drop (AB) in potential such as the one that exists in the Helmholtz layer.

Adjacent to this single-ion layer but farther away into the bulk of liquid, there is the second part of Stern's double layer which is diffuse in character.

Here the charges may be of the same sign as, or opposite to, that of the adsorbed layer. Because the electrostatic field at the surface results in a preferential adsorption of the oppositely charged ions, the distribution of positive and negative ions in the diffuse part of the double layer is non-uniform. Thermal agitation in this part of the double layer allows the particles to translocate freely. Also, the diffuse part is free to move when the whole soil system is subjected at boths its ends to an externally applied potential difference.

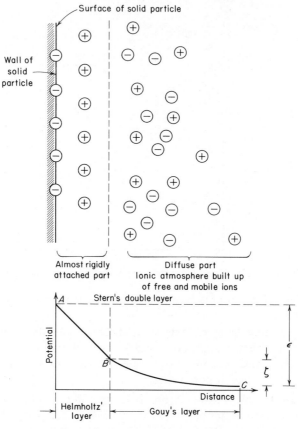

FIG. 10-23   Stern's double layer.

Freundlich[22] has some comments to make relative to the dependence of the electrokinetic phenomena upon the nature and concentration of the electrolyte present in the solution. It is his opinion that at high concentrations of electrolytes the electrokinetic phenomena will become insignificant and may disappear for the simple reason that the double layer will no longer reach far enough into the liquid; that at the point where the layer of liquid adhering to the wall passes over into the mobile liquid, appreciable differences of potential will no longer exist. Besides the influence of concentration, the increase in conductivity causes a diminution in electrokinetic action.

10-27. The Structure of Colloidal Particles. In order to elucidate the nature of water-film attached to the surface of a colloidal (mineral) soil particle, it is necessary to familiarize one's self with the present-day concepts of the structure of a colloidal particle and the mutual interaction of mineral particles with the aqueous solution which surrounds the particles. These concepts are borrowed from colloid science and are utilized for the explanation of the so-called electrokinetic phenomena in soils, particularly in fine-particled soils such as silts, clays, and clay colloids.

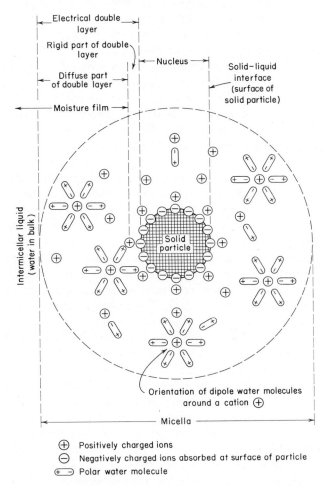

Fig. 10-24 Schematic sketch of a colloidal micella.

When solid particles such as those of a colloidal clay are dispersed in liquids, as may occur with soil *in situ*, then there are many individual systems which consist of a charged nucleus surrounded by adsorbed and more-or-less extended diffuse ionic atmosphere (Fig. 10-24).

According to a suggestion made by J. Duclaux (see Ref. 22), the individual colloidal particle in a disperse system as described above is termed a colloidal *micella*. The disperse phase is termed the *intermicellar liquid*, which is in equilibrium with the micella. The intermicellar liquid may contain electrolytes as well as non-electrolytes.

ELECTRO-OSMOSIS

10-28. Fundamental Principle. Consider a cylindrical column, $ABCD$, Fig. 10-25, of an ideal porous soil system, the particles, S, (shown here idealized as spheres) of which are surrounded by moisture films, m. Assume that this soil system is placed between the two electrodes, 1-1 and 2-2, in an electrical field, E, brought about by a source of direct electrical current. This is to say that the soil system is subjected externally, at its ends, to an electric energy or to an electrical potential difference. Upon the application of an external, primary electric potential, the positive charges (cations) in the diffuse double layer are attracted by the negative electrode (cathode) and thus will tend to translocate in the electric field towards the cathode (the minus-pole), and the negative ones (anions) towards the anode (Fig. 10-25).

The positive ions of the electrical diffuse double layer translocating upward in the pictured soil system drag with them the oriented water molecules, thus setting the positively charged water layer (or the mobile part of the moisture film) into upward motion and dragging the rest of the liquid along the immobile part of the moisture film. One sees that the direction of flow depends upon whether the liquid carries positive or negative charges, and upon the position of the poles of the source of the direct current. The tendency of the positive charge in the water to set itself in motion and to translocate the water along with it, together with the enclosed column of neutral water (free water, or water in bulk) is resisted by the viscosity of the water. The resistance to motion of the water molecules is assumed to follow Newton's law of viscous flow. Hence the movement of the mobile part of the moisture film over the immobile part of the moisture film surrounding the soil particle is a tangential slip by overcoming the shearing resistance of the liquid.

The velocity of the soil moisture flow in the film phase depends upon the magnitude of the applied electric potential difference and the viscosity of the liquid medium. The amount of moisture transferred by means of film flow, it can be understood, is also proportional, among other things, to the specific surface area of the soil particles in a unit of a given volume or weight (one gram, for example). The finer the soil particles, the more specific surface there is in a unit of volume, or in unit weight, which in its turn means more films, and hence more film moisture transferred.

The term *electro-osmosis* is used to describe the electrokinetic phenomenon of liquid (water) moving through a system of a porous medium relative to a fixed solid (i.e., the colloidal soil particles are prevented from moving) under the influence of a primary, externally applied electrical field. The derivation of this term is based on an analogy with osmotic phenomena which take place through organic and inorganic membranes, diaphragms, or porous plugs. Therefore such a movement of liquids through a porous plug under the influence of an electric potential is called "electric osmosis" or electro-osmosis. The porous system, such as soil, may be thought of as bundles of complicated, interconnecting passages of diverse ways.

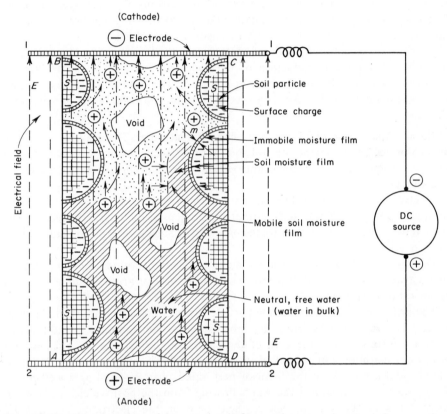

FIG. 10-25   Translocation of ions and soil film moisture under the influence of an electrical potential.

From the foregoing discussion it can be understood that in electro-osmosis the mechanism for the translocation of soil moisture is possible due to the existence of the electric diffuse double layer in a moist soil system. The application of an electric potential at the ends of the soil system results in the displacement of the charged mobile moisture films relative to the immobile ones. Because the mobile part of the moisture film is free to move, whereas the soil particles are not, a flow of moisture takes place. The direction of moisture flow depends upon whether water is charged with positive or negative ions.

10-29. Historical Notes. The electro-osmotic phenomenon was discovered by Professor F. F. Reuss in 1808 (op. cit.) but he did not explain the phenomenon.

Systematic research on electro-osmosis was performed by Wiedemann[23] in 1852. Quincke made in 1861 quantitative measurements at a single capillary (op. cit.). Quincke also realized that the electro-osmotic phenomenon has a connected phenomenon, termed the *streaming potential*. The phenomenon of the *streaming potential is the converse of electro-osmosis.*

Also, Quincke gave the original electrical double layer theory and explained it. As may be gathered from the review of the various double layer theories, Quincke's original theory is a fundamental one to which, generally, only a few improvements were made and a few extensions were added.

Quincke's theory was formulated mathematically in 1878/79 by H. Helmholtz (op. cit.). With the introduction of the dielectric constant in the Helmholtz double layer theory by Smoluchowski in 1893[24], the Helmholtz theory by and large is still valid, particularly as a special case, or as a component part in other theories.

10-30. Application of Electro-osmosis in Engineering. The application of the electro-osmotic phenomenon to soil and foundation engineering has been studied by Leo Casagrande,[25,26] Schaad and Haefeli,[27] Winterkorn,[28] Preece,[29] Vey,[30] and others.

Electro-osmosis is utilized for the de-watering of silty and clayey soils difficult to drain by gravity. These soils cannot be drained easily by gravity because the relatively large surface tension forces of water in such soils tend to retain water in their voids.

De-watering of soil is pursued to facilitate laying of foundations in a dry pit or excavation, for the stabilization of soil in natural or artificial slopes, as well as for other purposes.

The principle of de-watering fine-particled soils electrically is illustrated in Fig. 10-26. To keep the excavation dry, positive electrodes (anodes) in the form of rods are installed near the toes of the slopes of the excavation. The negative electrodes (cathodes) are installed in the mass of soil away from the slopes of the cut and are made in the form of perforated pipes resembling a well-point. Their function is to collect the water flowing from the positive electrode when there exists in the soil an electric field between the electrodes, i.e., a D.C. circuit. The collected water in the negative electrode is pumped out and discharged.

One well-known example in engineering practice and technical literature of the successful application of electro-osmosis in soil mechanics is the de-watering of a silt with unfavorable physical properties by the Germans during the Second World War at Trondheim, Norway, for the construction of their U-boat pens (see Ref. 26).

The volume, V, of water moved per unit of time by electro-osmosis is directly proportional to the applied electric current, the dielectric constant, and inversely proportional to the viscosity and electro-conductivity of water:

$$V = \frac{\zeta DI}{4\pi\eta\lambda}, \qquad (\text{cm}^3/\text{sec}) \qquad (10\text{-}38)$$

where ζ = zeta potential
D = dielectric constant of water
I = current
η = dynamic viscosity of water.
λ = specific conductivity of water.

If the current is kept constant, the flow of water is independent of the length and area of the capillaries.   Note that all these factors are functions of temperature.

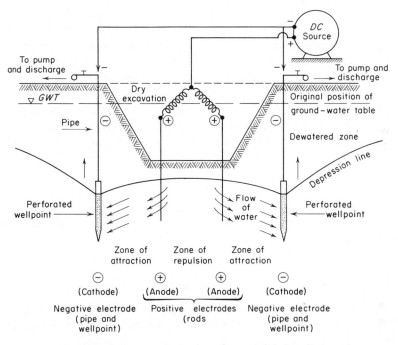

FIG. 10-26.   Principle of de-watering of a fine-particled soil by electro-osmosis.

STREAMING POTENTIAL

10-31. Induced Electrical Potential.   In electro-osmosis, the application of a primary electrical potential causes in a moist porous system (which may be imagined as a fixed porous plug inside an imaginary cylinder) the motion of the liquid relative to the fixed solids.

Conversely, the motion of a liquid forced mechanically through a fixed porous plug, say a clay diaphragm, by means of a certain energy (heat energy, for example), induces an electrical potential difference or electromotive force, E.M.F., between the two ends of the plug. A process of soil moisture translocation brought about by means of a primary thermal potential is termed *thermo-osmosis*.

Because the film liquid is electrically charged, the translocation of the liquid through the porous soil system is accompanied by an induced electric current. The electric diffuse double layer is swept along by the flow of the mobile film water, so that opposite charges are built up at opposite ends of the system of the porous plug. This induced electric potential difference in a thermo-osmotic process is termed the *streaming potential*, which may be regarded as the converse phenomenon of electro-osmosis.

Hence it can be expected that an externally applied primary potential, for example, a thermal potential, will induce between the two ends of the porous system a secondary potential, namely an electric potential, upon displacing the mobile film. This principle was discovered by Quincke in 1859. The streaming liquid displaces the positive charges of the water molecules relative to the solid particles and thus induces an electrical potential along the height of the column of the moist, porous soil system. The induced E.M.F. is related with the zeta-potential.[31] Likewise, the amounts of film moisture transferred are thus connected with the zeta-potential. This phenomenon, converse to electro-osmosis, seems to be less known to the engineering profession than electro-osmosis. Yet, the phenomenon of induced electric potentials gives one an important basis on which to rest the theory of the mechanism for the translocation of soil moisture in the film phase (unsaturated flow), particularly upon freezing.

The induced streaming potential, E_s, by a thermal gradient is expressed as

$$E_s = \frac{\xi PD}{4\pi\eta\lambda}, \quad \text{(volts)} \tag{10-39}$$

where all symbols are the same as in electro-osmosis, and P = net pressure necessary to stop the flow. This pressure is also called the *thermo-osmotic* or *driving pressure* of water.

REFERENCES

1. F. Zunker, "Das Verhalten des Bodens zum Wasser". Blanck's *Handbuch der Bodenlehre*, Die physikalische Beschaffenheit des Bodens, Berlin, Julius Springer, 1930, vol. 6, p. 70.
2. F. Zunker, *Bautechnik*, Berlin, Springer, 1935, p. 74.
3. L. G. Briggs, "Absorption of Water Vapor and Certain Salts in Aqueous Solution by Quartz", *Journal of Physical Chemistry*, 1905, vol. 9, pp. 617-64.
4. S. Odén, "Note on the Hygroscopicity of Clay and the Quantity of Water Adsorbed per Surface Unit", *Transactions of the Faraday Society*, London, 1921, vol. 17, pp. 18-21.
5. J. W. Bain, R. C. Bacon, and H. D. Bruce, *Journal of Chemical Physics*, 1938, vol. 7, p. 818.
6. W. E. Forsythe, *Smithsonian Physical Tables*, The Smithsonian Institution, Washington, D.C., 1954, p. 361-362.
7. *Handbuch der Physik*, vol. 7, "Mechanik der Flüssigen und Gasförmigen Körper", Berlin, Julius Springer, 1927.
8. National Research Council: *International Critical Tables of Numerical Data, Physics, Chemistry, and Technology*, 1st ed., vol. 4, New York, McGraw-Hill Book Co., 1929.
9. H. Freundlich, *Colloid and Capillary Chemistry*, New York, E. P. Dutton and Co., 1922, p. 28.
10. G. Beskow, *Tjälbildningen och Tjällyftningen*, Statens Väginstitut, Stockholm, 1935, pp. 134-135.

11. P. J. W. Debye, *The Collected Papers of P. J. W. Debye*, New York, Interscience Publishers, Inc., 1954.
12. P. J. W. Debye, "The Structure of Matter", trans. by F. M. Denton, *The University of New Mexico Bulletin*, Albuquerque, New Mexico, 1934, vol. 1, no. 2, October 1, 1934.
13. P. J. W. Debye, *Polar Molecules*, New York, The Chemical Catalog Co., Inc., 1929.
14. J. R. Partington, *An Advanced Treatise on Physical Chemistry*, vol. 5 (Molecular Spectra and Structure; Dielectric and Dipole Moments). London, Longmans, Green and Co., 1954.
15. F. F. Reuss, "Sur Un Nouvel Effet de l'Électricité Galvanique". Notice lue le 15 Avril 1808, *Mémoires* de la Societé Impériale Des Naturalistes de Moscou, 1809, à Moscou, de l'Imprimerie de l'Université Impériale, vol. 2, pp. 327-337.
16. G. Quincke, "Über die Fortführung materieller Teilchen durch strömende Elektrizität". Poggendorffs *Annalen der Physik und Chemie*, J. A. Barth, Leipzig, 1861, vol. 113, no. 8, pp. 513-598.
17. H. Helmholtz, "Studien über electrische Grenzschichten", G. Wiedemann's *Annalen der Physik und Chemie*. J. A. Barth, Leipzig, 1879. Neue Folge, vol. 7, pp. 337-382.
18. M. Gouy, "Sur la Constitution de la Charge Electrique à la Surface d'un Electrolyte", *Journal de Physique Théoretique et Appliquée*, Paris, 1910, vol. 9, pp. 457-468.
19. D. L. Chapman, "A Contribution to the Theory of Electrocapillarity, Sixth Series", *The London, Edinburgh, and Dublin Philosophical Magazine and Journal of Science*, April, 1913, vol. 25, no. 148, pp. 475-481.
20. A. J. Rutgers, *Physical Chemistry*, New York, Interscience Publishers, Inc., 1954.
21. O. Stern, "Zur Theorie der elektrolytischen Doppelschicht", *Zeitschrift für Elektrochemie und angewandte physikalische Chemie*, Leipzig-Berlin, 1924, pp. 508-516.
22. H. Freundlich, *Colloid and Capillary Chemistry*. Trans. by H. S. Hatfield, E. P. Dutton and Company, Inc., New York, 1922, p. 371.
23. G. Wiedemann, "Über die Bewegung von Flüssigkeiten im Kreise der geschlossenen galvanischen Säule" and J. C. Poggendorffs *Annalen der Physik und Chemie*, J. A. Barth, Leipzig, vol. 87, no. 11, 1852, pp. 321-352, vol. 99, no. 10, 1856, pp. 177-233.
24. M. Smoluchowski, "Elektrische Endosmose und Strömungsströme, in Graetz's *Handbuch der Elektrizität und des Magnetismus*, J. A. Barth, Leipzig, 1914, vol. 2, p. 366.
25. L. Casagrande, *Die elektrische Entwässerung feinkörniger Böden*, Deutsche Wasserwirtschaft, 1941, vol. 36, pp. 556-559.
26. L. Casagrande, *The Application of Electro-osmosis to Practical Problems in Foundations and Earthworks*. Building Research Technical Paper no. 30, H.M. Stationary Office, London, 1947.
27. W. Schaad, and R. Haefeli, *Elektrokinetische Erscheinungen und ihre Anwendung in der Bodenmechanik*, no. 13, Mitteilungen aus der Versuchsanstalt für Wasserbau und Erdbau an der Eidgenössischen Technischen Hochschule in Zürich, Leeman und Co., 1947.
28. H. F. Winterkorn, "Fundamental Similarities between Electro-osmotic and Thermo-osmotic Phenomena", *Proceedings*, 27th Annual Meeting of the Highway Research Board, held at Washington, D.C., December 2-5, 1947, pp. 443-454.
29. E. Vey, "The Mechanics of Soil Consolidation by Electro-osmosis, *Proceedings*, 29th Annual Meeting of the Highway Research Board, held at Washington, D.C., December 13-16, 1949, pp. 579-589.
30. E. F. Preece, "Geotechnics and Geotechnical Research", *Proceedings*, 27th Annual Meeting of the Highway Research Board, held at Washington, D.C., December 2-5, 1947, pp. 384-416.
31. A. E. Alexander, and P. Johnson, *Colloid Science*, Oxford, At The Clarendon Press, 1949, vol. 1, pp. 340-343.

QUESTIONS AND PROBLEMS

10- 1. Distinguish between various kinds of soil moisture.

10- 2. Distinguish between groundwater and perched groundwater.

10- 3. What is the reason for water to rise in a capillary tube?

10- 4. How high will water rise in a capillary tube?

10- 5. In what direction does capillary moisture generally flow?

10- 6. Distinguish between water in bulk and film water.

10- 7. What happens to the capillary fringe if the soil becomes inundated?

10- 8. What is the cause for groundwater to flow?

10- 9. What is surface tension?

10-10. What is capillary moisture in soil, and what is the cause of rise of capillary moisture in soil?

10-11. Derive the analytical expression for the height of ascent of water in a capillary tube.

10-12. Explain the performance of Daytona Beach sand used for automobile races.

10-13. If the angle of wetting is zero, and the surface tension of water at 20°C is $T = 75$ dynes per cm, and the capillary diameter is 0.10 mm, calculate, in cm, the height, h, of the capillary rise.

10-14. Calculate h at 10°C, and at 30°C, all other conditions being the same as in Problem 10-16.

10-15. In what condition is the capillary system if the angle of wetting is zero?

10-16. What is the pressure deficiency in the capillary water at 20°C?

10-17. If the radii of curvature of an irregular capillary are $r_1 = 0.05$ and $r_2 = 0.10$ mm, what is the surface tension across the meniscus formed by this double curvature?

10-18. What are the applications of the capillary tube theory to soil engineering?

Chapter 11

FROST ACTION IN SOILS

11-1. Frost Problems in Soil. In fine-particled soils, particularly in silts, the moisture of the upward capillary and/or film flow, if frost penetrates downward into the capillary fringe, forms ice lenses under certain freezing conditions. The growing ice lenses expand and cause frost heaves and frost boils which might be very detrimental to highway and airfield runway pavements, sheeted excavations, and to the stability of slopes of cuts and fills (Fig. 11-1).

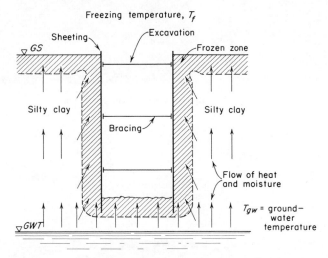

FIG. 11-1   Freezing of soil around a sheeted excavation.

The frost penetration depths in soil can be approximately calculated by means of the heat transfer theory based on heat conduction in the steady state flow of heat; in the unsteady state flow of heat, by means of F. Neumann's theory (which also is based on the theory of heat transfer); by means of Stefans solution (which is a special case of Neumann's theory); by Ruckli's "suction force" theory, and possibly other methods—methods which are subjects of graduate study, and therefore are not treated in this book. For the aforementioned theories and solutions refer to the author's work *The Frost Penetration Problem in Highway Engineering.*[1]

   In this book, only the qualitative and the research aspects of freezing soil systems and the associated phenomena, such as thawing and soil moisture migration induced by an energy potential, will be dealt with. Experience shows that shortly after the thawing of the soil beneath the pavement, the soil loses its bearing capacity for a certain period of time. This phenomenon is known as the "spring break-up" (Figs. 11-2 and 11-3).

FIG. 11-2   Spring "break-up" on earth roads.

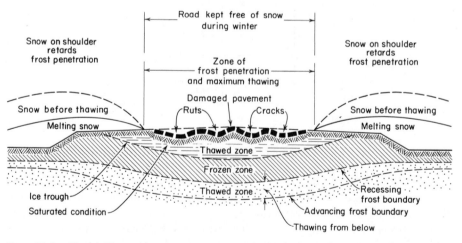

FIG. 11-3   Sketch illustrating freezing and thawing damage to a road. Thawing causes spring "break-up".

Because silt particles are small enough to provide a comparatively high capillary rise, and, at the same time, large enough to furnish voids of such a size as to allow a quick flow of moisture through the silt, silt absorbs moisture rapidly. This phenomenon causes, in turn, a rapid saturation of the voids of the soil, saturation which subsequently results in rapid loss of bearing capacity of the silty soil.

Thus, the determination of the height to which moisture would ascend in a certain soil is of great importance for the evaluation of the frost susceptibility of soils and their bearing capacity in highway, airfield, railway, canal, and other earthwork engineering.

On the other hand, the presence of unsaturated moisture in a soil without the presence of and/or access to free groundwater or other supply may not be distinctly harmful if the moisture binds the soil particles rather than lubricates them.

From the foregoing discussion, in general, two things strike one immediately upon starting to study a freezing soil system. These are: first, the profound influence of temperature upon the soil moisture; and second, the observation that the substance water contributes considerably to the performance of the soil, particularly when under freezing conditions. These two factors—temperature, or rather heat exchange with the surroundings of the freezing soil system on the one hand, and soil moisture migration induced by a thermal potential on the other hand—interact mutually, an interaction which endows the freezing soil system with great complexity, and consequently makes it very difficult to study. Therefore, freezing soil systems are often studied experimentally— in the field, as well as in the laboratory.

In studying frost effects upon soil it must also be remembered that there is something else involved besides merely the solid particles of the soil, viz., soil texture (refer to the textural criterion of frost-susceptible soils, for example). As just mentioned, in the soil freezing process an important factor, among others, is the soil moisture, and what seems to be more important, the interaction of physical forces between the surface of soil particles and the soil moisture films surrounding the soil particles. This is of particular significance in studying the soil moisture transfer in the film phase upon freezing.

It seems that the key to the secrets of the freezing soil system lies in the substance water itself. Thus the liquid phase of the soil is not just an important constituent part of the soil under load, but it also plays an important role when subjected to temperature changes. Temperature, it is known, changes the properties of water. Variation in temperature starts a thermal potential which induces the soil moisture to migrate, and to create an electrical potential between the ends of the freezing soil system. Therefore, to understand better the soil moisture migration phenomenon upon freezing, one should become somewhat familiar with the structure of the water molecule, the diffuse double layer theory as well as with the methods of research used in studying freezing soil systems.

In much of its functioning, water is commonplace. However, odd as it sounds, commonplace things usually are the least appreciated and the most difficult to understand. It is known that water is the most abundant liquid on the earth and that it is used daily because it is an absolute necessity for sustaining life.

However, when it comes to the studies of freezing soil systems and their associated soil moisture migration, water, particularly in the film phase, turns out to be the least understood factor pertaining to the freezing process.

SOIL FREEZING

11-2. Factors Contributing to Freezing Soils. When a soil is subjected to freezing temperatures, several phenomena take place, the intensity of which depends upon the intensity of freezing temperatures:

1) Moisture is translocated by upward flow from the groundwater to the growing ice lenses (change in soil moisture content).
2) Upon freezing, water is converted to ice (change in phase). On freezing, water increases by 9% in volume.
3) Frost penetrates the soil.
4) Upon penetrating the soil, frost causes frost heaves (change in volume of soil) on the soil or ground surface and pavements.

Some of the factors which affect the frost action in soil are the soil type itself, proximity of groundwater (or perched groundwater), the initial soil temperature, the air temperature above the ground surface (microclimate), exposure, vegetative cover, type of pavement cover on the soil, depth of snow (insulating cover) on the soil, if any, and the density of the snow.

The principal effects of frost action on a highway are freezing and thawing of the pavement supporting soil. Frost action not only causes local heaving and breaks pavements, but also causes loss in load-carrying capacity because of subsequent softening of the soil and localized settlements brought about by thawing.

FIG. 11-4   A black-top road damaged by frost action.

Figs. 11-2 and 11-4 illustrate various types of roads in poor condition even though they have an excellent cross section and apparently good side drainage. The frost penetration in combination with high moisture content in the soil is directly responsible for the failure of these roads.

Thawing causes loss of bearing capacity of soil and so-called "spring break-ups" on roads built on and of improper soil. Thus it can be inferred that frost action imposes difficulties in design, construction, exploitation, and maintenance of roads. It also impairs traffic safety. In addition, repairs to roads damaged by frost usually cost huge sums. It becomes necessary, therefore, in highway and airport engineering, to estimate, among other factors, the frost penetration depth in soil to provide either for proper insulation or adequate drainage courses underneath the pavement to take care of the thawing waters, and to determine the necessary amount by which the groundwater table should be lowered. If the groundwater table is sufficiently low, upon freezing the height of the upward translocated soil moisture from the groundwater will not be intercepted by the depth of the maximum frost penetration which is known to prevail in the region under consideration.

The so-called practical method of replacing frost-susceptible soils by gravel in a great many instances does not bring about the desired results. The first question that arises in such a replacing operation is how much or how thick a layer of the frost-susceptible soil should be excavated out of the roadbed and replaced. Then there are observations that in certain areas gravel for replacing frost-susceptible soils and for other uses of highway construction is getting scarcer and scarcer, and that soon no gravel will be available. Border-line materials in lieu of gravel are being considered.

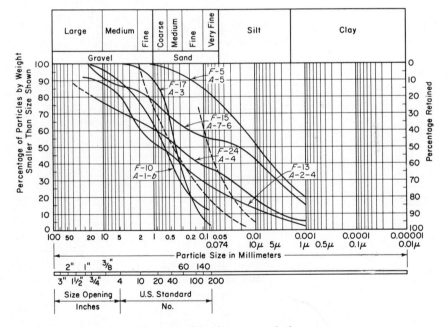

FIG. 11-5   Particle size accumulation curves.

The other important question is this: how shall the subgrade soil be protected from the adverse effect of frost? It appears that the frost penetration problem in highway soils is not merely a mechanical problem, but is primarily a thermal-hydraulic problem involving a complex soil-moisture-temperature system.

The solution of any problem in heat transfer, such as the frost penetration problem in highway soils, cannot be assumed without some theoretical basis, for example, without knowledge of the thermal conductivity or diffusivity of the soil medium, as well as of some fundamental laws of heat transfer.

Interest in studying frost penetration problems is usually concentrated upon the following factors:

1) the depth to which frost penetrates the varing ious soils;
2) the intensity and duration of the freezperiod;,
3) the temperature variation of the air, road surface and soil, and
4) the position of the groundwater table and proximity to other water

    sources.

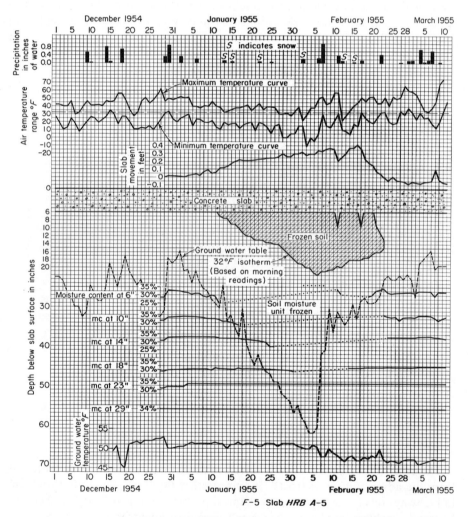

F-5 Slab *HRB A-5*

FIG. 11-6   Changes in soil A-5 upon freezing.

Besides the heat transfer aspect our attention should also be directed to the phenomenon of how the soil moisture is supplied to the growing ice lenses, and the question of the nature of the driving force, or mechanism causing the migration of soil moisture towards a cold isothermal boundary surface and inaugurated by a freezing thermal gradient.

Fig. 11-5 shows 6 particle-size accumulation curves of soils studied by the author during the years from 1952 to 1955. The symbol, F, with the sample number means a soil used in frost action studies. The soil designated as F-5 is a sandy, silt-clay mixture, derived from old glacial lake bed sediments. Soil F-10 is a mixture of coarse, medium, and fine sands containing a considerable amount of gravel and some silt and clay, derived from gneissic glacial materials which have been reworked by water.

Soil F-13 is a sandy gravel with considerable silt and clay content, derived from basalt and diabase (gravel size is large; fragments are angular).

Soil F-15 is a silt-clay mixture, derived primarily from underlying Triassic argillite.

Soil F-17 is a mixture of coarse, medium, and fine sands, derived from coastal plain sediments.

Soil F-24 is a well-graded mixture of gravel, sand, silt, and clay, derived from till containing much limestone.

The dotted lines in Fig. 11-5 indicate A. Casagrande's criterion of frost susceptibility of soils.

A graph resulting from these studies and showing precipitation, air temperatures, slab displacement (heave), frost penetration depth in soil, soil moisture content, groundwater level, and groundwater temperature of soil F-5, classed as A-5 (sandy silt-clay), is shown in Fig. 11-6.

The studies of frost action in these six soils generally revealed the following:

1) Coarse, granular, non-plastic soils react to changes in air temperature more quickly than fine-particled soils, i.e., in coarse, granular, non-plastic soils frost penetrates sooner than in clayey soils and, upon thawing, frost leaves such a soil sooner than from clayey soils.

2) Frost penetrates through a concrete slab more rapidly than through a soil of the same thickness as the slab (because the thermal conductivity of a concrete slab is greater than that of an equal depth of soil); for the same reason, the soils thaw faster beneath the slabs.

3) A concrete slab over a granular soil responds most quickly to cold and warm spells. A shoulder of fine-particled soil shows little reaction to cold and warm spells when compared with the preceding combination of slab and granular material.

4) The freezing isotherm (0°C = 32°F-line, or rather, plane) penetrates to a greater depth in granular soils than in fine-particled soils.

5) There is a lag between the minimum air temperature of winter and the maximum penetration of the 32°F-line. In the cases studied the lag was one day; in some of the shoulders of fine-particled soils the time lag was several days.

6) Maximum heaving does not necessarily occur at the time of the maximum depth of the 32°F-line.

7) The silty *A*-4 soils are most susceptible to frost heaving. The granular *A*-1-*b* and *A*-3 soils heave the least.

8) Most thawing in soil occurs from the top downward during thaw periods; however, some thawing takes place from the bottom.

9) As a frozen layer of soil thaws from top and bottom, this fact is of particular importance because the greater rate of thawing beneath pavement slabs may form "pockets" of thawed soil at high moisture content from which the water cannot drain. Consequently, the soil bearing capacity is reduced because of the saturated state of the soil. This observation implies a drainage problem concerning base and subbase courses to be solved with particular reference to drainage of water produced by the melting of the frozen soil moisture from underneath the road pavement.

10) Soil freezes at temperatures slightly lower than 0°C.

11) Temperature studies indicate the necessity of measuring and knowing the surface temperature of the slab or ground surface (microclimate) for calculating heat transfer, frost penetration depths, icing of pavements, and other possible purposes.

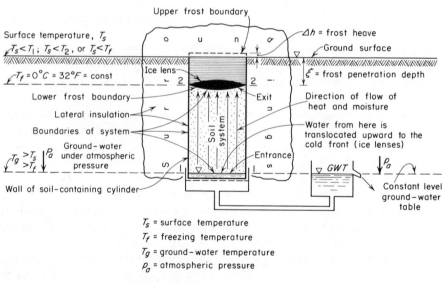

T_s = surface temperature
T_f = freezing temperature
T_g = ground-water temperature
P_a = atmospheric pressure

FIG. 11-7   Freezing soil system.

11-3. Theoretical Considerations on the Freezing Soil System. The changes induced by surface temperature, T_s, are usually effectuated by a temperature potential as a driving force.[2,3] The freezing soil system is illustrated in Fig. 11-7.

If a vertical column of a soil system is subjected to freezing from its top downward, as occurs in highway soils in winter, several changes take place in the following manner. A curvilinear temperature gradient, $\partial T/\partial x$, sets in across the freezing soil system, from the top down, Fig. 11-8. There takes place an upward heat transfer from a region of higher temperature, T_g, in the soil system (groundwater) towards a region of colder temperature, T_f, (frozen layer of soil, for example). The thermal energy, in its turn, initiates the upward migration of soil moisture in the porous soil system.

Upon freezing of the soil moisture, latent heat is released. Likewise the thermal properties of soil, water, and ice change, as do the density, viscosity, and dielectric constant of the water.

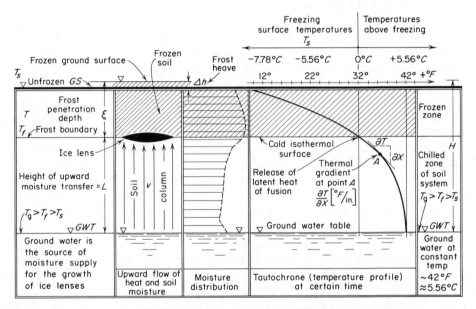

FIG. 11-8   Sketch illustrating the concept of unidirectional upward flow of soil moisture upon freezing. Open system.

Some Modes of Soil Moisture Translocation Upon Freezing. Depending upon the state of packing of the soil, soil moisture can be translocated upward through the porous medium of soil upon freezing by one or another mechanism: 1) as a vapor, 2) as a liquid (in bulk or by film), or 3) in a simultaneous combination of vapor and liquid.

The manner in which the soil moisture migrates through a porous medium such as soil during a freezing process is termed "the mechanism" of moisture transfer.

Vapor Diffusion. If the voids of the soil are relatively large, and there is no continuous moisture in the liquid form in the voids connecting the groundwater with the downward freezing ice lenses, then the soil moisture from the groundwater is transported upward by way of the mechanism of vapor diffusion. Here the driving pressure is the vapor pressure difference between the vapor pressure at the warmer end of the freezing soil system (the free water surface = groundwater table) and the vapor pressure in the upper region of the soil system just below the ice, where it can be very small, or even negligible as compared with that of the free surface.[4] This is to say that moisture migration takes place in the direction along the drop of the thermal gradient. The vapor pressure decreases from the groundwater table up curvilinearly as the temperature decreases from the groundwater up to the freezing isothermal surface.

EXPERIMENTAL STUDIES OF FREEZING SOIL SYSTEMS

11-4. Purpose of Experiment. The main purpose of a soil freezing experiment is to learn the interrelationships of the various factors involved in the soil moisture translocation and freezing processes, and to try to find a relationship between the driving pressure and the amount of soil moisture supplied from the groundwater via the moisture films to the freezing zone of the soil. The amount of water transferred should be a well-defined function of the driving pressure to permit reasonable calculations of frost problems on roads. Also, these studies would permit one to learn and to describe the mechanism for the upward translocation of the soil moisture in the film phase in a freezing soil system.

In order to learn the interrelationships of the various factors involved in damage to roads by frost in interaction with soil moisture, particularly when the translocation of soil moisture from warmer regions to colder ones is more effective than the other moisture transfer mechanisms, a certain soil was subjected to freezing experiments. Because of the many unknown and obscure factors involved in the behavior of a freezing soil system, the freezing soil systems were studied in their entirety, evaluating their performance by the total, net end result of the system as a whole between the entrance and exit of the system.

During the course of upward migration, induced by a freezing thermal gradient, the flowing water loses some of its driving pressure. This means that the driving pressure in the system's flow performs some mechanical work which goes lost. Thus, in doing external, over-all work, the entire freezing soil system loses some of its energy, so that the system in nature does not work with 100% efficiency. It also appears that the factors governing the energy losses (or drop in driving pressure) accompanying the upward migration of soil moisture upon freezing are not quite susceptible to exact mathematical analysis, for the time being. Therefore, to understand the frost effects in soil, the freezing soil system must be studied experimentally.

Principle of Experiment. It is the author's strong belief that the freezing soil system should be studied as an organic entity. This is to say, the freezing experiment should be so arranged as to simulate nature as closely as possible. If there is groundwater in the field available from which, upon freezing, the soil can "draw" water, the experiment should be set up accordingly. Likewise, if in the field the soil freezes from its top vertically downward, then these should be the conditions in the experiment. If it can be assumed that in the field there is no lateral flux of heat through the soil, then proper boundaries should be provided in the experimental freezing soil system to assure such a condition.

If the organic entity of soil in the field suggests an open system, then the soil freezing experiment should be performed with an open soil system. If there is no groundwater source present in the field, or the groundwater is inaccessible for the supply of water to the downward freezing ice lenses, then the experiment should be performed accordingly. Also, moisture transfer from places of higher concentration to lower ones upon freezing in the vapor phase, or by capillarity, or by film flow, or by a combination of all of these mechanisms must be clearly kept in mind, and the experiment arranged accordingly.

FIG. 11-9. Soil freezing equipment.

Experiments. The freezing experiments of the soil system were accomplished by applying an external, primary potential (a freezing thermal potential) to the upper horizontal surface of a vertical soil cylinder 12 in. high and 6 in. in diameter, the lower end of which was inserted in a water bath (at $T = +8°C$, which is the average annual groundwater temperature at the "frost yard" of Rutgers, the State University, at University Heights, New Jersey) to simulate the source of groundwater. Hence, the soil system was an open one. Immediately after the commencement of freezing, measurements were made of temperature within the soil and its environment, driving pressure differences, induced electrical potential differences (E.M.F.) across the soil system (secondary potential), the supply of groundwater from a burette consumed during freezing, and frost heave. The soil system was prepared of Dunellen soil—a silt-containing glacial outwash soil in New Jersey.

The general view of a freezing equipment with auxiliary apparatus for performing such soil freezing experiments is illustrated in Fig. 11-9.

Experimental Results. In the soil freezing experiment described here, the following data were recorded:

a) time,

b developed sub-pressures,

c) soil temperatures at various levels,

d) surface temperature above the soil specimen (microclimate),

e) groundwater temperature,

f) laboratory air temperature,

g) quantity of water transferred from the groundwater reservoir into the soil specimen upon freezing,

h) induced secondary electrical potentials, and

i) frost heave.

Fig. 11-10a shows the positions where temperatures, sub-pressures, and induced electrical potentials were measured.

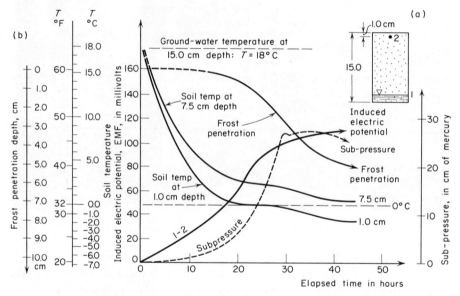

FIG. 11-10 Soil freezing experiment data.

Fig. 11-10b shows a graphical representation of the soil freezing experiment data. This graph indicates that as the temperature in the soil decreased the sub-pressure and the induced electrical potential between both ends 1-2 of the freezing soil system increased. The order of magnitude of the induced electrical potentials was measured by the author in various freezing soil systems from 40 to 120 millivolts. The sub-pressures, depending upon the physical conditions of the soil, temperature, pressure and humidity environment, and care of experiment were observed for the Dunellen soil as high as 32 cm mercury.

11-5. Soil Moisture Transfer as a Function of Porosity and Packing. Depending upon the state of packing of the soil, the moisture transferred by one or another mechanism is more accentuated. Moisture diffusion by the vapor phase would take place in a soil with larger void sizes rather than in one with fine void sizes. If the soil is fully saturated with water, the moisture migration cannot take place in the vapor phase. If the packing of the soil is very dense, moisture transfer in the vapor phase is ineffective.

The foregoing is illustrated by the following experiment performed by the author. Soil samples, 12 in. high and 6 in. in diameter, Fig. 11-11, were prepared at various porosities and subjected to freezing under similar temperature conditions. The lower ends (entrance of systems) were placed in "groundwater" (see the two recep-tacles at the bottom of the freezing cabinet, Figs. 11-9 and 11-12), and the soil cylinders were laterally insulated to minimize the lateral flux of heat. Then the surfaces of the soil samples were subjected to freezing, and the supply of "groundwater" consumed during the freezing experiment was measured. The soil-freezing systems were all open systems.

FIG. 11-11   Soil system with thermistors and moisture sensing elements.

11-6. Film Transport. In a very dense, close packing of soil (for which there is a theoretical and practical limit), where the soil particles are packed so close to each other (small porosity) that the moisture around and between the soil particles forms uninterrupted liquid films through the entire soil system down to the groundwater supply, then, depending upon the texture of the soil (whether silt, silty clay, clayey silt, or clay) the film transport mechanism becomes more effective than that of the vapor mechanism (Fig. 11-13). The process of the up-ward moisture translocation via the moisture films in the freezing soil is slow, of course. However, as evidenced by the author's studies, a considerable amount of soil moisture can flow from the groundwater upward during a relatively long period of time, for example, during a freezing season. It is the slow process of flow, indeed, which often is overlooked and forgotten, and which is one of the main factors where the danger of damage to highways and runways lies. Note that in the film-transport mechanism, the ice lenses are connected via the moisture films with the groundwater (or perched groundwater) supply, Figs. 11-12 and 11-14.

If there is no groundwater present, the soil freezing is then a drying process until all of the soil moisture has been transferred to the freezing isothermal region.

11-7. Combination of Various Modes of Moisture Transport. Depending upon the texture and gradation of the soil, and the degree of packing, or the presence

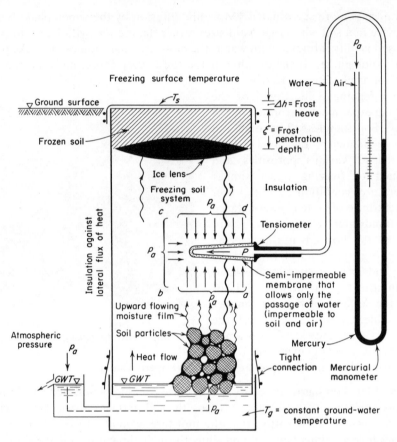

FIG. 11-12 Soil-tensiometer-water system (open system); (a-b-c-d-) = free body diagram.

of a multi-layered soil-system, a combination of the various soil moisture transport mechanisms may exist simultaneously upon freezing. For example, with large porosities, it is more likely that upward soil moisture transport in the vapor phase will be more effective than a film flow. In a densely packed clayey silt or silty clay the film-transport mechanism may be more effective than vapor flow. Between the maximum possible and minimum possible densities, and for different textures of soil, and in various combinations other than gravel and clay, there may set in several upward soil moisture transfer mechanisms in various proportions. There are no sharply defined boundaries between the various modes of moisture transport mechanisms and processes. It is quite reasonable to assume, rather, that a transition from one mode to another constitutes the combination of the simultaneously acting various modes of transport.

11-8. Summary of the Study of the Possible Mechanism for the Translocation of Soil Moisture in the Film Phase Upon Freezing. The studies performed hitherto by the author on freezing soil systems have convinced him that the

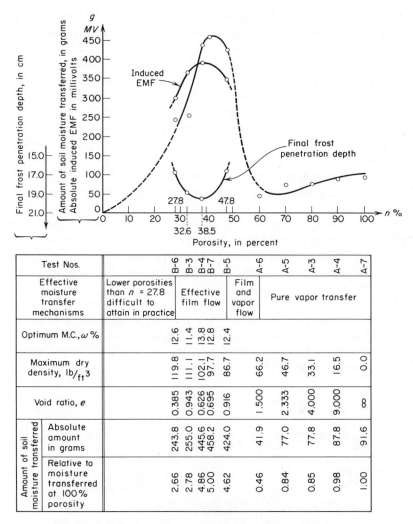

FIG. 11-13. Amount of soil moisture transferred upon freezing as a function of porosity of soil.

electric, diffuse double-layer theory may be considered as the basis for studying freezing soil systems and hints as a possible mechanism for the upward translocation of soil moisture in the film phase upon freezing.

At the present stage of studies, some of the assumptions upon which the theory of the mechanism is based can be summarized as follows:

1) Water is the continuous liquid phase in the porous soil system.
2) There exists in the water around the solid soil particles an electric, diffuse double layer of the Gouy-Chapman or Stern type.
3) The surfaces of the solid soil particles are ordinarily charged negatively; the negative ions are adsorbed on the surfaces of the solid particles.

4) There are free positive charges in the diffuse part of the double layer.
5) The complex, tortuous network of voids in the soil is assumed to be bundles of ideal capillaries.
6) Through the voids of the soil an idealized flow of soil moisture can take place in a direction parallel to the axis of the cylindrical column of soil. The flow is slow enough for the inertia forces to be neglected; the flow should, however, be considered as the overall flow of the system.
7) The motion of soil moisture in the film phase is induced by means of an external, primary potential, viz., a thermal potential, freezing—for example.
8) The translocation of the soil moisture takes place by friction, i.e., a viscous flow takes place within the double layer and in the bulk of the free liquid.
9) There is no slip of film water at the boundary surfaces of the solid particles.
10) The thickness of the double layer (i.e., the distance normal to the interface over which zeta-potential differs appreciably from that in the bulk of the liquid) is small compared with the radius of curvature at any point of the surface.
11) The mobile part of the moisture film is set in motion tangentially past the immobile part of the film by a freezing temperature gradient.
12) The translocating moisture, displacing the positive ions of the water molecules, induces an electric potential (secondary potential) along the columnar system of soil.

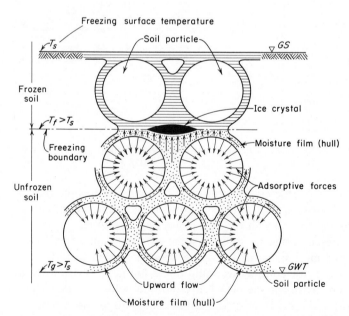

FIG. 11-14   Sketch illustrating the concept of the upward flow of soil moisture by way of film toward an ice crystal.

13) Soil freezing experiments have shown that upon freezing and at the proper packing water is transferred from groundwater to the cold front via the soil moisture films.

14) Also, experiments have shown that upon freezing an electrical potential is induced between the two ends of the freezing soil system.

15) There exist certain relationships between the experimental driving pressure, induced electrical potential, and amount of water transferred; these relationships are still to be studied.

11-9. Frost Penetration Depth. J. Stefan (see Ref. 1) gives a simple formula for the formation of ice in calm water. This formula can be applied for computing approximately the frost penetration depth, ξ, in soil as a function of time:

$$\xi = \sqrt{\frac{2K_1}{Q_L \rho_1} (T_f - T_s)t}, \qquad [\text{ft}] \qquad (11\text{-}1)$$

or

$$\xi = \sqrt{\frac{2c_1 \alpha_1}{Q_L} (T_f - T_s)t}, \qquad [\text{ft}] \qquad (11\text{-}2)$$

where K_1 = thermal conductivity of frozen soil, in B/(ft)(hr)(F),

Q_L = latent heat of fusion for ice per unit weight, in B/lb, where B = British thermal unit;

ρ_1 = unit weight of water, in lb/ft^3;

T_f = Freezing temperature = 32°F;

T_s = Temperature at the road or ground surface, in F°;

t = time, in hours; viz., duration of cold;

c_1 = specific heat of the frozen soil per unit weight, in B/(lb)(F), and

α_1 = thermal diffusivity of the frozen soil, in (ft)^2/hr.

Stefan's formula is good when the conditions are such that the temperature gradient in the frozen zone (ice layer) is linear, the soil moisture present is motionless, and the surface temperature (air temperature) or the temperature of the microclimate, T_s, is constant.

Illustrative Problem. Calculate the frost penetration depth by means of Stefan's approximation.

Given. $K_1 = 1.34[\text{B/ft}^2\text{F}^{-1}\text{hr}^{-1}/\text{ft}]$ for frozen soil;

$Q_L = 144$ B/lb;

$\rho_1 = 62.4$ lb/ft^3 for water;

$n = 0.33$ = porosity of soil, assumed to be fully saturated;

$T_s = 14°\text{F}$;

$T_f = 32°\text{F}$;

$t = 7$ days = 168 hours.

Then, by Equation (11-1), and introducing in the denominator porosity n, the frost penetration depth, ξ, is:

$$\xi = \sqrt{\frac{2K_1}{nQ_L \rho_1} (T_f - T_s)t} = \sqrt{\frac{(2)(1.34)(32 - 14)}{(0.33)(144)(62.4)}} \sqrt{168} = \underline{1.65 \text{ (ft.)}}$$

11-10. Ice Segregation. The amount of segregated ice in a frozen soil system (number, thickness, and distribution of visible ice layers or lenses) depends very much upon the intensity and rate of freezing. When the soil system is frozen quickly, say 8 in. of frost penetration in three days at a temperature difference of 45°F between surface and groundwater, no ice layers are visible. The whole soil sample may be frozen solidly through. But upon splitting the soil sample longitudinally immediately after the test, examination of the frozen soil sample by eye or with the aid of a magnifying glass does not reveal any ice segregation in layers, although the moisture content in the soil after the freezing experiment is larger than before the experiment, and the moisture contents are larger at the ends of the soil cylinder than at its mid-height. Slow freezing, on the contrary, brings about clearly visible ice layers of various thicknesses.

Ice segregation in soil also takes place under cyclic freezing and thawing conditions when the thawed ice waters freeze again.

Of course, ice segregation is influenced by differing thermal properties of the soil material and by the various types of soil moisture and electrolyte, as well as the ice in soil or, rather, the properties of the frozen soil itself. Heat conduction through unfrozen and frozen soil particles is different from that through unfrozen water, chilled water, and ice. Thus, ice lenses develop in the downward freezing soil in jump-wise layers, leaving unfrozen water between two separately spaced ice layers or lenses. Hence, in a frozen soil there may be ice as well as unfrozen water at the same time. As the temperature conditions may still change in a negative direction, some of the unfrozen (under-cooled) water may also freeze as time passes or the frost intensity increases.

FROST CRITERIA

11-11. Criteria for Evaluating the Susceptibility of a Soil to Frost. Frost criteria serve to identify and evaluate in advance, by simple means, the frost susceptibility of soils used for engineering purposes.

Among other criteria, those by Taber[5] and A. Casagrande[6] are the better known. Taber showed that "the size of soil particles is one of the most important factors controlling segregation of water during freezing." For the upper limit Taber gives the particle size of 0.07 mm which, under favorable conditions, is able to produce ice layers. Casagrande's frost criterion has already been given in Chapter 9, and therefore will not be repeated here.

Beskow,[7] based on extensive laboratory experiments with Swedish soils, tried to separate frost-susceptible soils from non-frost-susceptible ones by means of soil particle size and height of capillary rise.

Although any one of these frost criteria makes possible a diagnosis of frost susceptibility of the particular soil under consideration, none of them indicates the degree of frost susceptibility and its intensity.

In construction work, however, it is very often desirable to know the depth to which frost may be expected to penetrate the soil in a given locality, and to predict the amount of heaving. Therefore, it is necessary to introduce the quantitative concept of a "degree of frost danger", η.

This characteristic can be found experimentally in the laboratory by determining the rate of heave, $\Delta h/t$ (ft/hr), and the rate of frost penetration, ξ/t (ft/hr).

The quotient of the above two quantities multiplied by 100 is then defined as the degree of frost danger:

$$\eta = \frac{\Delta h}{\xi}\,100\,\%. \qquad (11\text{-}3)$$

The greater the degree of frost danger, the greater is the upward flow of soil moisture towards the ice lenses, which means that the heaving is greater.

Unfortunately, no grouping limits for the classification of the degree of frost danger are available at present.

REMEDIAL MEASURES

11-12. Some Remedial Measures Against Frost Damage to Roads. The practical objective of remedial measures against frost damage to roads is to try to keep the damage down to a minimum. As to such measures: relocation of a route, replacement of frost-susceptible soils, raising the grade, drainage, lowering groundwater table, insulation courses and membranes, chemical treatment of the soil, and other possible means are generally applied.

It appears that effective drainage is of importance to all soils upon which and of which roads are built.

REFERENCES

1. A. R. Jumikis, *The Frost Penetration Problem in Highway Engineering*, New Brunswick, New Jersey, Rutgers University Press, 1955.
2. A. R. Jumikis, "The Soil Freezing Experiment", Highway Research Board Bulletin no. 135, *Factors Influencing Ground Freezing*, National Academy of Sciences-National Research Council, Publication 425, Washington, D.C., 1956, pp. 150-165.
3. A. R. Jumikis, "Some Concepts Pertaining to the Freezing Soil Systems", Highway Research Board Special Report no. 40, *Water and its Conduction in Soils*, National Academy of Sciences-National Research Council, Publication 629, Washington, D.C., 1958, pp. 178-190.
4. A. R. Jumikis, "Soil Moisture Transfer in the Vapor Phase Upon Freezing", Highway Research Board Bulletin no. 168, *Fundamental and Practical Concepts of Soil Freezing*, National Academy of Sciences-National Research Council, Publication 528, Washington, D.C., 1957, pp. 96-115.
5. S. Taber, "Freezing and Heaving of Road Pavements", *Public Roads*, 1930, p. 118.
6. A. Casagrande, "Discussion on Frost Heaving", *Proceedings*, Highway Research Board, Washington, D.C., 1932, Part I, p. 169.
7. G. Beskow, *Tjälbildningen och Tjällyftningen*, Stockholm, Meddelande 48, Statens Väginstitut, 1935, p. 132, p. 152.

QUESTIONS AND PROBLEMS

11- 1. What are the three basic factors necessary for bringing about frost heaves, viz., damage to roads?

11- 2. What is the nature of frost damage to roads, their pavements, and to railroads and canals?

11- 3. Describe the various possible soil moisture transfer mechanisms upon freezing.

11- 4. Under what conditions do visible ice lenses form in a freezing soil?

11- 5. What is a freezing soil system?

11- 6. Distinguish between primary and induced (secondary) potentials.

11- 7. Distinguish between thermo-osmosis and electro-osmosis.

11- 8. In which soil does *capillary* moisture rise higher, a coarse-particled soil or a fine-particled one? Why?

11- 9. What happens to a capillary fringe in a soil if the whole soil profile up to the ground surface becomes inundated?

11-10. Illustrate and describe what happens to an earth road when the frost penetration depth overlaps a part of the capillary fringe?

11-11. Which kind of placing of anti-frost heave sand layer is correct, on left or right in Fig. Problem 11-11? Why?

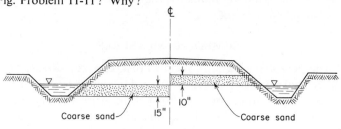

Fig. Problem 11-11.

11-12. Of what value are laboratory experiments on soil freezing?

Chapter 12

GROUNDWATER

12-1. Permeability of Soil. Permeability is defined as the property of a porous material which permits the passage or seepage of fluids such as water and/or oil, for example, through its interconnecting voids.

In soil, the nature of groundwater flow may be either laminar or turbulent. A flow is laminar if the adjacent flow lines of water are parallel. The laminarity or turbidity, depends mostly upon the resistance to flow offered by the soil, through which the flow takes place.

The resistance to flow depends upon the type of soil, size and shape of the soil particles (rounded, angular, or flaky), the degree of packing (density of soil, and, thus, upon the size and geometry of the voids. Also, the resistance is a function of the temperature of water (viscosity and surface tension effects).

Soils, the textural sizes of which are smaller than fine gravel, are considered as preventing turbidity. Therefore, for practical purposes in studying groundwater flow through soils, only laminar flow is usually considered. Coarse-textured soils are more pervious than fine-textured soils.

Generally, the groundwater flow may be steady or unsteady, under pressure or under no pressure. An example of pressure flow is artesian water flowing under pressure head between two confining impermeable layers of soil or rock, for example, causing an artesian condition. Seepage underneath a massive dam, or through an earth dam, at the beginning of flow will be of an unsteady nature. Only after some time lag does the flow attain a steady character.

A water flowing with a free, open surface, would be under no pressure, or rather under atmospheric pressure—for example, seepage through an earth dam after the flow has attained a steady character.

In this book, only the steady flow of groundwater is considered, which includes flowing by gravity, as well as artesian flow.

Although theoretically all soils are more or less porous, in practice the term "permeable" is applied to soils which are porous enough to permit the flow of water through such a soil. Conversely, soils which permeate with great difficulty are termed "impermeable".

In soil mechanics, the coefficient of permeability, k, expresses the degree of permeability of a soil. The coefficient of permeability, k, has a velocity dimension in (cm/sec), for example.

12-2. Darcy's Law. The flow of seepage water is calculated by means of

Darcy's law of artificial filtration through a uniform, unstratified soil. The quantity v, in cm/sec expressing flow velocity

$$v = ki \qquad (12\text{-}1)$$

is termed Darcy's law.[1] It can be seen that the coefficient of permeability, k, is the filter velocity of laminar flow of water at a hydraulic gradient of $i = 1$. In other words, Darcy's law of permeability of saturated soil ($S = 1$) to water is directly proportional to the hydraulic gradient, i. This velocity is the ration of flow with respect to the unit gross cross-sectional area of the soil cylinder.

The proportionality in Darcy's law is valid for laminar flow up to a certain critical gradient, i_{cr}, at which the flow velocity is critical, v_{cr}, Fig. 12-1. Beyond

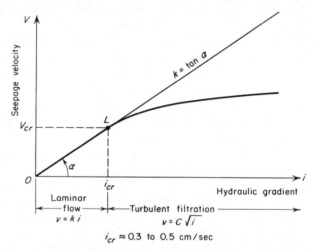

FIG. 12-1   Laminar region of Darcy's law from O to i_{cr}.

point L, where $i > i_{cr}$, the filtration is turbulent, with a seepage velocity, $v > v_{cr}$. In the turbulent region the seepage velocity can be approximately expressed as $v = c\sqrt{i}$, where c is a coefficient characterizing the seepage medium, the soil, and the turbidity of flow. The geometric representation of Darcy's law is shown in Fig. 12-2.

A water particle possesses energy in the following major forms:

potential energy owing to its position, height, or elevation;

pressure energy because of its weight or rather pressure, and also

kinetic energy due to its velocity of flow.

If the velocity of the groundwater flow were zero, then all of the water levels in the piezometric tubes would be at the same elevation, which coincides with the free, horizontal surface of the groundwater. With flowing groundwater, the water level in each of the consecutive piezometric tubes is at a lower elevation than in the preceding one. The difference in these pressure heads, $h = h_1 - h_2$, between both ends of a streamline represents the loss in potential energy along the length, L, used up in overcoming frictional resistance to flow in the voids and in the constrictions in soil.

In order that a flow of water through soil can take place, a driving pressure, p, is needed, viz., a difference in pressure, $p = p_1 - p_2$, between two points on the flow path. The quantity

$$\frac{p}{L} = \frac{p_1 - p_2}{L} = i_p \qquad (12\text{-}2)$$

is termed the pressure gradient.

Because the kinetic energy of the flow of groundwater associated with small seepage velocities is small, in practice it is not taken into consideration in seepage theory.

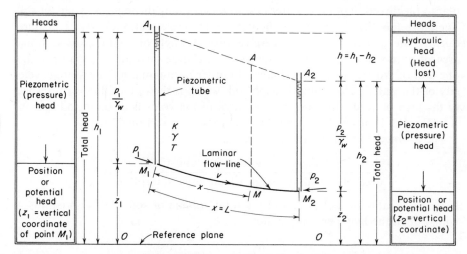

FIG. 12-2   Terminology and geometric representation of Darcy's law $v = kh/L = ki$.

The head lost, h, in overcoming the frictional resistance in soil to seeping water is then, calculated from Fig. 12-2 by means of Bernoulli's principle, that the total head of the energies of a liquid is the sum of potential head, pressure head and velocity head (here = 0), as

$$h = \left(z_1 + \frac{p_1}{\gamma_w}\right) - \left(z_2 + \frac{p_2}{\gamma_w}\right) = h_1 - h_2 \qquad (\text{cm}), \qquad (12\text{-}3)$$

where the quantities involved are shown in the figure. Here z_1 and z_2 are position heads, or geodetic heights; p_1/γ_w and p_2/γ_w are piezometric heads (head lost) and $h = h_1 - h_2$ is the hydraulic head.

As seen from Eq. (12-3), Bernoulli's equation for groundwater flow contains terms usually expressing potential energy of flow and loss in head by frictional resistance of soil.

The stress at point M_1 is $u_1 = \gamma_w p_1/\gamma_w = p_1$ in g/cm^2, or kg/cm^2, depending upon the units used. This stress, a hydrostatic water pressure, is termed the *neutral stress*. Similarly, the neutral stress at point M_2 is $u_2 = p_2$.

Average Flow Velocity. Recall that in hydraulics, the flow velocity of water is expressed as

$$v = \frac{Q}{A} \quad \text{(cm/sec)}, \tag{12-4}$$

where Q = volume of flowing water in cm^3 per unit of time, which in hydraulics is called the discharge, and

A = gross cross-sectional area, in cm^2, for which the discharge is calculated. Relative to flow through soil, obviously the average velocity calculated by Eq. (12-4) is not the actual velocity of the flowing water through a porous medium. Considering a unit gross cross-sectional area (solids + voids) in soil perpendicular to the direction of flow, water in soil can flow only through the voids in soil. Therefore the "live", or net, or the permeating cross-sectional area A. Consequently the actual velocity of permeability through one unit cross-sectional area of pure voids is greater for the same discharge quantity, Q, than through one unit of gross cross-sectional area. In order to obtain a unit or average velocity of the water permeating through soil, which is the rate of flow with respect to the area of voids, the actual "live" area of the voids is to be introduced for A in Eq. (12-4), instead of using the full gross cross-sectional area, A.

The average flow or filtration velocity is

$$\frac{\text{Discharge in volume per unit time}}{\text{area of the soil through which flow takes place}} = ki.$$

If the void ratio of soil is e, and the total volume of soil is $(1 + e)$ (solids + voids), then the live, permeating area, A_p, is

$$A_p = \frac{e}{1 + e} A \quad \text{(cm}^2\text{)}, \tag{12-5}$$

where $e/(1 + e)$ is the relative volume of voids. Then the actual, average permeating flow velocity is

$$v_{ave} = \frac{Q}{A_p} = \frac{Q}{A} \frac{1 + e}{e} = v \frac{1 + e}{e} \quad \text{(cm/sec)} \tag{12-6}$$

For example, water flows through a soil of a cross-sectional area of 1 cm^2 (solids + voids) with a velocity of 1 cm^3/sec. Hence, the seepage velocity is $v = 1$ cm/sec. The void ratio of this soil is given as $e = 0.80$. Then the unit average velocity per 1 cm^2 of voids is

$$v_{ave} = v \frac{1 + e}{e} = (1) \frac{1 + 0.8}{0.8} = 2.25 \quad \text{(cm/sec)}.$$

Total Discharge. The total discharge, Q, of the permeating water through a soil, the gross cross-sectional area of which is A, and during time, t, in seconds is

$$Q = vAt = kiAt \quad \text{(cm}^3\text{)}. \tag{12-7}$$

For example, if the seepage velocity at a given hydraulic gradient is $v = 0.35$ cm/sec, and the cross-sectional area through which seepage takes place is $A = 100$ cm $\times$ 60 cm $= 600$ cm^2, then during one day $= 86,400$ seconds the discharge is

$$Q = (0.35)(600)(86,400) = 18,144,000 \text{ cm}^3 = 18,144 \text{ liters } =$$

$$= 18.144 \text{ cu m} = 35.31 \text{ cu ft} \times 18.144 =$$

$$= 640.66 \text{ cu ft} = 7.481 \text{ gal} \times 640.66 =$$

$$= 4,792.78 \text{ gal}$$

Problem. Given a free surface, steady, parallel, horizontal groundwater flow. Calculate total discharge per day per $b = 100$ cm width of a uniform water-bearing stratum resting on a horizontal, impermeable layer. The soil is a medium sand. Its coefficient of permeability is $k = (5)(10^{-3})$ cm/sec. Two observation wells are spaced 275 m apart. The pertinent geodetic data are shown on Fig. 12-3. Also, calculate and plot the depression line.

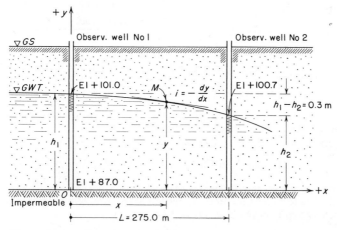

FIG. 12-3   Groundwater flow over a horizontal impermeable layer. Elevations in meters.

Solution 1. Based on Dupuit's theory[2] which for this case is identical with Darcy's law of filtration of water through a uniform soil, the unit discharge of groundwater for one unit of width perpendicular to the drawing plane can be expressed in the following differential form:

$$q = -ky\frac{dy}{dx}, \tag{12-8}$$

where x and y are coordinates of the point, M, on the free surface of the flowing groundwater and L is the length of a section of the water-bearing stratum. Here the minus sign means that with the increase in flow distance, x, the pressure head decreases. Therefore, dy is negative. Or, in this coordinate system, the slope of a tangent in the second quarter is negative.

It is pertinent to note that Dupuit assumed that the filter velocity depends only upon the surface gradient (slope), i.e., upon the tangent dy/dx instead of sine of the angle of the slope (see Eq. 12-14).

The quantity, h_2, in Fig. 12-3, may also be considered as the stage of water in a river or canal.

Separation of variables in Eq. (12-8) and integration yields:

$$q = k \frac{h_1^2 - h_2^2}{2L} \tag{12-9}$$

The equation of the depression line of the flowing groundwater surface is obtained by applying the principle of continuity of flow by writing

$$q = k \frac{h_1^2 - h_2^2}{2L} \quad \text{and} \quad q = k \frac{h_1^2 - y^2}{2x} \tag{12-10}$$

Then

$$y = + \sqrt{h_1^2 - \frac{x}{L}(h_1^2 - h_2^2)}. \tag{12-11}$$

Continuing the solution of the numerical problem, the unit discharge is

$$q = k \frac{(h_1 + h_2)(h_1 - h_2)}{2} = $$

$$= (5)(10^{-3})(10^{-2}) \frac{(101.0 - 87.0) + (100.7 - 87.0)}{2} \tag{12-12}$$

$$\frac{(101.0 - 87.0) - (100.7 - 87.0)}{275.0} = $$

$$= 7.54(10^{-7})(m^3/sec) = 6.52(10^{-2})(m^3/day).$$

The factor (10^{-2}) in the above equation is needed to convert the coefficient of permeability k from cm/sec to m/sec.

For $b = 100$ m width the total discharge is

$$Q = qb = (6.52)(10^{-2})(100) = 6.52 \ (m^3/day).$$

Complete the depression line by means of Eq. 12-11.

Solution 2. The foregoing method of solution of this problem suggests, by Eq. (12-12) that the discharge can simply be expressed as

$$q = kiA = k = i(1 \times h), \tag{12-13}$$

where

$$i = \frac{h_1 - h_2}{L} = \frac{0.3}{275} = 0.00109$$

is the hydraulic gradient, and

$$h - \frac{h_1 - h_2}{2} = \frac{14.0 + 13.7}{2} = 13.85 \ (m)$$

is the average thickness of the water-bearing stratum.

Then the unit discharge is

$$q = (5)(10^{-3})(10^{-2})(0.00109)(13.85) = (7.54)(10^{-7})(m^3/sec) =$$
$$= (6.52)(m^3/day).$$

For a 100 m width the discharge is, as before,

$$Q = (6.25)(10^{-2})(100) = 6.52 \ (m^3/day).$$

12-3. Inclined Flow. Assume a uniform flow of groundwater through a uniform soil under conditions as illustrated in Fig. 12-4. The thickness, or depth, of the flowing sheet of water is d throughout, and the grade of the free surface of the flowing water is the same as that of the impermeable layer, and constant. Also assume the width of the groundwater stream to be constant.

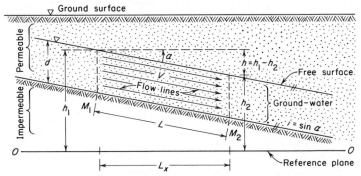

FIG. 12-4   Uniform groundwater flow with free surface.

Under these conditions, and going from one live cross-section to another one, the magnitude of the hydrostatic heads varies for all streamlines by the same amount. This means that the hydraulic gradient is the same for all flow lines. The difference in the levels, h, of water between two points on the flow path causes the groundwater to flow. With a constant coefficient of permeability, k, the flow velocity then depends only upon the hydraulic gradient, i, i.e., the filtration velocities for all streamlines in a uniform groundwater flow are equal.

This discharge is calculated as

$$Q = Av = Aki \qquad (\text{cm}^3/\text{sec}). \qquad (12\text{-}13)$$

If the width, b, of the soil mass through which the flow takes place (perpendicularly to the drawing plane) is greater than d, then the discharge is calculated as

$$q = \frac{Q}{b} = kid = vd = kd \sin \alpha \qquad (12\text{-}14)$$

cm^3/sec per cm width,
where $i = \sin \alpha = \text{const.}$

Problem. Calculate the discharge per day of a uniform, parallel flow along an incline of $i = 0.003$ for a $b = 100$-ft shore line (perpendicularly to the drawing plane). The thickness of the water sheet is 5 m. The coefficient of permeability is $k = (5)(10^{-3})$ (m/sec).

Solution. By Eq. (12-13), the discharge is

$$Q = kiA = (5)(10^{-3})(0.003)(5 \times 100)(86,400) =$$
$$= 648.0 \qquad (\text{m}^3/\text{day}).$$

12-4. Artesian Groundwater Flow. If the groundwater flowing under pressure through a pervious layer of soil is fully *confined* from its top and bottom between impermeable geologic formations, such a groundwater is termed *artesian water*

(Fig. 12-5). The pervious soil layer is termed the *aquifer*. If a well is drilled into the soil until groundwater in the aquifer is reached, then, depending upon the magnitude of the pressure, p, at the well-point, artesian water will flow up through the well. The height of rise, $h_f = p/\gamma_w$, of artesian water may be higher than the

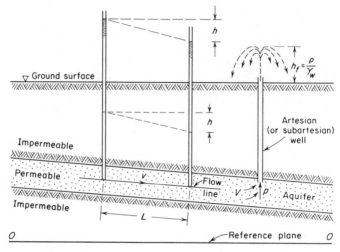

FIG. 12-5   Artesian (or subartesian) groundwater flow.

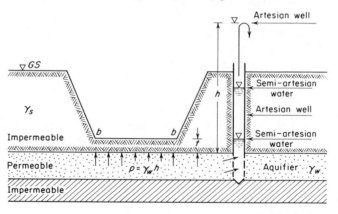

FIG. 12-6   Effect of artesian water on stability of bottom of pit.

ground surface. In such a case one speaks of a fountain of water. Or, the height of rise of artesian water may be less than the elevation of the ground surface. In such a case one speaks of *semi-artesian water*.

The need can be easily seen for establishing the position of the groundwater table before the commencement of foundation operations. If excavation in soil is carried down so deep that the bottom of the excavation pit is broken through by the pressure of the artesian water, then usually there is very little one can do to correct the conditions in the spoiled pit. Usually such sites are abandoned and a new site is sought if costly foundation methods are to be avoided.

The danger of the presence of artesian water at a construction site relative to excavation and stability of the bottom of the pit is illustrated in Fig. 12-6. To prevent the bottom of the pit from being broken through by water, the minimum thickness, t, of the bottom at pressures in equilibrium should be:

$$\uparrow \gamma_w h = \downarrow \gamma_s t, \tag{12-15}$$

or

$$t = \frac{\gamma_w}{\gamma_s} h \quad \text{(cm)} \tag{12-15a}$$

at an uplift coefficient of $\alpha = 1$. That is, the bottom of the pit, viz., clay, is then considered as absolutely impermeable, so that the bottom surface, b-b, receives the full, undiminished pressure. With an uplift coefficient of $\alpha < 1.0$, t then comes out less than $(\gamma_w/\gamma_s)h$.

If the porosity of the soil is $n = 30\%$, then the uplift coefficient, α, is theoretically calculated as[3]

$$\alpha = (1.21)n^{2/3}. \tag{12-16}$$

This calculation shows the thickness, t, to be less than before, namely:

$$\alpha = (1.21)(0.3)^{2/3} = 0.54,$$

and

$$t_\alpha = \alpha \frac{\gamma_w}{\gamma_s} h = (0.54)(t). \tag{12-17}$$

However, because of the uncertainties in the uniformity of porosity distributions, and to avoid an unpleasant experience with damaged pit-bottoms, it is safer to operate with an $\alpha = 1.00$, if the elevation of the structure permits one to do so.

Pile driving in soil containing artesian water is also troublesome. Cases are known where, upon the removal of the pile-driving rammer, the pile was pushed out of the soil by the pressure of artesian water.

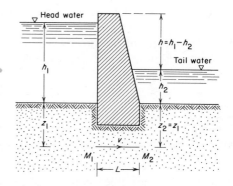

FIG. 12-7   Confined flow under a structure.

The discharge through the aquifer in the direction of flow, again, is calculated as

$$Q = vA = kiA \quad \text{(cm}^3/\text{sec)},$$

where $i = h/L$.

An example of a *partly confined* groundwater flow under pressure and with no free surface is illustrated in Fig. 12-7. The hydraulic gradient, i, is here calculated as

$$i = \frac{h_1 - h_2}{L} \tag{12-18}$$

12-5. Seepage Connected to Groundwater. Figure 12-8 illustrates a condition where seepage water from a body of water (river, canal, reservoir) is hydraulically connected to groundwater. This case occurs also with sinks in soil upon heavy rainfalls, and with groundwater recharge basins. The seepage water may have a surface water-table, m-s, or a capillary water-table (surface of menisci, m-m).

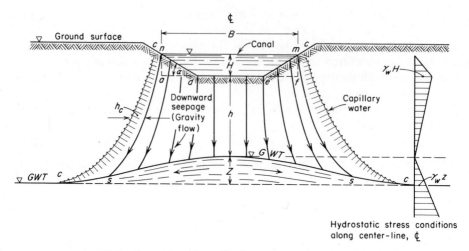

FIG. 12-8   Seepage and capillarity connected to groundwater.

The velocity of the downwards translocating seepage water through a horizontal section of a uniform soil column, according to Darcy's law is

$$v = k_{aw} \frac{H + h}{h} \quad \text{(cm/sec)},\qquad (12\text{-}19)$$

where h = height of the column of soil above the groundwater table,

H = depth of water in the water-basin, in cm, and

k_{aw} = coefficient of the system's permeability of soil the voids of which are filled partly with air, and partly with water.

According to Zunker,[4] the value of k_{aw} is

$$k_{aw} = \frac{k}{2},\qquad (12\text{-}20)$$

where k = the permeability of the uniform soil system to water.

As soon as the air content in soil becomes so large that the air bubbles cling to the hygroscopic and water-film moisture, surface menisci develop (boundary surface between liquid and gas) and a capillary sub-pressure is induced within the seepage water. The hydraulic stress conditions in water are also illustrated in Fig. 12-8.

Of course, the method of calculating seepage discharge from canals depends very much upon the geological conditions under consideration.

Example. Refer to Figure 12-8. A navigable canal of trapezoidal cross section is dug into a pervious soil. A soil sample taken 2 ft below the bottom level of the canal is tested in the undisturbed state in the laboratory and is found to have a coefficient of permeability $k = 2$ m/day. There is a seepage of water through the bottom and sides of the canal. The width of the canal at the water level is $B = 30$ m. The slopes of the canal are made vert.: horiz. $= 1 : n = 1 : 2.5$. The depth of the water in the canal is $H = 3.5$ m. The groundwater table, after the seepage flow from the canal has stabilized, is at a depth of $h = 8.0$ m below the bottom. Further, assume that the loss of water by capillarity makes up 55% of the total seepage lost from the canal save for the loss by evaporation. Calculate the total loss of water from canal to soil per one linear meter along the shore line of the canal.

Solution.

a) The coefficient of the system's permeability of the soil, k_{aw}, the voids of which are filled partly with air and partly with water, by Eq. (12-20) is

$$k_{aw} = \frac{k}{2} = \frac{2.0}{2} = 1.0 \qquad \text{(m/day).}$$

b) The velocity of the downward translocating seepage water, by Eq. (12-19) is

$$v = k_{aw}\frac{H + h}{h} = (1.0)\frac{3.5 + 8.0}{8.0} = 1.425 \qquad \text{(m/day).}$$

c) The filtrating area, A, at the level, c-d-e-f, at the bottom of the canal is assumed to be approximately the horizontal projection of the wetted perimeter, which is equal to the width of the canal, $B = 30.0$ m :

$$A = (cf)(1.0) = (B)(1.0) = (30.0)(1.0) = 30.0 \qquad \text{(m}^2\text{).}$$

d) The discharge quantity of the seepage is

$$q = vA = (1.425)(30.0) = 42.75 \qquad \text{(m}^3\text{/day)}$$

per 1 m running shore line.

e) If the loss of water by capillarity is given as 55% of the total loss of water from the canal to the soil, then the 42.75 m³/day loss of water by seepage alone represents 45% of the total. Hence, the loss by capillarity is

$$42.75 \times 55/45 = 52.24 \qquad \text{(m}^3\text{/day),}$$

and

f) the total loss from the canal to the soil is

$$42.75 \text{ m}^3\text{/day} + 52.24 \text{ m}^3\text{/day} = 94.99 \text{ m}^3\text{/day}$$

per one running meter along the shore line of the canal.

12-6. Permeability Through Stratified Layers of Soil

The Problem. In soil, foundation, and highway engineering compound-layer systems in several strata, rather than single, unstratified ones, are often encountered (Fig. 12-9). In such a case the permeability to water of each of the particular single component soil layers of the stratified soil system may be, and usually is, different because of the various types of soil. Besides, the permeability perpendicular to the stratified soil layers or bedding planes (usually approximately in the vertical direction) is different from that parallel (usually approximately in the horizontal direction) to the stratification. Therefore, it appears necessary to determine a weighted coefficient of permeability for the compound, stratified soil system.

Permeability Perpendicular to Stratification. If the groundwater flows through a compound soil layer consisting of several different types of soil, and each layer being of different permeability perpendicular to stratification of the layered soil system, then an average system's coefficient of permeability can be calculated if the permeabilities $k_{1\perp}$, $k_{2\perp}$, $k_{3\perp}$, . . . $k_{n\perp}$ are known.

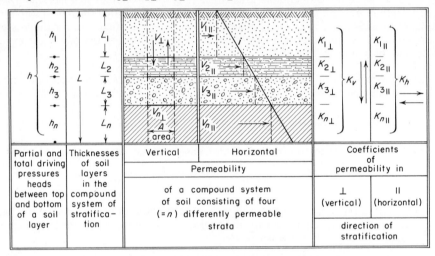

FIG. 12-9   Compound system of soil layers.

With the symbols as shown in Fig. 12-9, the average coefficient of permeability, k_v, perpendicular to the bedding planes, is calculated on the principle of continuity of flow: the flow velocity, v, perpendicular to stratification, must be the same in all layers because the cross-sectional area A under consideration, which is parallel to the stratification and through which the flow takes place, remains the same and constant at all times. Hence,

$$v = k_{1\perp}\frac{h_1}{L_1} = k_{2\perp}\frac{h_2}{L_2} = k_{3\perp}\frac{h_3}{L_3} = \cdots = k_n\frac{h_n}{L_n} = k_v\frac{h}{L}, \qquad (12\text{-}21)$$

where $k_{1\perp}, k_{2\perp}, k_{3\perp}, \ldots k_{n\perp}$ are the coefficients of permeability of the individual
    component layers,
    $h_1, h_2, h_3, \ldots h_n$ are the singular losses in pressure heads between the top
    and bottom of each component stratum,
    h is the total pressure head, and
    $L_1, L_2, L_3, \ldots L_n = L$ are the thicknesses of the layers.
Also, from Darcy's law, $v = k(h/L)$, the following relationship exists:

$$\frac{h_1}{v} = \frac{L_1}{k_{1\perp}}; \quad \frac{h_2}{v} = \frac{L_2}{k_{2\perp}}; \quad \frac{h_3}{v} = \frac{L_3}{k_{3\perp}}; \quad \cdots \quad \frac{h_n}{v} = \frac{L_n}{k_{n\perp}}. \qquad (12\text{-}22)$$

Adding these latter equations obtain

$$\frac{h_1}{v} + \frac{h_2}{v} + \frac{h_3}{v} + \cdots + \frac{h_n}{v} = \frac{L_1}{k_{1\perp}} + \frac{L_2}{k_{2\perp}} + \frac{L_3}{k_{3\perp}} + \cdots + \frac{L_n}{k_{n\perp}}, \quad (12\text{-}23)$$

or

$$\frac{1}{v}(h_1 + h_2 + h_3 + \cdots + h_n) = \frac{h}{v} = \frac{L_1}{k_{1\perp}} + \frac{L_2}{k_{2\perp}} + \frac{L_3}{k_{3\perp}} + \cdots + \frac{L_n}{k_{n\perp}}. \quad (12\text{-}24)$$

Substitution of v from Eq. (12-21) into Eq. (12-24) yields the average coefficient of permeability, k_v, of the compound soil layer perpendicular to stratification:

$$k_v = \frac{L}{\dfrac{L_1}{k_{1\perp}} + \dfrac{L_2}{k_{2\perp}} + \dfrac{L_3}{k_{3\perp}} + \cdots + \dfrac{L_n}{k_{n\perp}}} \quad (\text{cm/sec}). \quad (12\text{-}25)$$

The discharge through a unit area perpendicular to stratification is

$$q = v = k_v \frac{h}{L} = \frac{h}{\dfrac{L_1}{k_{1\perp}} + \dfrac{L_2}{k_{2\perp}} + \dfrac{L_3}{k_{3\perp}} + \cdots + \dfrac{L_n}{k_{n\perp}}} \quad (\text{cm}^3/\text{sec}). \quad (12\text{-}26)$$

If the permeability, $k_{n\perp}$, of any one of the single soil layers in the compound layer is relatively very low, then this $k_{n\perp}$ determines the magnitude of the denominator in Eq. (12-26), namely: if any one of the k's is approaching zero, then the corresponding quantity $(L/k_\perp)_n$ approaches a very large value, so that practically all other $(L/k_\perp)$ terms in the denominator can be neglected. Then v becomes very small. Thus, it can be understood that the least permeable layer in the compound layered soil system, no matter how thin, has a considerable influence on the flow velocity, viz., discharge perpendicular to stratification.

12-7. Permeability Parallel to Stratification. If the groundwater flows through a compound soil layer of different permeabilities parallel to the stratification or bedding planes, then all flow lines are also hydraulically parallel to the boundaries of the stratification. Besides, the hydraulic gradient, i, is the same at every point of each layer, because in this case i does not depend upon the permeability of the soil layer. Therefore, the average flow velocity, v_h, for an L-unit thick compound layer of soil is calculated based on the following considerations: The total average unit discharge per area $a = 1 \text{ cm}^2$ is

$$q = va = v1 = v \quad (\text{cm}^3/\text{sec}). \quad (12\text{-}27)$$

This q can be considered as consisting of the sum of partial unit discharges through each of the single layers in the compound layer:

$$q = q'_1 + q'_2 + q'_3 + \cdots + q'_n. \quad (12\text{-}28)$$

The partial discharges $q'_1, q'_2, q'_3, \ldots q'_n$, are calculated as follows:

Compute a hypothetical total discharge, q_1, parallel to stratification which would flow through the entire compound-layered system the total thickness of which is $L_1 = L$. Assume that all of the single layers of the compound layer are of the same soil with the same coefficient of permeability k_{h_1}. Then calculate the hypothetical total flows $q_2, q_3, \ldots q_n$ corresponding to a permeability of $k_{h_2}, k_{h_3}, k_{h_4}, \ldots k_{h_n}$, respectively, assuming that the total thicknesses of the corresponding layers are $L_2 = L, L_3 = L, \ldots L_n = L$, respectively.

The portion q'_1 flowing through the layer L_1 units thick is

$$q'_1 = q_1 \frac{L_1}{L}. \tag{12-29}$$

This principle of calculation is now applied to velocities, viz.,

$$v'_1 = v_1 \frac{L_1}{L}, \tag{12-30}$$

because q is proportional to v.

The portions $v'_2, v'_3, \ldots v'_n$ flowing through the corresponding layers of thickness $L_2, L_3, \ldots L_n$, respectively, are

$$v'_2 = v_2 \frac{L_2}{L}, \tag{12-30a}$$

$$v'_3 = v_3 \frac{L_3}{L}, \tag{12-30b}$$

$$\cdots \cdots \cdots$$

$$v'_n = v_n \frac{L_n}{L}. \tag{12-30n}$$

Then the total average velocity, v, according to the symbols used in Fig. 12-9, is

$$v = k_h i = v'_{1\,\|} + v'_{2\,\|} + v'_{3\,\|} + \cdots + v'_{n\,\|} =$$

$$= \frac{1}{L} (v_{1\,\|} L_1 + v_{2\,\|} L_2 + v_{3\,\|} L_3 + \cdots + v_{n\,\|} L_n) =$$

$$= \frac{1}{L} (k_{1\,\|} i L_1 + k_{2\,\|} i L_2 + k_{3\,\|} i L_3 + \cdots + k_{n\,\|} i L_n), \tag{12-31}$$

and

$$k_h = \frac{k_{1\,\|} L_1 + k_{2\,\|} L_2 + k_{3\,\|} L_3 + \cdots + k_{n\,\|} L_n}{L} \quad \text{(cm/sec)}, \tag{12-32}$$

where k_h = average coefficient of permeability for the entire compound layer of soil parallel to stratification (usually horizontally);

i = hydraulic gradient of the stream of groundwater, assumed constant and the same for all strata in the compound layer of soil;

L = total thickness of the compound soil layer;

$L_1, L_2, L_3, \ldots L_n$ = thicknesses of individual soil layers making up the compound layer of soil;

$v_{1\parallel}$, $v_{2\parallel}$, $v_{3\parallel}$, ... $v_{n\parallel}$ = flow velocities through each of the soil strata making up the compound layer; and

$k_{1\parallel}$, $k_{2\parallel}$, $k_{3\parallel}$, ... $k_{n\parallel}$ = coefficient of permeability of each of the respective component soil layers in the layered system.

The discharge through the compound soil layer is

$$q = k_h i. \qquad (12\text{-}33)$$

In the case of parallel (horizontal) permeability through a layered soil system, the discharge quantity is influenced by that component which has the largest coefficient of permeability because, as in Eq. (12-32), these coefficients are in the nominator contributing to the k_h-values. This means that in cohesive soils the magnitude of the discharge quantity is determined by the thinner layers of sand.

The average coefficient of permeability of the entire thickness of the layered system, k_{ave}, is calculated as the geometric average of k_v and k_h:

$$k_{\text{ave}} = \sqrt{k_v k_h}. \qquad (12\text{-}34)$$

Example. Given a massive weir placed on a horizontal system of layered soil as shown in Fig. 12-10.

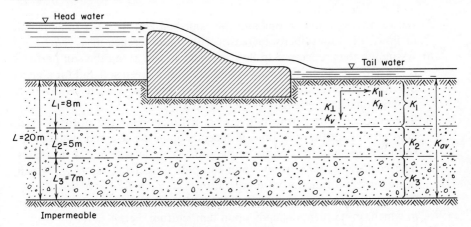

12-10 Seepage through a layered system of soil.

The coefficients of permeability of soil representing each of the three layers are:
1) perpendicular to bedding planes:
 $k_\perp$: $k_1 = 0.010$ m/sec
  $k_2 = 0.020$ m/sec
  $k_3 = 0.030$ m/sec
2) parallel to bedding planes:
 $k_\parallel$: $k_1 = 0.040$ m/sec
  $k_2 = 0.050$ m/sec
  $k_3 = 0.090$ m/sec
Determine the average coefficient of permeability of the layered soil system.
Solution.
a) The system's coefficient of permeability, k_v, perpendicular to stratification is, by Eq. (12-25):

$$k_v = \frac{L}{\dfrac{L_1}{k_1} + \dfrac{L_2}{k_2} + \dfrac{L_3}{k_3}} = \frac{20.0}{\dfrac{8.0}{0.010} + \dfrac{5.0}{0.020} + \dfrac{7.0}{0.030}} = 0.0156 \quad \text{(m/sec)}.$$

b) The system's coefficient of permeability, k_h, parallel to stratification, is, by Eq. (12-32):

$$k_h = \frac{k_{1\parallel}L_1 + k_{2\parallel}L_2 + k_{3\parallel}L_3}{L} = \frac{(0.040)(8.0) + (0.050)(5.0) + (0.090)(7.0)}{20.0} =$$
$$= 0.060 \quad \text{(m/sec)}.$$

c) The system's average coefficient of permeability, k_{ave}, by Eq. (12-34) is

$$k_{ave} = \sqrt{k_v k_h} = \sqrt{(0.0156)(0.060)} = 0.0306 \quad \text{(m/sec)}.$$

12-8. Discussion of Darcy's Law.

1) Darcy's law is valid as long as a laminar flow exists.
2) It applies to soil textures which are finer than fine gravels.
3) In soil, the flow of water is possible if there is a difference in pressure heads between two points on the flow path.
4) When $h_1 > h_2$, flow will take place from a point with h_1 to a point with h_2 (Fig. 12-2).
5) Between two points, in one and the same soil and with the same length of flow, the flow velocity increases with the difference in $h = h_1 - h_2$.
6) Assuming that resistance to flow of water in soil along the soil particles is constant, it can further be assumed that for a given soil and for a given difference in pressure heads, $h = h_1 - h_2$, the flow velocity is inversely proportional to the length of the flow path, L.
7) The coefficient of permeability, k, is a function of the porosity, viz., void ratio, e, of the soil; thus, it depends upon the size and shape of the soil particles, and the density of the soil. With decrese in e, k decreases.
8) The coefficient, k, depends upon the unit weight of water, γ_w, which, in its turn, is a function of temperature, i.e., $\gamma_w = f(T)$.
9) The coefficient, k, depends also upon the dynamic viscosity of water, η, which, in its turn, depends upon temperature, i.e., $\eta = f(T)$.
10) The coefficient of permeability, k, also depends upon the amount of entrapped air and/or gas in the voids of the soil, as well as on the water itself.
11) The coefficient of permeability, k, of soil in the direction parallel to stratification is usually many times (2 to about 30) greater than that perpendicular to the stratification.
12) Because of irregularities in texture and densities of the soil deposits, permeability varies greatly from point to point. Therefore, it is extremely difficult to determine.
13) Thus it can be concluded that the coefficient of permeability of soil depends very much upon the type of soil, as well as on climatic, hydrologic, and geologic conditions.
14) The coefficient of permeability is best determined experimentally.

DETERMINATION OF COEFFICIENT OF PERMEABILITY

12-9. Determination of k Experimentally in the Laboratory. Many methods of determining permeability of soil are described and discussed in a "Symposium on Permeability of Soils" of the American Society for Testing Materials,[5] and in "Procedures for Testing Soils" by the same society. Therefore, only the basic theoretical principles upon which such tests are based are discussed here.

a) *Constant-Head Vertical Permeameter.* A permeameter is an apparatus used for determining the coefficient of permeability of soil.

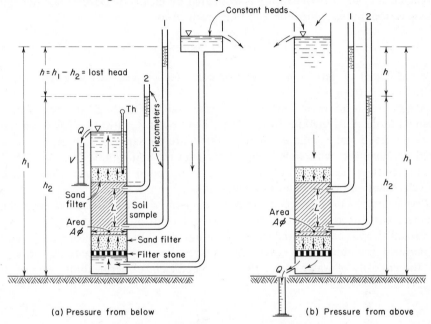

(a) Pressure from below   (b) Pressure from above

FIG. 12-11   Constant-head permeameters.

A constant-head permeameter consists of a vertical cylinder containing the soil sample for which the coefficient of permeability is to be determined, Fig. 12-11. The soil sample can be in a disturbed state, or in an undisturbed state. Two or more piezometric tubes are attached to the permeameter cylinder spaced a distance, L, apart. The horizontal cross-sectional area of the cylinder, viz., soil sample, perpendicular to the direction of flow of water through the soil sample is A cm^2. The test cylinder is connected through its bottom by means of a pipe to a water or pressure reservoir, Fig. 12-11a, distant h units above the soil sample. Note that h is constant. Thus, water pressure is applied, and water enters the permeameter from below the soil sample giving an upward flow. The amount of water, V, in cm^3 flowing during a certain time, t seconds, is collected in a graduate cylinder; the temperature of the water is measured; the pressure difference $h = h_1 - h_2$ is determined, which is the loss in head spent for overcoming the resistance to flow over a length of flow, L, through the soil sample, and the following quantities calculated:

Discharge $\qquad\qquad Q = \dfrac{V}{t} \qquad$ (cm^3/sec) $\qquad\qquad$ (12-35)

Seepage velocity $\qquad v = \dfrac{Q}{A} \qquad$ (cm/sec) $\qquad\qquad$ (12-36)

Hydraulic gradient $\qquad i = \dfrac{h}{L} \qquad$ (cm/cm). $\qquad\qquad$ (12-37)

The coefficient of permeability is evaluated by means of Darcy's law per unit cross-sectional area, unit time and unit gradient as

$$ k = \frac{v}{i} = \frac{Q}{Ai} \qquad \text{(cm/sec).} \qquad\qquad (12\text{-}38) $$

The coefficient of permeability is to be corrected for viscosity and reported at 20°C: $k_{20} = (k)(\eta/\eta_{20})$.

A constant-head permeameter with water seeping through the soil sample from its top is illustrated in Fig. 12-11b. The flow is downward. The quantities to be observed and calculated to determine k are the same as with the constant-head permeameter with water seeping through the soil sample from below.

The constant-head permeability test is more suited for coarse soils such as gravelly sand and coarse and medium sand.

Permeability Correction for Temperature. In soil mechanics research and practice, for purpose of comparison, the coefficient of permeability, k, is conventionally reported at a standard temperature of +20°C. Therefore, coefficients of permeability obtained at other temperatures than standard are to be corrected for the viscosity of water at +20°C. The coefficient of permeability at +20°C, k_{20}, is calculated as

$$ k_{20} = k\,\frac{\eta_T}{\eta_{20}}, \qquad\qquad (12\text{-}39) $$

where k = coefficient of permeability obtained at some temperature $T \ne 20°C$,

$\quad \eta_T$ = coefficient of dynamic viscosity, in g/(cm sec) = poises at some temperature $T \ne 20°C$, and

η_{20} = coefficient of dynamic viscosity at +20°C.

Values of viscosity correction coefficients η_T/η_{20} at atmospheric pressure are given in Appendix III. The values in this table were prepared by the author from viscosity figures as given in the International Critical Tables, and interpolated for values not shown in these ICT tables, and also interpolated between full degrees to give η and η_T/η_{22} for decimal degrees. The temperature correction table contains viscosity correction factors for undercooled water down to $-10°C$, and for ordinary water up to +40°C.

Example. A soil sample representing a sand has been tested in a constant-head permeameter. The inside diameter of the container holding the sand is $D = 10.2$ cm. The head loss, h, over a distance $L = 12.5$ cm between two piezometers is 86.0 cm. The amount of the permeating water collected during a time of 2 minutes is $V = 733$ cm³. The temperature of the permeating water was 15°C.

Compute discharge, Q, and the coefficient of permeability of this sand.
Solution.
1) Discharge

$$Q = \frac{V}{t} = \frac{733}{(2)(60)} = 6.1 \qquad (cm^3/sec).$$

2) Cross-sectional area of soil sample:

$$A = \frac{\pi D^2}{4} = (0.785)(10.2)^2 = 81.6 \qquad (cm^2).$$

3) Hydraulic gradient

$$i = \frac{h}{L} = \frac{86.0}{12.5} = 6.88.$$

4) Coefficient of permeability

$$k_{15} = \frac{Q}{Ai} = \frac{(6.1)}{(81.6)(6.88)} = 0.01085 \qquad (cm/sec) =$$
$$= (1.085)(10^{-2}) \qquad (cm/sec).$$

5) Coefficient of permeability at standard temperature of 20°C, by Eq. (12-39) is

$$k_{20} = k_{15} \frac{\eta_{15}}{\eta_{20}} = (0.01085)(1.13432) = (1.23)(10^{-2}) \qquad (cm/sec).$$

b) *Falling-Head Permeameter.* A falling-head or variable-head permeameter consists of a vertical test cylinder of cross-sectional area A in cm^2 containing the soil sample to be tested for permeability. To the test cylinder there is attached a vertical, transparent tube of constant diameter, viz., cross-sectional area, a, in cm^2, throughout (Fig. 12-12). The test cylinder is placed in an overflow container to maintain the tail water at constant level. The sample is allowed to saturate; the standpipe filled to a certain height with water, h_1; the height of the water is marked, and time is clocked. If no more water is added, the height in the standpipe drops as the water seeps through the soil sample. During an elapsed-time interval between t_1 and t_2, the elevation of the water in the standpipe will drop from height, h_1, to height, h_2, measured from tail-water table, by an amount of h. The drop in head means decrease in volume of water in the standpipe.

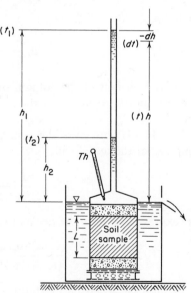

Fig. 12-12   Falling-head permeameter.

The calculation of the coefficient of permeability, k, from a falling-head permeability test is performed as follows.

Let h equal the head at any time, t. During the next time interval, dt, the height of the column of water in the standpipe drops by an amount of $(-dh)$. The minus sign means that height, h, decreases as time, t, increases. The differential volume, dQ, of water lost (discharge) from the standpipe is

$$dQ = -a\,dh \qquad (\text{cm}^3), \tag{12-40}$$

where $a =$ cross-sectional area of the standpipe, in cm^2.

By the principle of continuity, during the time interval, dt, this amount of water, Q, flows through the soil sample, the height of which is L cm:

$$dQ = kAi\,dt = kA\,\frac{h}{L}\,dt, \tag{12-41}$$

where $h/L = i =$ hydraulic gradient, in cm/cm.

Hence, Eq. (12-40) can be equated to Eq. (12-41):

$$-a\,dh = kAi\,dt. \tag{12-42}$$

Separating variables, h and t, this equation can be integrated between the limits of h_1 and h_2 for h, and t_2 and t_1 for t:

$$\int_{h_2}^{h_1} \frac{dh}{h} = -\frac{k}{L}\frac{A}{a}\int_{t_2}^{t_1} dt, \tag{12-43}$$

yielding

$$\ln\frac{h_1}{h_2} = \frac{k}{L}\frac{A}{a}(t_2 - t_1). \tag{12-44}$$

Here $h_1 =$ height of the column of water in the standpipe at the beginning of the test, and $h_2 =$ height of the column of water in the standpipe at the end of the test.

Eq. (12-44) now gives the general expression for the coefficient of permeability, k, of the tested soil:

$$k = \frac{L}{(t_2 - t_1)}\frac{a}{A}\ln\frac{h_1}{h_2} \qquad (\text{cm/sec}), \tag{12-45}$$

or, expressed in terms of decimal logarithms,

$$k = \frac{(2.3026)L}{(t_2 - t_1)}\frac{a}{A}\log_{10}\left(\frac{h_1}{h_2}\right) \qquad (\text{cm/sec}). \tag{12-46}$$

In the case when permeability is tested by means of an artificially applied pressure, the pressure head of which, h_a, is measured by means of a mercury barometer, for example, then k is calculated as

$$k = \frac{(2.3026)L}{(t_2 - t_1)}\frac{a}{A}\log_{10}\frac{h_1 + (13.6)h_a}{h_2 + (13.6)h_a}, \tag{12-47}$$

where $13.6 = \gamma_{\text{Hg}} =$ unit weight of mercury.

If the coefficient of permeability, k, of a soil is tested at a temperature different from $+20°C$, then it has to be corrected for viscosity, viz., temperature, and reported as

$$k_{20} = k \frac{\eta_T}{\eta_{20}}, \qquad (12\text{-}48)$$

where η_T/η_{20} = viscosity correction coefficient.

The falling- or variable-head permeability test is more suited for fine sands, silts, and clays. This type of apparatus is very convenient to work with if the drop in head in the vertical tube does not exceed 1 cm/sec. The amount of water seeping through the soil sample in this test need not be collected because it can be calculated from the cross-sectional area of the standpipe, and the drop in height of the water column in it.

The presence of air in the voids of cohesive soils, particularly clays, when determining their permeability, is a very disturbing factor.

Example. An undisturbed clay sample of cylindrical shape has been tested for its permeability in a falling-head permeameter. The diameter of the soil sample was 5.0 cm, and its thickness, viz., height was 2.5 cm. The inside diameter of the standpipe of the permeameter was 12.5 mm. At the start of the permeability test, the reading of the water column in the standpipe was 45.0 cm. Seven minutes and 25 seconds later the reading was 43.0 cm. The temperature of the permeating water was 20°C.

1) Sketch the test arrangement.
2) Calculate the coefficient of permeability of the clay sample.

Solution.

1) The principal sketch of the falling-head permeameter is like that shown in Fig. 12-12.
2) The coefficient of permeability, k, is calculated by Eq. (12-46) as

$$k = \frac{a}{A} \frac{L}{t} (2.3) \log_{10}\left(\frac{h_1}{h_2}\right).$$

a) The cross-sectional area of the soil sample:

$$A = \frac{\pi D^2}{4} = (0.785)(5.0)^2 = 19.6 \qquad (\text{cm}^2).$$

b) The cross-sectional area of the standpipe:

$$a = \frac{\pi d^2}{4} = \frac{(3.14)(1.25)^2}{4} = 1.23 \qquad (\text{cm}^2).$$

c) The thickness of the soil sample:

$$L = 2.5 \qquad (\text{cm}).$$

d) The time, t, to drop in head from 45.0 cm to 43.0 cm:

$$t = t_2 - t_1; \quad t_1 = 0.$$
$$t_2 - t_1 = t = (7 \times 60) + 25 = 445 \qquad (\text{sec})$$

e) Falling head ratio:

$$\frac{h_1}{h_2} = \frac{45}{43} = 1.048.$$

f) $\ln(1.048) = (2.3)\log_{10}(1.048) = (2.3)(0.020361) = 0.0468$.
g) The coefficient of permeability of the clay sample tested at 20°C is;

$$k_{20} = \frac{(1.23)(2.5)}{(19.6)(445)}(0.0468) = \underline{(1.64)(10^{-4})} \quad \text{(cm/sec)}.$$

Note.   To judge whether this calculated permeability is high or low, it would be helpful for the engineer to know the density and porosity, or void ratio, of the soil.

One realizes that there is a difference in the magnitudes of k tested under load and without a superimposed load. Here the time factor is involved, namely: it takes a longer time to drop the water in the same amount of head through a loaded soil sample. Hence, the coefficient of permeability of a loaded soil sample is less than that of an unloaded sample.

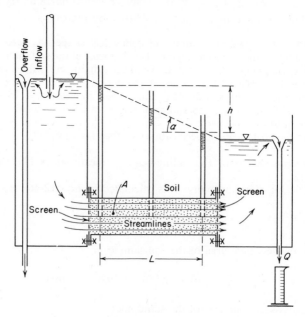

FIG. 12-13   Horizontal permeameter.

c) *Horizontal Permeability Test.* A basic sketch of a horizontal permeameter is shown in Fig. 12-13. The discharge, Q, head loss, h, temperature, T, are observed. The filtration length, L, between any two points along the flow path can be established as being constant, and the cross-sectional area perpendicular to the horzontal direction of flow can be ascertained. The coefficient of permeability, k, is then calculated as

$$k = \frac{V}{i} = \frac{Q}{Ai} = \frac{Q}{A(h/L)} \quad \text{(cm/sec)}. \qquad (12\text{-}4)$$

The horizontal permeability test is well suited for sand.

Example. In Fig. 12-13, the cross-sectional area of a soil sample, tested in a 30 cm long horizontal permeameter, was $A = 100$ cm^2, and the discharged volume of water was $V = 750$ cm^3, at a head loss of $h = 60$ cm. The duration of this test was 10 min. The temperature of the water was measured as $T = 20°C$. Determine the coefficient of permeability of this soil.

Solution. By Eq. (12-49),

$$k_{20} = \frac{(750)(30)}{(10 \times 60)(100)(60)} = \underline{(6.25)(10^{-3})} \quad (cm/sec).$$

d) *Coefficient of Permeability by Consolidation Test.* The coefficients of permeability of some cohesive soils are very low, so that measurable quantities of discharge, viz., drop in head in a standpipe, can be ascertained only by the application of large hydraulic gradients. Such soils, as well as those subjected to heavy loads, can be tested for their permeability to water by subjecting them to a consolidation test, which, in essence, is a drainage or permeability test.

An idea of the principle underlying the performance of permeability test on a cohesive soil by means of a consolidation test apparatus is given in Chapter 15 of this book dealing with the topic of consolidation of soil.

12-10. Values of Coefficients of Permeability. For orientation purposes some relative values of coefficients of permeabilities for textural fractions in soil are given in Table 12-1. The classification of the ranges of permeability by various degrees is here adopted after Terzaghi and Peck.[7] This table shows that a composite soil consisting of various textural fractions and in various proportions, may have k-values which can vary within a very wide range. Therefore these k-values are not suitable for use in design of hydraulic structures, earthworks, and foundation engineering. For design work actual values of coefficients of permeability of soil are to be obtained.

TABLE 12-1. RELATIVE VALUES OF SOIL PERMEABILITIES

Degree of Permeability	Range of Coefficient of Permeability k cm/sec	Approximate Textural Soil Fraction
1	2	3
High	$>10^{-1}$	Medium and coarse gravel.
Medium	10^{-1} to 10^{-3}	Fine gravel; coarse, medium and fine sand; dune sand.
Low	10^{-3} to 10^{-5}	Very fine sand, silty sand, loose silt; loess, rock flour.
Very low	10^{-5} to 10^{-7}	Dense silt; dense loess; clayey silt; clay.
Impervious	$<10^{-7}$	Homogeneous clays.

A graphical presentation of values of coefficients of permeabilities of different types of soils, the application of k's to earth dams, and the method of determination of k's is shown after A. Casagrande and Fadum[8] in Fig. 12-14.

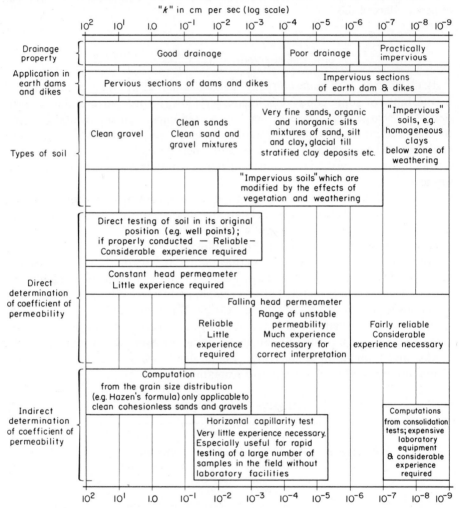

FIG. 12-14   Coefficient of permeability (After A. Casagrande, and R. E. Fadum, Ref. 8).

REFERENCES

1. H. P. G. Darcy, *Les fontaines publiques de la ville de Dijon*, Paris, Victor Dalmont, Éditeur, 1856, pp. 570, 590, 594.
2. J. Dupuit, *Études théoretiques et pratiques sur le mouvement des eaux dans les canaux decouverts à travers les terrains permeables*, Paris, Dunod, 1863, pp. 229, 260.
3. F. W. Hanna and R. C. Kennedy, *The Design of Dams*, New York, McGraw-Hill Book Co., 1931, p. 107.
4. F. Zunker, "Das Verhalten des Bodens zum Wasser", in Blanck's *Handbuch der Bodenlehre*, Berlin, Julius Springer, 1930, vol. 6, p. 181.

5. *Symposium on Permeability of Soils*, Special Technical Publication no. 163, by the American Society for Testing Materials, Philadelphia, 1955.
6. *Procedures for Testing Soil*, American Society for Testing Materials, Philadelphia, April, 1958.
7. K. Terzaghi and R. B. Peck, *Soil Mechanics in Engineering Practice*, New York, John Wiley and Sons, Inc., 1948, p. 331.
8. A. Casagrande and R. E. Fadum, *Notes on Soil Testing for Engineering Purposes*, Cambridge, Mass., Harvard University, Publication no. 268, 1939/40, Fig. 11, p. 23.

QUESTIONS AND PROBLEMS

12-1. Compute the value of a conversion factor for permeability of soil, k, to convert cm/sec into m/day, ft/sec, ft/min, ft/day.

12-2. Convert the values of k as given in Table 12-1 into ft/sec. What is the conversion factor?

12-3. State the principle of Darcy's law of permeability.

12-4. What are the assumptions for the validity of Darcy's law?

12-5. A canal, the surface elevation of which is $+85$ (in ft), runs parallel to a river, the elevation of the water table of which is $+81$. All other conditions necessary for the solution of this problem are shown on the accompanying sketch, Fig. Problem 12-5. The coefficient of the horizontal permeability of the undercut sand layer is $k_h = 0.02$ ft/min, and the vertical permeability of this sand layer is $k_v = 0.004$ ft/min. Calculate the loss of water from canal to river per 100 run of shore per day. Indicate remedial measures to decrease the seepage loss of water from the canal.

12-6. A sample of sand, 5.0 cm in diameter and 10.0 cm thick, was subjected to a permeability test. The test apparatus was of the constant-head type. The test lasted 10 sec, under a hydrostatic head of 100 cm and at 20°C. The weight of the collected discharge water was 600 g. Determine the coefficient of permeability, k, in cm/sec of the specimen of sand. Sketch the test apparatus.

12-7. Given falling-head permeability data, obtained from testing a (-4)-material compacted in a standard permeability testing mold at 12.0% moisture content.
Diameter of soil sample: $D = 10.12$ cm.
Thickness (length of sample): $L = 11.84$ cm.
Inside diameter of tube: $d = 1.08$ cm.
Specific gravity of soil particles: $G = 2.65$.
Volume of sample: $V = 952.0$ cm³.
Weight of dry sample: $W_d = 1804$ g.

Trial Nos.	Temperature of Water °C	Soil °C	Elapsed Time in sec	Head at Start of Test h_1 cm	End h_2 cm
1	21.2	21.2	0	80.0	
2	23.8	23.4	57.6		70.9
3	25.4	25.4	14.0	70.9	70.1

Determine the coefficient of permeability to water of this soil at a standard temperature of 20°C. Give your opinion about the test data as given above. Sketch the test arrangement.

12-8. Given a permeability test apparatus as shown in Fig. Problem 12-8.

Calculate k. $\left(\text{Answer: } k = \dfrac{2Q}{a}\dfrac{L}{h_1{}^2 - h_2{}^2}\right).$

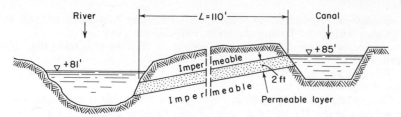

FIG. Problem 12-5.

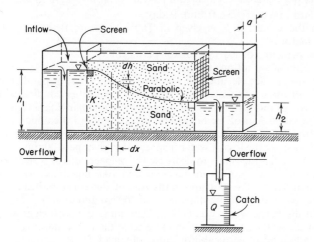

FIG. Problem 12-8.

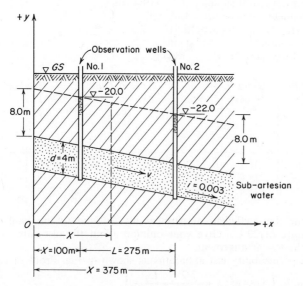

FIG. Problem 12-9.

12-9. Given: inclined artesian groundwater flow as shown in Fig. Problem 12-9. The piezometer level in observation well No. 1 is at elevation -20.0 (in m). The piezometer level in observation well No. 2 is at elevation -22.0. The thickness of the confined aquifer is $d = 4.0$ m. The coefficient of permeability of the soil is $k = 0.005$ m/sec.

Calculate discharge in m³/day per one meter of shore line for a downgrade of the impervious layer of $i = -0.003$, and the same for an upgrade of the impervious layer of $i = +0.003$.

Chapter 13

THEORY OF WELLS

13-1. Determination of Permeability Experimentally in the Field

Pumping Tests. Where the soil conditions in the field are non-uniform, laboratory test results of soil permeability may turn out to be erratic. More reliable coefficients of permeability of soil can be obtained by the method of special full-scale pumping tests: a) water is pumped out of a test well (discharge well), and b) water is pumped into a test well (recharge well).

These pumping methods are extensively used by water supply engineers, and are now also gaining in popularity among foundation and hydraulic structures engineers.

Well. A well is an artificial, usually vertical, cylindrical, perforated hydraulic structure, provided with a screen that taps groundwater from the voids of the soil which it penetrates. Both types of vertical wells are lined to prevent them from caving in. A well, sunk into a water-bearing stratum and tapping free-flowing groundwater having a free groundwater table under atmospheric pressure, is termed an *ordinary*, or *gravity*, or *discharge*, or *unconfined* well. An ordinary well is a well in which the surface of the water inside and outside the well, when not being pumped, is under atmospheric pressure—the inside and outside of the well being connected through the well screen.

A well sunk into and tapping water from an aquifer where the groundwater flows confined between two impermeable soil layers, and under pressure greater than atmospheric, is termed an *artesian*, or *pressure*, or *confined* well. In the casing of an artesian well, water rises under pressure to a considerable height above the ceiling of the stratum to which it was confined before being relieved by the construction of the artesian well to a height equivalent to the hydrostatic pressure under which the flow takes place.

The groundwater flow to a well, or out of it, is assumed to be radial. A radial flow is one where the direction of flow at every point is towards, or from, some point on the axis of symmetry of the well system. The axis of symmetry coincides with the longitudinal axis of the vertically installed well.

Pumping of Water out of a Single Well. The method of pumping water out of a test well for the purpose of ascertaining a reasonable value of the coefficient of permeability, k, can more properly be described as the radial, groundwater gravity flow to a single, central well. In this test, a single test well is installed in a horizontal permeable soil layer. A certain quantity of water, Q, is continuously pumped out of the well. The pumping takes place, depending upon soil properties, for a period of a few days to a fortnight, until the groundwater flow to the well is stabilized, i.e., a steady state of flow is attained and the depression funnel or cone of the lowered groundwater table around the well established. The stabilized depression surface, viz., depression line of the lowered groundwater

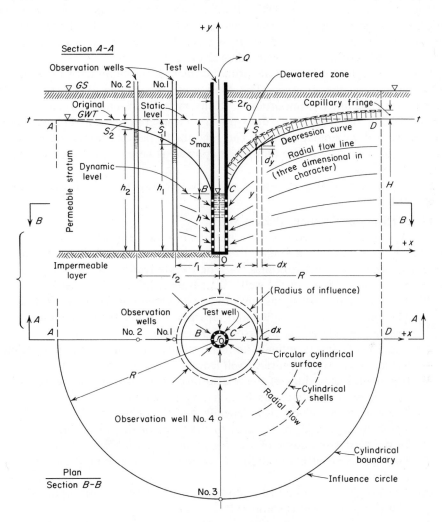

FIG. 13-1   Ordinary, perfect well.

table, is established by means of observing the position of the groundwater table, the draw-down, s, of the groundwater in several observation wells spaced around the test well on two radial lines, Fig. 13-1, one of which may be selected parallel to the groundwater flow, and the other one perpendicular to the flow direction. The maximum lowering or draw-down, s_{max}, of the groundwater table is at the well.

A minimum of two observation wells is needed, which then permits the calculation of the coefficient of permeability, k, of the soil to water.

The lowered groundwater table in the test well is called the working or pumping level.

The draw-down decreases with distance from the test well. The depression line dies out gradually, and forms, theoretically, a circle around the test well as the circle of influence. Its radius, R, is termed in the theory of hydraulics of wells the radius of influence of the depression cone.

In water supply engineering the prime problem is to obtain a certain quantity of water out of the ground. The draw-down associated therewith is then a matter of secondary importance. Conversely, in foundation engineering, the important problem is the draw-down of the groundwater table necessary to achieve a dry foundation pit. The amount of pumped water, save for the necessity of determining the pump horsepower, is here otherwise of secondary importance only.

In both instances, the process of groundwater flow in the soil and into the well is the same.

13-2. Theory of Ordinary Perfect Wells.

Assumptions. The theoretical-mathematical treatment of a radial gravity flow of groundwater to a single, ordinary, perfect well is based on Dupuit-Thiem's theory of well hydraulics.[1,2] For the derivation of an analytical expression for the yield, Q, of the well, viz., permeability of soil, k, assume:

1) The soil is a homogeneous, uniform, porous medium of infinite areal extent.
2) The perfect well is installed and taps groundwater from the entire thickness of the permeable, water-bearing stratum.
3) There exists an unconfined, uniform, steady, laminar, and radial groundwater flow to the cylindrical well from a concentric boundary.
4) For small inclinations of the free surface of the groundwater gravity-flow system, the streamlines can be taken as horizontal.
5) The horizontal velocity is independent of the depth.
6) The hydraulic gradient is equal to the slope of the tangent at any point on the depression curve of the free groundwater table.
7) The coefficient of permeability, k, of the soil is constant at all times and at all places.
8) The well is being pumped continuously at a uniform rate until the flow of water to the well is stabilized.

Disregarding the limiting assumptions, Dupuit-Thiem's theory can be applied to practical problems relative to groundwater flow. Of course, the success of this theory depends, to a great extent, upon how the assumed conditions underlying it are met in nature.

Flow into an Ordinary, Perfect Well. The flow of water into an ordinary, perfect well is a gravity flow where the groundwater table is exposed to atmospheric pressure. Because the radial flowlines to a circular well are three-dimensional in character, this flow problem cannot be treated by means of flow nets, but must be studied analytically.

Assume a single, perfect well system as illustrated in Fig. 13-1. The outside radius of the well is r_0. The original static groundwater table, which at the same time is the zero draw-down, is at elevation, t-t. The thickness of the water-bearing strata is H units. Upon pumping, the water table in the well lowers by an amount of s, termed the draw-down. At the same time, the groundwater table around the well also lowers. The de-watered zone in the soil, $ABCDA$, takes the form of an inverted funnel or cone of depression. The maximum draw-down, s_{max}, is at and within the well. The depressed line, $ABCD$, representing the groundwater table is called the *depression line*, known also as the *pumping groundwater table*. The radial distance, R, where draw-down, s, is zero, is termed the *radius of influence* of the well.

The rate of flow, Q, of water into the well at stabilized flow upon pumping, expressed by means of Darcy's law, is

$$Q = vA = kiA \quad (m^3/sec), \tag{13-1}$$

where v = flow velocity in m/sec,
$\quad A$ = flow area, in m^2,
$\quad i = dy/dx = \tan \alpha$ = hydraulic gradient,
$\quad dy$ = change in y-coordinate of the depression curve, and
$\quad dx$ = change in x-coordinate of the depression curve.

The area, A, through which the flow of water to the well takes place, is a vertical, circular, cylindrical surface (below the depression curve) with a radius, x, and height, y:

$$A = 2\pi x y. \tag{13-2}$$

While a particle of water approaches the center of the well by an amount of dx, the groundwater table experiences a depression, or loss in gradient = dy.

If there exists a continuous, uniform, radial flow over an impermeable stratum, then the rate of flow across any cylindrical area, A, is equal to the, Q = flow, into the well and, in turn, pumped out of it:

$$Q = k \frac{dy}{dx} 2\pi x y. \tag{13-3}$$

Separation of variables gives the following differential equation:

$$y \, dy = \frac{Q}{2\pi k} \frac{dx}{x}. \tag{13-4}$$

The boundary conditions for integrating Eq. (13-4) are evaluated as follows (see Fig. 13-1): where the depression line intersects the vertical, outside surface of the well, $x = r_0$ and $y = h$; here h = depth of the water in the well. Where the draw-down line joins the original position of the unlowered groundwater table (at points A and D), $x = R$ and $y = H$.

Integrating Eq. (13-4) between limits as indicated:

$$\int_h^y y \, dy = \frac{Q}{2\pi k} \int_{r_0}^x \frac{dx}{x} \tag{13-5}$$

obtain

$$y^2 - h^2 = \frac{Q}{\pi k} \ln \frac{x}{r_0}, \tag{13-6}$$

which is the *general equation of the depression line.*
Integrating between $x_1 = r_0$ and $x_2 = R$, and between $y_1 = h$ and $y_2 = H$, obtain

$$\int_h^H y \, dy = \frac{Q}{2\pi k} \int_{r_0}^R \frac{dx}{x}, \tag{13-7}$$

$$H^2 - h^2 = \frac{Q}{\pi k} \ln \frac{R}{r_0}, \tag{13-7a}$$

from which discharge, Q, can be calculated as

$$Q = \pi k \frac{H^2 - h^2}{\ln \dfrac{R}{r_0}} = k\pi \frac{(H + h)(H - h)}{\ln \dfrac{R}{r_0}}. \tag{13-7b}$$

Hence, the discharge of groundwater into a well is directly proportional to the product of the sum times the difference of the natural and artificial stages of the groundwater, and inversely proportional to the natural logarithm of the R/r_0-ratio.

In practice, R is to be substituted by such a distance from the well at which, after pumping a certain amount of water, the depression of the natural water table in the water-bearing soil layer has no longer any practical significance.

Equation of Depression Line. Eq. (13-6) gives the equation of the depression line, viz., the free surface of the groundwater:

$$y = \sqrt{H^2 - \frac{Q}{\pi k} \ln \frac{R}{x}} \qquad \text{(m)}. \tag{13-8}$$

In this equation, when $x = r_0$, $y = h$ which is the ordinate of the depression line at the wall of the well, or the depth of water in the well:

$$h = \sqrt{H^2 - \frac{Q}{\pi k} \ln \frac{R}{r_0}} \qquad \text{(m)}. \tag{13-9}$$

When $x = R$, $\ln(R/R) = \ln 1 = 0$, and $y = H$,
Draw-down. Because draw-down is

$$s = H - y, \tag{13-10}$$

it can now be expressed an any point $(x; y)$ by means of Eq. (13-8):

$$s = H \pm \sqrt{H^2 - \frac{Q}{\pi k} \ln \frac{R}{x}}, \tag{13-11}$$

or in the system of decimal logarithms

$$s = H \pm \sqrt{H^2 - \frac{(2.3)Q}{\pi k} \log_{10} \frac{R}{x}}. \qquad (13\text{-}12)$$

For pumping water out of the well (lowering of groundwater table) use the minus sign before the square root. For recharge of water into the well (and soil) use the plus sign. When $x = R$, then $s = 0$. When $x = r$, $y = h$.

Equations (13-11) and (13-12) also show that the less the thickness of the water-bearing soil stratum, H, the greater is the draw-down, s. Maximum draw-down at well casing, upon pumping out of the well, is

$$s_{max} = H - h = H - \sqrt{H^2 - \frac{(2.3)Q}{\pi k} \log_{10} \frac{R}{r_0}}. \qquad (13\text{-}13)$$

Yield Capacity of the Well. The capacity of the well is calculated by Eq. (13-7b) as

$$Q = \frac{\pi k(H^2 - h^2)}{\ln(R/r_0)}, \qquad (13\text{-}14)$$

or

$$Q = \frac{\pi k(2H - s_{max})s_{max}}{\ln(R/r_0)}. \qquad (13\text{-}15)$$

Equation (13-15) shows that the greater is the coefficient of permeability of the soil, k; the thickness of the water-bearing layer, H; the maximum draw-down, s_{max}; the radius of the well, r_0; and the less is the radius of influence, R, the greater is the rate of the radial flow, Q, into the well.

Eq. (13-15) can be rewritten as follows:

$$Q = (2.73) \frac{kHs}{\log_{10}(R/r_0)} \left(1 - \frac{s}{2H}\right) \qquad (13\text{-}16)$$

For very thick water-bearing layers, when $H \to \infty$ and $s/2H \to 0$, the term $s/2H$ can be omitted as being small as compared with the unity. In such a case discharge

$$Q = (2.73) \frac{kHs}{\log_{10}(R/r_0)}. \qquad (13\text{-}17)$$

Q is a maximum when $(d^2 Q)/(ds^2) < 0$.

Setting $(dQ)/(ds)$ equal to zero,

$$\frac{2\pi k}{\ln(R/r_0)}(H - s) = 0, \qquad (13\text{-}18)$$

find that for an extreme quantity of Q, maximum or minimum, and because $(2\pi k)/\ln(R/r_0) \neq 0$,

$$H - s = 0, \quad \text{and} \quad s = H.$$

The second derivative is

$$\frac{d^2Q}{ds^2} = \frac{2\pi k}{\ln(R/r_0)}(-1) < 0. \tag{13-19}$$

Therefore at $s = H$, the Q-function is at its maximum,

$$Q_{max} = \frac{2\pi k}{\ln(R/r_0)} H^2, \tag{13-20}$$

(see point B in Fig. 13-2). Here discharge, Q, is shown as a function of draw-down, s. Although Q is zero when $s = 0$ and when $s = 2H$, Q is real only between the values of $s = 0$ and $s = H$. This means that practically only the first one-half of the parabola is valid. Note that H is the maximum draw-down at which maximum discharge, Q, can be attained.

The same conclusion could have been arrived at by inspection upon setting in Eq. (13-15) $s_{max} = H$.

The parabolic relationship between discharge, Q, and draw-down, s, can also be seen by forming a ratio between two discharge quantities, Q_1 and Q_2, expressed by Eq. (13-15), measured at two different draw-downs, s_1 and s_2:

$$\frac{Q_1}{Q_2} = \frac{(2H - s_1)s_1}{(2H - s_2)s_2}, \tag{13-21}$$

or

$$Q_2 = Q_1 \frac{(2H - s_2)s_2}{(2h - s_1)s_1}. \tag{13-22}$$

The parabolic relationship indicates that the inflow of groundwater into the well increases to a lesser degree than the draw-down.

Problem. Upon pumping an ordinary, perfect well at $Q_1 = 4$ m³/hour, a draw-down of $s_1 = 1.5$ m has been attained. Calculate the yield of the well, Q_2, at a draw-down of $s_2 = 3.0$ m, if the thickness of the water-bearing stratum is $H = 7.0$ m.

Solution. By Eq. (13-22),

$$Q_2 = Q_1 \frac{(2H - s_2)s_2}{(2H - s_1)s_1} = (4) \frac{[(2)(7) - 3]3}{[(2)(7) - 1.5]1.5} = 7.04 \qquad \text{(m³/hr)}.$$

This calculation shows that upon increasing the draw-down by 100%, the increase in yield is only

$$\frac{7.04 - 4.00}{4.00} 100 = 76\%.$$

Specific Yield of Well. As seen from Eq. (13-15), Q is a second degree function of draw-down, s, i.e., Q is a parabolic function, Fig. 13-2. The specific yield of a well, q, is defined as its yield per unit length (1 m) of draw-down in the well, or the gross yield per working head (s_{max}), i.e., $q = (dQ)/(ds)$.

Specific yield, q, can theoretically be calculated by differentiating Q in Eq. (13-15) after s:

$$dQ = \frac{\pi k}{\ln(R/r_0)} d[(2H - s)s], \tag{13-23}$$

or

$$dQ = \frac{\pi k}{\ln(R/r_0)} 2(H - s)\,ds, \qquad (13\text{-}24)$$

and specific yield is then

$$\frac{dQ}{ds} = \frac{2\pi k}{\ln(R/r_0)} (H - s). \qquad (13\text{-}25)$$

Graphically, the quantity $(dQ)/(ds)$ is the slope of the tangent at a point A, Fig. 13-2, whose coordinates are $(s; Q)$.

Note in Eq. (13-25) that the greater the draw-down, s, the less the specific yield, q, of the well (flat slope of tangent to the Q-curve, Fig. 13-2.

When, as in Eq. (13-25) and in Fig. 13-2,

$s \to 0$, then $(dQ0/(ds) \to \infty$,

$\qquad$ i.e., $Q \to 0$.

When

$s \to H$, then $(dQ)/(ds) \to 0$,

$\qquad$ i.e., $Q \to$ max.

With $s = 1$ m, the specific yield is

$$q = \frac{dQ}{ds} = \frac{(2.73)k}{\log_{10}(R/r_0)} (H - 1) \qquad (13\text{-}26)$$

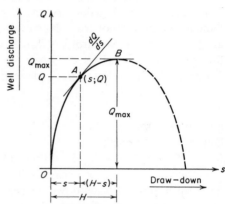

FIG. 13-2   Discharge of an ordinary, perfect well as a function of draw-down.

Example. Determine the yield capacity, Q, of an ordinary perfect well at a draw-down of $s_{max} = 3.5$ m. The radius of the well is $r_0 = 0.1$ m. The thickness of the water bearing stratum is $H = 7.0$ m. The radius of influence is $R = 100$ m. The coefficient of permeability is $k = 0.005$ m/sec. Plot the depression curve.

Solution. By the Dupuit-Thiem theory, Eq. (13-14),

$$Q = \frac{\pi k(H^2 - h^2)}{\ln(R/r_0)} = \frac{(\pi)(0.005)[7^2 - (3.5)^2]}{(2.3)\log_{10}(100/0.1)} =$$

$$= 0.0836 \quad (\text{m}^3/\text{sec}) = 83.6 \quad (\text{liters/sec}).$$

The depression curve coordinates for an ordinary perfect well are calculated by Eq. (13-8), assuming several x-values and calculating the corresponding y-ordinates.

x	y
m	m
75.0	6.88
50.0	6.73
25.0	6.45
10.0	6.06
1.0	4.95
$r_0 = $ 0.1	3.51
$R = $ 100.0	$H = $ 7.00

13-3. Radius of Influence. The radius of influence of the depression cone, R, is to be estimated from experience, or it is to be found by observation in several bore holes made at different distances from the test well. According to Sichardt,[3] for stabilized flow condition, R is given in meters as

$$R = 3000s\sqrt{k}, \tag{13-27}$$

where s = maximum draw-down in meters, and
     k = coefficient of permeability of soil, k, in m/sec.
This equation, giving conservative R-values, has no theoretical support, and dimensionally it is not true. However, in most cases in practice, when R-values are not available, Sichardt's R-values are used with relatively good success as they exclude large errors.

For larger draw-downs in single wells Weber's equation[4]

$$R = c\sqrt{Hk(t)/n} \qquad (m) \tag{13-28}$$

gives more precise values.
Here $c \approx 3$, a coefficient;
     H = thickness, in m, of the water-bearing stratum;
     k = coefficient of permeability of soil, in m/sec;
     t = time of draw-down, in sec; and
     n = porosity of soil, which varies from 0.25 (coarse sand) to 0.34 fine sand). An average coefficient of porosity of $n = 0.30$ can be used.
Also, Weber's equation has no true dimensions. Although Weber's R does not seem to depend upon the pumping quantity, Q, which looks odd, his R-equation is much quoted in the technical literature.

Example. Determine the radius of influence of a depression cone after an ordinary, perfect well has been pumped for 24 hours. The thickness of the water-bearing stratum is 7.0 m. The coefficient of permeability is $k = 0.005$ m/sec. The porosity of the soil is $n = 0.30$.
Solution. The radius of influence is calculated by Weber's Eq. (13-28):

$$R = c\sqrt{Hk(t/n)} = (3)\sqrt{(7)(0.005)(86400/0.30)} = \underline{301.2} \qquad (m).$$

Kozeny[3] gave an expression for the calculation of the radius of influence, R, in terms of time, t, during which a yield from the well of Q m³/sec has been attained:

$$R = \sqrt{\frac{12t}{n}}\sqrt{\frac{Qk}{\pi}} \qquad (m). \tag{13-29}$$

Here 12 = a coefficient,
     n = porosity of soil, in decimal fractions,
     k = coefficient of porosity of soil, m/sec, and
     $\pi = 3.14$.
The radius of influence increases with the fourth root of discharge, Q, and permeability, k.
As can easily be seen, Kozeny's equation contains true dimensions for R in meters.

Example. Calculate the radius of influence, R, if the following data were obtained from a pumping test:

$$\text{yield:} \qquad Q = 0.06421 \text{ m}^3/\text{sec}$$
$$\text{permeability:} \quad k = 0.005 \text{ m/sec}$$
$$\text{porosity:} \qquad n = 0.30$$
$$\text{duration of test:} \ t = 24 \text{ hr} = 86,400 \text{ seconds.}$$

Solution. By Kozeny's equation, the radius of influence of the depression cone is calculated as

$$R = \sqrt{\frac{(12)(86400)}{0.30}} \sqrt{\frac{(0.06421)(0.005)}{3.14}} = \underline{186.8} \qquad \text{(m).}$$

Example. Given: yield out of well: $Q = 0.06421 \text{ m}^3/\text{sec}$
thickness of water-bearing stratum: $H = 7.0$ m
permeability: $k = 0.005$ m/sec
hydraulic gradient: $i = 0.00175$.

Determine the radius of influence, R.

Solution. The hydraulic gradient suggests that groundwater flows along a slope of an impermeable soil stratum. In such a case the radius of influence can approximately be calculated as

$$R = \frac{Q}{2\pi Hki} = \frac{0.06421}{(2)(3.14)(7)(0.005)(0.00175)} = \underline{166.8} \qquad \text{(m)}$$

According to Schoklitsch,[6] the values of the radius of influence of the depression cone for various soils are about as follows:

in coarse gravel $R \leq 500$ m = 1640 ft
in fine gravel $R = 100$ m to 500 m = 330 ft to 1640 ft
in sand $R = 50$ m = 165 ft, and
in dune sand $R = 5$ m to 10 m = 15 ft to 30 ft.

Slichter[7] gives an R-value as 600 ft. Muscat[8] indicates $R = 500$ ft when no specific information is available, the error in the resultant computed value of k being only 10% if the correct magnitude is either half or twice 500 ft. And Tolman[9] suggests $R = 1000$ ft.

Upon the lack of any data for R, in preliminary calculations the R-values can be used as indicated in Table 13-1. The R-values are collected from many sources; they are evaluated and adjusted for the soil classification system according to the Bureau of Soils, U.S. Department of Agriculture.

Whatever the R-values may be, the influence of R on the rate of flow, Q, is relatively insignificant because it enters into the Q-equation under the sign of logarithm, but logarithms of numbers, particularly of the R/r_0-ratios, vary very slowly. For example, if

$$R/r_0 = 10, \ 100, \ 1000, \ 10000,$$

then $\log_{10}(R/r_0) = 1, 2, 3,$ and 4.

13-4. Coefficient of Permeability. Eq. (13-7a) or Eq. (13-3) permits one to calculate the coefficient of permeability, k, of soil:

$$k = \frac{Q}{\pi(H^2 - h^2)} \ln \frac{R}{r_0}, \qquad \text{(m/sec)} \qquad (13\text{-}30)$$

or, expressed in decimal logarithms,

$$k = \frac{(2.3)(Q)}{\pi(H^2 - h^2)} \log_{10} \frac{R}{r_0}.$$ (13-31)

If the maximum draw-down, s_{max}, at a certain Q is known, then $s_{max} = H - h$, and

$$H^2 - h^2 = (H + h)(H - h) = (H + h)s_{max} = (2H - s_{max})s_{max},$$

and

$$k = \frac{(2.3)Q}{\pi(2H - s_{max})s_{max}} \log_{10} \frac{R}{r_0}.$$ (13-32)

TABLE 13-1. RADIUS OF INFLUENCE IN VARIOUS SOILS

Soil		Radius of Influence R, in meters
Description	Particle Size d in mm	
1	2	3
Coarse gravel	>10	>1500
Medium gravel	2 to 10	500 to 1500
Fine gravel	1 to 2	400 to 500
Coarse sand	0.5 to 1	200 to 400
Medium sand	0.25 to 0.5	100 to 200
Fine sand	0.10 to 0.25	50 to 100
Very fine sand	0.05 to 0.10	10 to 50
Silty sand	0.025 to 0.05	5 to 10

Example. Given: a system consisting of one test well 0.4 m in diameter. The well is installed in a medium sand so that it represents an ordinary, perfect well. The thickness of the groundwater bearing stratum is 7 m. Upon a draw-down in the well of 3.5 m, the yield of the well is 301 m³/hr. The observed radius of influence is $R = 200$ m.

Determine the system's coefficient of permeability of soil.

Solution. By Eq. (13-32),

$$k = (0.732)(301) \frac{\log_{10} 1000}{[(2)(7) - 3.5](3.5)} = 17.99 \text{ (m/hr)} = 0.005 \quad \text{(m/sec)}.$$

Because of the uncertainties in the values of radius of influence of the depression cone, R; because it is difficult to determine R precisely, and because of the sensitivity of the factor, k, in calculating Q, two observation wells, as indicated on Fig. 13-1 for the determination of k can be used. With the two pairs of coordinates r_1/h_1 and r_2/h_2 of the points on the depression line obtained from observation in the two observation wells Nos. 1 and 2, respectively, Eq. (13-5) can be integrated between the distance between these two wells to obtain the following equation:

$$\int_{h_1}^{h_2} y \, dy = \frac{Q}{2\pi k} \int_{r_1}^{r_2} \frac{dx}{x},$$ (13-33)

or

$$h_2{}^2 - h_1{}^2 = \frac{Q}{\pi k} \ln \frac{r_2}{r_1}, \qquad (13\text{-}34)$$

which is the equation of the depression line.

The coefficient of permeability, k, is calculated as

$$k = \frac{Q}{\pi} \frac{(\ln r_2 - \ln r_1)}{h_2{}^2 - h_1{}^2}, \qquad (13\text{-}35)$$

or, because $\qquad\qquad (h_2 - h_1) \approx (s_1 - s_2), \qquad (13\text{-}36)$

$$k = \frac{Q}{\pi} \frac{\ln \dfrac{r_2}{r_1}}{(h_2 + h_1)(s_1 - s_2)}, \qquad (13\text{-}37)$$

where s_1 and s_2 are draw-downs at observation wells Nos. 1 and 2, respectively. Expressed in the system of decimal logarithms,

$$k = \frac{(2.3)Q}{\pi} \frac{\log_{10}(r_2/r_1)}{(h_2 + h_1)(s_1 - s_2)}, \qquad (13\text{-}38)$$

or

$$k = (0.732)(Q) \frac{\log_{10}(r_2/r_1)}{(h_2 + h_1)(s_1 - s_2)}, \qquad (13\text{-}39a)$$

or

$$k = \frac{Q}{1.365} \frac{\log_{10}(r_2/r_1)}{(h_2 + h_1)(s_1 - s_2)}. \qquad (13\text{-}39b)$$

Note that the coefficient of permeability, k, represents the over-all permeability of the entire water-bearing stratum in the vicinity of the test well and is influenced by the pumping operations. Therefore, k is the "system's" permeability.

In this method of determination of k the draw-down is usually brought about in three stages, each of them yielding a k-value, so that a total of three k-values is obtained. If the pumping operations have been performed correctly and carefully enough, the three k-values will differ little among themselves. The average of the three k-values is then reported as the coefficient of permeability of the soil.

Values of Coefficients of Permeability. In the nature the values of the coefficient of permeability vary between $k = 0.01$ m/sec for coarse gravel to $k = 0.0001$ m/sec for dune sand. Soils with $k < 0.0001$ m/sec are not practicable groundwater sources, and soil de-watering by the method of lowering the groundwater table is seldom applied. In such cases the methods of pneumatic foundations, or pouring of concrete under water, chemical waterproofing of soil between sheet piling, and even artificially freezing the soil are applied.

Some k-values are compiled in Table 13-2.

TABLE 13-2. COEFFICIENTS OF PERMEABILITY, k, OF SOIL

Soil Type	k m/sec
1	2
Coarse gravel	5×10^{-3} to 1×10^{-2}
Coarse gravel with lenses and pockets of sand	4×10^{-3} to 5×10^{-3}
Medium gravel	3.5×10^{-2}
Fine gravel	3.0×10^{-2}
Coarse river sand	2×10^{-3} to 8.8×10^{-3}
Sand, 4-8 mm	3.5×10^{-2}
2-4 mm	2.5×10^{-2} to 3×10^{-2}
Fine sand + clay	8×10^{-4} to 3×10^{-3}
Fine, clean, sharp sand + some clay	5×10^{-4} to 1×10^{-3}
Dune sand	2×10^{-4}
Very fine sand	1×10^{-4}
Silty fine sand	1×10^{-3} to 1×10^{-4}
Loess, $e = 1.3$	1×10^{-3}
Loess, $e = 0.55$	2×10^{-7}
Clays	2×10^{-7} to 1×10^{-10}

Example. Calculate the flow of groundwater into the well, Q. The well penetrates a 7.0 m thick water-bearing stratum of medium sand. The coefficient of permeability is $k = 0.005$ m/sec. The radius of the well is $r_0 = 0.1$ m. The required maximum draw-down is $s_{max} = 3.5$ m. Also, construct the depression line.

Solution. Radius of influence, by Eq. (13-27):

$$R = 3000s\sqrt{k} = (3000)(3.5)\sqrt{0.005} = 805 \quad \text{(m)}.$$

Flow into a 0.1 m radius well, by Eq. (13-15), expressed for any s, and in the system of decimal logarithms:

$$Q_{0.1} = \frac{(1.365)k(2H - s)s}{\log_{10}(R/r_0)} =$$

$$= \frac{(1.365)(0.005)(2)(7) - (3.5)3.5}{\log_{10}(805/0.1)} = \underline{0.06421 \ (\text{m}^3/\text{sec})} =$$

$$= \underline{231.156 \ (\text{m}^3/\text{hr})}.$$

If the radius of the well were $r_0 = 0.20$ m $= 8''$, and $R = 805$ m, then

$$Q_{0.2} = \frac{0.25082}{\log_{10} 4025} = 0.06958 \quad (\text{m}^3/\text{sec}) = 250.488 \quad (\text{m}^3/\text{hr}).$$

One sees that the size of the well is of less influence on Q than might be assumed, as can be seen from the following Q-ratio:

$$\frac{Q_{0.2}}{Q_{0.1}} = \frac{250.488}{231.156} = 1.087.$$

Note here that with an increase in the radius of the well by 100%, the increase in discharge into the larger well is only 8.7%.

Assuming a radius of influence for medium sand from Table 13-1 as $R = 200$ m, the discharge into a well of radius $r_0 = 0.1$ m is

$$Q_{200} = \frac{0.25082}{\log_{10}(200/0.1)} = 0.07598 \quad (\text{m}^3/\text{sec}) = 273.535 \quad (\text{m}^3/\text{hr}),$$

and

$$\frac{Q_{805}}{Q_{200}} = \frac{231.156}{273.535} = 0.845.$$

Thus one sees that the magnitude of the radius of influence, R, has also relatively little effect upon Q: upon increasing the radius of influence four times, the discharge decreases by 15.5%.

ARTESIAN WELLS

13-5. Description. An artesian well is one which is installed in a permeable, groundwater bearing stratum confined between two impermeable strata, one above and one below the confined aquifer. The groundwater flows under the influence of artesian pressure. The well is sunk through the upper impermeable layer, and may extend down through the entire thickness of the water-bearing stratum. Such a well is called a perfect artesian well. Or, the well may penetrate the water-bearing stratum only partially; or it may penetrate only down to the contact surface between the upper impermeable layer and the aquifer.

13-6. The Hydraulics of a Perfect Artesian Well. The mathematics for the calculation of discharge into an artesian well, Fig. 13-3, or for computing the coefficient of permeability of soil, is based, like many other hydraulic structural engineering problems, on the linear filtration law by Darcy, expressed in a differential form as

$$Q = kA \frac{dy}{dx}, \tag{13-40}$$

where Q = discharge or yield, in m³/sec;
   $A = 2\pi x h_a$ = cross-sectional area perpendicular to flow, in m²;
   h_a = thickness of aquifer, in m, and
   $dy/dx = i$ = hydraulic gradient.

The flow towards the central well with a permeable casing and closed bottom is radial, with no gravity component (practically).

The filtration velocity, v, is

$$v = \frac{Q}{A} = \frac{Q}{2\pi x h_a} = k \frac{dy}{dx}, \tag{13-41}$$

and separation of variables gives

$$dy = \frac{Q}{2\pi k h_a} \frac{dx}{x}. \tag{13-42}$$

Integration of Eq. (13-42) yields

$$\int_h^H dy = \frac{Q}{2\pi kh_a} \int_{r_0}^R \frac{dx}{x},$$

(13-43)

or

$$H - h = \frac{Q}{2\pi kh_a} \ln \frac{R}{r_0}.$$

(13-44)

From here, yield

$$Q = \frac{2\pi kh_a(H - h)}{\ln(R/r_0)} = (2.73)\frac{kh_a(H - h)}{\log_{10}(R/r_0)} = (2.73)\frac{kh_a s_{max}}{\log_{10}(R/r_0)}$$

(13-45)

in m^3/sec.

Note that the yield from an aquifer under pressure is directly proportional to the draw-down, s:

$$Q = Cs.$$

(13-46)

Thus, the Q-function in the case of free groundwater is parabolic, but that of artesian water is linear.

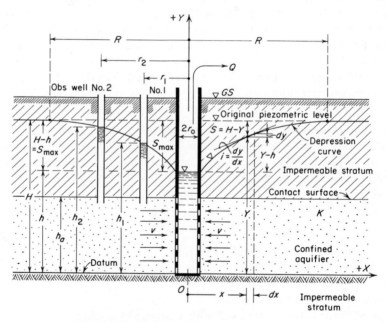

FIG. 13-3   Perfect artesian well. Radial flow.

In these equations (Fig. 13-3),

H = elevation of water table in well (or imaginary piezometer from a datum plane), in m;

h = elevation of water table in well after pumping, in m;

$s_{max} = H - h$ = maximum draw-down at well, in m;

R = radius of influence, in m; and

r_0 = radius of artesian well, in m.

Equation (13-45) shows that for various draw-downs, s, the discharges are also different. Remembering that the radius of influence of the depression cone forming the piezometric surface varies very little upon pumping, its variation at different s can be considered negligible. This permits one to formulate that various discharges from the same well are proportional to their draw-downs, Eq. (13-46), i.e.,

$$\frac{Q_1}{Q_2} = \frac{Cs_1}{Cs_2} = \frac{s_1}{s_2}. \tag{13-47}$$

Note the difference in this respect between artesian waters and free ground water Eq. (13-21).

Permeability. By Eq. (13-44), the permeability, k, is calculated as
a)

$$k = \frac{Q}{(2.73)(h_a)} \cdot \frac{\log_{10}(R/r_0)}{s_{max}} \quad \text{(m/sec)}. \tag{13-48}$$

b) The coefficient of the system's permeability, k, from two observation wells installed in artesian water is

$$k = \frac{Q}{(2.73)(h_a)} \frac{\log_{10}(r_2/r_1)}{(s_1 - s_2)} \quad \text{(m/sec)}, \tag{13-49}$$

where r_1 and r_2 are the distances of observation wells Nos. 1 and 2, respectively, from the central test well, and s_1 and s_2 are the draw-downs in observation wells Nos. 1 and 2, respectively.

c) Upon pumping one test well and observing one observation well, the coefficient of permeability, k, is

$$k = \frac{Q}{(2.73)(h_a)} \frac{\log_{10}(r_1/r_0)}{(s_{max} - s_1)} \quad \text{(m/sec)}. \tag{13-50}$$

Equation of Depression Line. By Eq. (13-44), the equation of the depression line of the cone of depression is (setting $H = y$, and $R = x$):

$$y = h + \frac{Q}{2\pi k h_a} \ln \frac{x}{r_0}, \tag{13-51}$$

(see Fig. 13-3).
Velocity of Flow.

$$v = \frac{Q}{A} = \frac{Q}{2\pi r_0 h_a}. \tag{13-52}$$

Example. Calculate the artesian groundwater flow into a perfect artesian well Maximum draw-down is 3.5 m; thickness of aquifer, $h_a = 7.0$ m. Coefficient of permeability, $k = 0.005$ m/sec. Radius of well: $r_1 = 0.1$ m. Radius of influence is $R = 200$ m.

Solution. By Eq. (13-45),

$$Q = (2.73)\frac{(0.005)(7.0)(3.5)}{\log_{10}(200/0.1)} = \underline{0.10131 \text{ (m}^3\text{/sec)}} =$$

$$= 364.716 \text{ (m}^3\text{/hr)}.$$

Note. If Q were known along with other pertinent data, the coefficient of the aquifer-soil permeability, k, in this example could be calculated by Eq. (13-48) as

$$k = \frac{Q}{(2.73)(h_a)} \frac{\log_{10}(R/r_0)}{s_{max}} = \frac{(0.10131)}{(2.73)(7.0)} \frac{\log_{10}(200/0.1)}{3.5} =$$
$$= 0.005 \text{ (m/sec)}.$$

Example. Determine k from two observation wells.
Given: radius of a perfect artesian well, $r_1 = 0.1$ m;
       height of water column in artesian well, $h = 0.9$ m;
       thickness of aquifer, $h_a = 7.0$ m;
       yield, $Q = 0.10131$ m³/sec.
       Draw-downs in, and distances of observation wells are:

Observation Well Nos.	Distance from Test Well, r, m	Draw-down, s, m
1	$r_1 = 40$	$s_1 = 0.71$
2	$r_2 = 100$	$s_2 = 0.29$

Solution.
a) By Eq. (13-49),

$$k = \frac{Q}{(2.73)(h_a)} \frac{\log_{10}(r_2/r_1)}{(s_1 - s_2)} = \frac{0.10131}{(2.73)(7)} \frac{\log_{10}(100/40)}{(0.71 - 0.29)} =$$
$$= (0.0053)(0.947) = 0.005 \quad \text{(m/sec)}.$$

b) If only one observation well is used, for example, $r_1 = 100$ m, and the maximum draw-down in the test well is $s_{max} = 3.5$ m, then

$$k = \frac{Q}{(2.73)(h_a)} \frac{\log_{10}(r_1/r_0)}{(s_{max} - s_1)} = (0.0053) \frac{\log_{10}(100/0.1)}{(3.50 - 0.29)} = \underline{0.005 \text{ (m/sec)}}.$$

LOWERING THE GROUNDWATER TABLE

13-7. The Problem. One of the greatest opponents and hazards in foundation engineering operations is the groundwater. Unfavorable groundwater conditions may threaten the entire construction program. The inflow of water into the excavated foundation pit causes difficulties not only in earthwork operations but it also causes the loosening up of sandy soils, loss of cohesion and also the strength of the cohesive soils. Therefore, all methods of construction of deep foundations have for their purpose either 1) to combat effectively the inflow of water into an open foundation pit, or 2) to provide conditions so that foundations can be laid in dry pit.

The first objective is achieved by temporarily lowering the groundwater table. The second objective is achieved by means of open or pneumatic caissons.

When the footings of foundations are to be laid in an open foundation pit in a finely textured soil deep below the groundwater table, the pit can be kept dry by means of lowering the groundwater table. The groundwater table is usually drawn down about 50 cm $\approx$ 20 in. below the elevation of the base of the footing. Lowering the groundwater table is brought about by means of a well point system from which the inflowing water is pumped out and discharged.

13-8. Wellpoint System. A wellpoint system consists basically of
1) a row of several wells or wellpoints, usually installed around the perimeter of the foundation pit;
2) riser pipes;
3) swing joints;
4) header pipe lines to which the wells are connected;
5) pumps, and
6) discharge pipes.

The radii of influence of the wellpoints overlap. The wellpoint consists of a metal pipe, usually 2 in. in diameter, which, when installed in the soil (vertically, horizontally, or inclined, as in mines or in slopes of water-bearing cuts, for example, collects the ground water flowing into it.

The lower end of the pipe, or casing, particularly the wellpoint proper, is perforated over a length of 1.5 to 2 m (or about 4.5 to 6 ft), and is covered with a fine filter of metallic mesh screen. The screen is made of phosphor-bronze, or copper, or brass, to resist the aggression of chemical compounds dissolved in groundwater. The mesh is protected by an external screen of a heavy, perforated brass plate. Metallic filters quickly become clogged by fine-particled soil. Therefore, they are protected by building around them a gravel-sand filter. This is accomplished by penetrating into the soil to a proper depth a tubular filter casing from the inside of which the native soil is jetted out. In this casing the wellpoint is installed, and selected filter material of coarse aggregate such as coarse sand, and/or gravel is poured in place around it. Upon installation, the filter casing is removed, leaving the wellpoint with the filter material in position. Gravel filters around wellpoints are also installed in non-uniform and stratified soils.

In fine-particled soil, upon pumping, the action of the surface tension of water between the soil particles tends to retain the water within the voids of the soil, thus retarding the flow.

The spacing of the wellpoints depends upon the type of soil and its permeability. In clean sand with a depth of water up to about 15 ft, wellpoints are installed in a row along the header line from 4 to 5 ft apart. The top end of the screened length is usually jetted in about 3 to 4 ft below the bottom of the excavation.

The well is installed in the ground at the swing joint points by way of jetting, using water pressure from hydrant or from a special jetting pump. For that purpose, the bottom of the well casing is provided with a ball-type check valve (Fig. 13-4). Such a valve allows for an unimpeded downward flow of water through the inside of the casing out into the soil through the nozzle located at the lower end of the well when jetting the wellpoint into position. The ball-type check-valve closes the nozzle automatically when water is pumped out of the well. Almost every manufacturer of such equipment has his own patented wellpoint of a particular internal design.

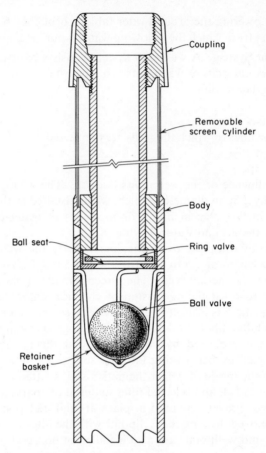

FIG. 13-4 Wellpoint (Moretrench System) (Courtesy of the Moretrench Corp., Rockaway, N.J.)

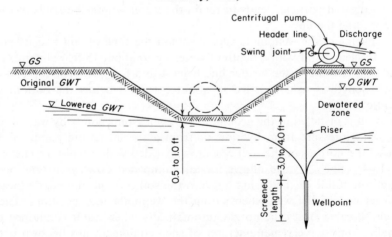

FIG. 13-5 Single-stage asymmetrical wellpoint system.

The water pressure, upon jetting the wellpoint, washes out a cavity in the soil and sinks the wellpoint into the ground to a desired depth. The sinking of the wellpoint is speeded up by bouncing the casing up and down, and by rotating it. Jetting a wellpoint into position is a quick operation, requiring under normal conditions only about 40 seconds per point. All wellpoints are jetted to the same

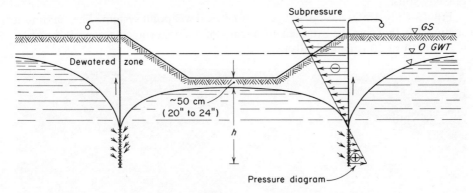

FIG. 13-6   Symmetrical wellpoint system.

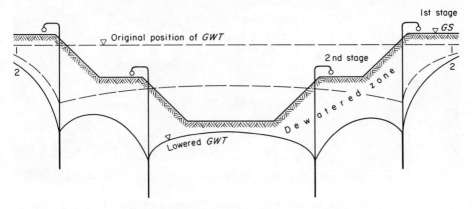

FIG. 13-7.   Two-stage de-watering system.

depth, viz., elevation, and deep enough below the bottom of the pit. This is a necessary requirement to prevent entering of air into the vacuum lines through a "high" wellpoint during de-watering operations in soil. The presence of air in the wellpoint system decreases its efficiency. However, since the inflow into the wellpoints cannot be voided entirely, because the voids of the de-watered soil contain atmospheric air, at least air should be kept to a minimum.

Pumping in a Single Stage. A single-stage wellpoint system is one where the header and pumps are arranged in one tier. Fig. 13-5 illustrates a single-stage asymmetrical wellpoint system used for de-watering narrow trenches. Upon pumping, the wellpoint system is under subpressure, i.e., below atmospheric pressure, and depression curves of the groundwater table results. The well-points should be spaced so that depression lines intercept, thus forming a continuous de-watered zone.

The method of providing dry foundation pits by means of the wellpoint system is suitable for conditions from the finest sandy soils to the coarsest gravelly soils.

Fig. 13-6 illustrates a single-stage, symmetrical wellpoint system. The maximum suction lift that can be attained by means of a single-stage de-watering system is about 18 to 20 ft (practically).

FIG. 13-8 Multiple-stage de-watering system (Courtesy of the Moretrench Corp., Rockaway, N.J.)

Pumping in Multiple Stages. For depths greater than 18 to 20 ft, a multiple-stage de-watering system is used. A multiple-stage system consists of two or more tiers of single-stage de-watering systems (Fig. 13-7). With n stages, a lowering of the groundwater table of $(n \times 18)$ ft can be achieved. Sometimes 5 or 6 stages are applied for de-watering deep foundation pits, Fig. 13-8.

The installation of a multiple-stage wellpoint system is accomplished in this way: a single-stage tier of wellpoints is installed around the excavation pit, the groundwater table is lowered, and the first part of the excavation is dug. Then another row or tier of wellpoints is installed, and the excavation work continued downward, see Fig. 13-7.

When necessary, a third and/or n^{th} tier of wellpoints is installed. At the bottom of the pit, a last tier of wellpoints might be needed to keep the bottom of the excavation sufficiently dry to permit the operation of heavy construction equipment.

After the foundations have been carried up above the groundwater table, it is no longer necessary to continue lowering the groundwater table, and the wellpoint installation is dismantled.

Application of Wellpoint Systems. The wellpoint systems are applied for lowering the groundwater table in excavating pits under dry conditions for the construction of foundations of bridge piers and abutments; dry docks; water pumping stations and sewerage treatment plants; cofferdams; to facilitate pile-driving operations where dry conditions are needed; for constructing sewer lines, tunnels, and de-watering of mines; structural underpinning operations to cope with "quicksand" conditions, and to permit quick, effective excavation in operating heavy equipment under dry conditions. The de-watered slopes of the excavation are usually stable.

13-9. Comments on the Wellpoint System. The following comments are pertinent to the operation of wellpoint installations for the purpose of lowering the groundwater table in foundation engineering activities:

1) Suction pumps cannot suck water much above 20 ft. Therefore, the practical suction height limit should not exceed 15 to 20 ft.
2) To lift water to a greater height, deep-well pumps, termed submerged or immersion pumps, are used. Such pumps are lowered into the water in the casing of the well. The water can then be pushed to a considerable height. The disadvantage of such an installation is its cost.
3) For lifting water from a greater depth than 20 ft, a multiple-stage de-watering system is more effective.

The following are some of the advantages of wellpoint systems.

1) Although the planning and design of a wellpoint system is a very specialized job, the method of lowering the groundwater table by means of wellpoints is safe, effective, and simple to supervise.
2) Rapid jetting permits quick and easy installation of the wellpoint system.
3) De-watering of soil by the wellpoint method transforms a wet soil into a "firm" one, thus permitting the excavation of the earthworks under dry conditions and also permitting substructure construction operations under dry conditions.
4) Excavation in dry soil is less expensive than in wet soil.
5) Lowering the groundwater table permits earthwork excavations all year round.
6) De-watering usually eliminates partly or wholly sheeting and/or shoring, and avoids cave-ins.
7) Each wellpoint can be excluded from the general operation of the well-point system, inspected, and repaired.

The following are some of the disadvantages of a wellpoint system.

1) The initial installation cost is relatively high.

2) In the wellpoint system the replacement cost in case of failure is also high.

3) If the well is not properly gravel-treated, there exists, upon pumping, a danger of sand being pumped into the wellpoint.

4) Comprehensive boring operations in soil are necessary if the operation is worked in stages.

5) The construction site is jammed with pumps, pipes, and associated equipment.

6) Every lowering of the groundwater table causes settlement of soil and adjacent structures. It must be checked whether settlements are tolerable.

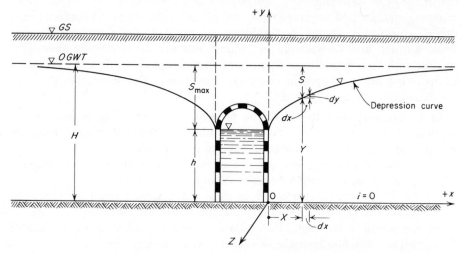

Fig. 13-9   Ground-water table lowering by means of horizontal galleries.

13-10. Lowering the Groundwater Table by Means of Horizontal Galleries.
The groundwater table can also be lowered by means of horizontal galleries dug in the ground. Assume that the gallery is dug down to the impervious soil layer, Fig. 13-9. The velocity of the water flowing into the trench at any point on the depression line $(x; y)$ is:

$$v = k \frac{dy}{dx}, \qquad (13\text{-}53)$$

and the quantity of water flowing into the trench from one side along one linear foot of shoreline is

$$q = vA, \qquad (13\text{-}54)$$

where $A = zy$ is the cross-sectional area at point $(x; y)$, and z is the length of the trench, viz., canal.
Then

$$q = zyk \frac{dy}{dx}. \qquad (13\text{-}55)$$

Integrating this equation for y between the limits $y_1 = h$ and $y_2 = H$, and for $x_1 = 0$ and $x_2 = R$, obtain:

$$q = zk \frac{H^2 - h^2}{2R}.$$ (13-56)

The quantity of water flowing into the gallery from both sides is

$$Q = 2q = zk \frac{H^2 - h^2}{R}.$$ (13-57)

When the water table in the gallery drops or rises, the shape of the depression curve also changes. When the water table drops, i.e., h decreases, then R increases, and vice versa. Upon increasing h, R decreases.

Example. Given: $H = 7.0$ m, $h = 2.0$ m, $R = 400$ m, $k = 0.001$ m/sec. Calculate the discharge into the gallry per $z = 1$ meter shore length, and plot the depression line. What is the maximum draw-down?
Solution.
a) By Eq. (13-56), for one-sided inflow

$$Q_1 = zk \frac{H^2 - h^2}{2R} = (1)(0.001) \frac{(7.0)^2 - (2.0)^2}{(2)(400)} =$$

$$= (5.625)(10)^{-5} \quad (\text{m}^3/\text{sec from one side}).$$

For two sides of the gallery,

$$Q = 2Q_1 = (2)(5.625)(10)^{-5} \quad (\text{m}^3/\text{sec}).$$

b) The equation of the depression curve is:

$$y^2 = H^2 - \frac{2}{z} \frac{Q_1}{k} (R - x)$$ (13-58)

Substituting for the known quantities, obtain

$$y = +\sqrt{(4.00) + (0.1125)(x)}$$ (13-59)

c) The maximum draw-down at the gallery is

$$s_{max} = H - h = 7.0 - 2.0 = 5.00 \quad (\text{m}).$$ (13-60)

13-11. Settlement. Upon lowering the groundwater table to a certain extent, a volume change in soil takes place. Thus an important question arises whether, because of the volume change of soil, the soil, viz., the ground surface, will or will not settle. In a submerged condition, before the lowering of the groundwater table, soil particles are subjected to buoyancy. Upon lowering the groundwater table, the buoyancy is removed and the soil mass between the original and the lowered position of the groundwater table becomes apparently heavier and exerts its full pressure upon a horizontal supporting surface, real or imaginary, by an amount which is approximately 1.6 times as much as that before lowering the groundwater. This pressure exerted upon a compressive layer of soil gives rise to compression, viz., volume change of the soil, which, in its turn, causes a consolidation settlement of the soil, even though no external load is applied at the ground surface.

The apparent increase in pressure, viz., unit weight of soil after lowering the groundwater table, can be seen from the following simplified calculation:
Dry unit weight of soil (degree of saturation: $S = 0$) after lowering the groundwater table:

$$\gamma_d = (1 - n)G\gamma_w, \tag{13-61}$$

where γ_d = dry unit weight of soil,
       n = porosity,
       G = specific gravity of soil particles, and
       γ_w = unit weight of water.
Submerged unit weight of soil before lowering the groundwater table:

$$\gamma_{sub} = (1 - n)(G - 1)\gamma_w \tag{13-62}$$

Ratio:

$$\lambda = \frac{\gamma_d}{\gamma_{sub}} = \frac{(1 - n)G\gamma_w}{(1 - n)(G - 1)\gamma_w} = \frac{G}{G - 1} > 1, \tag{13-63}$$

or, assuming for quartz sand $G = 2.65$, the ratio is

$$(\gamma_d/\gamma_{sub}) = 1.606,$$

which means that the dry unit weight of the soil is approximately 1.6 times greater than the submerged unit weight.

For a saturated soil, shortly after draw-down of the groundwater table, and with an average porosity of $n = 30\%$,

$$\frac{\gamma_{sat}}{\gamma_{sub}} = \frac{(1 - n)G\gamma_w + n\gamma_w}{(1 - n)(G - 1)\gamma_w} = 1.865 \tag{13-64}$$

times heavier than the submerged weight.

THE SUBSIDENCE OF MEXICO CITY

13-12. Cause of Subsidence. The settlements of soil and structures and the subsidence of this modern Mexican metropolis, the Federal District of Mexico City—a city of four million people and one of the largest cities in North America —are very well known. They are very celebrated and spectacular examples of large-scale soil consolidation frequently cited by soil and foundation engineers.

Mexico City, called by the Aztecs Tenochtitlán, and founded by them in 1325 on a small island in Lake Texcoco, is situated in a large valley basin of about 3110 square miles. The surface of this elliptical plateau is about 7400 ft above sea level. The deepest point of the basin is about 7225 ft above the sea level.[10]

The general process of subsidence of this area began long ago in pre-Spanish and Spanish times after the installation of dikes and drainage canals to cope with floods in that city. To protect the city from floods, the Aztecs in 1449, under the rule of Montezuma I, began to build a dam 10 miles long. After the conquest of Mexico by the Spaniards, the latter, too, were engaged in flood protection work, mainly by means of canals. There occurred extensive floods in Mexico City in 1555, 1580, 1607, 1629, and later.

The subsiding process of Mexico City was accelerated about 1789 when the plateau was drained. The subsidence still takes place at an alarming rate caused by the installation and pumping of about 3500 sub-artesian wells throughout the Federal District of Mexico City starting about 1910 to increase the

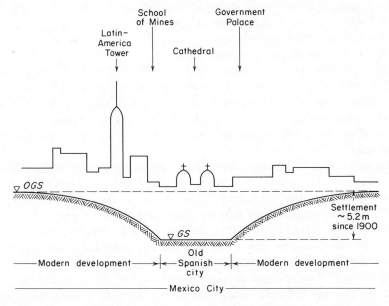

FIG. 13-10   Illustrating the concept of the subsidence of Mexico City.

water supply. The depth of these wells is 50 to about 500 ft. Some of them are supposed to be 700 ft deep. Since 1900, when the new sewerage system was installed, and when the settlement of the soil had attained about three-quarters of an inch, Mexico City has sunk more than 16 ft. In 1944, the rate of pumping of the wells was 7 m^3/sec $\approx$ 1850 gallons per sec, or about 237 ft^3/sec (according to Mexican engineers). Mexico City settles now at an unbelievable rate of 2 ft a year, or more than 1 mm per day. From 1900 to about 1957 buildings have settled in some places about 25 ft below the ground surface. Speaking in hyperbole, there is no talk about the rate of settlement of the city, but rather about the rate of disappearance of it.

Actually, the settlement, viz., subsidence, of Mexico City began with the erection of the old Spanish City. Although the structures in the old Spanish City in Mexico City are generally neither high nor heavy (save for a few cathedrals), the great settlements in this part of the city took place during the many centuries that passed since the application of the city load on the very compressible soil. The development of the modern Mexico City took place around the old Spanish city. Fig. 13-10 illustrates the concept of the subsidence of Mexico City. The tall and heavy structures inevitably settle regardless of whether they are founded on piles or not.

The reason for the subsiding of Mexico City is in part the load of the city and the nature of the soil deposit in the large, flat Mexico Valley surrounded by mountains. Borings in the city indicate that the soil consists of a layered system of gravel, sand, silt, and clay, the latter of which is mostly of volcanic origin, containing montmorillonite. This clay ranges in depth from 30 to 600 ft.

The particularly conspicuous characteristics of this "gelatine-like" clay are:

    a) the very low unit weight in moist condition,

    b) the high moisture content, and

    c) a very low coefficient of permeability.

This clay contains commonly about 200% to 500% of moisture by dry weight in undisturbed samples. Some soil samples have a void ratio as high as $e = 15$. The soft clays form confined aquifers. The coefficient of this soft clay is of the order of magnitude of $k = 10^{-7}$ cm/sec. Rabe[11] gives a figure of 2×10^{-9} cm/min. The clay is often interspersed with thin sand layers and pockets of sand lenses.

When asked what is the reason for these aggravating settlements, the Mexican replies: "Jaboncillo", meaning a mass of soap, i.e., the soap-like, slippery, oily soil. This term was introduced by the Aztecs to denote the extensive lake of mud—the soil, meaning the bentonite clay when wet.

Another factor contributing to the subsidence is the increased rate of pumping of the wells which extend down through the clay into the coarse, permeable soil materials, as well as the weight of the buildings expelling water out of the voids of the soil. The intensive evaporation of soil moisture through the ground surface in this high elevated valley also causes the soil to consolidate and to settle.

13-13. Soil Profile and Soil Properties. Soil exploration borings have penetrated the soil of Mexico City to nearly 2000 ft without hitting bedrock. Dependable soil material, in the usually accepted sense, exists in Mexico City only at great depth. Some reasonably satisfactory bearing material can be found at depths of from 110 to 230 ft (Fig. 13-11). At a depth of about 165 ft there is a layer of gravel and sand cemented with fine clay. Other sediments in the soil profile of Mexico City are volcanic ashes and water-deposited layers (lacustrine volcanic clay). The volcanic ashes, fine in texture, settled in the lake basin very slowly thus forming a very spongy textural structure. These volcanic ash clays, a 33 to 66 ft thick layer, overlie the cemented sand and gravel. On top of the volcanic clay, a layer about 16 ft thick of volcanic sand is deposited, and on top of this more volcanic ash has been deposited (about 100 ft thick). This clay layer possesses bentonite characteristics. Above these expansive clays, there exists a layer about 35 ft thick of transported clay and artificial fill. This fill has been filled by Aztecs and Spaniards as flood protective measures.

According to Cuevas.[12] Carillo,[13] Gonzalez,[14] Albin[15] and Zeevaert,[16,17] the soil properties underneath Mexico City can be approximately described as follows.

The upper layer—the top soil— varies in thickness from a few inches to several yards. The unit weight of this soil ranges from about 88 lb/ft³ to 150 lb/ft³ (~ 1400 kg/m³ to ~ 2400 kg/m³). The next layer (Fig. 13-11) consists of clay and marl, about 32 ft to 105 ft in thickness, and is classed as a clayey silt. It is bright in color, turning to gray or brown on being exposed to the oxidation of air.

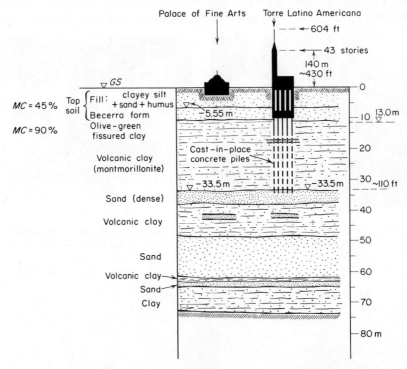

FIG. 13-11   A sketch profile of soil from Mexico City. A freely prepared sketch after Zeevaert, Ref. 17.

The clay shrinks in air by an amount of ⅛ of its original volume. The porosity, and void ratio, e, of this clay is high: it varies from $e = 2$ to $e = 12$, and in some cases to $e = 15$. Such large void ratios result in very low submerged unit weights of the soil. The unit weight of this soil is about 38 lb/ft³ (≈ 609 kg/m³). This explains the high compressibility of the volcanic ash. The fine volcanic ash in the Mexico Valley has decomposed into thixotropic bentonite clay containing about 20% of the mineral montmorillonite, about 50% ashes, diatoms, and minute marine crustacea, about 10% organic colloids, and other substances. The clay is about 40% finer than 2 microns.

Then follows a thin layer of sand, about 5 ft thick, and then another clay layer, 65 ft. thick, another sand layer 13 ft in thickness, and another layer of compressible volcanic clay of very great thickness.

The *seat of settlement* of the upper clay layer is in its lower part at a depth between 92 ft and 108 ft (28 and 33 m). The second clay layer contributes the largest part of the soil settlement in Mexico City. Both clay layers gave between 1949 and 1953 a total settlement of 36 in. ($\approx$ 93 cm).

13-14. Nature of Damage. The subsidence of Mexico City has brought with it many engineering problems. Under settlement conditions the bench marks become unreliable. Hence, it is difficult to perform precise settlement studies in the field. Also, the settlement of Mexico City's soil results in disastrous breakage of the city's sewer system and pipe lines; in undulating streets (Avenida

Fig. 13-12   The building of the former National Engineers' School, School of Mines, Mexico City.

Fig. 13-13   Three-stage pavement and the position of the street-light pole indicate settlement of the street. Mexico City.

Fig. 13-14   The tilted Guadalupe National Shrine, Mexico.

Juarez, Avenida Tenochtitlán, for example) and cracking pavements and structures; tilting and settlement of monumental buildings such as churches, cathedrals (among them the Guadalupe National Shrine and the cathedral on the Plaza de la Constitucion), monuments, museums, theaters, the ex-school of Mines, Fig. 13-12, and the Palace of Fine Arts, the first floor of which is now the basement. The Y.M.C.A. building settles because of the pumping from several adjacent wells 700 ft deep. Even the most modern buildings in Mexico City, such as the Department of Hydraulic Resources Building, and the building which houses the United States of America Embassy on the Paseo de la Reforma, are victims of the subsidence.

Fig. 13-13 shows a three-stage pavement and the position of the street-light pole erected on the original (first) pavement.

Fig. 13-14 shows the tilted Guadalupe National Shrine. This indicates how difficult it is to design and construct foundations on soils and areas previously described. The settlement of the soil of Mexico City can thus be regarded as a large-scale consolidation test.

13-15. Recent Development. To cope with the unfavorable soil conditions in Mexico City engineers are now trying to build "floating" foundations— hollow, cellular, concrete boxes—which are placed in the upper clay stratum. The term "floating" or "compensating" foundation carries the idea of compensating the weight of the excavated soil by an equivalent, total weight of the new structure. This principle has been applied to the building of the National Lottery of Mexico,[18] and several other structures. Where the structures are lighter than the excavated soil, they are lifted up, as for example the pumping station "La Condesa". Also, cases are known where in that city the casings of the subartesian wells were lifted up above the ground surface, so that the projecting tops, to assure the proper operation of the wells, had to be cut off. Sometimes, because of the hydrostatic

FIG. 13-15 Torre Latino Americana, Mexico City.

pressure and swelling pressure of the soil, the bottoms of excavations of foundation pits burst through.

Lately, tilting and settlement of floating structures are controlled, among other methods, by pumping water into and out of the cells which settled less than the other end of the structure.

The partly floating foundation of the Tower Latino Americana, Fig. 13-15, consists of a reinforced concrete mat supported on 361 concrete point-bearing piles driven to a depth of 33.5 m into a firm layer of sand.

REFERENCES

1. J. Dupuit, *Études théoretiques et pratiques sur la mouvement des eaux dans les canaux découverts et a travers les terrains perméables*, 2nd edition, Paris, Dunod, 1863, pp. 229; 254.

2. A. Thiem, "Über die Ergiebigkeit artesischer Bohrlöcher, Schachtbrunnen und Filtergalerien", *Journal für Gasbeleuchtung und Wasserversorgung*, 1870, p. 455.
3. W. Kyrieleis and W. Sichardt, *Grundwasserabsenkung bei Fundierarbeiten*, Berlin, Julius Springer, 1930, p. 30.
4. H. Weber, *Die Reichweite von Grundwassersenkungen mittels Rohrbrunnen*, Berlin, Julius Springer, 1928, p. 11.
5. J. Kozeny, *Theorie und Berechnung der Brunnen*, Wasserkraft und Wasserwirtschaft, 1933, vol. 28, p. 104.
6. A. Schoklitsch, *Hydraulic Structures*, trans. S. Shulits, New York, The American Society of Mechanical Engineers, 1937, vol. 1, p. 179.
7. C. Slichter, *19th Annual Report*, 1899, U.S. Geological Survey, Part 2, p. 360.
8. M. Muscat, *Flow of Homogeneous Fluids Through Porous Media*, New York, McGraw-Hill Book Co., Inc., 1937, p. 95.
9. C. F. Tolman, *Ground Water*, New York, McGraw-Hill Book Co., Inc., 1937, p. 387.
10. W. H. Rabe, "Die Geschichte der Hochwassersicherung der Stadt Mexico", *Die Bautechnik*, no. 17/18, April 8, 1941, p. 192.
11. W. H. Rabe, "Der Baugrund der Stadt Mexico und die Senkungen ihrer Gebäude", *Die Bautechnik*, no. 28, 1941, p. 300.
12. J. A. Cuevas, "Foundation Conditions in Mexico City", *Proceedings*, First International Conference on Soil Mechanics and Foundation Engineering, vol. 3, June 22 to 26, 1936, Cambridge, Mass., p. 233.
13. N. Carillo, "Influence of Artesian Wells in the Sinking of Mexico City", *Proceedings*, Second International Conference on Soil Mechanics and Foundation Engineering, June 21 to 30, 1948, Rotterdam, vol. 7, p. 157.
14. M. Gonzalez, "level Control in Buildings by Means of Adjustable Piling", *Proceedings*, Second International Conference on Soil Mechanics and Foundation Engineering, June 21 to 30, 1948, Rotterdam, vol. 4, pp. 152-156.
15. P. Albin, Jr., "Special Foundations Support Mexico City's Buildings on Highly Compressible Clay", *Civil Engineering*, 1949, vol. 19, no. 8, pp. 25-28.
16. L. Zeevaert, "Pore Pressure Measurements to Investigate the Main Source of Surface Subsidence in Mexico City" (Disc.), *Proceedings*, Third International Conference on Soil Mechanics and Foundation Engineering, August 16 to 27, 1953, Zürich, vol. 2, pp. 299-304.
17. L. Zeevaert, "Foundation Design and Behaviour of Tower Latino Americana in Mexico City", *Geotechnique*, vol. 7, no. 3, September, 1957, pp. 115-133.
18. J. A. Cuevas, "The Floating Foundation of the New Building for the National Lottery of Mexico: An Actual Size Study of the Deformations of a Flocculent-Structured Deep Soil", *Proceedings*, First International Conference on Soil Mechanics and Foundation Engineering, June 22 to 26, 1936, Cambridge, Mass., vol. 1, pp. 294-301.

QUESTIONS AND PROBLEMS

13-1. What is the practical limit for lowering groundwater table in one tier?

13-2. Derive according to the Dupuit-Thiem theory the differential equation of the depression curve which would result upon lowering the groundwater table. The well is extending down to an impervious layer. The aquifer is under atmospheric pressure. Also, integrate the differential equation for full and efficient operation of this soil-well system. The system pertains to an ordinary, perfect well.

13-3. Discuss assumptions and limitations of the Dupuit-Thiem theory of wells.

13-4. Calculate stress conditions (effective, neutral, and total stresses) in soil algebraically before and after lowering groundwater table. Disregard capillary effects, and tabulate results. Consider the soil to be a fine, homogeneous sand.

Chapter 14

SEEPAGE THEORY

14-1. Seepage Through Earth Dams. Assumptions. Seepage can occur to lower-lying lands from natural water courses and/or the sea; from artificial water reservoirs, underneath various hydraulic structures, and from leakage of artesian wells.

Darcy's law of permeability of water can also be applied to calculate discharge of gravity flow through earth dams. In designing and constructing earth dams the engineer is interested in their stability against sloughing and washing out of slopes. Particularly, he is interested in the loss of water through the earth dam by seepage, as well as in the height of the outcrop point of the uppermost flow or seepage line. This uppermost flow line is also called the saturation line, or the phreatic line.

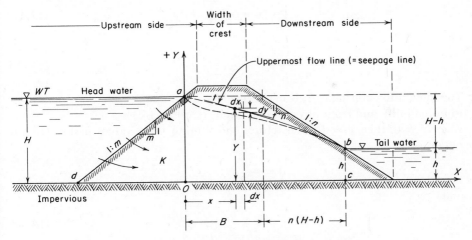

FIG. 14-1   Sketch of a homogeneous dam.

The uppermost flow line is a free water surface forming the upper boundary of flow by seepage. Above the saturation line there exists atmospheric pressure. Below this line there exists hydraulic pressure. Below the outcrop point the downstream slope of the earth dam must be protected from washing out.

Suppose that an engineer has to determine the seepage quantity or discharge of water through an earth dam as illustrated in Fig. 14-1. Assume that the dam is homogeneous, and permeable; that the dam rests on an impervious layer of soil, or rock; and that the system's permeability is k m/sec.

The curved line, *a-b*, is the uppermost flow line, or simply the seepage line. At point *b*, on the downstream side, the seepage line crops out of the dam. The height *b-c* (*h*) is the height of the outcrop point of the seepage line above the impervious stratum. The water sheet, the thickness of which is *h*, or < *h*, is termed the tailwater.

The slope of seepage line is

$$i = -\frac{dy}{dx}. \tag{14-1}$$

Derivation of Discharge Equation. The rate of filtration, *v*, according to Darcy's law, is

$$v = ki = k\left(-\frac{dy}{dx}\right). \tag{14-2}$$

The discharge through the dam per one unit of length along the shore line is

$$q = vA = vy(1) = -ky\frac{dy}{dx}, \tag{14-3}$$

where $A = y(1) = $ area perpendicular to flow.

Separation of variables and integration of Eq. (14-3) yields

$$q\int_0^x dx = -k\int_0^y y\,dy, \tag{14-4a}$$

or

$$qx = -\frac{k}{2}y^2 + C. \tag{14-4b}$$

The integration constant, *C*, is determined by reasoning as follows:
in Eq. (14-4b), and from physical conditions (see Fig. 14-1):
when $x = 0$, then $y = H$. Therefore, substituting these values in Eq. (14-4b) obtain *C*:

$$0 = -\frac{k}{2}H^2 + C,$$

and

$$C = \frac{k}{2}H^2. \tag{14-4c}$$

Substituting Eq. (14-4c) into Eq. (14-4b), obtain

$$q = \frac{k}{2x}(H^2 - y^2), \tag{14-4}$$

which is the discharge equation per unit length of shore line. Note that in this derivation a vertical, cross-sectional area (through point *a*) through which the water seeps is substituted for the upstream face (*a-d*). Also, the triangular part on the downstream side of the dam has been neglected in deriving the discharge formula. These two neglected triangular parts of the dam, however, also consume a certain magnitude of the pressure head to overcome the friction in these parts of the soil. However, the convenience in calculating the discharge outweighs the errors thus introduced.

Equation of Seepage Line. From Eq. (14-4), the equation of the uppermost flow line, or seepage line, or depression line, is obtained:

$$y^2 = H^2 - \frac{2qx}{k}. \tag{14-5}$$

Also, note that the position of the uppermost seepage line (*a-b*) cannot yet be determined because of the unknowns of x, y, q, and h.

Check of Equation (14-5)
  a) When $x = 0$, then $y = +H$.
  b) When $x = B + n(H - h)$, then $y = h$.

Determination of Outcrop, h. The position of the outcrop, h, viz., the position of the seepage line, is determined so that the discharge, q, through the vertical face, *b-c*, is a maximum. Therefore, in the q-function, Eq. (14-4), x is to be substituted by $B + n(H - h)$, and y is to be substituted by h:*

$$q = \frac{k}{2x}(H^2 - y^2) = \frac{k}{2}\frac{(H^2 - h^2)}{B + n(H - h)}. \tag{14-6}$$

The discharge is at its maximum when q is differentiated after h, and when this derivative is set equal to zero, i.e., $dq/dh = 0$, and when the second derivative of the q-function is less than zero, i.e., $(d^2q)/dh^2 < 0$.

The first derivative of the q-function is set equal to zero as shown:

$$\frac{dq}{dh} = \frac{k}{2}\left\{\frac{[B + n(H - h)(-2h)] - [(H^2 - h^2)(-n)]}{[B + n(H - h)]^2}\right\} = 0. \tag{14-7}$$

This fraction can be equal to zero in the following cases:
  1) the nominator should be zero, or
  2) the denominator should be ∞.

It is obvious that $k/2 \neq 0$, and that by design or construction the denominator is not equal to an infinitely large number. For the same reasons, $n \neq \infty$ also. It follows, therefore, that the brackets in the nominator must be zero:

$$nh^2 - 2(B + nH)h + nH^2 = 0. \tag{14-8}$$

The solution of this quadratic equation gives such a height of the outcrop, h, that q becomes a maximum:

$$h = \left(H + \frac{B}{n}\right) - \sqrt{\left(H + \frac{B}{n}\right)^2 - H^2}. \tag{14-9}$$

In order that h be physically a real quantity, use a minus sign before the radical. Equation (14-9) reveals that h, to accommodate the maximum discharge, depends upon the geometry of the dam only.

* See A. Schoklitsch, *Hydraulic Structures*, translated from the German by S. Shulits, published by the Am. Soc. of Mech. Engineers, New York, 1937, p. 193.

The second derivative, $(d^2q)/(dh^2)$, is < 0, as one can check by differentiating Eq. (14-7) once more.

Note that in Eq. (14-9) the height of the outcrop of the seepage line is the same no matter what the material used for building the dam. The discharge, however, is a function of k (see Eq. 14-4).

Discharge. Now that h is known, and based on the principle of continuity of flow, the discharge, q, can be calculated by Eq. (14-6):

$$q = \frac{k}{2} \frac{(H^2 - h^2)}{B + n(H - h)}. \tag{14-10}$$

When q is known, then by Eq. (14-5) the ordinates, y, of the seepage line $(a\text{-}b)$ can be calculated and plotted by assuming various x-values. Of course, the system's permeability, k, must be known.

Direction of Velocity Vector at Outcrop Point. To ascertain the direction of the seepage velocity vector, V, reason as follows: assume that the vector of seepage velocity, V, forms an angle, δ, with the face of the downstream slope of the dam as indicated in Fig. 14-2.

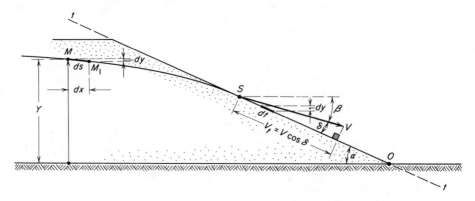

FIG. 14-2   Velocity vector at outcrop point.

The projection of the seepage velocity vector on the slope $t\text{-}t$ is

$$V_t = V \cos \delta. \tag{14-11}$$

The seepage velocity anywhere on the curved part of the seepage line is

$$V = k \sin \beta. \tag{14-12}$$

It is calculated based on Darcy's law "$v = ki$" as shown below. Here k is the coefficient of the system's permeability, and i = hydraulic gradient.

Velocity at point M:

$$V = ki = -k \frac{dy}{ds}, \tag{14-13}$$

where ds is the differential length of the seepage curve, MM_1; but, from Fig. 14-2,

$$-\frac{dy}{ds} = \sin \beta, \tag{14-14}$$

where β = angle formed by the velocity vector, V, with the horizontal drawn through the point of tangency.
Then

$$V = k \sin \beta, \tag{14-15}$$

Q.E.D., which is the expression for seepage velocity at any point on the depression curve. Eq. (14-15) indicates that seepage velocity on the depression curve always has a finite value and cannot be greater than k.

At the outcrop point, S, the two velocity projections, namely $V_t = V \cos \delta$, and $V_t = k \sin \beta \cos \delta$, obviously are equal, i.e.,

$$V \cos \delta = k \sin \beta \cos \delta. \tag{14-16}$$

Between the points of outcrop, S, and the toe, O, of the dam, the velocity, according to Darcy's law, is:

$$V_t = ki = -k\frac{dy}{dt} = k \sin \alpha, \tag{14-17}$$

where dt is a differential length on line t-t between points S and O, and $i = dy/dt = \sin \alpha$.

Equating Eq. (14-16) and Eq. (14-17), obtain

$$k \sin \beta \cos \delta = k \sin \alpha, \tag{14-18}$$

or because, by geometry,

$$\beta = \alpha - \delta,$$

$$\sin(\alpha - \delta)\cos \delta = \sin \alpha. \tag{14-19}$$

This equation is satisfied for slopes the slope angles of which are equal to or less than vertical ($\alpha \le 90°$) and when $\delta = 0$.

Hence, it can be deduced that the seepage velocity vector at the outcrop point, S, of the uppermost flow (seepage) line is directed along the line of the downstream slope. In other words, at the outcrop point, S, the velocity vector and the slope segment, S-O, are tangent to the curved seepage line, M-M_1-S

14-2. Graphical Determination of the Seepage Line. If the shape and position of the uppermost flow line $B_1 B_2 RS$ in the cross section of an earth dam is known (Fig. 14-3) then, as was seen in the previous section, the discharge quantity of seepage water through the dam can be calculated.

Besides determining the shape of the seepage line analytically, it can also be constructed graphically, or established in the laboratory—experimenting with a model dam of its prototype, as well as by the method of electrical analogy.

Parabolic Seepage Line. Because the seepage line for most of its length resembles a parabolic curve, A. Casagrande suggests for practical purposes that the real seepage line can be replaced by a parabola[1]. However, the substitute curve deviates from the true seepage line at the upstream and downstream faces of the dam. The assumed parabolically shaped seepage line, BB_2ESAV, is termed the basic parabola. The parabola is a curve whose every point is equidistant from a fixed point, termed the focus, and a line, termed the directrix.

Construction of Parabolic Seepage Line. The graphical construction of the parabolic seepage line is based on the properties of the parabola. For that purpose one must know a point on the parabola, for instance, point B, and the position of the focus, F, of the parabola.

According to A. Casagrande, the location of the parabolic point, B, with its coordinates $(x; y = H)$ is at the surface of the impounded water and distant 0.3 times the projection, $D_1 B_1$, of the upstream slope $B_1 D$, of the dam and away from point B_1 as shown in Fig. 14-3.

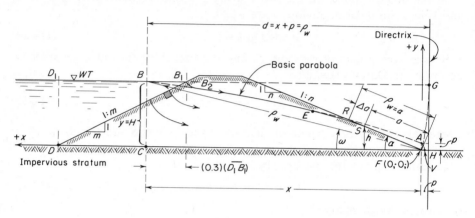

Fig. 14-3   Basic parabola (adapted after A. Casagrande, Ref. 1).

The position of the focus, F, of the basic parabola is usually chosen at the intersecting point of the lower boundary flowline (horizontal in this case) and the discharge face, which is the downstream slope of the dam.

The following are some of the important properties of a parabola (Fig. 14-4). A point (B) on the parabola is equidistant from the focus and from its directrix, i.e., $\rho = d$, where ρ is the radius-vector, from F as a pole to the point on the parabola in question, and ω is its amplitude.

The vertex, V, of the parabola halves the subtangent: $FV = VH = p/2$. The value of the focal ordinate is equal to the half-parameter, p, of the parabola.

The angle of the slope of the tangent, t-t, at a point whose coordinates are $\xi = p/2$ and $\eta = p$ is $45°$, or its slope is $\tan 45° = 1$.

Equation of Parabola. The equation of the parabola in the canonic form with the vertex at the point of origin of coordinates (V) in the rectangular coordinate system is

$$\eta^2 = 2p\xi, \tag{14-20}$$

or

$$\xi = \frac{\eta^2}{2p}, \tag{14-21}$$

where ξ and η are the flowing coordinates, and $2p$ is the parameter of the parabola.

To fit the parabola to the physical problem (the focus, F, is assumed to be located at the toe of the downstream slope), it is convenient to translate the η-axis from the vertex, V, to the focus, F, and to write the equation of the parabola relative to its focus as a point of origin of the coordinates. Thus, the new coordinate system is now xFy, whereas the old coordinate system was $\xi V\eta$.

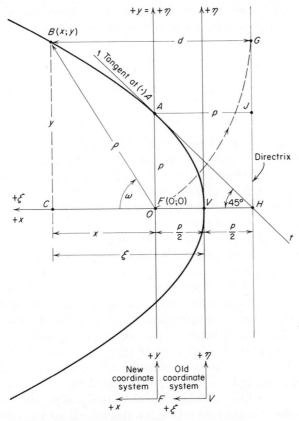

FIG. 14-4   Some properties of a parabola.

The transformation of the abscissas is

$$\xi = x + p/2,\qquad(14\text{-}22)$$

see Fig. 13-4, and because there is no transformation of coordinates in the vertical direction, then in the new coordinate system

$$y = \eta.\qquad(14\text{-}23)$$

Substituting Eq. (14-22) into Eq, (14-21),

$$x + p/2 = y^2/(2p),\qquad(14\text{-}24a)$$

and

$$x = \frac{y^2 - p^2}{2p},\qquad(14\text{-}24)$$

which is the equation of the parabola with the point of origin of coordinates at the focal point of the parabola.

Expressed in terms of x, the equation of the parabola is

$$y = \sqrt{2px + p^2}. \tag{14-25}$$

From Eqs. (14-24) and (14-25) one notes that before the parabola can be constructed, the half-parameter, p, of the parabola must be known. From geometry, in Fig. 14-4, $\rho = d$, or

$$\sqrt{x^2 + y^2} = x + p, \tag{14-26a}$$

and

$$p = \sqrt{x^2 + y^2} - x. \tag{14-26}$$

Construction of a Parabola for $\alpha > 30°$. The half-parameter, p, can now be constructed. With the radius, ρ, from a point, B, on the parabola as the center, swing an arc, FG, to intersect the line, d, at point G drawn from point B parallel to the x-axis. Then draw through point G a line perpendicular to the x-axis (parallel to y-axis). Line GH is the directrix of the parabola. Section FH is the half-parameter, p, of the parabola.

An ordinate, p, at F gives point A on the parabola. The bisecting point of FH on the x-axis gives the position of the vertex, V, of the parabola.

Now that p is known, other points which would lie on the parabola can be found graphically by means of the property of the parabola: namely, that every point on the curve is equidistant from the focus and from the directrix. One proceeds as follows: draw an ordinate, y, at any arbitrary abscissa-point (C) on the x-axis. Take the distance ($x + p$) as a radius, ρ, and draw from $F(0; 0)$ an arc, FB, for example. The intersection of ($x + p$) with the y-ordinate gives point B, which lies on the parabola. Repetition of this method with other values of ρ will give enough points to trace out the parabola.

Outcrop of Seepage Line. The intersection of the basic parabola with the downstream face of the dam at point R (Fig. 14-3) is calculated according to A. Casagrande as ($a + \Delta a$), where $a = VS$ is the wetted part of the downstream face, and point S is the intersection of the actual seepage line with the downstream face (or the outcrop point of the seepage line). Note that the quantity ($a + \Delta a$) is nothing else than a special radius vector, ρ, the amplitude, ω, of which is equal to the angle of slope, α, of the downstream face. Thus,

$$a + \Delta a = \rho_{\omega=\alpha}, \tag{14-27}$$

where Δa is the distance, SR, above the wetted part of the downstream face. The ratio

$$\frac{RS}{RF} = \frac{\Delta a}{a + \Delta a} = c \tag{14-28}$$

is a function of α, where α is the angle of the discharge face of the dam.

Slope Angles of Downstream Slopes. The dam as shown in Fig. 14-3 has no drainage structure or gallery at the downstream discharge. If the drainage structure at the toe of the dam is as illustrated in Figs. 14-5a and b, then the slope angles of the discharge face are $\alpha = 90°$ and $\alpha = 135°$, respectively. If there is a discharge gallery, Fig. 14-5c, then the slope angle is $\alpha = 180°$. The slope angle is, by convention, the clockwise angle between the base of the dam and the face of discharge. Note that in each case the intersection of the base line of the dam (bottom flow line) with the discharge face, F, is used as the focus of the basic parabola.

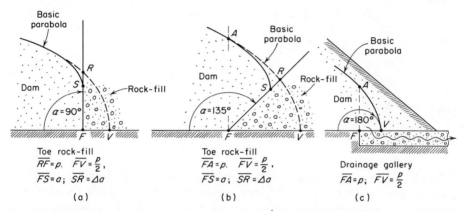

Toe rock-fill
$\overline{RF} = p.$ $\overline{FV} = \dfrac{p}{2},$
$\overline{FS} = a;$ $\overline{SR} = \Delta a$

(a)

Toe rock-fill
$\overline{FA} = p.$ $\overline{FV} = \dfrac{p}{2},$
$\overline{FS} = a;$ $\overline{SR} = \Delta a$

(b)

Drainage gallery
$\overline{FA} = p;$ $\overline{FV} = \dfrac{p}{2}$

(c)

FIG. 14-5   Slope angles for various drainage structures (after A. Casagrande, Ref. 1).

The c-values for various α's are given by A. Casagrande in Fig. 14-6 for any slope from 30° to 180°. Knowing α, which is given by construction of the dam, determine from Fig. 14-6 the c-value, which then permits one to calculate Δa:

$$\Delta a = (a + \Delta a)c. \qquad (14\text{-}29)$$

This quantity, Δa, in its turn, permits the determination of the position of point S at which the seepage line crops out of the downstream face of the dam. The outcrop ordinate is h.

The outcrop point, S, is connected to the basic parabola by sketching a short transition curve, ES. Point E on the curve is selected by eye.

Point B_1—intersection of the upstream water level with the face of the upstream slope of the dam—is also connected to the basic parabola, viz., seepage line at point B_2, by sketching a transition curve in between points B_1 and B_2. This transition curve, being the uppermost flow line, must be perpendicular to the upstream slope at

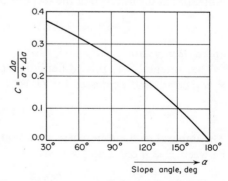

FIG. 14-6 $c = f(\alpha)$ (after A. Casagrande, Ref. 1).

point B_1. This is because the slope is an equipotential line. According to the flow net theory, the tangents at point B_1 drawn to the equipotential and flow line intersections must be mutually perpendicular.

Discharge Through Dam for Slope Angles of $\alpha > 30°$. After the seepage line, BB_1B_2ES, is established, the seepage discharge through the dam per one unit of length of shoreline can be calculated:

$$Q = vA = kiA = kA \frac{dy}{dx}, \tag{14-30}$$

where

$$A = y(1) = y = \sqrt{2px + p^2}, \tag{14-31}$$

and

$$\frac{dy}{dx} = \frac{p}{\sqrt{2px + p^2}}. \tag{14-32}$$

Then

$$Q = k\sqrt{2px + p^2}\,\frac{p}{\sqrt{2px + p^2}} = k\,p, \tag{14-33}$$

Discharge Through Dam for Slope Angles of $\alpha < 30°$. If the angle, α, of the downstream slope is less than $30°$, then, according to Schaffernack-Casagrande's method[2] one proceeds to determine the outcrop point, S, of the seepage line as follows. First note that points O and B are on the seepage line (Fig. 14-3). To simplify the matter, assume that part of the seepage line, $OS = a$, is a straight line. A tangent at point O under an angle, α, coincides over the length, OS, with the seepage line, viz., parabolic curve. Then express, according to Dupuit, the discharge through any cross section per unit time (see Fig. 14-7a):

$$Q = ky \frac{dy}{dx}. \tag{14-34}$$

Note that at the outcrop of the seepage line from the downstream face of the dam

$$y = ha \sin \alpha, \tag{14-35}$$

and $dy/dx = \tan \alpha$.

The integral of this differential equation (14-34) between $x = 0$ and $x = a \cos \alpha$, and expressed for Q, is

$$Q = ka \sin \alpha \tan \alpha. \tag{14-36}$$

The integral of the differential equation (14-34), after separation of variables, is, between $x = a \cos \alpha$ and $x = d$:

$$Q \int_{a\cos\alpha}^{d} dx = k \int_{a\sin\alpha}^{H} y\,dy, \tag{14-37}$$

the solution of which is

$$Q(d - a \cos \alpha) = \frac{k}{2}(H^2 - a^2 \sin^2 \alpha). \tag{14-38}$$

Position of the Outcrop Point of the Seepage Line Analytically for $\alpha < 30°$.
By the principle of continuity of flow the discharge quantities on both sides of
the outcrop height, h, must be equal, i.e.,

$$Q = ka \sin \alpha \tan \alpha,$$

and

$$Q = \frac{k(H^2 - a^2 \sin^2 \alpha)}{2(d - a \cos \alpha)}$$

must be equal. Equating the latter two equations obtain a quadratic equation
relative to a:

$$a^2 \sin^2 \alpha - 2\,ad \sin \alpha \tan \alpha + H^2 = 0. \tag{14-39}$$

The solution of this equation gives the length, a, which determines the outcrop
point, S, of the seepage line at the downstream slope of the earth dam:

$$a = \frac{d}{\cos \alpha} - \sqrt{\frac{d^2}{\cos^2 \alpha} - \frac{H^2}{\sin^2 \alpha}}. \tag{14-40}$$

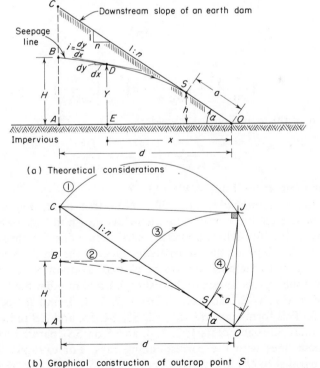

(a) Theoretical considerations

(b) Graphical construction of outcrop point S

FIG. 14-7   Determination of the outcrop point S, for $\alpha < 30°$.

Determination of the Outcrop Point Graphically for $\alpha < 30°$. The position of the outcrop point, S, viz., discharge length, a, can be determined graphically based on Eq. (14-40) as follows (Fig. 14-7).

Extend the H-ordinate above point B (which is a point on the seepage line), and intersect it at point C with the downstream slope of the dam. On OC as a diameter, draw a semicircle. Find point G on the downstream slope by intersecting it with a line from point B drawn parallel to the base, AO, of the dam. With point O as a center, and with a radius of OG, point G is transferred onto the semi-circle obtaining point H. Then, from point C as center and with a radius, CH, point H is transferred onto the downstream slope, viz., diameter, to give the outcrop point, S, of the seepage line.

Note that $\measuredangle\ CHO$ is $90°$: $OG = OH$, and $CH = CS$. Then the proof for the graphical construction of Eq. (14-40) is, from geometry as in Fig. 14-7b,

$$(OJ)^2 + (CJ)^2 = (OC)^2. \tag{14-41}$$

But
$$OJ = OG = H/(\sin \alpha), \tag{14-42}$$

$$CJ = CS = \frac{d}{\cos \alpha} - a, \tag{14-43}$$

and

$$OC = \frac{d}{\cos \alpha}; \tag{14-44}$$

therefore

$$\left(\frac{H}{\sin \alpha}\right)^2 + \left(\frac{d}{\cos \alpha} - a\right)^2 = \left(\frac{d}{\cos^2 \alpha}\right)^2. \tag{14-45}$$

The solution of this equation for a yields:

$$a = \frac{d}{\cos \alpha} - \sqrt{\frac{d^2}{\cos^2 \alpha} - \frac{H^2}{\sin^2 \alpha}}, \tag{14-40}$$

which is the same as the Eq. (14-40), Q.E.D.

Construction of Parabola for $\alpha < 30°$. Now that d, H, and a are known, the parabolic seepage line can be constructed as shown in Fig. 14-8.

Draw $SS_1 \perp OA$ through S, and $BS_1 \parallel OA$. Draw line OT through S which is the line of the slope of the downstream face of the dam. Simultaneously, line OT is tangent to the parabola (to be plotted) at point S. Then divide SS_1 and RT into equal divisions (six in this example), and number the division points as indicated in Fig. 14-8. Connect points 1, 2, 3, 4, 5, and B (located on TB) with point S. This forms rays ST, $S1$, $S2$, $S3$, $S4$, $S5$, and SB radiating from S. Then draw lines through points 1, 2, 3, 4, and 5 on SS_1 parallel to S_1B ($\parallel OA$). Intersect these lines with the corresponding rays. For example, intersect the line drawn parallel to OA and through point 5 on SS_1 with ray $S5$ to give point 5_o. Point 5_o is a point on the parabola. In a similar way construct parabolic points 4_o, 3_o, 2_o, and 1_o. Points B and S are already given as points on the parabola (on seepage line). The tracing of a curve through points B, 5_o, 4_o, 3_o, 2_o, 1_o, and S results in a parabola which is the sought seepage line, BS, above its outcrop at S.

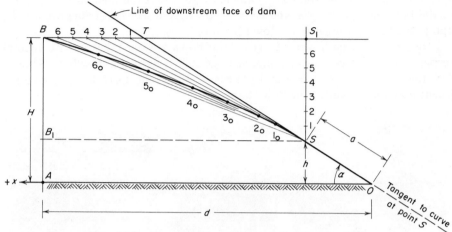

FIG. 14-8   Construction of seepage line for $\alpha < 30°$.

14-3. The Hydrodynamic Flow Net.

Flow Net. Seepage studies through earth dams can also be performed by means of a flow net. A flow net is a system consisting of two sets or families of mutually orthogonally intersecting curves (Fig. 14-9). One set of these curves, designated as the ψ-curves, are the so-called flow lines or stream lines. The other set of curves, designated as the Φ-curves, are the so-called equipotential lines.

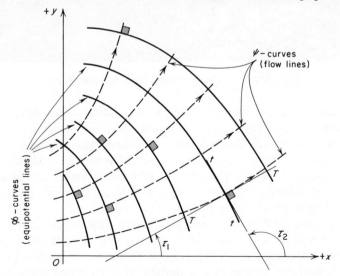

FIG. 14-9   Flow net.

The pattern formed by a flow net represents the direction of seepage flow and the hydraulic head prevailing at any point in a cross section of a soil mass through which seepage takes place. A flow net, thus, is a graphical device used in the study of seepage through soil and earth dams.

A flow net can be obtained mathematically, or experimentally, or by the method of sketching by trial and error. Flow nets in seepage studies are usually applicable to two-dimensional flow (flow in plane).

Flow Line. The path which a particle of flowing water takes in its course of seepage through a porous medium, such as soil, is termed a flow line. Thus, a flow line defines the direction and pattern of flow. The space between two adjacent flow lines is called the flow channel.

FIG. 14-10   Experimentally obtained flow lines.

Theoretically, there can be an infinitely large number of flow lines. However, for convenience in studying as well as for practical purposes, only a few pattern-forming flow lines are arbitrarily selected and used. Mathematically, the selection of the number of flow lines is done by giving the general ψ-function a particular parameter. Graphically, the selection of the number of flow lines is done arbitrarily by sketching a few, say 4, 5, or 6, flow lines. Likewise, experimentally, it is practical to select not more than 4-6 flow lines.

Experimentally, the flow lines through a model dam, confined in a tank with a transparent wall, can be made visible by injecting through the dam from its upstream face and from selected points a dye, fluorescein. The flow lines formed by the dye follow the same path as a particle of water which enters the dam at the same selected points where the dye is introduced.

The complete flow lines are traced on the transparent face of the seepage tank with a colored (white) china-marking pencil. Such an experimentally obtained flow net is shown in Fig. 14-10. The flow lines and the equipotential lines obtained by the dam model test can then be plotted or photographed for study.

As can be understood, the advantage of obtaining the uppermost flow (seepage) line by modelling a dam is that the seepage line can be obtained directly. However, the capillarity in soil above the seepage line may not reveal sharply the true position of the seepage line. This is so chiefly because of the presence of capillary moisture above the true seepage line which separates the saturated part of the soil from the unsaturated part. Other reasons for a poorly defined seepage line may be a wide dyeline, or when the dye-injecting point is not inserted precisely at the point where the upstream level intersects the upstream face of the dam model.

From model experiments with earth dams one gets the idea that water loss by capillary seepage in a model dam may be considerably more than through its prototype dam in nature.

Equipotential Line. An equipotential line is one which is passed through all points of equal piezometric head. Piezometers installed anywhere along an equipotential line should show equal head (Fig. 14-11).

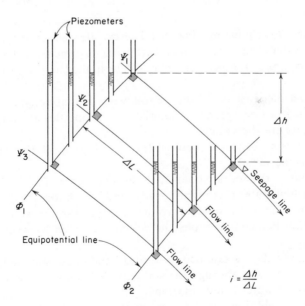

FIG. 14-11   Hydraulic gradient, i.

The total head is the sum of the pressure head, geodetic or elevation head, and a neglible velocity head. Thus, equipotential lines can be considered potential contours.

There is an infinitely large number of equipotential lines present. An arbitrary number of equipotential lines can be chosen

a) mathematically by giving the Φ-function some particular parameters,

b) by sketching them by the method of trial and error, and

c) by determining them experimentally.

Over the distance, ΔL, between two adjacent equipotential lines, Φ_1 and Φ_2, in the direction of flow there takes place a drop in hydraulic head, Δh, viz., a loss in driving pressure, or a drop in potential. It is generally understood that water translocates from higher elevations to lower ones; or, in other words, from higher energy levels to lower ones, and hence along the direction of the maximum energy gradient—the shortest path from one position to another one. Note that the excess hydrostatic pressure, $\gamma_w \Delta h$, is the force which drives the water through the soil.

Because the hydraulic gradient is expressed as $i = (\Delta h)/(\Delta L)$, i.e., the gradient equals the loss in head divided by the distance a water particle travelled, ΔL, the gradient has a maximum value along a flow line perpendicular to the equipotential lines owing to the shortest ΔL (the smaller is ΔL, the greater is i at same Δh). Hence, the flow lines must intersect equipotential lines at right angles (see point A, Fig. 14-9 and Fig 14-11). Because the intersecting lines are curves, the clause of right angles means that the tangent, T-T, to the flow curve at the point of intersection (at point A, Fig. 14-9) and the tangent, t-t, to the equipotential curve at the same point A should be mutually perpendicular.

14-4. Short Description of Flow Net Theory. Because in most cases seepage problems of water in soil and through earthworks can be treated two-dimensionally, the description of the flow net theory will be limited here to a two-dimensional flow.

The flow net theory is based on the following assumptions:

a) the soil is a homogeneous material (soil properties at every point in the soil mass are the same);

b) the soil is an isotropic material (permeability in all directions in the soil mass is the same);

c) all voids in the soil are completely filled with water;

d) the flow of water is laminar, steady, and continuous;

e) the soil is incompressible (no volume change in soil mass, nor in its voids);

f) the water is incompressible (the volume occupied by water remains constant);

g) the fluid (water) is assumed to be ideal, and of constant density;

h) the flow of water through the soil mass follows Darcy's law, and

i) the flow of water is not rotational.

Under these conditions, and based on the principle of continuity of flow, the quantity of water which enters an elementary, or differential, soil prism must be equal to the quantity of water which leaves the prism. Also, the flow depends upon the x- and y-coordinates.

The set of the equipotential lines and the set of the flow lines form together a net which characterizes the given flow. This net is termed the hydrodynamic flow net.

The properties of a hydrodynamic flow net are:

1) The two sets of curves (the equipotential and the flow curves) are orthogonal. From the orthogonality of the flow net, it follows that the velocity vector of filtration flow is directed normal to the equipotential line.

2) In an orthogonal, quadratic flow net the drop in pressure head, Δh, between any two adjacent equipotential lines (if they are equally spaced) is the same and constant. This drop in pressure head equals a fraction of the total drop in head, h, between the entrance and exit of the seepage system of the soil:

$$\Delta h = \frac{h}{N}, \tag{14-41}$$

where N is the number of equal potential drops along a flow channel, or the number of squares between two neighboring flow lines.

3) The hydrostatic head, h_n at any point under consideration can be determined from the flow net, or calculated as

$$h_n = n \frac{h}{N} = n(\Delta h), \tag{14-42}$$

where $h/N = \Delta h$ is the equal drop in pressure head between two equipotential lines, and n = number of equal potential drops between the point under consideration and zero potential.

4) This discharge quantity of water flowing between any two adjacent flow lines is constant.

If the pressure difference between any two equipotential lines of a square is the same, for example, dh, then the hydraulic gradient for a square, say at point A, Fig. 14-12, is

$$i = \frac{dh}{dn}. \tag{14-43}$$

This discharge, dq, between two parallel flow lines spaced at a distance dm apart and two parallel planes parallel to the drawing plane spaced one unit of length apart is, according to Darcy's law,

$$dq = v\,dA = ki\,dA = k\frac{dh}{dn}(dm)(1), \tag{14-44}$$

where v = flow velocity,

dA = differential area perpendicular to flow,

k = coefficient of permeability of soil to water, and

dh, dn, and dm are elements as in Fig. 14-12.

If the flow lines are drawn so that the discharge between adjacent flow lines is everywhere the same, and if the equipotential lines are drawn so that the pressure difference between successive lines is likewise everywhere the same, then

$$dq = (\text{const})\frac{dm}{dn} = \text{const.} \tag{14-45}$$

This means that in the flow net of rectangles the ratio of the sides $(dm)/(dn)$ must be constant.[3]

If the ratio is made $(dm)/(dn) = 1$, then the rectangles become squares. Hence, from the above reasoning it is concluded that in an orthogonal system of squares the discharge, q, between any two equally spaced, adjacent flow lines (or through every flow channel) is a constant quantity throughout the flow net. Thereby, the discharge is a constant fraction of the total seepage through the soil: $q = Q/M$, where M is the number of flow channels.

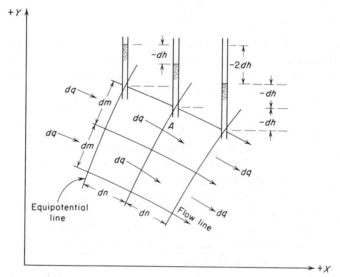

FIG. 14-12   Flow lines, equipotential lines and drop in piezometric head.

5) Forchheimer[4] has shown that the network of squares can be used to determine seepage under dams, sheet piling, cofferdams, and other earth structures. For example, if there are N squares in a strip between two adjacent flowlines (number of equal drops in potential), the head loss, or loss of potential (drop in pressure) along the flow line side of a square is $dh = h/N$, where h is the difference between headwater and tailwater levels, or more generally h is the total hydrostatic head. The hydraulic gradient along a *square* the sides of which are equal to $(dn =) dm$ is

$$i = \frac{dh}{dn} = \frac{dh}{dm} = \frac{\frac{h}{N}}{dm}. \tag{14-46}$$

The discharge through such a strip of one flow channel is

$$dq = v\,dA = k\,\frac{h}{N\,dm}\,dm = k\,\frac{h}{N}. \tag{14-47}$$

If there are M such strips (number of flow channels) in the dam (also = number of squares between two adjacent equipotential lines), the total discharge per unit length of dam along the shoreline is

$$Q = M \, dq = M \, \frac{kh}{N} = kh \, \frac{M}{N},\qquad\qquad (14\text{-}48)$$

as has been shown by Forchheimer.[5]

14-5. Seepage Analysis by Method of Trial and Error. This method consists of sketching flow and equipotential lines after the uppermost flow line has been established mathematically, or experimentally, or graphically by constructing the seepage parabola.

In applying the sketching method in seepage analysis, it is satisfactory enough to use only 5 to 6 flow lines. No improvement in precision is attained in using

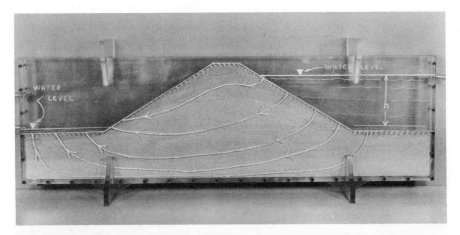

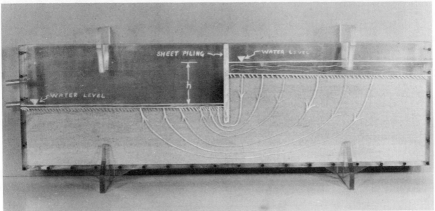

Fig. 14-13 Seepage line training models. *Top:* Seepage through a dam model. Note hump in the uppermost flow line brought about by surface tension forces. *Bottom:* Seepage around sheet piling.

more than the indicated number of flow lines because the method of sketching is not a precise one anyway.

14-6. Seepage Models. Experimental models can be used to great advantage for the student to visualize and understand the theory of seepage through earth dams and other earthworks, as well as for the purpose of training in obtaining flow lines on laboratory-scale models, which are used in the author's teaching work, and are shown in Figs. 14-13a and b. These pieces of apparatus, which serve also as a means of demonstration, consist of transparent training models, $34'' \times 10\frac{1}{2}'' \times 1\frac{1}{4}''$ in size, of various shapes. Fig. 14-13a shows flow lines actually traced in the process of seepage of water through a dam model made of sand. Fig. 14-13b illustrates flow lines obtained experimentally with a sheet piling model. Accessory equipment includes a metal tamper and a wooden mallet for compacting the sand, fluorescein dye, plastic tubing, dye injection device, stands, graduated cylinder, timer, and other items.

FIG. 14-14   Model dam with an underdrain carpet.

Such two-dimensional models permit one to observe clearly the exact course of flow lines that exist, under the conditions of the experiment, upon seepage of water through earthwork models.

The equipotential lines are sketched in the report drawing by the students according to Forchheimer's method of trial and error. In his instruction the author also assigns to students a seepage tank such as illustrated in Fig. 14-14. Its size is $74'' \times 24'' \times 6''$, and it is equipped with intake and outflow, adjustable overflow devices at both the upstream and downstream sides; with dye injection points and a board with mounted piezometer tubes for measuring potential head. Head measurements at points in the dam are used in determining the equipotential lines. With such a seepage tank experiments can be performed on dam models with homogeneous cross sections, or dam models provided with drainage galleries, or on dams with permeable shells on the downstream slope, or with sheet piling or clay cores in the dam. Experimental results from models are evaluated to the natural scale of dams by means of the theory of similitude, as well as compared with those results obtained theoretically.

The advantage of the hydraulic model over an electric one is that in the hydraulic model the Q-quantities can be clocked and the system's permeability, k, calculated. Besides, the hydraulic model permits observation of erosion and sloughing of the slopes of the dam should they occur. The electrical analog device, however, renders the flow net quickly.

Example. The application of the flow net theory to hydraulic structures on permeable soils is illustrated by a seepage problem around a sheet piling driven into the bottom of a water basin, for example, a river, for the purpose of obtaining a pit with a reasonably dry bottom by means of pumping out the enclosure (Fig. 14-15). The seepage water flowing through the soil around the sheet piling is collected in a sump from which it is pumped out.

In this example, the total drop in head is $h = 15$ ft, and the coefficient of the system's permeability in this example is given as $k = 0.125$ ft/day. The system's flow net is also given. It is required to calculate seepage flow into the enclosure in cu ft/day per 1 running ft of the wall of sheet piling.

Solution. There are $N_f = M = 6$ flow channels in this flow net, and $N_e = N = 15$ equal drops in head. The discharge quantity of seepage from the upstream side to the downstream side (pit) is by Eq. (14-48)

$$q = kh\,\frac{M}{N} = (0.125)(15)(6/15) = 0.75 \qquad \text{(ft}^3\text{/day)}$$

per 1 running ft of wall of sheet piling, a quantity which may be considered small or large depending upon the length of the perimeter of the enclosure by sheet piling.

SEEPAGE PRESSURE

If water within a soil mass is at rest, its effect upon the soil particles is limited to the hydrostatic uplift. However, if water flows or seeps through a mass of soil, the flowing water exerts upon the soil particles a hydrodynamic seepage pressure which acts in the direction of flow, and tangentially to a flow line. The magnitude of the seepage pressure is a function of the prevailing hydraulic gradient.

14-7. Derivation of Seepage Pressure Equation. Assume in a saturated soil mass such as an earth dam, for example, a differential flow channel whose length is dL and whose net cross-sectional area is dA (Fig. 14-16). The seepage flow takes place under the action of a driving pressure, dp, at the entrance face of the differential flow channel. The pressure is caused by the difference in head, dh, between the entrance and exit of the flow channel, as seen from the difference in piezometric levels at the ends of the channel.

The driving pressure, expressed as a function of head, is

$$dp = \gamma_w\,dh\,dA, \qquad\qquad (14\text{-}49)$$

where γ_w = unit weight of water.

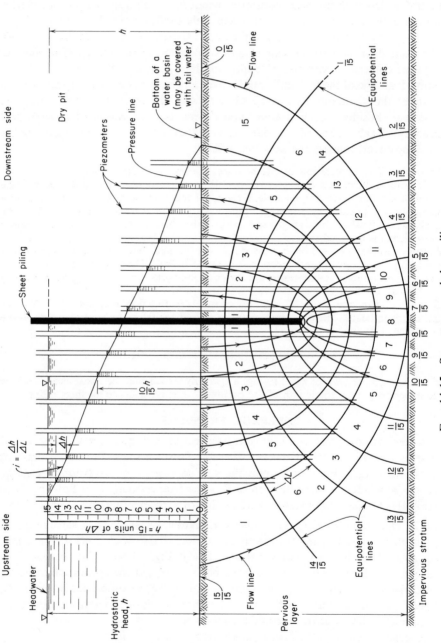

FIG. 14-15 Seepage around sheet piling.

Pressure, dp, is the total hydrodynamic pressure of seepage flow, known also by the term seepage pressure.

This pressure can be related to a unit volume:

$$\frac{dp}{dV} = \frac{dp}{dA\,dL} = \frac{\gamma_w\,dh\,dA}{dA\,dL}. \qquad (14\text{-}50)$$

Because ordinarily the seepage velocities in soils are low, the inertia force of the moving water is here neglected.

Designating $(dp)/(dA\,dL)$ by D, obtain the equation of seepage force per one unit of volume as

$$D = \gamma_w i \qquad \text{(in tons/m}^3\text{, for example)}, \qquad (14\text{-}51)$$

where $i = dh/dL$ is the hydraulic gradient. Note that the seepage force is a mass or body force and distributed over the volume of the body of the soil mass, and has the dimensions of a unit weight (tons/m^3, or g/cm^3, or lb/ft^3), depending upon the system of units of measurements used.

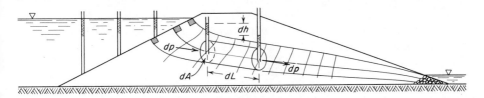

FIG. 14-16   Seepage pressure.

The hydrodynamic pressure, D, acts along the direction of flow of water. As Eq. (14-51) indicates, this pressure is a function of the unit weight of water, γ_w, and the prevailing hydraulic gradient, i, of the flow system, which, in its turn, is a function of head, h, and filtration length, L. Eq. (14-51) also shows that the seepage force, D, does not depend upon the velocity of flow nor the permeability of soil, k. This means that the hydrodynamic force is the same in non-cohesive as well as in cohesive soils, although flow velocities through these soils differ considerably.

To summarize the derivation of seepage force, it can be said that water seeping through the porous soil encounters a frictional resistance to flow by the soil skeleton. In overcoming this resistance, the seeping water exerts a hydrodynamic or seepage pressure, D, upon the skeleton of the porous material through which water flows.

Seepage Force Obtained From a Flow Net. By Eq. (14-51), the seepage pressure acting upon a volume made up of a square area, $A = abcd$, in a flow net, times one unit thick perpendicular to the drawing plane, Fig. 14-17, is

$$D_s = DA(1) = \gamma_w i A(1) = \gamma_w \frac{\Delta h}{\Delta n} \Delta n \Delta m(1) = \gamma_w \, \Delta h \Delta m \text{ (tons)}, \qquad (14\text{-}52)$$

where Δh = difference in head between the entrance and exit of a differential volume [$A(1)$] formed by a square, $A = abcd$, in a flow net;

Δn = dimension of square, $A = abcd$, in the direction of flow;

$\Delta h/(\Delta n) = i$ = hydraulic gradient across the square, and

Δm = dimension of square (ab) perpendicular to flow.

Hence, the flow net permits the calculation of the hydrodynamic pressure, viz., seepage force, exerted by water flowing through an earth mass.

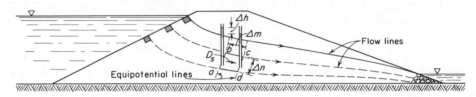

FIG. 14-17   Seepage force in a flow net.

Combination of Seepage Force with Gravity Force. Seepage forces can be combined with gravity (inertia) forces to give resultant forces. For example, the combination of $D = \gamma_w i$ lb/ft^3 with weight, of a soil mass, W lb/ft^3, results in a resultant body force, R:

$$R = \sqrt{D^2 + W^2 + 2DW \cos \alpha} =$$
$$= \sqrt{(\gamma_w i)^2 + (\gamma_{\text{soil}})^2 + (2)(\gamma_w i)(\gamma_{\text{soil}})(\cos \alpha)} \qquad \text{(lb/ft}^3\text{)}, \qquad (14\text{-}53)$$

where the physical quantities involved are as shown in Fig. 14-18.

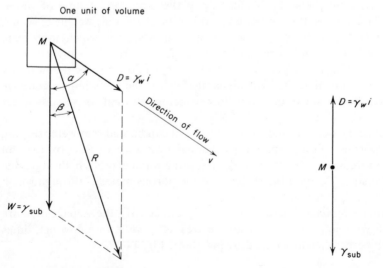

FIG. 14-18   Combination of seepage force with gravity force.

FIG. 14-19   Oppositely directed vectors.

The angle, β, between the resultant force, R, and the vertical is calculated as

$$\beta = \arctan \frac{D \sin \alpha}{W + D \cos \alpha}. \tag{14-54}$$

If $\alpha = 90°$, then

$$R = \sqrt{D^2 + W^2}, \tag{14-55}$$

and

$$\beta = \arctan \frac{D}{W}. \tag{14-56}$$

Seepage forces must not be forgotten when performing stability analyses of earth structures through which seepage of water takes place.

14-8. Effect of Hydrodynamic Pressure Upon The Stability of Soil. Hydrodynamic pressure has a great influence upon the stability of soil. Depending upon the direction of the flow of water through the soil, the hydrodynamic pressure can be thought of as being able to alter considerably the unit weight of the soil. For example, upon vertical downward flow, the resultant unit weight of soil can be thought of as being increased by the magnitude of the hydrodynamic pressure. Hence, in such a case, the seepage force has a densifying effect upon the soil mass. This fact, plus the effect of the surface tension forces acting in soil, explain the excellent beach sand conditions at Daytona Beach, Florida, on which heavy autoraces are run.

Upon a vertical, upward flow of water through a soil mass, the phenomenon converse to densification takes place. The hydrodynamic pressure "reduces" the effective weight of the soil mass (note the oppositely directed vectors of $D = \gamma_w i$ and γ_{sub}, Fig. 14-19). In other words, the hydrodynamic pressure, D, decreases the pressure of soil, caused by its self-weight, γ_{sub}.

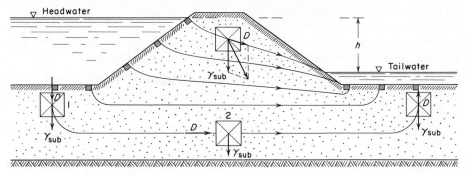

FIG. 14-20 Hydrodynamic pressure conditions of seeping water in soil.

The effect of D upon a unit weight of soil through which seepage takes place is illustrated in Fig. 14-20. At point No. 1, or rather, where the flow line is downward and vertical, the effective unit weight of the soil is

$$\gamma_{eff} = \gamma_{sub} + D, \tag{14-57}$$

indicating densification of soil.

At point No. 2, or rather anywhere on a horizontal flow line, the two vectors, D and γ_{sub}, act perpendicularly to each other, resulting in an obliquely inclined resultant vector. The inclination is slanted towards the tailwater. One sees that the flow, or hydrodynamic pressure underneath the earth dam, or under any other foundation where seepage takes place, decreases the resistance to horizontal displacement of the dam.

At point No. 3, where the flow is upward and vertical, the hydrodynamic pressure acts vertically upward against the submerged unit weight of soil, γ_{sub}:

$$\gamma_{eff} = \gamma_{sub} - D. \tag{14-58}$$

Here, when $D = \gamma_{sub}$, the soil appears weightless, and instability of the soil mass is impending. In such a case a special hydraulic condition prevails termed *critical*, at which there is a *critical hydraulic gradient*, i_c, and, consequently, a critical flow velocity, v_c; then

$$D = \gamma_w i_c. \tag{14-59}$$

When the flow velocity, v, exceeds the critical one, v_c, i.e., when $v > v_c$, then $D > \gamma_{sub}$, and γ_{eff} (in Eq. 14-58) becomes negative. This means that the soil particles are loosened, buoyed, and lifted up, resulting in a "boiling" or "quick" condition. This phenomenon is known as the "quicksand" condition. The reader is cautioned to remember that quicksand is not a type of sand. Rather, quicksand is a hydraulic condition in soil when there is an upward flow of water at a critical velocity. The latter depends upon a corresponding, critical hydraulic gradient. Thus, in general, a quick condition of a soil mass may be attained under certain circumstances. Structures founded on soil where quick condition exists sink down by their own weight because at quick condition the loosened soil mass loses its bearing capacity.

The discussion of the hydrodynamic pressure conditions of seeping water in soil at points Nos. 1, 2, and 3 reveals that a sand mass may be very stable or may become "quick" depending upon the direction of the seepage flow.

14-9. Position of Hydrodynamic Force in a Ruptured Seeping Slope. If a rupture of a seeping slope of an earthwork should occur, as in Fig. 14-21, the

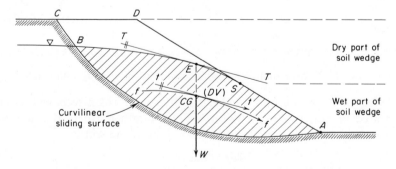

FIG. 14-21 Position of hydrodynamic force in a ruptured seeping slope.

hydrodynamic force, D, is one of the driving forces, among others, tending to cause the ruptured soil wedge, $ABCDA$, to slide out and down.

Because D is a mass force, the point of its application is the center of gravity, CG, of the wet part of the sliding soil wedge, $ABESA$. The direction of D is assumed variously: some engineers take it in the direction of the tangent t-t drawn to the flow line at point CG, whereas others transfer the point CG vertically upward on the seepage line to obtain point E. A tangent, T-T, is drawn at point E to the seepage curve. Then a line is drawn through point CG, parallel to T-T. This line through CG gives the direction of action of the hydrodynamic force. Note that the directions of D obtained by the two methods are not necessarily parallel. The resultant hydrodynamic force to be applied at CG is in magnitude equal to (DV), where V is the volume of the wet part of the soil wedge, i.e., part $ABESA$.

THEORY OF QUICKSAND CONDITION

14-10. Quick Condition.

Occurrence of Quick Conditions. Quick conditions of soil brought about by seepage forces are frequently encountered at the bottoms of foundation excavations in fine sand below the water table of a natural water basin, for example, in cofferdam work. Also, quick conditions may occur on the downstream slope of a dam, or a water saturated cut when the outcrop of the seepage line occurs above the toe of the slope, in open and pneumatic caissons, in tunnels and pipe trenches, as well as in other kinds of earthwork operations.

It is also quite possible that a foundation pit excavated in a fine sandy soil during the late summer, when the position of the groundwater table is low, is almost dry. But in the early spring, when the position of the groundwater table is high, seepage caused by the increased hydrostatic head of the raised groundwater table may create a quick condition.

Critical Hydraulic Gradient. In the previous discussion on hydrodynamic pressure it was pointed out that this pressure can change the equilibrium of a soil mass. At equilibrium, the downward-acting force, $W = \gamma_{sub}$, which is the weight of one unit of volume of the submerged soil, is equal to the upward-acting seepage force, $D = \gamma_w i_c$, i.e.,

$$W\downarrow - D\uparrow = 0, \qquad (14\text{-}60)$$

where $i_c =$ critical hydraulic gradient at the above force equilibrium.

The magnitude of the weight of the submerged soil is calculated as

$$W = \gamma_{sub} = (1 - n)(G - 1)\gamma_w = \frac{G - 1}{1 + e}\gamma_w, \qquad \text{(say in lb/ft}^3\text{)} \qquad (14\text{-}61)$$

where $n =$ porosity of soil,
$\quad G =$ specific gravity of soil particles,
$\quad e =$ void ratio of soil, and
$\quad \gamma_w =$ unit weight of water.

334   WATER IN SOIL

Substitution of the γ_{sub} and $D = \gamma_w i_c$ values into Eq. (14-60) yields:

$$\frac{G-1}{1+e}\gamma_w - \gamma_w i_c = 0, \tag{14-62}$$

and the critical hydraulic gradient, i_c, is calculated as

$$i_c = \frac{G-1}{1+e}. \tag{14-63}$$

The "critical hydraulic gradient" is defined as the minimum hydraulic gradient which will cause a quick condition within a certain type of soil.

The expression, i_c, shows that the critical hydraulic gradient depends only upon the specific gravity of the solid particles and the void ratio, e, viz., porosity, n, of the soil mass, but not upon the size of the soil particles, nor upon the coefficient of permeability of the soil. With $G = 2.65$ for quartz sand, and an average value of the void ratio of $e = 0.65$ (or $n = 0.393$) for a relatively medium-dense state of packing of the soil, the critical hydraulic gradient has an average value equal to unity:

$$i_c = \frac{G-1}{1+e} = \frac{2.65-1}{1+0.65} = 1.00. \tag{14-64}$$

Hence, when a hydraulic gradient is attained the value of which is $i = i_c = 1.00$, a loosening of the soil particles within the soil mass begins to take place, and a hydraulic ground-break, or "quick" condition, is imminent.

Eq. (14-63) may also suggest that an upward hydraulic gradient will bring about a quick condition in coarse gravel as readily as in a fine-particled sand, although it is well known that the quicksand phenomenon occurs more frequently in fine sands than in coarse soil material. Fine-particled sand is usually relatively uniform and in a loose state of packing. Consequently, such a soil material has a relatively high void ratio and a correspondingly low critical hydraulic gradient.

Factor of Safety. With a factor of safety of $\eta = 3$ to 4, the prevailing hydraulic gradient in a soil mass through which seepage of water takes place should be

$$i \leq \frac{i_c}{\eta}, \tag{14-65}$$

i.e., less than the critical hydraulic gradient, i_c.

Example. Given: a sand mass the void ratio of which is $e = 0.70$, and the solid particles the specific gravity of which is $G = 2.66$. Calculate the critical hydraulic gradient for that soil. Also, with a factor of safety, $\eta = 3$, compute the safe hydraulic gradient for the given flow system.

Solution. By Eq. (14-63), the critical hydraulic gradient is

$$i_c = \frac{G-1}{1+e} = \frac{(2.66)-(1)}{(1)+(0.70)} = \underline{0.976}.$$

Safe hydraulic gradient: $i = i_c/\eta = (0.976)/3 = 0.325.$

THE STUDY OF THE QUICKSAND PHENOMENON IN THE LABORATORY

14-11. Quicksand Apparatus. The quicksand phenomenon can be studied most effectively in the laboratory by means of an apparatus called the "quicksand tank" such as illustrated by Fig. 14-22. For the purpose of visibility such

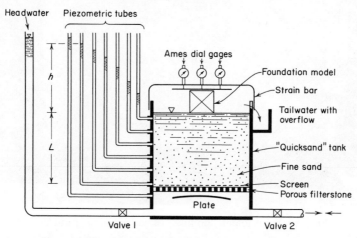

FIG. 14-22   Diagram of quicksand condition tank.

a tank is made of transparent lucite. The tank, $18'' \times 18'' \times 18''$, is connected with inlet and outlet pipes and control globe valves, and provided with seven piezometers to measure the loss of pressure head. The globe valves are delicate enough to maintain any constant hydraulic gradient. The flow conditions in the quicksand tank, depending on the position of the two valves, are summarized in Table 14-1.

To support the sand in the tank, the latter is provided with a porous filter stone through which water can enter the tank flowing upward, and can drain out downward. The tank is filled with sand to be tested, and the sand rests on top of the filter stone. To create the quicksand phenomenon, an upward flow of water is introduced into the tank under pressure from the space below the filter stone.

On the top of one side of the tank, opposite the piezometers, is a tailwater overflow weir to carry off any water which may filtrate upward to the free surface of the sand. Such water, upon reaching the surface of the soil, becomes ineffective in bringing about a quicksand condition, and must be carried away. The weir can also be used to measure the discharge flowing upward through the sand.

The open top of the tank is spanned with a brass strap or strain bar supporting three Ames dial gauges by which the settlement or rise of structural models, resting on the surface of the sand and subjected to upward or downward flow of water through the tank, may be measured.

A water-tight brass foundation model can be used in quick condition studies. The model can be filled with shot to give various constant pressures on the soil.

Fig. 14-23   Violent "boiling" of sand in quicksand tank.

To prevent the shot from shifting as the model settles and tilts, the inside of the model is provided with compartments.

Also, a square cofferdam, both ends open, can be used in performing various interesting experiments. The soil can be packed into the apparatus at various densities, viz., void ratios, and the critical hydraulic gradients, i_c, calculated.

Qualitative Description. Upon creating an upward flow through the sand the water has a certain velocity. For a certain upward flow velocity, there is in the composite soil a certain size of particles which has a similar downward terminal velocity and which will, therefore, stay suspended, or float in the upward stream. All finer-sized particles than those suspended will be carried by the stream up and away, whereas all coarser ones will sink and settle out. Thus, for the floating particles a critical flow velocity, v_c, viz., critical hydraulic gradient, i_c, is attained in the upward flow of water through the sand.

Upon further increase of the hydraulic gradient, one observes through the transparent walls of the apparatus that the sand starts to "boil" violently (Fig. 14-23), piping, channeling, and funneling up from bottom to top. Occasionally, at high flow pressures, a ground-break (air gap) in the sand occurs (Fig. 14-24). Also, because of the upward flow pressure, F, and weight, G, of the soil particle, a rotational motion of asymmetrical sand particles can be observed, causing a total rearrangement of the sand particles. The rotational motion is caused by the mechanical moment applied to an asymmetrical soil particle, as illustrated in Fig. 14-25. If rotation of a particle does not take place, this means that the rotation is usually prevented by the frictional forces between the contact points of the soil particles.

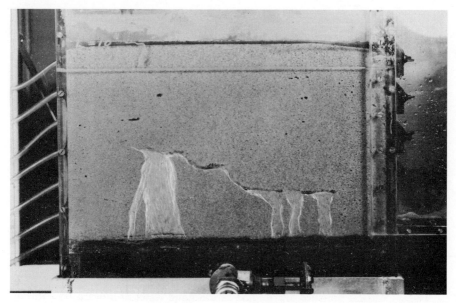

FIG. 14-24   A "ground-break".

Fine sand can start to "boil" in any open foundation pit if the groundwater rises toward the bottom of the pit at a hydraulic gradient greater than its critical value.

The rearrangement of the mobile soil particles and their flowing out from underneath the footing of a foundation brings about a loosening of the soil structure, which, in its turn, alters the admissible bearing capacity of the soil for the worse, and causes the structure to sink into the water-saturated soil.

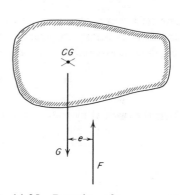

FIG. 14-25   Rotation of an asymmetrical particle of sand.

14-12. Hydrodynamics of Flow Conditions in the Quicksand Apparatus. When water flows upward through a quicksand tank (valve No. 1 open; valve No. 2 closed), referring to Fig. 14-26, the following hydrodynamic relationship exists: with specific gravity of sand, G, its void ratio, e, unit weight of water, γ_w, and volume of sand, $V = AL$ (A = horizontal cross-section of sand in apparatus and L = thickness of sand in apparatus), the submerged weight of sand, W, acting downward, is

$$W\downarrow = \gamma_{sub}AL = \frac{G-1}{1+e}\gamma_w AL. \tag{14-66}$$

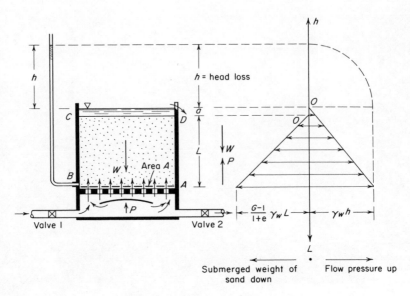

FIG. 14-26   Vertical pressure distribution in sand and water at upward flow through sand.

Assume that there is no friction on the sides of the lucite tank. The faster the upward flow of water, the greater are the hydraulic gradient, i, and the upward vertical flow pressure, P. This pressure is

$$P\uparrow = \gamma_w h A. \tag{14-67}$$

When the critical hydraulic gradient, $i_c = h/L$, is attained, then

$$P\uparrow = W\downarrow,$$

or

$$\gamma_w i_c L A = \frac{G-1}{1+e}\gamma_w A L, \tag{14-68}$$

and the critical hydraulic gradient is

$$i_c = \frac{G-1}{1+e}. \tag{14-69}$$

Fine sand usually consists of uniform particle size and is encountered in a loose or open state of packing. Therefore, fine sand has a relatively high void ratio, e, and a consequently low critical hydraulic gradient, i_c.

The various flow conditions through sand in the quicksand apparatus are compiled in Table 14-1.

TABLE 14-1. FLOW CONDITIONS IN QUICKSAND TANK

Case Nos.	Positions of Valves No. 1	No. 2	Flow Conditions in Sand or Direction of Flow of Water in Sand	Stability of Soil
1	2	3	4	5
1	Closed	Closed	Sand submerged. No flow in sand. Hydraulic gradient $i = 0$.	Stable condition. Filterstone carries weight of submerged sand and water.
2	Open	Closed	Pressure head $(L + a + h)$ $> (L + a)$. Upward flow. Hydraulic gradient $i = h/L$.	At v_c the condition is unstable or quick. Filterstone carries weight less than submerged weight of sand.
3	Closed	Open	Pressure head $= 0$. Downward flow. Hydraulic gradient $i = \dfrac{L + a}{L}$.	Stable condition. Filterstone carries submerged weight of sand and filtration pressure $(L + a)\gamma_w$. When the water table has dropped to elevation C-D (surface of sand), the hydraulic gradient is $i = L/L = 1$.
4	Open	Open	Depending upon the size of the ouflow pipe, water may or may not rise up into the soil.	Depending upon whether or not water surges up through the soil, the soil is or is not in a stable condition.

14-13. Other Uses of Quicksand Apparatus. The quicksand apparatus is useful for demonstrating several other kinds of phenomena associated with the quick hydraulic phenomenon in soil. For example, a study can be made of the effect of quicksand condition due to varying hydraulic gradients upon the stability of various model foundations with different contact pressures on the surface of the sand. Also, the behavior of a small concrete cofferdam can easily be studied by means of this apparatus. The cofferdam is placed in position so that the sand surface inside the cofferdam is a few inches below the surface of the sand outside the model. Fig. 14-27 shows a failure when the quicksand condition develops inside the cofferdam, and a sand suspension boils over its top onto the relatively stable outside. As the quick condition continues, the degree of instability of the cofferdam increases, and at final failure the model sinks into the tank below the ground surface. In this experiment, for instance, it is interesting to note that the upward boiling within the cofferdam starts in its corners, then approximately at the middle of the outside edge, then through the entire bottom of the model until finally the cofferdam model disappears below the surface.

A model structure can be supported on footings or on a mat, set on the sand, and caused to fail by a quick hydraulic condition. The same model can be set on piles and also caused to fail by the same agency. Observe that in both cases the critical hydraulic gradients are the same. The lesson from this experiment is that piles are of no value in fine-particled soils where quicksand conditions prevail. If piles are used, and it is economically feasible, they have to be driven down through the quicksand zone to and into a firm stratum. Under varying hydraulic conditions in sandy soil surveyors' bench marks may rise or settle.

FIG. 14-27   Failure of a cofferdam model.

The phenomenon of liquefaction of sand can also be demonstrated by means of the quicksand apparatus. A 2-kg weight is placed on a loosely packed and saturated, but yet barely stable, soil in the tank. Then the hydraulic gradient is slowly applied and gradually increased until its critical value is attained, so as not to disturb the weight. A rod is then quickly thrust into the sand, causing the weight immediately to sink (Fig. 14-28). This phenomenon would occur in practice where the action of heavy machinery, such as a pile driver, causes a sudden shock to the soil; or where vibrations and/or blasting takes place; or other dynamic forces such as earthquakes and the like act—each can induce the structure to sink into the quick soil.

The liquefaction in fine, open-structure, and saturated sand, induced by a sudden shock, is explained as follows: the sudden shock means a suddenly applied shearing stress to the soil mass. Upon receiving the shock, the sand tends to decrease rapidly in volume. Simultaneously, the water in the voids of the sand—termed pore water—receives a suddenly applied pressure, or stress.

FIG. 14-28   Liquefaction of sand by a sudden shock.

In soil mechanics, stress carried by water is termed *neutral stress*. Upon the increase in neutral stress, some of the weight of the soil mass, which might be considered as furnishing the normal effective or intergranular stress entering into the shearing process of soil, is transmitted to the pore water pressure. According to Coulomb, the shear strength of a non-cohesive soil, τ, can be expressed in an analytical form as

$$\tau = (\sigma_n - u)\tan\phi, \tag{14-70}$$

where $(\sigma_n - u)$ = normal effective (intergranular) stress, in kg/cm^2, or in lb/in.^{2}, whichever system of units of measurements is used;

   σ_n = total normal stress;

   u = pore water pressure, or neutral stress, and

   $\tan\phi$ = coefficient of internal friction of a non-cohesive soil, which for one and the same material is considered to be constant.

From this equation, it can easily be seen that upon the increase in neutral stress, u, the effective or intergranular stress of the soil, $(\sigma_n - u)$ decreases, and the shear strength of the soil, τ, decreases. The decrease in shear strength means decrease in bearing capacity of the soil.

14-14. Remedial Measures Against a Quick Condition. Concerning the critical hydraulic gradient in connection with the quicksand phenomenon,

$$i_c = h_c/L, \tag{14-71}$$

where h_c = critical hydraulic head, and L = length of seepage path, the problems of the foundation engineer center around two factors: 1) he may vary the value of the length of the seepage path, L, by means of engineering operations in the field, and 2) nature, or the engineer, may vary the value of the pressure head, h, during construction or after construction is completed.

Thus the methods used to prevent a quicksand condition are based directly upon the fundamental i_c equation (14-71). The larger is L, the smaller is i. The smaller is h, the smaller is i.

The increase in length of the seepage path, L, is achieved by enclosing the excavation with one or two rows of sheet piling driven to some distance below the grade of excavation (Fig. 14-29). By this increase in L the velocity of seepage, as well as the hydraulic gradient, are decreased. A problem for calculating a possible quicksand condition is worked out in the following example.

Example. Given an excavation surrounded by a system of sheet piling. The hydrostatic head, seepage length, depth of sheet piling below excavation grade, types of soil, and their coefficients of permeabilities are shown in Fig. 14-29. Evaluate the possibility of quicksand conditions in this excavation.

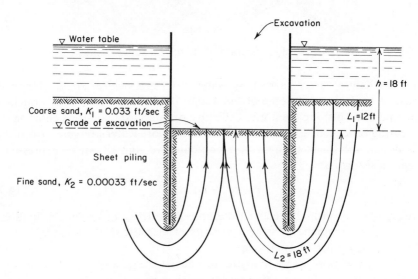

FIG. 14-29   Excavation.

Solution. The solution of this problem is based on Darcy's law in determining the critical hydraulic gradients in the two sand layers.

1) Darcy's filter velocity:

$$v = ki = k\,\frac{h}{L} \tag{14-72}$$

2) From here, the hydrostatic pressure head is

$$h = v\,\frac{L}{k}, \tag{14-73}$$

or, relating to our seepage system, $h = h_1 + h_2$, where h_1 and h_2 are the corresponding losses in head in the coarse and fine sands, respectively. Based on this equation, the system's head, h, is

$$h = h_1 + h_2 \quad \text{(ft).} \tag{14-74}$$

3) The filtration length, L, for this given system is

$$L = L_1 + L_2 \quad \text{(ft)}. \tag{14-75}$$

4) By Eq. (14-72) and Eq. (14-75), the system's average seepage velocity, v, is calculated as

$$v = \frac{h_1 + h_2}{\dfrac{L_1}{k_1} + \dfrac{L_2}{k_2}} = \frac{18}{\dfrac{12}{0.033} + \dfrac{18}{0.00033}} = \underline{(3.27)(10^{-4})/(\text{ft/sec})}.$$

5) Pressure head lost in coarse sand:

$$h_1 = v\frac{L_1}{k_1} = (0.000327)\frac{12.0}{0.033} = \underline{0.1189 \text{ (ft)}}.$$

6) Pressure head lost in fine sand:

$$h_2 = v\frac{L_2}{k_2} = (0.000327)\frac{18.0}{0.00033} = \underline{17.53 \text{ (ft)}}.$$

7) Hydraulic gradient for coarse sand:

$$i_1 = \frac{h_1}{L_1} = \frac{0.1189}{12.0} = 0.0099 \approx \underline{0.01}.$$

8) Hydraulic gradient for fine sand:

$$i_2 = \frac{h_2}{L_2} = \frac{17.53}{18.0} = 0.9794 \approx \underline{0.98}.$$

9) Because

$$i_{2=0.98} > i_{1=0.01},$$

there exists the possibility of a quick condition of the fine sand in the excavation. The sand will flow up through the bottom of the excavation. Therefore, the sheet piling should be driven deeper.
10) In practice, based on a rule of thumb, sheet piling is often driven to a depth in the soil as great as the height of the lateral loads of hydrostatic and/or earth pressure it supports.

The lesson from this problem is that there is danger of the occurrence of a quick condition in a layered system where the layers have differing coefficients of permeability. The hydraulic conditions are particularly unfavorable when water flows first through a very permeable layer with a high k-value under little loss of head, and then continues to seep through a less permeable layer of soil under a great loss of head. This means that the flow takes place here under a great hydraulic gradient.

The prolongation of the length of the seepage path can also be achieved by placing at the bottom of the excavation, where seepage lines converge, a clay blanket or other impermeable material according to the principle as illustrated in Fig. 14-30. However, the effect of such a blanket in decreasing the amount of seepage is small—about 20%.[6]

The hydrostatic pressure head, h, can be decreased by means of relief wells as has been done along the levees of the Mississippi River.[7] Seepage can also be intercepted and reduced inside an excavation by means of a wellpoint system. Besides many other field methods, a quicksand condition may be prevented by increasing the downward-acting force. This is achieved by placing a load on the surface of the soil at the place of seepage discharge. Metal or timber mats can be loaded for this purpose in open excavations.

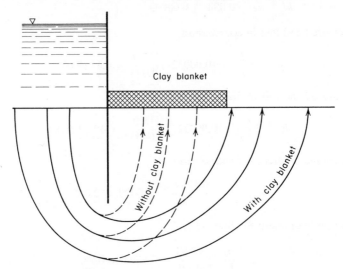

FIG. 14-30 Prolongation of the length of the seepage path.

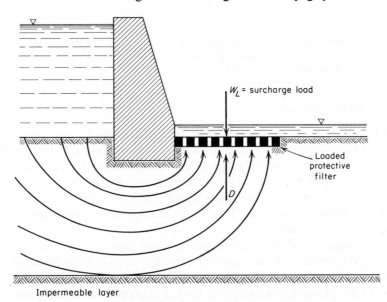

FIG. 14-31 Seepage underneath a foundation.

The weight of the soil can also be increased by densifying the soil. Quick conditions can, under some circumstances, be controlled by freezing the earth walls and bottom of the excavation, or by injecting stabilizing chemicals into the soil.

The placing of an underwater surcharge load, W_L, on the surface of the quicksand is equivalent to an increase in unit weight of the sand. This, consequently, increases the value of the critical hydraulic gradient. The force equilibrium in such a case is (Fig. 14-31):

$$D\uparrow - W_{\text{soil}}\downarrow - W_L\downarrow = 0, \tag{14-76}$$

or

$$D - \frac{G-1}{1+e}\gamma_w - W_L = 0. \tag{14-77}$$

The critical hydraulic gradient is then:

$$i_c = \frac{W_{\text{soil}} + W_L}{\gamma_w} = \frac{G-1}{1+e} + \frac{W_L}{\gamma_w}. \tag{14-78}$$

The surcharge can be made to act as a loaded filter through which water can filter upward.

REFERENCES

1. A. Casagrande, *Seepage Through Earth Dams*, New England Water Works Association, vol. 51, no. 2, June, 1937, pp. 136, 137.
2. *Ibid.*
3. A. Schoklitsch, *Graphische Hydraulik*, Leipzig und Berlin, B. G. Teubner, 1923, p. 16.
4. Ph. Forchheimer, *Hydraulik*, Leipzig, B. G. Teubner, 1914, p. 448.
5. *Ibid.*
6. L. White and E. A. Prentis, *Cofferdams*, New York, Columbia University Press, 1950, p. 35.
7. W. J. Turnbull and C. I. Mansur, "Relief Well Systems for Dams and Levees", *Proceedings*, vol. 79, ASCE, New York. Sept., 1953.

QUESTIONS AND PROBLEMS

14- 1. What is force of gravity?
14- 2. What is an inertia force?
14- 3. What is a body force?
14- 4. What is seepage force?
14- 5. Classify earth dams.
14- 6. Give the essential features of an earth dam.
14- 7. What is the difference between an earth dam and an ordinary fill or embankment?
14- 8. Why is a pervious shell section considered necessary on the upstream face of an earth dam?
14- 9. What is a flow net?
14-10. What is a seepage line? What is a flow line? What is an equipotential line?

14-11. Of what value are flow nets?

14-12. Estimate the amount of seepage of the homogeneous earth dam sketched in Fig. Problem 14-12 per foot of shore line. Given:
unit weight of saturated soil mass, $\gamma_{sat} = 120$ lb/ft³,
unit weight of water: $\gamma_w = 62.4$ lb/ft³,
average coefficient of permeability, $k_{ave} = 0.15$ ft/day.

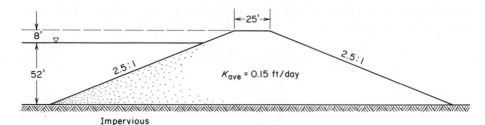

FIG. Problem 14-12.

14-13. For the earth dam shown in Fig. Problem 14-12, develop analytically an expression for seepage discharge. After you have established the uppermost flow line, calculate discharge in cu ft/day per ft of shore line. The coefficients of permeability at a standard temperature of 20°C are:
$k_h = 0.1350$ ft/day, and $k_v = 0.0500$ ft/day.
Also, determine the magnitude of the total seepage pressure, and show on an appropriate figure its point of application and direction of action.

14-14. Given a homogeneous earth dam as shown sketched on Fig. Problem 14-14. $G = 2.70$; $e = 0.75$.
   a) Construct the basic parabola and determine the uppermost flow line.
   b) Construct a flow net and compute seepage in cu ft/day per 100 ft shoreline; $k_v = 0.0002$ cm/min; $k_h = 0.0008$ cm/min.
   c) If there were no drainage gallery, and if the uppermost flow line would leave the dam at point E, what are the hydraulic and stability conditions of the dam at that point?
   d) Determine the factor of safety, η, of the dam relative to a quick condition at point E.

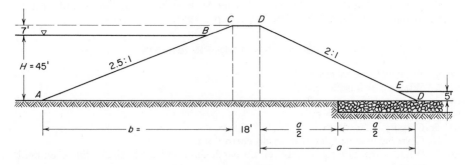

FIG. Problem 14-14.

14-15. What is the function of the drainage gallery in an earth dam?

14-16. If $Q_0 = 332$ cm³/hr cm, $Q = 767$ cm³/hr cm, $L_0 = 75$ cm and the net driving head is $H = 27.0$ cm, calculate by means of Fig. 14-10 the system's permeability,

k, in cm/sec for that system shown. The experimental model dam is built of Raritan sand, South Brunswick, New Jersey. Q_0 pertains to 1 cm width of seepage tank. Subscript zero ($_0$) refers to a homogeneous dam.

14-17. In the Problem 14-16, assume that $L = L_f = 75.0$ cm. Calculate discharge Q if $k = 27$ cm. Index f means "filter".

14-18. Given data as in Problem 14-16. The dam has no underdrain facilities. Calculate the discharge, Q_0, if $k = 1.88$ cm/sec. Consult Fig. 14-10. Note in this figure the hump in the experimentally obtained, uppermost flow line brought about by surface tension forces. Also, note that here the position of the basic parabola constructed by the A. Casagrande method is above the uppermost flow line.

14-19. Given: an earth dam as shown on Fig. Problem 14-19. The difference of head in upstream and downstream levels is 85 ft. The coefficients of permeability to water of the dam material are: $k_h = 200$ ft/day, and $k_v = (0.5)k_h$. Porosity of dam: $n = 30\%$. Specific gravity of the soil particles: $G = 2.68$.

Required:

1) The amount of loss of water from the reservoir by seepage in cu ft/day per 100 ft of run of the dam.

2) From your flow lines in the flow net drawn to scale of the dam (establish a linear scale!) determine:

   a) the actual hydraulic gradient which exists in your first (or upper) flow channel between the first two flow lines and for each of your consecutive equipotential drops;

   b) the critical hydraulic gradient of the system, and

   c) the factor of safety, η, against the possibility of developing a quick condition in the area of the head of the filter gallery (point C).

3) Prepare a separate sketch similar to the one shown here, and indicate by vectors all the forces, and their points of application, necessary to be considered in a stability analysis of a slope of an earth bank, relative to rupture along a circularly curved sliding surface. Describe briefly the nature of the various forces pertaining to such a stability or instability problem.

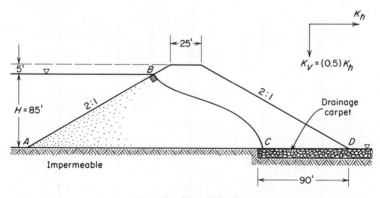

FIG. Problem 14-19.

14-20. What is the effect of a rapid draw-down of water on the upstream side relative to the stability of the dam?

14-21. Given: a 60-ft long overflow weir, resting on a pervious layer of soil as shown in Fig. Problem 14-21. The overall coefficient of permeability of the soil is

$k = 3.0 \times 10^{-3}$ cm/sec. Calculate discharge, Q, in cm³/sec/m of shore line of the weir. Also, prepare an uplift pressure diagram underneath the weir.

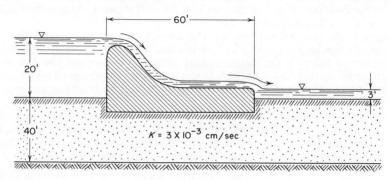

FIG. Problem 14-21.

14-22. What is the technical meaning of the term "quicksand"?

14-23. Plot a critical hydraulic gradient curve as a function of the void ratio of the soil, $i_c = f(e)$, and discuss what inferences can be drawn from the plotted curve. The specific gravity of the soil in question is $G = 2.65$.

14-24. Draw pressure diagrams for the flow conditions through sand in a quicksand apparatus as compiled in Table 14-1.

14-25. Given two cylinders filled with sand as shown in Fig. Problem 14-25a and b. One of the two cylinders is closed at its bottom. Through the other, water can filtrate through it downward. Draw hydrostatic and hydrodynamic pressure diagrams for the given conditions, showing pressure ordinates algebraically. What are the principal differences in these two pressure diagrams?

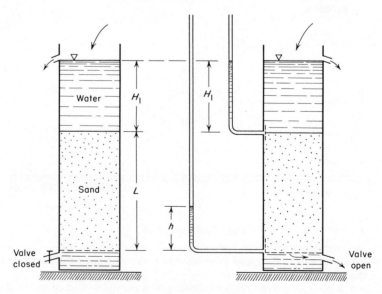

FIG. Problem 14-25.

14-26. 1) Derive the equation expressing the critical hydraulic gradient in terms of G and n
2) Derive this gradient as a function of G and e.
3) Explain what physical conditions govern the i_c-relationship.
4) Does i_c depend upon the system's coefficient of permeability?
5) Analyze the i_c-equation in the light of physical conditions that occur in a quicksand apparatus. Consider in your analysis the way in which i_c is limited by the apparatus.
6) What does it mean mathematically and physically if $i_c = 1$?
7) What consistency has sand when $i_c = 1$?
8) How can equation $i_c = (1 - n)(G - 1)$ be applied practically?
9) In Fig. Problem 14-26, there is a 2 cm wide gap or ground break in the soil in the middle of the thickness of the soil in the quicksand apparatus. The soil is loaded on its surface with a permeable mat load of $G = 124.8$ lb/ft³. Complete the sketch, and draw pressure diagrams. Calculate critical hydraulic gradient. $G = 2.65$; $e = 0.70$. What is the pressure in water in the gap?

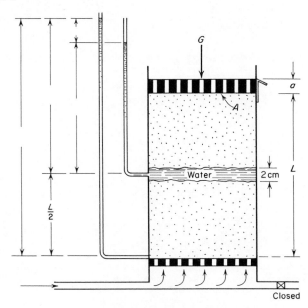

FIG. Problem 14-26.

14-27. What is the critical hydraulic gradient to cause a quick condition in a soil mass, the void ratio of which is 0.80, if the specific gravity of the soil particles is 2.66?

14-28. If the critical hydraulic gradient of a soil is $i_c = 0.32$, and the actual hydraulic gradient of a given system is $i = 0.47$, what should the surcharge load be in order to arrive at a factor of safety of $\eta = 3$ against a quicksand condition?

14-29. What is a protective filter in foundation engineering? Illustrate.

PART IV

Consolidation of Soil
and Settlement of Structures

Chapter 15

PERFORMANCE OF SOIL
UNDER COMPRESSIVE LOAD

15-1. Introduction. Structural loads are transmitted to soil through the foundation of the structure. The loads, compressing the underlying soil, tend to deform the soil structure by relatively displacing the soil particles from their original position, or by bringing the soil particles closer together, resulting in a decrease in volume of the soil. If a clayey, saturated soil is subjected to a structural compressive load, then the volume change in the soil is attributed mainly to the expulsion of water out of the voids of the cohesive soil. Volume changes in the vertical direction bring about a settlement of the soil, viz., settlement or a compressive deformation of the soil structure. Thus, settlement of soil may be defined as the vertical, downward displacement of soil, or movement of structure on that soil, brought about by a volume change in the soil due to a decrease in the volume of the voids in the soil, occurring after the beginning of construction.

The settlement of a foundation, in its turn, may be defined as the change in elevation of the base of the footing. As the soil settles, so does the foundation. Thus the magnitude of the settlement of the foundation is the same as for the soil upon which the foundation rests. In other words, settlement is the sinking of a structure due to a compressive deformation of the underlying soil.

If the contact pressure at the base of the footing on the soil is uniform, and uniformly distributed, settlements may be tolerable if the type of structure and/ or its exploitation can withstand such settlements. In contradistinction, non-uniform, or differential settlement of a structure may be disastrous, leading to cracking of the structural members, impairment of the structural rigidity of the building, and eventually to the collapse of the structure. This is particularly true with statically indeterminate structures such as continuous beams on more than two supports, frames, arches, vaults, and others. In these structures, settlement of a support induces supplemental moments, and if these additional bending moments are not taken into account in proportioning the structural members, the structure may turn out to be too weak to resist the additional moments, and may start to crack. A tall building may lean because of unequal, or differential settlements of the soil, and so would two adjacent structures of equal size of foundation bases and of equal weight, as for example, two oil storage tanks built next to each other: these tanks would lean toward each other because of the pressure distribution overlap in soil from these two tanks.

However, uniform, tolerable settlements should not be construed as a failure because settlement of a soil as a function of load is a normal physical phenomenon.

Uniform settlement is settlement which is brought about when the entire structure, under uniform pressure distribution on a uniform, homogeneous soil structure settles evenly without causing additional stresses in the structure.

The term differential settlement is used then when some parts of a structure settle more than others.

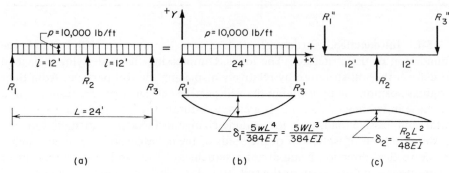

FIG. 15-1   Static system.

15-2. Effect of Settlement of Support on a Structure. The following example illustrates the difference in magnitude of the bending moments of a continuous beam on three suports, with and without a settlement of the center support, as shown in Fig. 15-1. The given static system is resolved into two simpler ones as shown.

Case. I. No settlement of supports.

Reactions of beam (a) are calculated based on the condition that the resultant deflection at the center of the beam is zero.

1) *Deflection at center of beam:*

$$\frac{5WL^3}{384EI} - \frac{R_2L^3}{48EI} = 0, \qquad (15\text{-}1)$$

where W = total load on the beam,
   L = length of the beam,
   E = modulus of elasticity of the material of the beam, and
   I = moment of inertia of the cross section of the beam.

2) *Center reaction:*

$$R_2 = (\tfrac{5}{8})W = (0.625)(10000)(24) = \underline{150,000 \text{ (lb)}}$$

3) *End Reactions:*

$$R_1 = R_3 = \frac{pL - R_2}{2} = \frac{(10000)(24) - 150,000}{2} = \underline{45,000 \text{ (lb)}}$$

4) *Bending moment at center of beam:*

$$M_2 = \left(R_1 \overset{+L}{\tfrac{+L}{2}} - p\frac{L}{2}\frac{L}{4}\right) = (45,000)(12) - (10,000)(12)(6) = \underline{-180,000 \text{ (ft-lb)}}.$$

Case II. Settlement of one supports.
Assume that the center support has a downward settlement of 0.5 in. Thus, there is a differential settlement between the center- and end-supports of 0.5 in.

1) *Resulting deflection, δ, of beams (b) and (c):*

$$\delta = \delta_b - \delta_c,$$ (15-2a)

or

$$\frac{5WL^3}{384EI} - \frac{R_2L^3}{48EI} = 0.5''.$$ (15-2)

2) *Center reaction:*
Assuming for steel $E = (30)(10^6)$ lb/in^2 and $I = 1373$ in^3, obtain

$$R_2 = (\tfrac{5}{8})W - \frac{192EI}{8L^3} = \frac{(5)(10,000)(24)(24)^3(12)^3 - (192)(30 \times 10^6)(1373)}{(8)(24)^3(12)^3} =$$
$$= 108,617 \text{ (lb)}.$$

3) *End reactions:*

$$R_1 = R_3 = \frac{(10,000)(24) - 108,617}{2} = 65,692 \text{ (lb)}.$$

4) *Total bending moment, M_b^s,*
at point of center support including the effect of settlement of the center support by 0.5 in.:

$$M_b^s = R_1\frac{L}{2} - p\frac{L}{2}\frac{L}{4} = (65,692)(12) - (10,000)(12)(6) = +68,300 \text{ (ft-lb)}.$$

Change in bending moment M_s,
due to settlement of center support by 0.5 in.:

$$M_s = M_b^s - M_2 = +68,300 - (-180,000) = +248,300 \text{ (ft-lb)}.$$

Note the change in sign, and the great change in magnitude of the bending moment at the center support because of a 0.5-in. settlement of the center support.

The foregoing example illustrates vividly that design engineers should be interested in the type and magnitude of settlement of the foundation on each particular soil; that they should avail themselves of settlement studies on soils in the laboratory as well as in the field; and that they should use the results of settlement tests and studies in their designs, in order to avoid distress to structures.

In particular, large amounts of settlement and differential types of settlement for various parts of foundations must be taken into account when structures are built on very compressible soils.

15-3. Causes of Settlements. Some of the main factors contributing to settlement of soils are:
1) static loads on soil;
2) dynamic forces from vibrations excited by machinery, traffic, pile driving operations, explosions, earthquakes, and various impacts on soil due to collapse of structures and/or earthworks. These factors loosen the structural strength of the soil, particularly the strength of non-cohesive soils;
3) fluctuations in the elevation of the groundwater table. This factor can be further subdivided into
   a) normal natural fluctuation, by drought;

b) artificial lowering of the groundwater table as, for example, for providing a dry foundation pit, river regulation or operations for drainage of an area, through radiation of heat from blast and other furnaces (drying, shrinking of soil);

c) raising the groundwater table artificially by impounding water in a reservoir, by tides, floods (may cause heave of soil), breaks in water mains;

d) subsidence of soil caused by mining and tunneling operations (subways and vibrations);

4) settlement from frost-heaved soils:

a) natural: from thawing;

b) artificial: under refrigeration houses;

5) other possible factors.

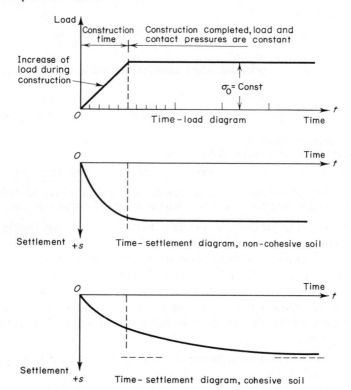

FIG. 15-2   Nature of course of settlement of a structure of non-cohesive and cohesive soil.

Fig. 15-2 illustrates schematically the nature of the course of uniform consolidation settlement of structures founded on non-cohesive and on cohesive soils. On non-cohesive soils, the settlement almost ceases during and at the end of the time of construction, whereas full settlements of structures founded on a cohesive soil are attained after a very long time. The latter is due to the long time needed for the expulsion and draining of water out of the voids of the cohesive soil at a certain load intensity (contact pressure) transmitted to the soil by the foundation of the structure.

Some Reasons for Intolerable Settlements. From soil mechanics theory on settlement of soils it is known that the magnitude of the settlement depends not only on the compressibility of the soil, but also upon the size and shape of the footings of foundations, upon the stresses in the soil underneath the foundations, water regimen in the soil, and other factors. Compression of soil is manifested in settlement of foundations.

Some of the reasons for differential and/or intolerable settlements are:

1) geologic and physical non-uniformity, or anomalies, in type, structure, thickness, and density of the soil medium (alluvial soils, clay, gravel, pockets of sand in clay, clay lenses in sand, wedge-like soil strata, ice lenses in soil, and effects of thawing of such ice lenses); admixture of organic matter; peat; muck;

2) non-uniform pressure distribution from foundation to soil due to non-uniform loading, and consequent differential performance of soil under the given configuration and structure of the works (part of structure is founded on piles, and part on shallow foundations);

3) water regimen at the construction site;

4) overstressing of soil at adjacent site by heavy structures built next to light ones (towers, spires, skyscrapers, silos);

5) overlap of stress distribution in soil from adjoining structures, and

6) other possible factors.

From the above discussion it can be inferred that foundation design is a very complex problem, in the solution of which one must consider many factors involved and also some "possible impossible conditions".

The prevailing trend in the engineering profession now is to require that plans of every important structure designed on compressible clay should be accompanied by an estimate of the possible settlements which may occur at various points under the foundations, the rate of settlement, and the magnitude of the final settlement.

In order to protect one's self from unpleasant surprises when laying foundations in clays, one should be aware of the seat of settlement of a compressed clay. Therefore a theory, whether approximate or rigorous, on the settlement phenomenon of a clay layer may prove to be an indispensable tool to the engineer, by means of which the factors determining the order of magnitude and the distribution of settlements can be recognized.

In settlement studies two broad groups of settlements are distinguished, namely:

1) settlement from consolidation (including also settlements caused by the lowering of the groundwater table) of soil, and

2) settlements brought about by the lateral expulsion of a soil mass from underneath the base of the footing of the foundation (sidewise and upward). The latter mode of settlement is especially marked when the load

is applied at the ground surface of the soil (in sandy soil particularly) over relatively small areas. The smaller the area, the more marked is the influence of lateral displacement.

THE MECHANICS OF CONSOLIDATION OF A LAYER OF CLAY

15-4. Two Important Questions of Interest. In studying the performance of cohesive, saturated soils under load, two questions in the consolidation (and settlement) processes come to the fore, namely: 1) the magnitude of the final settlement of the soil as a function of the compressive stress inflicted upon the soil, and 2) the rate of settlement during the presence of a constant load applied to the soil (progressive settlement).

The first question is of practical interest in foundation engineering in determining the full settlement of the structure, and in selecting such contact pressures on the soil as would not cause intolerable settlements, but settlements which would permit the satisfactory function and exploitation of the structure. The magnitude of settlement is primarily a function of the compressibility of the soil.

Compressibility of soil means the reduction in volume of a soil (dry, wet, or saturated) by the application of an external pressure on the soil.

Relative to the magnitude of the tolerable or allowable settlements of various types of structures, the significant observation one can make is that neither the building codes nor the German Industrial Norms (DIN) tabulate the magnitudes of harmless settlements of structures.

Some foreign ordinances indicate the following allowable settlements of various types of structures:[1]

Auxiliary structures for industrial plants	20 to 40 cm
Statically determinate structures with massive foundation	12 to 20 cm
Apartment houses of bricks, and structures with statically determined girders	8 to 12 cm
Apartment houses and industrial structures of statically indetermined systems	5 to 8 cm
Sensitive industrial structures subjected to dynamic stresses	3 to 5 cm

An older Viennese ordinance sets 3 to 4 cm as an allowable settlement.

Thornley,[2] discussing the demands of the superstructure, classifies structures according to permissible foundation settlements into 5 classes. For example, for monumental structures, cathedrals, large power plants, foundations for heavy machinery, grain elevators, large concrete tanks, office buildings, hotels, and stores of 10 or more stories in height and all of reinforced concrete or structural steel; warehouses of multiple-story, retaining walls, concrete arches for bridges, and hangars—the requirement relative to differential settlement under working load must be held within a maximum limit of $\frac{1}{8}''$, and gross settlement under working load to a maximum of $\frac{1}{2}''$.

For bridges of structural steel or of the suspension type, steel frame buildings, piers, and docks, the differential settlement under working load should be kept within a maximum of $\frac{1}{4}''$.

For factories, stores, apartment buildings, hotels, churches, schools, warehouses, machine shops, and highway structures, the differential settlement under working load should be not more than $\frac{1}{2}''$.

Owing to the nature of soil properties which may vary from foot to foot, and which are influenced very much by the moisture content in soil, it is very difficult indeed to set any standards for allowable amounts of settlements of structures on soil.

The second question of interest is to know the length of time before settlements will practically cease or fade out. The rate of settlement is primarily a function of the permeability of the soil. The rate of settlement decreases with time.

15-5. The Mechanical Spring and Water Analogy. According to Terzaghi:[3] "Every process involving a decrease in the water content of a saturated soil without replacement of the water by air is called a process of *consolidation*. The opposite process is called a process of swelling, which involves an increase in the water content due to an increase in the volume of the voids".

The change in the volume of voids and the volume of water in the voids is brought about either by the self-weight of the soil, or static loads. Thus, consolidation is the process of adjustment of the volume of the soil pore water (volume change) under an applied load on soil.

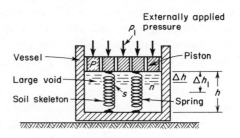

FIG. 15-3   Mechanical consolidation model.

In order to understand better the settlement problem of soil, a problem which is associated with the so-called consolidation phenomenon of a soil, the principle of the consolidation process of a clay will now be explained by means of a mechanical model.

The details of the working of the mechanical spring model can be found described in Terzaghi and Fröhlich's theory on the settlement of clay layers.[4]

The mechanical consolidation model, Fig. 15-3, consists of a vessel provided with a perforated piston, P. The piston is supported on one or several helical metallic springs, S. The springs function according to the theory of elasticity. In analogy with soil, the volume of the vessel represents the voids of the soil with a porosity of n. If the volume of the vessel underneath the piston is filled with water (pore water), then, by analogy to soil, this means that all of the voids of the soil are fully saturated with water.

The metal springs are imagined to be the solid soil particles, or the soil skeleton. The perforations in the piston can be imagined, with reference to soil, as the capillary passages through which water can be expelled out of the voids of the soil, or, under special conditions, water can flow into the soil.

Let us consider two conditions in the vessel: first, the vessel is dry, and second, the vessel is full with water.

1) *The Space in the Vessel Below the Plunger is Empty.* Upon the application

of an external compressive stress, p kg/cm^2 (without impact), the metal springs undergo a quick compression by an amount of Δh. Note that the externally applied load is fully carried by the springs (representing the intergranular stress transmission from particle to particle in contact), i.e., the stress carried by the springs is the effective, intergranular stress.

2) *Space Below Piston Filled with Water.* At the very first instant that the external load is applied to the piston, this load is fully transferred to water (assume that water is incompressible). Hence, water is stressed, but the springs are not. Thus, the reaction of water to external pressure means that at this instant water carries the full external load, i.e., $u = p$, where u is the neutral stress. As time goes on water will escape through the perforations made in the piston, out of the vessel . The velocity of water flow out of the vessel also depends, among other things, upon the size or area of the perforations. With larger perforations the water escapes under pressure at a faster rate than through smaller areas of the same number of perforations. With large perforations, as said, water escapes faster, and the springs will start to receive and to carry some of the externally applied load sooner than with the slow escape of water. Besides, the faster the water leaves the vessel, the sooner the springs will carry the externally applied load, p, in full, and thus the sooner they will attain their full deformation, Δh. Thus, by analogy, large perforations mean a coarse-particled soil with large voids and good drainage facility; small perforations mean a fine-particled, cohesive (clay) soil with poor drainage characteristics.

The part, p_1, of the total external load, p, the springs carry at any certain time, t, after the application of the external load, p, is by proportion

$$p_1 = p\, \frac{\Delta h_1}{\Delta h},\qquad (15\text{-}3)$$

where p_1 = effective stress carried by the springs, and

Δh_1 = the deformation of the springs (settlement of piston) at this certain time, t.

Because the load-spring-water system is, at any instant, in equilibrium, then the algebraic sum of all pressures acting on the system is equal to zero:

$$\downarrow \quad \uparrow \quad \uparrow$$
$$p - p_1 - u = 0,\qquad (15\text{-}4)$$

i.e., the total stress p equals the sum of the effective stress, p_1, and the neutral stress, u, or

$$u = p - p_1,\qquad (15\text{-}5)$$

where u = difference in pressures between external load and spring reactions, a difference which must be taken up by an excess hydrostatic pressure of water:

$$u = p - p_1 = p - p\,\frac{\Delta h_1}{\Delta h} = p\,\frac{\Delta h - \Delta h_1}{\Delta h}.\qquad (15\text{-}6)$$

This water pressure, u, is also termed the neutral pressure.

In Eq. (15-6), at time $t = 0$, $\Delta h = 0$, and $u = p$ (the total stress equals the neutral stress; there is no effective or intergranular stress). As the settlement of the piston increases, u decreases because Δh_1 increases and $\rightarrow \Delta h$. In such a case $u \rightarrow 0$, i.e., the springs then carry the full external load, and water carries no stress from the applied load, p, and the consolidation process of the "clay" can now be considered completed. Any intermediate stage in the consolidation process is termed the *degree of consolidation*, and is expressed in percents of the full consolidation. Note from this example that the system has one drainage face, i.e., there exists one-way drainage: namely, upward.

FIG. 15-4   Mechanical spring-consolidation model.

Likewise, in respect to the stress, in soil mechanics the compressive stress externally applied to a mass of a soil is termed the *total stress*, p. Part of this total stress, which during the consolidation process (drainage process) of a soil is taken up by water, is termed the *neutral stress*, u. The other part of the total stress, which is transferred intergranularly on the soil particles, is termed the *effective stress*, p_e. Then

$$p = p_e + u. \tag{15-7}$$

It is obvious that within the process of consolidation, a gradual decrease in neutral pressure takes place, along with a gradual increase in effective pressure. Their sum, however, is at all times constant and equal to the total pressure in magnitude, and is

$$p = p_e + u = p'_e + u' = p''_e + u'' = \cdots = \text{const.} \tag{15-8}$$

The constancy, of course, depends upon the total stress, p.

Teaching Aid. The consolidation phenomenon in soil can most readily be studied experimentally by a teaching aid such as illustrated in Fig. 15-4. Such a mechanical consolidation model is easily made, and the variations in effective and neutral stress as a function of the externally applied load, as well as the drainage phenomenon, effectively studied. In such a model, the neutral stress can be determined either by a small gage installed in a plastic cylinder, in which the spring and piston are located, or by means of a piezometric tube attached to that cylinder. Lead weights are used as the load. In Fig. 15-4, the lead weight happens to be 5.412 kg.

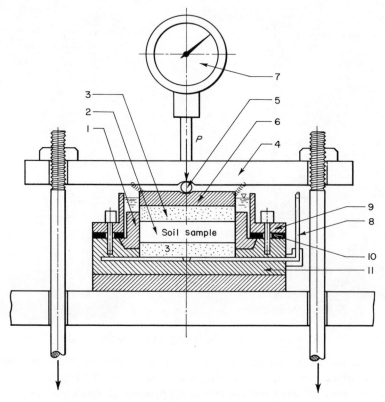

FIG. 15-5   Cross section of consolidometer.

Although the mechanical spring-consolidation model with a cohesive soil is a very crude mechanical device, for the purpose of analogy it nevertheless helps one to gain a pretty good insight into the consolidation processes which take place in a saturated, laterally confined layer of clay.

15-6. Consolidometer. The compressive properties of a soil are usually studied by means of a device termed the consolidometer, Fig. 15-5.

A consolidometer consists of a ring (1), into which is placed a soil sample (2), undisturbed or remolded, whichever may be the assigned problem. Here the soil sample is in a laterally confined state. On top and at the bottom of the soil sample there are porous filter stones (3), one on each side of the sample, to permit a two-way drainage of water expelled out of the voids from the soil sample under a vertical load, P. The axial, vertical load is applied on the soil sample by means of a loading yoke (4). The load is transmitted centrally from the loading yoke through a steel ball bearing (5) which rests on a circular loading plate (6), providing a uniform pressure distribution on the soil sample. The soil sample is subjected to predetermined load increments.

The load externally applied on the soil sample compresses the soil, squeezes some water out from the voids of the soil, and the soil sample thus decreases in thickness. This volume change is measured by an Ames dial gage (7). The volume change readings are made at definite time intervals for each load increment.

Depending upon the thickness of the ring, soil samples 1 cm to about 4.5 cm thick (or high) may be subjected to such a laterally confined compression or consolidation test depending upon the thickness of the consolidation ring (1). Because drainage of thick layers of clay requires a relatively long period of time, consolidation tests in the laboratory are usually performed on thin samples, 1 to 2.5 cm in thickness. Consolidation of such samples under a certain intensity of load usually is accomplished within a few days, and sometimes even within 24 hours.

At the bottom of the soil sample, the water expelled from the soil flows through the filter stone, and is forced into the standpipe (8).

At the top, a well-jacket (a brass ring) (9), filled with water, is placed around the porous filter stone in order to prevent excessive evaporation from the soil sample during the test. Water is forced into this well-jacket through the upper filter stone upon compression of the soil. Thus, during the consolidation test the soil sample is kept submerged in a saturated condition. This is so practiced because soils have their lowest strength and greatest compressibility when they are in a fully saturated condition. Inundation of the soil would also exclude the resistance to compression by the apparent cohesion (surface tension forces). Besides, the Terzaghi-Fröhlich consolidation theory of clays is devised for a fully saturated condition of the soil; hence, the consolidation test must be performed accordingly.

The standpipe permits the performance of a direct soil permeability test to water during the progress of the consolidation test. In essence, this standpipe is a falling (or rising) head permeameter, and measures the amount of water which passes through the soil sample during a given period of time and under an established hydraulic gradient.

15-7. Consolidation Test. From the description of the consolidation apparatus, it can be inferred that the consolidation test of a soil is in essence a compression test on a laterally confined soil sample, and in a way also a drainage or permeability test under load. It is a model test, not a destructive test like the shear test.

The main purpose of the consolidation test is to obtain information on the compressible properties of a saturated soil for use in determining the magnitude and rate of settlement of structures.

Before and after the consolidation test, the moisture content and weight of the soil sample must be determined so that the void ratios for each load increment can be calculated and plotted. This also requires the determination of the specific gravity of the soil tested.

Because the consolidation process of a soil is essentially a drainage process, the temperature of the soil water must be recorded and all tests reported at a standard temperature of, say, $+20°C$.

In performing a consolidation test, each load increment is usually allowed to remain on the soil sample until the further consolidation is negligible, or, in other words, until a straight-line branch of the consolidation curve, representing the secondary consolidation, is well defined. For each load increment a separate time-consolidation curve is drawn. Although any ratio in load increments may be used, in the laboratory the following load increments, Δp, are customary: 0.1, 0.2, 0.4, 0.8, 1.6, 3.2, 6.4, 12.8, and at times 25.6 kg/cm². In principle, the successive pressure should be twice the value of the preceding load.

After a new load increment is applied to the soil sample, subsequent dial readings are recorded after elapsed times of 0.25, 0.5, 1.0, 2, 4, 8, 15, 30, 60, 120, 240, 480, and 1440 minutes.

For practical reasons, in laboratory work, a load increment is allowed to remain on a soil sample for a period of 24 hours = 1440 minutes, during which time the secondary consolidation has developed reasonably well. However, stiff clay specimens are encountered requiring a consolidation time of more than 24 hours.

For each load increment a separate time-consolidation curve is plotted. These curves are needed for plotting the pressure-void ratio curves.

The loading of the soil sample is continued up to and somewhat above the compressive stress in the soil anticipated from a contemplated structure.

After the greatest load required for the test has been applied to the soil sample, the load is removed in decrements to provide data for plotting the expansion curve of the soil in order to learn its elastic properties and the magnitude of plastic or permanent deformations.

Some detailed description of consolidation tests of soils can be found in Reference 5.

To summarize, the consolidation test of a soil should furnish the following information:

1) the relationship between time and percent consolidation, represented by the time-consolidation diagram;
2) the relationship between the increasing or decreasing load on the soil and the change in the void ratio of the soil, represented by the pressure-void ratio diagram (expansion diagram); and
3) data on permeability of the soil as a function of that particular load.

STRESS-STRAIN RELATIONSHIP IN A CONSOLIDATION PROCESS

15-8. Stress-Strain Diagrams. Soils, although they undergo compression like solid bodies, actually follow Hooke's law of deformation only within a relatively narrow load interval (compare the stress-strain diagrams for metal and for soil in Fig. 15-6,

where $P.L.$ = proportional limit

p_p = stress at proportional limit

$E.L.$ = elastic limit

p_y = yield point stress

$U.S.$ = ultimate strength (p_u)

L = length of steel bar

ΔL = deformation of steel bar

$\varepsilon = \Delta L/L$ = relative deformation, or strain

H = thickness of layer of soil

ΔH = absolute deformation (settlement) of soil

$\varepsilon = \Delta H/H$ = relative settlement of soil.

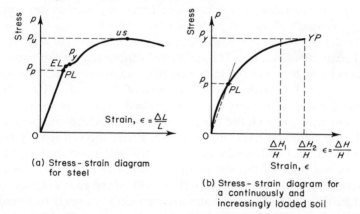

(a) Stress-strain diagram for steel

(b) Stress-strain diagram for a continuously and increasingly loaded soil

FIG. 15-6. Sketches of the shapes of stress-strain diagrams a) for steel and b) for soil.

The stress-strain curve for soil departs from the straight line as for steel, for example, indicating that soil departs from Hooke's law and that the deformation increases at a great rate after the so-called proportional limit, $P.L.$, is passed. At the yield point, $Y.P.$, the strain approaches an infinitely large value, i.e., the load or soil settles rapidly.

Water in the Voids of Soil. The voids of the soil may be filled with water. Upon compressing such a soil, water is expelled out of the voids of the soil. Depending upon the amount of water present, one distinguishes among three principal moisture conditions in soil, namely:

1) The soil contains a small amount of water, characterized by a degree of saturation, S, which is less than 100%. In such a case much air is also present in the voids of the soil. The air is connected freely to the atmosphere. This case is then a three-phase soil.

2) The soil contains large quantities of water in its voids. The water and the voids unoccupied by water contains a small amount of entrapped, isolated bubbles of air and/or gas. This condition can be considered as almost saturated one.

3) All voids of the given soil are fully saturated ($S = 100\%$) with water. Due to their inherent capillary properties, the voids of the cohesive soils are considered as always almost filled with water.

In the first soil moisture condition, compression of soil under an externally applied load on the soil in the field or in the laboratory takes place without expulsion of water from the voids of the soil (provided the load is far in excess of that magnitude necessary for consolidation of that soil when the amount of soil moisture makes the decreasing volume of voids saturated). In this case water and air freely escape out of the voids.

The resistance to compression of the soil is here made up of
a) the resistance friction between the soil particles in contact upon their displacement,
b) the resistance of the mutually attracting soil particles, and
c) the resistance of the moisture films, say, surface tension, at the contacts of the soil particles.

Under the second soil moisture condition, the process of soil compression is a very complex one. The difficulty is increased by the entrapped air bubbles which, under the increased pressure, dissolve in the water. The presence of air cushions in the interstices of a clay soil in its performance under compression is very disturbing indeed. The air in the voids endows the soil with some elastic properties very difficult to comprehend.

In the third soil moisture condition, where the soil is fully saturated, compression of soil obviously takes place only upon draining the water out of the voids of the soil under the influence of the compressive load externally applied to the soil. In the theory of soil consolidation, the solid soil particles as well as the water are considered as being imcompressible. The loading of saturated clays is thus always accompanied, at ordinary temperatures, by a decrease in soil moisture content, and thus by a decrease in volume of the soil. The process of expulsion of water from the voids of the soil is in itself a process of permeability of the clay to water, under the influence of the compressive load externally applied to the soil mass.

The water drains out of the voids of cohesive soils very slowly because of their low permeability.

Resistance to expulsion of water from the voids increases with the decrease in moisture content in the soil during the process of compression, or rather, using now the proper term with the soil mechanics connotation, the term of consolidation. As the consolidation process continues, there are established more points of contact between the soil particles at which their mutual interaction can take place. Also moisture films at points of contact add to the resistance to deformation by compression. It can now be inferred that with an increase in the compressive load on a clay soil the resistance to compression increases.

Cyclic Loading. From experiments on soils subjected to repetitional or cyclic loading, stress-strain curves can be plotted—the general features of which are illustrated in Fig. 15-7. Such a curve results when loading a soil in a lateral confinement, such as a pit surrounded by sheet piling, or in a soil consolidometer. The consolidometer is an apparatus for studying consolidation processes of soil in the laboratory.

The branch of the cyclic loading curve. 0-1, is the loading or compression curve, giving a settlement of a soil layer, marked by ΔH_1. Branch 1-2 is the unloading or swelling curve. Note that in this case the soil is unloaded to zero, and that the soil layer in question has experienced, after its first unloading, a

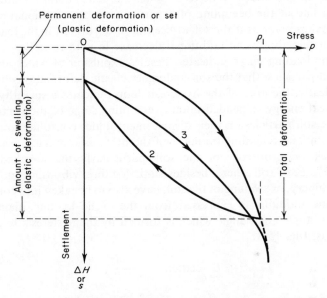

FIG. 15-7   Illustrating the cyclic loading curve of a soil.

permanent or plastic deformation or settlement, ΔH_2. This means that upon unloading the soil does not swell infinitely, but swelling ceases at a certain pore volume, or void ratio, point 2 on the curve, for example. Thus, upon unloading, the initial settlement, ΔH_1 does not disappear fully, i.e., the load, p_1, has caused a permanent decrease in the volume of voids. Only the elastic deformations disappear upon unloading the soil.

The permanent, or irreversible deformation, ΔH_2, is believed to be caused by soil particle translocation and readjustment. On the other hand, the elasticity of a soil refers to its ability to rebound, or to regain a part of its original form after the load is removed after compression.

In fully saturated soil, the elastic or reversible deformations vary greatly, and are explained as being due to the elastic deformations of the clay-water bonds between the soil particles. Some degree of elasticity in the soil is contributed by the solid, flake like particles of the soil: organic matter contents; peat; air; and soil moisture.

In partially saturated soil, the elastic behavior of the soil is also attributed to the elastic changes of the air bubbles in the aqueous vapor and to the pressure in the bubbles themselves, as well as to the vapor pressure in the voids.

The reloading of the soil, branch, 2-3, completes one full loading cycle. During unloading, the saturated clay takes up some water and "swells" (by osmotic filling of water into the voids after a certain amount of load has been removed). Upon reloading, some water is again expelled from the voids of the soil.

The loop of the stress-settlement curve is termed the *hysteresis loop*. Hysteresis loops brought about by cyclic loading are almost parallel among themselves for one soil sample under cyclic test. When the load, upon reloading, exceeds the value it had at the beginning of a particular cycle, additional compression of the soil takes place as if there had been no interruption in the loading. Thus the effect of reloading is an additional decrease in void ratio.

The cyclic loading curve indicates, besides expulsion of water and displacement of soil particles, that the soil undergoes elastic deformations by load.

Mechanically, the area of the hysteresis loop indicates a quantity of energy, probably heat energy, expended upon overcoming some of the frictional forces between the soil particles on their displacement under consolidation.

The loading and reloading branches of the hysteresis loop are used for evaluating the elastic properties of the soil, particularly the so-called "modulus of elasticity", E, of soil where, besides static loading, vibrations induced in the soil by machinery, or swelling of the soil, have also to be taken into consideration.

The elastic modulus is expressed from the cyclic loading diagram as the cotangent of angle ε, an angle which is formed by the hysteresis loops with the abscissa axis, Fig. 15-8:

$$E = \cotan \varepsilon = -\frac{dp}{de},$$
(15-9)

if instead of settlement, the corresponding void ratios are plotted.

Although, theoretically, the hysteresis loops should be parallel, i.e., E should be constant for any one material, the loops obtained from soil experiment are in fact not often quite parallel. As seen from the tangents E_1, E_2, and E_3 to the loading, unloading, and reloading branches, the "modulus of elasticity" of a soil is a variable factor depending upon load, viz., depth below the ground surface.

The course of the main branch of the cyclic stress-settlement curve depends also to a certain degree upon the speed with which the successive load increments are applied to the soil. Quick loading usually gives a more gentle curve than slow loading, Fig. 15-9.

The nature of a stress-settlement diagram for a cyclic loading of a granular soil is illustrated in Fig. 15-8. Note the point of proportional limit, p_p, and the yield stress, p_y. The proportional limit, p_p, is the stress at which the settlement curve begins to deviate markedly from a straight line. The proportional limit of cohesive soils is less than that of sands, and is arbitrarily taken to be about one-quarter the value of the yield point, i.e., $4p_p \approx p_y$.

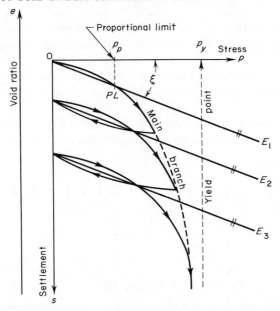

FIG. 15-8   Diagram of nature of settlement for a cyclic loading of granular soil.

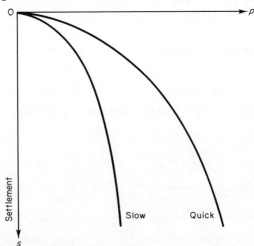

FIG. 15-9   Slow and quick loading curves.

Effect of Temperature on Consolidation. Because consolidation of soil is essentially a drainage process involving the concept of permeability, and permeability is affected by temperature, then, obviously, temperature must logically also have an effect upon the process of consolidation.

The dynamic viscosity tables in the Appendix of this book show that a change in temperature from 0°C to 25°C brings about a corresponding change in the values of dynamic viscosity of about double, i.e., from 0.01790 to 0.00894 (g)/(cm sec) = poises, respectively.

Hence, the higher the temperature of the soil under a consolidation test, the greater its drainage, the higher the compressibility, and the higher the rate of consolidation.

Therefore, upon subjecting a soil to a consolidation test, the soil temperature should be measured, test results corrected, and reported at a standard temperature, say, of $+20°C$.

Effect of Non-cohesive Soil Layers on a Sandwiched Cohesive Soil. If a cohesive soil layer is enclosed between two permeable layers of granular non-cohesive

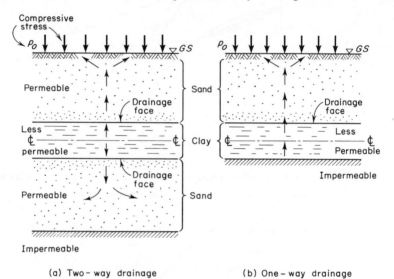

(a) Two-way drainage   (b) One-way drainage

FIG. 15-10. Two-way and one-way drainage.

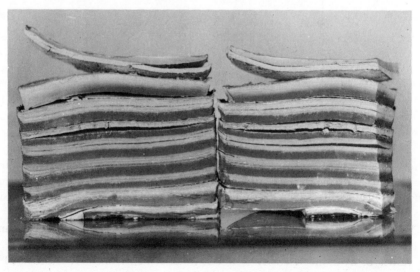

FIG. 15-11. Varved clay.

material, this condition facilitates drainage of water out of the soil by the fact that the clay has now two drainage faces through which to empty, as compared with one-way drainage, Fig. 15-10. Hence drainage and consolidation with two drainage faces can take place at a much more rapid rate than through one drainage face, assuming that all other conditions in both cases are the same.

Likewise, varved clays containing sandwiched layers of silt (Fig. 15-11) drain and consolidate faster and more effectively than a mass of solid clay of the same thickness.

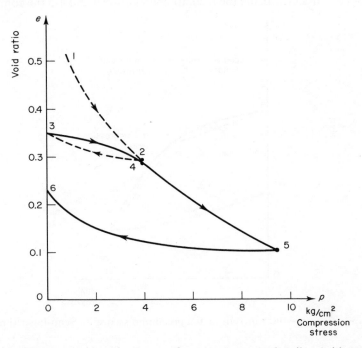

FIG. 15-12 Pressure-void ratio curve of a precompressed soil. Arithmetic scale.

15-9. Preconsolidation. It may so happen that a soil in nature has been previously loaded with a certain pressure (a sheet of glacial ice, for example[6]), p_{pr}, under which the soil had time to consolidate (point 2 on branch 1-2 of the pressure-void ratio curve, Fig. 15-12). In this example the compressive stress is $p_{pr} = 4.0$ kg/cm². It also could have happened that after the consolidation time elapsed the load on the soil was removed to zero, branch 2-3. Some time after the unloading it could be that a sample of this soil was taken and subjected to a consolidation test under loads from $p = 0$ to $p = p_t = 9.5$ kg/cm², branch 3-4-5, past the previous preconsolidation stress, $p_{pr} = 4.0$ kg/cm², that existed on the soil earlier. Branch 5-6 shows that the soil sample was unloaded to zero, resulting in a void ratio of $e = 0.23$. The amount of swelling (elastic deformation) is from $e_5 = 0.10$ to $e_6 = 0.23$. The amount of permanent (plastic) deformation is from $e_3 = 0.35$ to $e_6 = 0.23$.

This stress-void ratio curve thus indicates that, before the compression test, the soil had once before been subjected to a preconsolidation load the intensity of which was $p_{pr} = 4.0$ kg/cm^2.

The preconsolidation pressure is thus that pressure to which a soil has been subjected at some time previously, before the compression test. Note that the branches 1-2 and 2-3 on the stress-void ratio curve, when performing a consolidation test on a preconsolidated soil sample in the laboratory, do not appear on the graph. All that the consolidation test renders is the curve 3-4-5 (-6), branch 3-4 of this curve being the recompression branch and 4-5 the compression

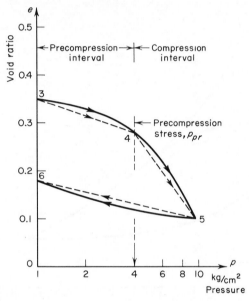

FIG. 15-13   Pressure-void ratio curve of a precompressed soil. Semi-logarithmic scale.

branch. Also, observe that up to the preconsolidation stress, p_{pr}, from zero to p_{pr}, the stress-void ratio curve (p-e curve) has a relatively flat slope, whereas past the preconsolidation stress the curve has a relatively steep slope. Such a graph is typical for preconsolidated and re-loaded clays. In soil engineering the nature of the slopes of the p-e curve on both sides of the preconsolidation stress indicates the following: up to the preconsolidation load this soil is less compressible than past the preconsolidation load. To illustrate this point simply, assume that on this soil a foundation is to be laid transmitting to the soil a contact pressure of $p_0 = 2$ kg/cm^2. Because in our illustration the contact pressure is less than the preconsolidation pressure, i.e., $p_0 = 2$ kg/cm^2 $< p_{pr} = 4$ kg/cm^2, the magnitude of the settlement of this clay can be expected to be small. If, however, the contact pressure at the base of the footings were, say, $p_0 = 7$ kg/cm^2, a case where the contact pressure is larger than the preconsolidation pressure ($p_{pr} = 4$ kg/cm^2), then much larger settlements of the clay can be expected than at contact pressures below the preconsolidation pressure.

The preconsolidation pressure is often very difficult to discover on the p-e curve if plotted to an arithmetical scale. To discover the preconsolidation pressure most readily, it is expedient to plot the p-e curve to a semi-logarithmic scale, where pressures (p) are plotted to a decimal logarithmic scale, and void ratios (e) to an arithmetical scale, Fig. 15-13. Then the preconsolidation stress, p_{pr}, appears theoretically as a point of break (point 4, Fig. 15-13) between two straight lines (see dotted lines 3-4 and 4-5), separating the preconsolidated part of the p-e curve (flat dotted line 3-4) from the consolidated part (steep dotted line 4-5).

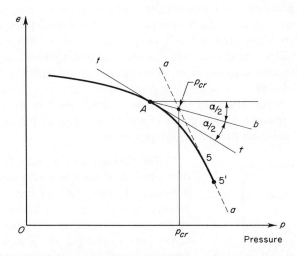

FIG. 15-14 Determination of precompression stress after A. Casagrande.

However, plots of consolidation test results to a semi-logarithmic scale often do not show up as straight lines, but as curved ones, such as the solid curve 3-4-5-6 on Fig. 15-13. In such a case the location of the point of the preconsolidation pressure does not show up clearly. To find the point representing the preconsolidation pressure on such curves, A. Casagrande suggested the following empirical method which locates the point in question approximately, see Fig. 15-14.[7] Locate by eye the point of the greatest curvature (point A on the recompression branch, for example). Through this point draw a horizontal line, A-h, and a tangent, A-t, to the curve. Bisect the angle, $\measuredangle hAt$, thus formed by the bisector, Ab. Then draw backwards, from point 5, the straight line part of the compression curve, 5-5' (straight dotted line, a-a), until it intersects the bisector line, Ab, to give point p_{pr}. This point then approximately determines the preconsolidation pressure.

A soil may have been preconsolidated during the geologic past by the weight of an ice sheet or glacier which has melted away, or by other geologic overburden and structural loads which no longer exist. For example, thick layers of over burdened soil may have been eroded away, or excavated away, or heavy structures may have been torn down. Also, capillary pressures which may have acted on the clay layers in the past may have been removed for one reason or another. Preconsolidation may also be caused by evaporation of water from the clay.

The practical significance of the preconsolidation load appears in calculating settlements of structures and in geological studies of unsolidified sediments which at some time in the geologic past may have been subjected to an over-burden load.

Sometimes in practice easily compressible soils upon which structures are to be built are artificially precompressed or prestressed, and then a structure is erected which will exert a pressure on the soil of somewhat less magnitude than the pre-stress pressure. For example, a three-hinge reinforced concrete arch bridge was constructed in the following way: the forms for the bridge had provisions for holding sand of such weight as would correspond to the final weight of the bridge. As the concrete for the bridge was poured, an equal weight of sand was shoveled into the river to maintain the soil upon which the bridge piers were founded at a reasonably constant, unchanged stress. The main reason for this was to avoid cracking the freshly poured concrete during the curing period, and to prevent ugly sagging of the arches due to increased weight as the pouring of concrete for the bridge progressed.

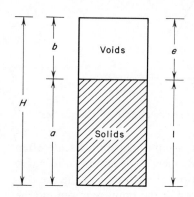

FIG. 15-15　Soil phase diagram.

15-10. Change in Void Ratio. Upon expulsion of water out of the voids of a soil by a certain intensity of load, the volume of the soil decreases, resulting· in a decrease in the height of the soil sample, or thickness of the soil layer; or, expressed in general terms, the decrease in volume is the settlement of the soil. Hence the void ratio also varies with the load. Note that before the application of the load the void ratio is larger than after its application, i.e., the void ratio before drainage is larger than after.

The change in thickness, H, of the soil layer can conveniently be expressed by means of the change in the void ratio, de. Refer to the soil phase diagram of a soil, Fig. 15-15.

Because the absolute thickness, H, (or relative thickness $1 + e$) of a saturated layer of soil is made up of the height of the absolute volume of solids, a (or relative height "1"), and of the height of the absolute volume, b (or relative height, e), it can be written that

$$H = a + b \quad \text{(cm)}. \quad (15\text{-}10)$$

Because the volume of solids is constant, and only the volume of voids, viz., void ratio, varies, the change in H is:

$$dH = d(b). \quad (15\text{-}11)$$

The relative compressive deformation (shortening, or settlement) in the thickness of the soil layer is

$$\frac{dH}{H} = \frac{db}{a+b} = \frac{de}{1+e} = s, \qquad (15\text{-}12)$$

where dH/H is the relative amount of loss of water per unit height of the soil prisma and s is the specific compression (per unit of height of the soil prisma). Substitution of e with an average void ratio e_{ave} yields

$$s = dH/H = \lambda \frac{de}{1 + e_{\text{ave}}} = \alpha d(e), \qquad (15\text{-}13)$$

where λ and α are coefficients.

This equation reads that the specific change in thickness (specific compression) is directly proportional to the change in pore volume, or void ratio. This rule, therefore, permits expressing the relative settlement of a soil layer caused by a consolidation load by means of the change in void ratio (viz., per volume), and plotting the pressure-void ratio curves as illustrated in Fig. 15-16.

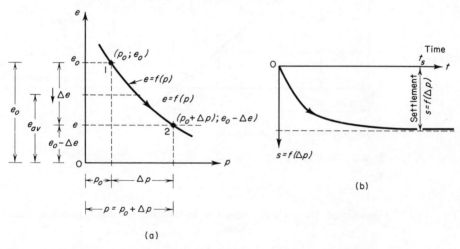

FIG. 15-16. Change in void ratio with change in pressure during time, t_s. a) Coordinates on a pressure-void ratio curve; b) Time-settlement curve.

If an initial void ratio is e_0 at an initial pressure of p_0, then a load increment, Δp, brings about a decrease in the void ratio by an amount of Δe. The final void ratio is then

$$e = e_0 - \Delta e \qquad \text{(dimensionless)}, \qquad (15\text{-}14)$$

or, in the differential form,

$$e = e_0 - d(e). \qquad (15\text{-}15)$$

If $d(e)$ could be expressed as a function of pressure, then Eq. (15-15) would permit one to calculate the void ratio for any pressure, if the initially given void ratio, e_0 at p_0 is known. This condition is characterized on the pressure-void ratio curve by two points, 1 and 2, the coordinates of which, respectively, are:

1) $(p_0; e_0)$ before applying the load increment, Δp, and

2) $(p_0 + \Delta p; e_0 - \Delta e)$ after the application of Δp, see Fig. 15-16a.)

Figure 15-21b, furthermore, indicates that the time, t_s, during which the reduction in void ratio by Δe took place, caused by a load increment Δp, brings about a settlement $s = f(\Delta p)$. The plot of settlement as a function of time gives the time-settlement curve.

This question leads to the problem of deriving an analytical pressure-void ratio equation.

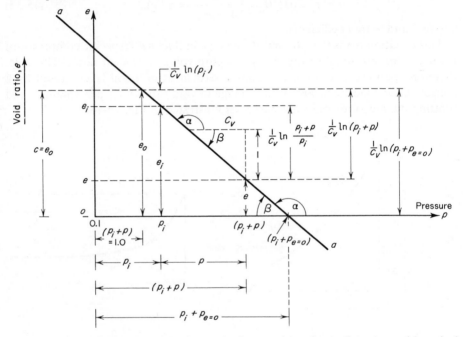

FIG. 15-17   Elements of straight line. Abscissas to ln-scale; ordinates to arithmetical scale.

15-11. Pressure-Void Ratio Equations. The pressure-void ratio curves are by nature approximately logarithmic. A plot of void ratios as functions of pressure in a semi-logarithmic coordinate system show these functions to appear as straight lines, a-a, for example, Fig. 15-17. The straight-line, pressure-void ratio equation can be written after the type

$$y = kx + c, \tag{15-16}$$

or

$$e = -\frac{1}{C_v} \ln(p_i + p) + c, \tag{15-17}$$

where e = void ratio at any pressure, $p_i + p$, and the index, v, at C meaning compression in the vertical direction; c and p_i are experimental parameters to be determined from consolidation tests. Mathematically, $(p_i + p)$ and e are running coordinates. Physically these parameters mean the following: $- 1/C_v = \tan \alpha = \tan (180° - \beta) =$ slope of line a-a (here tangent is in the second quarter, $\alpha > 90°$); the reciprocal of $\tan \alpha$ is termed the *coefficient of compressibility of soil*, and is independent of load. The coefficient of compressibility is sometimes termed the *compression index*. The physical units of coefficient of compressibility, C_v, are (g/cm^2).

$p_i =$ initial pressure to which a new applied load, p, is added; in cohesive soils, p_i depends upon the moisture content in the soil, whereas in sands —on the density of the sand; and

$c =$ cutoff on the ordinate axis.

This equation is generally meant to represent the main compression branch. The compression curve can then be defined by the parameters, c and $1/C_v$. Obviously, the quantity, c, must be of the nature of some kind of void ratio, which it actually is.

Also, this equation corresponds to one given by Terzaghi[8].

Equations for the unloading (swelling) branch and for the reloading branch of the consolidation curve can be derived in a way similar to that shown above for the compression branch.

The swelling curve is

$$e = e_0 - \frac{1}{C_s} \ln(p_i + p), \qquad (15\text{-}18)$$

i.e., the void ratio, e, decreases from its original, known value, e_0 proportionally to the natural logarithm of the consolidation pressure. The quantity $1/C_s$ in this equation is the expansion index, in (cm^2/g), the index, s, referring to swelling.

The reloading curve is very difficult to express by an equation. Approximately, however, its equation can be written as

$$e = e_0 - \frac{1}{C_v} \ln(p_i + p). \qquad (15\text{-}19)$$

Of course, the C_v-values for the loading and reloading branches of the consolidation curve have different values in each case, because the slopes of these curves are different.

Analysis of Equation

1°) When $p_i + p = 1$, then $c = e_0$.

Thus, c is a void ratio when the total load of the consolidating sample is $(p_i + p) = 1$. In such a case, Eq. (15-17) can be written as

$$e = e_0 - \frac{1}{C_v} \ln(p_i + p), \qquad (15\text{-}20)$$

i.e., the void ratio, e, decreases from its original, known value, e_0, proportionally to the natural logarithm of the consolidation pressure.

2°) When $p = 0$, then the initial void ratio, by Eq. (15-17), is

$$e_i = -\frac{1}{C_v} \ln(p_i) + c. \tag{15-21}$$

3°) Subtracting Eq. (15-21) from Eq. (15-17), obtain

$$e - e_i = -\frac{1}{C_v} \ln \frac{p_i + p}{p_i}. \tag{15-22}$$

In this equation the constant, c, has disappeared.

4°) The reciprocal of the slope of the line, $1/(\tan \beta)$, is termed the compression index, C_v. From Fig. 15-18,

$$\tan \alpha = \tan(180° - \beta) = -\tan \beta = -\frac{1}{C_v}. \tag{15-23}$$

Note again that the compression index, C_v, has the units of g/cm^2.

5°) When $e = 0$, designate the corresponding pressure as $p_i + p_{e=0}$. In such a case Eq. (15-17) transforms into

$$\frac{1}{C_v} \ln(p_i + p_{e=0}) = c, \tag{15-24}$$

and

$$p_i + p_{e=0} = e^{cC_v} \quad (\text{g/cm}^2). \tag{15-25}$$

Of course, the condition of a zero void ratio in soil cannot exist in reality.

6°) Differentiation of the general e-equation, Eq. (15-17), with respect to the applied vertical pressure, p, which is the first derivative of the e-function, gives the slope of the compression curve, sometimes also termed the consolidation curve:

$$\frac{d(e)}{d(p)} = -\frac{1}{C_v} \frac{1}{p_i + p} \quad (\text{cm}^2/\text{g}). \tag{15-26}$$

When $(p_i + p) = 1$, then

$$\frac{d(e)}{d(p)} = -\frac{1}{C_v} \quad (\text{cm}^2/\text{g}). \tag{15-27}$$

7°) The consolidation curve equation is satisfactory for practical purposes in foundation engineering but only within a narrow pressure interval. The equation, which is approximate by its nature, has, however, some rough inherent deficiencies, which are desirable to know (in order that one should know the tool he uses, and its limitations).

The equation in question is

$$e = e_0 - \frac{1}{C_v} \ln(p_i + p). \tag{15-20}$$

a) When $p \to \infty$, $e \to -\infty$, while the smallest possible value for e is $e = 0$. In reality even this ($e = 0$) value cannot be attained (refer to soil phase diagram).

b) If in Eq. (15-20) the void ratio is set $e = 0$, it follows that $(e_0 = c)$

$$p_i + p = e^{cC_v}, \tag{15-25}$$

(in this equation $e = 2.71 \ldots$, the base of natural logarithms), an expression which conveys that porosity seems to be equal zero at a definite value of pressure $(p_1 + p) = e^{cC_v}$. In reality the void ratio of a soil tends to approach, at a given pressure, a certain limit characterized by the maximum possible density of the given soil.

c) Differentiation of Eq. (15-17) or Eq. (15-20) yields

$$\frac{d(e)}{d(p)} = - \frac{1}{C_v} \frac{1}{p_i + p}, \tag{15-26}$$

or

$$\frac{d(p)}{d(e)} = -C_v(p_i + p) \tag{15-28}$$

(tangent is a straight line).

However, from the many experimental curves obtained in laboratory testing of a great many soil samples, one observes that the $d(p)/d(e) = f(p)$-curves are mostly curved, and are approximately straight lines only within a narrow pressure interval.

8°) The coefficients of compression and expansion (swelling) of cohesive and non-cohesive soils are, for informative purposes:[9]

Soil Type	Coefficient of Compression C_v kg/cm²	Coefficient of Expansion C_s kg/cm²
Clay	1- 20	8- 70
Sandy clay	15- 50	65-260
Silt	15- 20	25-130
Fine sand	15-100	130-260

One notes that the variation in the C_v- and C_s-coefficients is very wide. This indicates the need for testing separately each type of soil subject to consolidation.

9°) When the externally applied load, p, varies in small increments within narrow intervals, then the consolidation curves can be replaced in a semilogarithmic plot by a straight line, and the pressure-void ratio equation thus established, Eq. (15-17), can then be used to render results of sufficient accuracy in consolidation and settlement calculations in cohesive soils.

In contradistinction to the compression of sands, the compression of clays under a consolidation load takes place over a long period of time rather than immediately.

15-12. Simplified Pressure-Void Ratio Equation. When the external compressive load, p, is applied to the soil in small increments, Δp, then the decrement in void ratio, Δe, is also small. In such a case the soil compression curve, $\overset{\frown}{AB}$, can be approximately replaced by a straight line, or chord, AB, Fig. 15-18.

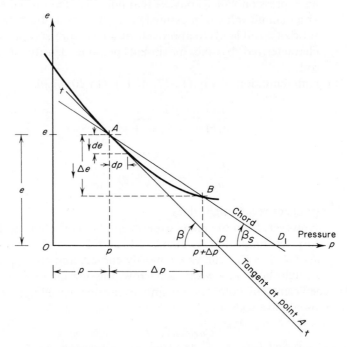

FIG. 15-18   Pressure-void ratio curve (compression branch, $\downarrow \Delta e$).

The slope of the chord with respect to the p-axis is:

$$\frac{\Delta e}{\Delta p} = -\tan \beta_s. \tag{15-29}$$

When the chord, AB, rotates through point A in the clockwise direction, then it approaches the tangent (at point A), AD, as a limit. The limiting value of the $(\Delta e)/(\Delta p)$ expression, when $\Delta p \to 0$, is

$$\lim_{\Delta p \to 0} \frac{e_2 - e_1}{(p + \Delta p) - p} = \lim_{\Delta p \to 0} \frac{-(e_1 - e_2)}{\Delta p} = \lim_{\Delta p \to 0} \frac{-(\Delta e)}{\Delta p} = -\frac{d(e)}{d(p)} =$$
$$= \tan \beta = a \qquad (\text{cm}^2/\text{g}), \tag{15-30}$$

which is termed the coefficient of compressibility. The minus sign indicates that with increasing pressure, p, the void ratio, e, decreases. Geometrically this means that the tangent goes through the second and fourth quarters.

This equation gives the differential change in void ratio, $d(e)$, as a function of differential pressure, dp, causing the change, $d(e)$, in e:

$$d(e) = -a\,d(p), \tag{15-31}$$

and it means that the change in void ratio is directly proportional to the change in pressure.

This $d(e)$-equation is analogous to Hooke's law of relative deformation of elastic materials, which is

$$\frac{\Delta H}{H} = \frac{1}{E}\,p, \qquad (\text{cm/cm}) \qquad (15\text{-}32)$$

where $\Delta H/H$ = relative deformation with respect to H, or strain;

$\quad\quad \Delta H$ = magnitude of longitudinal deformation;

$\quad\quad H$ = length or height of an elastic material (or H = thickness of a soil layer, or height of a test sample of soil);

$\quad\quad E$ = Young's modulus of elasticity, in g/cm^2, or in kg/cm^2, and

$\quad\quad p$ = stress, acting axially on the material.

Or else,

$$E = -\frac{dp}{dH}\,H. \qquad (15\text{-}33)$$

The analogy, of course, is more of a mathematical nature by the construction of Hooke's formula, and is not quite fulfilled for soils physically because of the variable nature of the so-called "modulus of elasticity", E, for soils. However, the specific compression, or relative deformation, or strain of soil may be written by Eq. (15-12) as

$$\frac{dH}{H} = \frac{de}{1+e}. \qquad (15\text{-}12)$$

Obviously here e is the initial void ratio.

Substituting $de/(1 + e)$ for dH/H in Eq. (15-33) obtain an expression for the *modulus of elasticity of soil*:

$$E = -\frac{dp}{de}(1+e) = \qquad (15\text{-}34)$$

$$= C_v(p_i + p)(1+e), \qquad (15\text{-}35)$$

(from Eq. 15-28), which expresses the E-quantity from the mathematical pressure-void ratio curve.

Writing Eq. (15-31) for the simplified pressure-void ratio curve,

$$-\frac{d(e)}{d(p)} = a, \qquad (\text{cm}^2/\text{g}) \qquad (15\text{-}36)$$

and eliminating $d(e)$ from Eqs. (15-36) and (15-12), obtain

$$\frac{dH}{H} = -a\,\frac{dp}{1+e}. \qquad (15\text{-}37)$$

Setting

$$\frac{a}{1+e} = v_v \quad (cm^2/g), \tag{15-38}$$

obtain

$$\frac{dH}{H} = -v_v \, d(p), \tag{15-39}$$

and

$$dH = -v_v H \, dp \quad (cm), \tag{15-40}$$

where the index at v means vertical compression. Note that here H is meant as a constant.

This equation expresses the decrease in height of the fully saturated soil sample, viz., decrease in pore volume in terms of a height of a column of water.

The quantity $v_v = a/(1 + e)$ represents the *specific loss of pore water*, or amount of linear compression of clay per unit of its original thickness, brought about by a pressure increase.

In one-dimensional pore water, flow, v_v, is the height of a pore water column, one unit in length, which is expelled by an increase of one pressure unit (1 lb/in², or 1 kg/cm², or 1 g/cm², or whatever units are being used) from a soil prism of an arbitrary cross section. Some authors call the v_v-quantity the modulus of volume change.[10]

The specific loss of pore water, v_v, is a fairly constant quantity within the interval of low pressures. For large pressures, however, v_v is no longer considered to be constant.

Now, with reference to the analogy of Hooke's law, which is

$$\frac{\Delta H}{H} = \frac{1}{E} \, p, \tag{15-32}$$

it can be written for soil that

$$\frac{dH}{H} = -\frac{1}{M_v} \, dp, \tag{15-41}$$

where

$$\frac{1}{M_v} = v_v \quad (cm^2/g), \tag{15-42}$$

and

$$M_v = \frac{1}{v_v} = \frac{1+e}{a} = -\frac{dp}{de}(1 + e) \quad (g/cm^2), \tag{15-43}$$

or by Eq. (15-28),

$$M_v = C_v(p_i + p)(1 + e). \tag{15-44}$$

As already said, the quantity, M_v, is termed the compression modulus of soil. As has already been mentioned, e is the initial void ratio. However, for increments, Δe and Δp, of tangible size, the initial void ratio may be found somewhat too large, but the final void ratio, e_f, may be somewhat too small. Therefore, instead of an initial e, an average e, e_{ave}, is used in these simplified calculations.

The compression modulus, M_v, is a variable quantity—a function of e. Thus, the compression modulus represents better the state of affairs of the variable elastic, as well as the plastic properties of soils, than the application of the concept of modulus of elasticity, E, for metals to soil.

The amount of settlement of soil using the simplified pressure-void ratio theory is then, by analogy to Eq. (15-40), in terms of load increments, is (after integrating Eq. (15-40) where settlement $s = -(H_f - H_i) = H_i - H_f$, H_i being the initial, and H_f the final height of the soil sample under consolidation):

$$s = v_v Hp = \frac{1}{M_v} Hp = \frac{pH}{C_v(p_i + p)(1 + e)} = \frac{a}{1 + e_{\text{ave}}} Hp = \frac{a}{1 + e_{\text{ave}}} A_{\text{ef}} \quad \text{(cm)},$$

$$(15\text{-}45)$$

where $A_{\text{ef}} = Hp =$ the effective pressure area, Fig. 15-19.

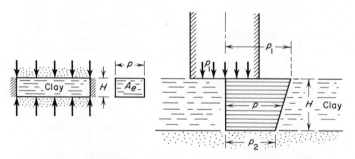

(a) In the laboratory   (b) In the field

FIG. 15-19   Illustrating effective pressure areas.

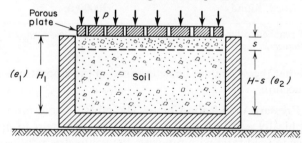

FIG. 15-20   Settlement consideration. One-way drainage (upward).

Eq. (15-45) can also be elucidated in the following way (Fig. 15-20): consider that upon compression of the soil the volume of the solids does not change. Hence, the volume of solids before and after compression is the same:

$$\frac{H}{1 + e_1} = \frac{H - s}{1 + e_2}. \quad (15\text{-}46)$$

$$\underset{\text{before}}{\phantom{\frac{H}{1+e_1}}} \quad \underset{\text{after}}{\phantom{\frac{H-s}{1+e_2}}}$$

where e_1 = void ratio before applying load, p, and

e_2 = void ratio after the application of load, p.

Then

$$s = \frac{e_1 - e_2}{1 + e_1} H = \frac{\Delta e}{1 + e_1} H \quad \text{(cm)}, \quad (15\text{-}47)$$

or

$$s \approx \frac{a p H}{1 + e_{\text{ave}}} = \frac{1}{M_v} H p. \quad (15\text{-}48)$$

This solution may be applicable if no lateral extrusion of soil from underneath the base of a footing can take place.

The approximate range of variation in the average compression modulus, M_v-values, for various soils is shown in Table 15-1 after Kögler and Scheidig.[11]

TABLE 15-1. COMPRESSION MODULUS, M_v.*

Soil Material	Compression Modulus M_v kg/cm²
1	2
Peat	1 to 5
Clay, plastic	5 to 40
Clay, stiff	40 to 80
Clay, medium hard	80 to 150
Sand, loose	100 to 200
Sand, dense	500 to 800
Gravel, sandy gravel, dense	1000 to 2000
Rock, fissured, jointed	1500 to 30000
Rock, sound	30000 to ∞

* Compiled after F. Kögler und A. Scheidig: *Baugrund und Bauwerk*, see Ref. 11.

It is advised that the M_v-values be determined in the laboratory on each particular soil in question.

15-13. The Pressure-Void Ratio Curve. The pressure-void ratio curve can be presented graphically as illustrated in Fig. 15-21. To help to appreciate the involved change in void ratio with pressure, the volumetric relationship between solids and water-saturated, void ratio, e, is shown to the left of the ordinate axis by way of the familiar soil phase diagram, which represents here a two-phase soil. The change in void ratio, Δe, is obtained by subtracting from the initial void ratio, e_i, the final void ratio, e_f. The latter is brought about by the load increment, Δp. An average void ratio, e_{ave}, as in Fig. 15-21, is then used for settlement calculations by Eq. (15-48).

Example. From the curve, Fig. 15-21, the magnitude of the settlement, s, of the soil represented on the graph is calculated as follows:

Coefficient of compressibility (slope of chord), a:

$$a = \left| \frac{-\Delta e}{p} \right| = \frac{e_i - e_f}{p_2 - p_1} = \frac{1.30 - 0.75}{4.70 - 2.20} = 0.22 \qquad (\text{cm}^2/\text{kg}).$$

Compression modulus, M_v:

$$M_v = \frac{1 + e_{\text{ave}}}{a} = \frac{1 + \dfrac{1.30 + 0.75}{2}}{0.22} = 9.2 \qquad (\text{kg/cm}^2.)$$

This low value of M_v indicates a very compressible soil. In Fig. 15-21, the absolute height of the soil sample tested, is $(s\text{-}s) = H = 2.0$ cm. (Note on the soil phase diagram that its relative height is $(1 + e)$. Also, at $p = 0$, the volume of voids in the soil was 1.65 times greater than that of the solids).

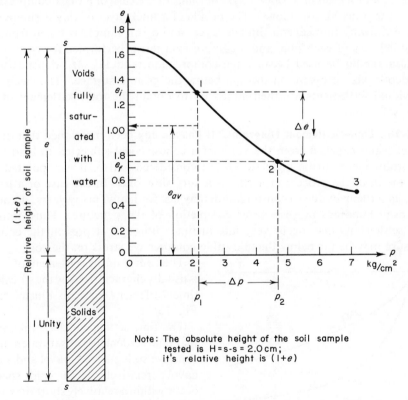

FIG. 15-21   Pressure-void ratio curve based on change in void ratio.

The pressure causing the change in void ratio is

$$p = \Delta p = p_2 - p_1 = 4.7 - 2.2 = 2.5 \qquad (\text{kg/cm}^2).$$

Settlement, s, by Eq. (15-48):

$$s = \frac{1}{M_v} Hp = \frac{1}{9.2} (2.0)(2.5) = 0.54 \qquad (\text{cm}).$$

The soil is very compressible because the soil sample tested under the confined compression condition settles by $(0.54)/(2.00) \times 100 = 27.0\%$ of its original thickness.

15-14. Settlement of Several Thin Layers of Soil. In the case of several thin layers of compressible soil encountered in the soil profile, pressure-void ratios have to be produced for each layer separately, settlements for each layer must then be calculated separately, and these separate settlements added to give the full settlement of the soil:

$$s = \sum_{1}^{n} (s), \quad \text{(cm)}, \quad\quad\quad (15\text{-}49)$$

where n = number of compressible layers.

15-15. Settlement of a Thick Layer of Soil. In the case of a thick compressible layer, one proceeds as follows. The profile of a thick layer of clay is subdivided on the drawing into several thinner layers and a soil sample is taken from the mid-thickness of each one, and a compression test is performed for each. This method should be used because the compression modulus, M_v, depends upon the depth, viz., pressure on the soil below the ground surface. The calculated individual settlements are then added up to obtain the total settlement of the thick soil layer.

15-16. Time-Settlement Diagrams. It has already been mentioned that drainage of water expelled from the voids of a cohesive soil subjected to load is an important factor to be understood and considered. Also, it was pointed out that the drainage process of a clay is a very slow one. In the case of a heavy clay, its settlement due to consolidation may last for many, many years; decades; and even hundreds of years after completion of the structure. Thus, intolerable settlements may occur very late in time, although at present the contact pressure may be far below the allowable compressive stress on the soil.

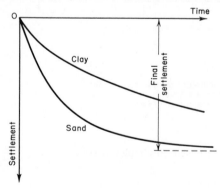

The course of the settlement of a soil is usually characterized by the so-called, time-settlement curve, as illustrated in Fig. 15-22.

The time-settlement diagram shows that final settlements of saturated, noncohesive soils such as gravel and sand, having relatively large void spaces, occur within a relatively short time after the application of the load (practically after the completion of the structure) as compared with cohesive soils, because water can drain freely out of the voids. For cohesive soils much more time is needed for the settlement curve to

FIG. 15-22 Time-settlement curves under constant load.

approach asymptotically a horizontal line parallel to the time-axis, indicating the cessation of settlement.

The effect of time on the settlement of a laterally confined clay can best be studied by keeping the load on the soil sample constant. On a time-settlement curve of a cohesive soil, such as illustrated in Fig. 15-23, three distinct parts

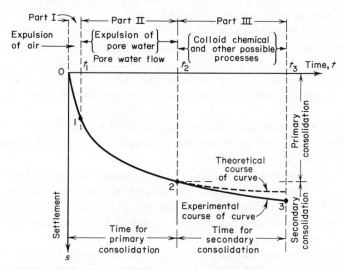

FIG. 15-23   Elements of a time-settlement curve of a cohesive soil at a constant load.

may be observed, namely parts I, II, and III, each falling within a certain time interval, namely:

Part I: Time from 0 to t_1, during which air is expelled from the voids of the soil after the external load has been applied. The presence of air in the voids of a clay is a very serious problem in the consolidation process, because air cushions retard permeability of soil to water.

Part II: Time from t_1 to t_2, during which the pore water is stressed (or pore water pressure is induced) and is expelled due to the applied load, resulting in the so-called main settlement or *primary consolidation* of the soil. The pore water becomes stressed because the application of a load of a certain magnitude usually takes place faster than the pore water can drain out of the voids and equalize within the voids, so the water in the voids is said to be under *excess hydrostatic pressure*. When, after some time, the excess water has been drained out, the soil reaches a state of equilibrium for that load. After the load is increased, the process of drainage from the soil begins again and continues under the new load until a new state of equilibrium is attained.

Part III. Time from t_2 to t_3, during which colloid-chemical processes and surface phenomena become active, such as the stressed moisture films around the soil particles, the moisture surface tension in the corners of the soil particles, viscosity and density changes in the stressed moisture films, molecular attractive forces between soil particles and moisture films, induced electrokinetic potentials, and other processes. All these processes are very slow by their very nature. This is to say, among other things, that the effect of the electric, diffuse double layer upon the draining flow of water now becomes more pronounced than before. The settlement brought about during the period of time of such processes is called the post-settlement or the *secondary consolidation.*

Because of the colloidal-chemical processes, the secondary consolidation process in nature requires long geologic periods of time, and therefore the secondary consolidation process also requires a long time to consolidate the soil fully in the laboratory. Thus one factor in the impossibility of simulating in the laboratory long, natural consolidation processes (into secondary consolidation) comes to the fore.

During the time of secondary consolidation, and because of the reasons mentioned before, the actual experimental, time-settlement curve is offset from its theoretical course, Fig. 15-23.

Secondary consolidation of mineral soils is usually negligible, but in the case of organic soils it may be considerable because of their colloidal nature.

A possible disintegration of clayey soil particles and other possible reasons and processes are also mentioned in the technical literature as probably contributing to secondary consolidation.

The possibility of the disintegration and the mechanical break-down of the soil particles, however, is somewhat in contradiction to one of the assumptions underlying the consolidation theory, namely, that soil particles are incompressible.

Much research, therefore, is still needed to elucidate the real nature of the process of secondary consolidation in clayey soils, and to determine how to cope with it analytically when describing the consolidation process mathematically.

15-17. Determination of Zero and 100% Consolidation. In practice, only the primary consolidation is usually reckoned with. In this connection there arises a certain difficulty in determining when and where on the time-settlement, viz., time-consolidation, graph the points of zero percent and that of 100% primary consolidation are located.

A. Casagrande's Method. Because the first part (upper branch of the time-percent consolidation curve) is approximately parabolic in shape when plotted to an arithmetical scale, then the zero percent consolidation coordinate may be found, according to A. Casagrande and Fadum[12] in the following way (Fig. 15-24). Select a point, P_1, on the time-percent consolidation curve (drawn to semi-logarithmic scale) corresponding to a certain time, t_1. Through this point (P_1/t_1) draw a horizontal line, A-P_1. Select point A so that it corresponds to time $t = (\frac{1}{4})t_1$. Ascertain the ordinate, $d = AP_2$, between the horizontal line A-P_1, and the curve. Then lay off this d-value above the curve from point P_2, to give point P_3: $P_2 - P_3 = d$. Through point P_3 should go the horizontally directed, theoretical, zero percent consolidation line. This construction should be repeated for 3 or 4 other arbitrary t-values on the curve, obtaining 3 or 4 other points such as P_7, P_8, P_9. The points P_3, P_7, P_8, P_9 so found above the curve should line up very closely in a horizontal line, P_3-P_9. This horizontal line, then, represents the theoretical zero percent consolidation.

The point of 100% consolidation is arbitrarily found by Ref. 12 by intersecting two tangents, one of which is drawn to the time-percent consolidation curve of the primary branch, and the other to the straight line part of the secondary consolidation branch, Fig. 15-24. The point of intersection, S, of the two tangents determines the position of the horizontal line on the graph of the 100% consolidation of the soil sample for any one load on the sample tested for its consolidation properties.

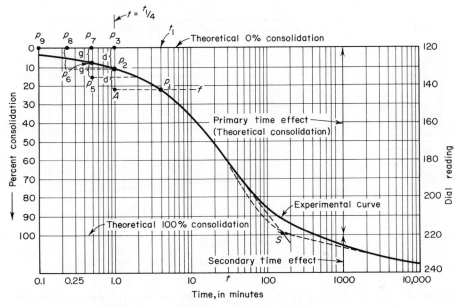

FIG. 15-24 Time-percent consolidation curve.

The distance between the zero percent and the 100% line is then divided into ten equal parts, each part meaning 10% consolidation.

The concept of percent, or degree, of consolidation is the ratio of settlement of a clay sample in the consolidometer, s_t, to its full or 100% settlement, s, after full consolidation at a certain pressure has been attained:

$$\frac{s_t}{s} \times 100. \tag{15-50}$$

The dial readings indicated on the vertical scale to the right of the time-percent consolidation curve, Figs. 15-24 and 15-25, are the record of the deformation in height of thickness of the soil sample (compression or expansion). For convenience, in its turn, the dial readings are then converted into percent consolidation of the soil sample (which in effect means changes in void ratios) as indicated on the left-side ordinate axis (Figs. 15-24 and 15-25). The amount of consolidation (compression) is calculated by subtracting each dial reading from the dial reading at zero time, say minutes.

The time-consolidation curve is useful in predicting rates of settlement of soil under certain magnitudes of load. The time-consolidation curve is usually plotted on a 5-cycle, semi-logarithmic paper with the "amount of consolidation", or "percent of consolidation", on the arithmetical scale and the corresponding *elapsed time* in minutes on the logarithmic scale.

A sample of a time-percent consolidation curve for a clay from Raritan, New Jersey, is shown in Fig. 15-25.

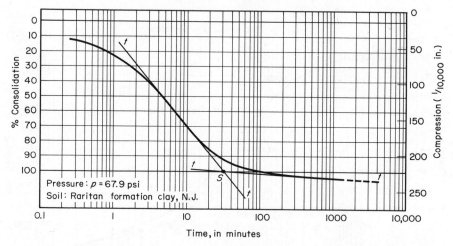

FIG. 15-25   Time-percent consolidation curve for a New Jersey clay.

Taylor's Square Root of Time Fitting Method. The zero percent and the 100% consolidation can also be determined by the so-called square root of time fitting method devised by Taylor.[13] In this method, all dial readings are plotted on the ordinate axis, and the corresponding square roots of time are plotted on the abscissa axis, Fig. 15-26.

Taylor observed that on the theoretical $\sqrt{t}$-percent consolidation curve a straight line exists to beyond 50% consolidation, while at 90% consolidation the abscissa is 1.15 times the abscissa of the straight line produced. Using Taylor's method, first the straight line, *t-t*, is drawn which fits best the early part of the experimental curve. The intersection of the *t-t* line with the ordinate axis yields the "corrected" point of zero percent consolidation. Then a straight line, *t'-t'*, is drawn which at all points has abscissas 1.15 times as great as those of the first line (*t-t*). The intersection of this second line with the experimental curve is taken as the 90% consolidation point. Its time value is t_{90}. One ninth of the vertical distance between the corrected zero point and the 90% point is added below the 90% point, to give the 100% consolidation point of primary consolidation.

The pressure-void ratio graph, which is needed for calculating the magnitude of the total settlement, is prepared by means of one of these two ways:

1) the void ratio for a particular load is calculated from dial readings recorded immediately before the new load increment is applied, or

2) by choosing a time point on the time-consolidation graphs so that the dial readings of each time-consolidation curve, corresponding to that chosen time point, are beyond the end of the primary consolidation, i.e., beyond the point of intersection, S, in the region of the secondary consolidation (Fig. 15-25).

The height of the soil sample is proportional to its volume. Therefore, the pressure-void ratio curve gives the relationship between change in volume of the soil sample and the load on it.

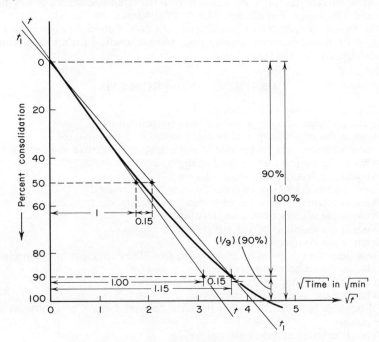

FIG. 15-26 Square root of time fitting method.

REFERENCES

1. H. Meischeider, "Setzungen von Ingenieurbauwerken", *Die Bautechnik*, 1954, no. 10, p. 324.
2. J. H. Thornley, *Foundation Design and Practice*, New York, Columbia University Press, 1959, pp. 29-32.
3. K. Terzaghi, *Theoretical Soil Mechanics*, New York, John Wiley and Sons, Inc., 1948, p. 265.
4. K. Terzaghi and O. K. Fröhlich, *Theorie der Setzung von Tonschichten*, Leipzig und Wien, Franz Deuticke, 1936, p. 2.
5. ASTM, *Procedures for Testing Soils*, April, 1958, Philadelphia, pp. 287-313.

6. E. Antevs, *The Last Glaciation*, Research Series no. 17, New York, American Geographical Society, 1928, p. 107.
7. A. Casagrande, "The Determination of the Pre-consolidation Load and its Practical Significance", *Proceedings*, First International Conference on Soil Mechanics and Foundation Engineering, Cambridge, Mass., June, 1936, vol. 3, pp. 60-64.
8. K. Terzaghi, *Erdbaumechanik auf bodenphysikalischer Grundlage*, Leipzig und Wien, Franz Deuticke, 1925, p. 87.
9. K. A. Redlich, K. Terzaghi, and R. Kampe, *Ingenieurgeologie*, Wien und Berlin, Julius Springer, 1929, p. 339.
10. G. P. Tschebotarioff, *Soil Mechanics, Foundations and Earth Structures*, New York, McGraw-Hill Book Co., Inc., 1951, p. 105.
11. F. Kögler and A. Scheidig, *Baugrund und Bauwerk*, Berlin, Wilhelm Ernst und Sohn, 1948, p. 59, p. 123.
12. A. Casagrande and R. E. Fadum, *Notes on Soil Testing for Engineering Purposes*, Soil Mechanics Series no. 8, Publication from the Graduate School of Engineering, Harvard University, Cambridge, Mass., 1939/40, no. 268, p. 37.
13. D. W. Taylor, *Research on Consolidation of Clays*, Publication from the Department of Civil and Sanitary Engineering, Massachusetts Institute of Technology, Cambridge, Mass., 1942, pp. 17-18.

QUESTIONS AND PROBLEMS

15- 1. Distinguish between the concepts of
a) compaction, b) compression, and c) consolidation.

15- 2. What is the objective of a consolidation test of a cohesive soil?

15- 3. Upon what does the magnitude of settlement of a cohesive soil depend?

15- 4. What is the basic equation used in the consolidation theory?

15- 5. What is the "coefficient of consolidation"?

15- 6. How can the coefficient of consolidation be determined?

15- 7. What is the meaning of the term "compressibility"?

15- 8. What is the coefficient of compressibility?

15- 9. What is the modulus of volume change?

15-10. What is the compression index?

15-11. How does the compression index differ from the coefficient of compressibility?

15-12. What is the compression modulus?

15-13. What is understood by excess hydrostatic pressure?

15-14. What are the assumptions underlying the consolidation theory of clays?

15-15. Distinguish between the use of the term "consolidation" by geologists and by engineers.

15-16. What is primary consolidation of soil?

15-17. Explain what is understood by secondary consolidation, and the possible reasons causing it.

15-18. What is the "degree of consolidation"?

15-19. Upon what does the rate of consolidation of a clay depend?

15-20. Upon what does the rate of settlement depend?

15-21. What is the spring analogy?

15-22. What basic law has the consolidation theory contributed to the compression of clays?

15-23. Under what conditions, and how, should a prototype clay sample be subjected to the consolidation test in the laboratory?

15-24. What is understood by "fitting the time curve" in consolidation theory?

15-25. Which are the factors determining the settlement of structures founded on clay?

15-26. How does M_v vary in a uniform soil with depth, increasingly or decreasingly? Show your reasoning by calculations, and illustrate by a sketch.

15-27. How does a vary in a uniform soil with depth, increasingly or decreasingly?
       Show your reasoning by calculations, and illustrate by a sketch.
15-28. What does a steep compression curve indicate?
15-29. What does a low value of M_v of a clay indicate?
15-30. What is the "virgin" curve?
15-31. What is precompression load?
15-32. How is the precompression load determined?
15-33. What is one-way drainage?
15-34. What is two-way drainage?
15-35. The initial void ratio of a 20 ft thick layer of cohesive soil is $e_i = 0.900$, and the
       final void ratio is $e_f = 0.800$ after the structure has been completed. What is
       the probable settlement of this structure?
15-36. Given three pressure-void ratio curves of a loess soil, Fig. Problem 15-36.

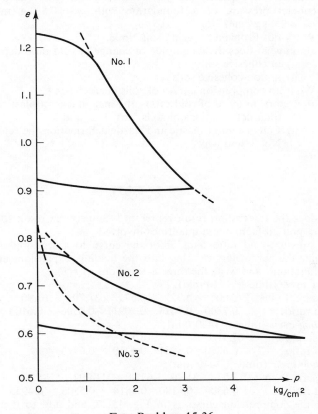

FIG. Problem 15-36.

Curves Nos. 1 and 2 (solid lines) represent two different types of undisturbed
loess soil. Curve No. 3 (dotted line), represents a disturbed wind-borne loess.
    Required. Analyze thoroughly the subject of pressure-void ratio curves.
Particularly:
       a) Describe the curves.
       b) Locate precompression loads on the diagrams, and report their magni-
          tudes.

c) Plot the three given curves on a semi-logarithmic graph paper. Locate preconsolidation loads, and compare with those obtained under b).

d) Establish the $e = f(p)$-equations for the given three curves
   i) for the loading branches, and
   ii) for the unloading branches.

e) What are the C_v and C_s-values in g/cm^2 and in kg/cm^2? Compare them with those published by Terzaghi. What are your observations?

f) What is the geometrical interpretation of the C_v-quantity?

g) What is the physical interpretation of the C_r-quantity?

h) If, on curve No. 1, under a compression process, the void ratio at $p = 1.5$ kg/cm² is $e_1 = ..$, what is the void ratio e_2 at $p = 2.5$ kg/cm²?

i) The same exercise as under f) and g), but relative to the unloading branch.

j) What is the expected soil performance if soil No. 1 were loaded by a contact pressure of a foundation with $p_0 = 0.5$ kg/cm², and with $p_0 = 2.0$ kg/cm²?

k) Work out Problem h), using soil No. 3.

l) Upon what does the magnitude of change in void ratio depend
   i) in cohesive soils?
   ii) in non-cohesive soils?

m) What do compression curves of soils characterize?

n) i) Report, in terms of void ratios, the magnitudes of plastic, elastic, and total deformations of soils Nos. 1, 2, and 3.
   ii) Can or cannot plastic and elastic deformations be reported for soil No. 3, and why?

15-37. Integrate:

$$de = - \frac{1}{C_v} \frac{dp}{p_i + p}$$

What does the integration result represent? Subject the result to an analysis, and interpret all factors and quantities involved.

15-38. Given pressure-void ratio data. Plot the curve to a semi-logarithmic scale; determine the parameters entering into the loading, expansion, and reloading curve equations, and write the three e-equations as $f(p)$.

Loading cycle (time = 1440 min):

Pressure, lb/in²:	0.00	4.72	13.57	31.70	67.90	114.02
Void ratio:	0.7500	0.7425	0.7091	0.6596	0.6103	0.5620

Unloading cycle (time = 1440 min):

Pressure, lb/in²:	67.9	31.70	13.57	4.72
Void ratio:	0.5760	0.5981	0.6319	0.6775

Reloading cycle (time = 1440 min):

Pressure, lb/in²:	13.57	31.70	67.90	114.02	285.00
Void ratio:	0.6500	0.6180	0.5814	0.5503	0.4955

15-39. Replot the compression curve as in Fig. 15-22, and add to it an unloading (expansion) branch defined by the following coordinates (for points on this curve following the course from left to right as the soil sample was unloaded):

Points	p kg/cm²	e
3	7.5	0.50
4	4.0	0.60
5	2.0	0.75
6	0.0	0.95

Calculate the amount of rebound (or swelling) of this soil when it is unloaded from $p_1 = 4.7$ kg/cm² to $p_2 = 2.2$ kg/cm². Report the coefficient of expansion in cm²/kg, and in cm²/g.

Also, report the magnitudes of plastic and elastic deformations after the soil sample is unloaded to $p = 0$ kg/cm².

15-40. Given a squared foundation as shown in Fig. Problem 15-40a. A pressure-void ratio curve is also given for the soil upon which the foundation is to rest. The base of the footing is to be at an elevation of three meters below the ground surface. Because the consolidation theory is developed in the metric system of units of measurement, the problem here will be given and is to be solved in the metric system. The load on the foundation is 225 metric tons. The unit weight of soil is $\gamma = 1800$ kg/m³. Find the amount of compression of the layer of clay 1.20 m thick between the hard shale and the base of the footing.

Hint for solution.

1) The vertical pressure of the weight of the soil before excavation at 3.00 m = 300 cm depth ($\gamma = 1800$ kg/m³ = 0.0018 kg/cm³):

$$p_1 = \gamma z = (0.0018)(300) = 0.54 \qquad (\text{kg/cm}^2).$$

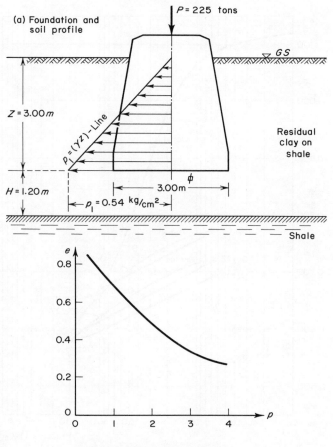

(a) Foundation and soil profile

(b) Pressure – void ratio curve

FIG. Problem 15-40.

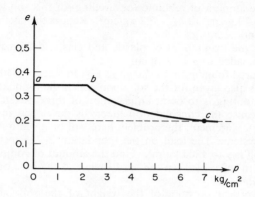

FIG. Problem 15-41.

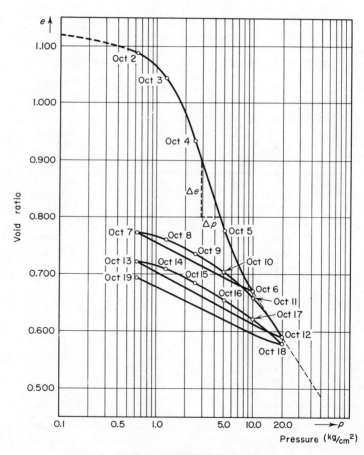

FIG. Problem 15-43.

2) The contact pressure on the soil from the foundation:

$$p_2 = \frac{P}{A} = \frac{(225)(1000)}{(300)^2} = 2.5 \quad (\text{kg/cm}^2),$$

where A = area of base of footing.

3) $\Delta e =$ 6) $a =$

4) $e_{ave} =$ 7) $M_v =$

5) $\Delta p =$ 8) $s =$

Note: consider whether it might be more practical to carry the foundation down to the hard shale.

15-41. Given a pressure-void ratio graph as shown in Fig. Problem 15-41.
   a) Interpret the nature of the curve representing a confined compression test of a cohesive soil.
   b) What does the horizontal part ($e = \cdots = $ const) of the graph mean?
   c) What is the magnitude of the precompression load, p_{pr}, and the probable reason for it?

15-42. A consolidation test on varved clay from Moonachie, New Jersey, gave the following data:

Point Nos.	Pressure, kg/cm²	Void Ratio, e
1	0.625	1.088
2	1.250	1.045
3	2.500	0.936
4	5.000	0.777
5	10.000	0.672
6	0.625	0.774
7	1.250	0.761
8	2.500	0.736
9	5.000	0.706
10	10.000	0.660
11	20.000	0.592
12	0.625	0.722
13	1.250	0.710
14	2.500	0.685
15	5.000	0.655
16	10.000	0.622
17	20.000	0.580
18	0.625	0.694

Plot the pressure-void ratio graph.

15-43. Study and discuss the pressure-void ratio curve, Fig. Problem 15-43, obtained from a consolidation test on Moonachie varved clay.
   a) Has the varved clay ever been preconsolidated?
   b) If this clay should occur in a glaciated area, what are the reasons for preconsolidation?
   c) If a preconsolidated clay should occur in a non-glaciated area, what may be the reasons for causing a preconsolidation load?
   d) Present your opinion as to the potential danger to the structural rigidity of a large city water tower, founded on varved clay. The tower exerts by its round mat foundation, 20 ft in diameter, a contact pressure of 2.5 t/ft² on the clay. The structure is a multiple-story reinforced concrete frame, with solid walls, 90 ft high. The tolerable settlement for this structure is $\frac{1}{4}$ in.

Chapter 16

ONE-DIMENSIONAL CONSOLIDATION THEORY; THE CONSOLIDATION PROCESS

16-1. The Consolidation Process-Hydraulic Problem. The expulsion of water from the voids of the saturated clay soil by an externally applied load in the consolidation process, and the change in volume associated with such a process, are essentially a hydraulic problem. More specifically, it is a problem of permeability of a soil to water. It is, therefore, expedient to supplement here the consolidation theory with the permeability aspect of soil, because permeability, besides compressibility, is one of the principal factors relative to settlement of a soil, viz., settlement of structure. By logic then, concerning the discussion on the theory of consolidation, it can be said that the magnitude of settlement depends upon the compressibility of the soil, whereas the rate of consolidation depends on both, namely: permeability and compressibility. The combined effect of permeability and compressibility is usually comprehended in one resulting factor, termed the *coefficient of consolidation.*

16-2. Assumptions Underlying the Consolidation Theory. Taking into consideration the permeability factor in soil consolidation, the following are the assumptions underlying the uni-dimensional consolidation theory of saturated, laterally confined clay soils subjected to axial, vertical loading.

1) The soil is a homogeneous material.
2) The voids in the soil are fully saturated with water and free of air.
3) Water in voids, and the solids of the soil, are incompressible; therefore the change in volume of the soil, when loaded, is effected by the change in volume of the voids.
4) The drainage in laterally confined soil brought about by an externally applied load on the soil takes place in a vertical direction only.
5) The coefficient of permeability of the soil to water is constant throughout the soil.
6) Darcy's law of permeability is applicable.

In reality these assumptions, of course, are not fully met. The results from consolidation studies, however, reveal that large discrepancies between theory and nature are brought about by the presence of a large volume of air in the voids of the soil.

16-3. The Clay System for Analysis. With reference to Terzaghi's spring-water analogy to a soil consolidation process, it was explained in Article 15-5, that the total pressure exerted on a consolidating soil equals the sum of the effective pressure and the neutral pressure, the sum being at all times constant:

$$p = p_e + u = \text{const.} \qquad (15\text{-}8)$$

Also, it can be understood, that the neutral pressure, u, is a function of two variables; the depth coordinate, z, below some reference surface (or line), and time, t. With reference to permeability and time, the magnitude of compression of soil, ΔH, takes place during a time interval from t_0 to $t_n = t$ simultaneously with an expulsion of a water column, the height of which is

$$\Delta H = v_v H \Delta p \qquad (\text{cm}).$$

This means that during this time interval a flow of the pore water takes place under a hydraulic pressure gradient,

$$i_u = \frac{\partial u}{\partial z}, \qquad (16\text{-}1)$$

or difference in excess hydrostatic pressure head, dh. Assume that for this flow the laws of hydrodynamics must apply.

Consider now a layer of clay whose thickness is $(2H)$, Fig. 16-1. The clay is enclosed between pervious sand layers or porous filter stones, and is laterally confined (natural soil, or the rigid walls of the consolidometer ring). Also, consider at the outset of this discussion that this clay is, to a certain degree, in a consolidated condition. Now, at a certain time, say $t = t_0 = 0$, the clay soil is subjected to an externally applied axial, vertical pressure, or pressure increment, Δp. Note in Fig. 16-1a, that the clay system has two drainage faces, namely: I-I' at the top, and II-II' at the bottom. Hence there exists in this clay system a two-way drainage, namely: upwards and downwards symmetrically to the central N-N' axis. The flow of water expelled out of the voids under the pressure, $\Delta p = p_t$, at time t is uni-directional. When an external pressure is applied to the clay, the clay compresses. Pore water is expelled from the voids and drained out of the soil upwards and downwards through the top and bottom surfaces of the clay layer into the pervious material. The clay undergoes a consolidation process, and as a result of this decreases in its confined height, or settles.

Because of the symmetrical flow of water, upwards and downwards, imagine, in order to simplify the mathematical analysis of the consolidation problem, that one-half of the originally $(2H)$-thick clay layer (namely the lower, NN'II'II, part below the horizontal axis of symmetry, N-N') is now removed, so that only the upper part, I I'$N'N$I, remains for consideration. The thickness of the upper part of the half remaining or reduced clay system is now $H = (2H)/(2)$. Imagine in the reduced clay system, because of the nature of the presupposed uni-dimensional flow, that plane N-N' now constitutes some sort of watershed, or an imaginary impervious layer. This reduced new clay system has now a one-way drainage only, and the discharge, Q, of the expelled pore water takes place in the same direction as before, namely upward (Fig. 16-1b).

In this reduced clay system, I I′ II′ II, for the sake of convenience in calculations, the z-axis (depth) is assumed to be directed positively upward, and the pressure axis positively to the right in the drawing plane, and along the axis of the horizontal symmetry, *N-N′*. Here z means the height coordinate above the *p*-axis, or central, horizontal lamina of clay.

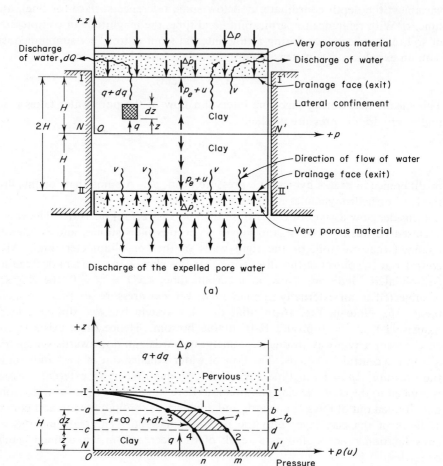

FIG. 16-1   Clay system.

16-4. Drainage and Pressure Conditions in Clay During Consolidation. For the purpose of analyzing the effect of the drainage and pore water pressure conditions on the consolidation process of a laterally confined clay subjected to a vertical, axial load, imagine an elementary, rectangular soil prism cut out of the reduced clay layer, as shown in Fig. 16-2. The base area, *a*, of this elementary soil prism is $a = 1 \times 1 = 1$ square unit. The height or thickness of the soil prism is *dz*. The two parallel unit surfaces of the prism, spaced a distance, *dz*, apart, are the two drainage faces of the elementary soil prism, one at the bottom (the entrance face), and one at the top of the prism (the face of exit). Thus, if the clay layer in the assumed system were subjected to an axial, vertical pressure, then the pore water expelled by this pressure from the voids of the soil would flow vertically upwards from the bottom and to and through the top drainage faces of the elementary soil prism.

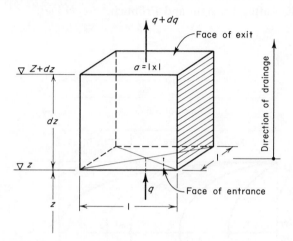

Fig. 16-2   Elementary soil prism.

Let us now pay attention to the process of water drainage during the period of the loading time of the clay by any pressure increment on the clay, Δp. Suppose that the consolidation of clay under a certain load increment, $\Delta p_{t<0}$, has been attained, and a new load increment, Δp, is applied on the surface of the clay. Remember that just before this new load increment, Δp, is applied, i.e., at time, *t*, just before it attains a 100% consolidation ($t < 0$), there is no flow of water out of the voids under the previous load increment, $\Delta p_{t<0}$, because the magnitude of the static excess pressure, *u*, of the water in the voids is $u_{t<0} = 0$.

An instant later, after the application of the new load increment, Δp, say at time $t = 0$, the magnitude of the hydrostatic excess pressure (neutral pressure), $u_{t=0}$, is equal to the externally applied load, Δp, i.e., $u_{t=0} = \Delta p$. The total applied load is carried in this first instance entirely by the pore water, and the effective, or intergranular stress, p_e, is equal to zero: $p_e = 0$. Thus, the total stress is expressed for $t = 0$ as

$$p_{t=0} = \Delta p = p_e + u_{t=0} = 0 + \Delta p \qquad (g/cm^2). \qquad (16\text{-}2)$$

After some lapse of time, *t*, since the application of the new load increment, Δp, on the clay, the pressures in the pore water and on the soil skeleton (hydrostatic excess or neutral pressure, and intergranular or effective pressure, respectively) distribute themselves curvilinearly (parabolically, or sinusoidally, depending upon the assumption used) as illustrated in Fig. 16-3. This is the case where the pore water can flow simultaneously and symmetrically with respect to the central axis N-N', towards the top and the bottom boundary surfaces, I-I', and II-II' of the layer of clay ($2H$) units thick.

The proportion of the neutral and effective stresses in clay between the beginning and end of consolidation (from time $t = 0$ to a very long time $t = \infty$) for a certain load increment, Δp, is delineated at a certain time, t, by a curved line, such as curve $\overset{\frown}{I m II}$, for example, or curve $\overset{\frown}{I n II}$ at time $t + dt$. These time curves are called, after Terzaghi and Fröhlich,[1] *isochrones*.

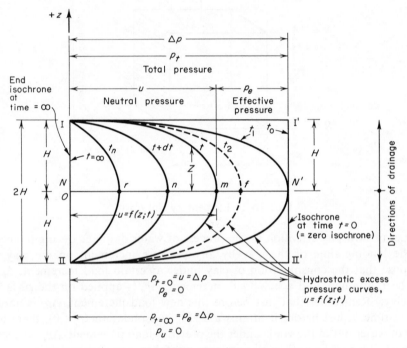

FIG. 16-3   Isochrones.

The isochrone at time $t = 0$ is represented in Fig. 16-3 by the vertical line I'N'II', and is termed the *zero isochrone*. The isochrone which sets in after a long time, say $t = \infty$, when the consolidation process is completed, is shown by the vertical line, IOII, and is termed the *end isochrone*. Between times from $t = 0$ to $t = \infty$, during which the consolidation process of the clay takes place, the isochrones are curved lines. As time passes the isochrones approach the vertical or z-axis, separating at any time, t, and for any depth, z, in a certain proportion the increasing effective stresses from the decreasing neutral stresses. Their sum (total stress) is always equal to the magnitude of the externally applied pressure increment, and is constant.

1°) Thus, at time $t = 0$ and $z = 0$, the total stress is

$$p_{t=0} = p_e + u_{t=0} = 0 + \Delta p = \text{const.} \qquad (16\text{-}3)$$

The ordinates on the O-p axis between the zero and a t-isochrone, (ordinates N'-f, or N'-m, or N'-n), or the end isochrone (N'-O) indicate an increase in normal effective pressure to which the solid particles of the clay are subjected during consolidation.

2°) At time $t = 0$ and height $z = z$, or $z = H$, the total stress is equal to the full neutral pressure by Pascal's law of pressure distribution in a fluid:

$$p_{t=0} = u_{t=0} = \Delta p = \text{const.} \qquad (16\text{-}4)$$

3°) At time $t = t$, and height $z = 0$, or $z = z$,

$$p_t = p_{e_{t=t}} + u_{t=t} = \Delta p = \text{const.} \qquad (16\text{-}5)$$

It is well here to note that during the time interval between $t = 0$ and $t = \infty$, the neutral pressure, u_t, drops from $u_{t=0} = \Delta p$ to $u_{t=\alpha} = 0$, i.e.,

$$\Delta p \gtrless u_t \geq 0. \qquad (16\text{-}6)$$

Simultaneously, the intergranular or effective stress increases from $p_e = 0$ to $p_e = p_t = \Delta p$:

$$0 \gtrless p_{e_{t=t}} \leq \Delta p. \qquad (16\text{-}7)$$

4°) At time $t = t$, and $z = H$, the neutral stress is zero, and the effective stress at the surface of the clay (drainage face) is equal to the total stress, $p_t =$ applied stress, Δp:

$$p_t = p_e + u_t = p_e + 0 = \Delta p = \text{const.} \qquad (16\text{-}8)$$

5°) After a long period of time, when $t = \infty$, and the consolidation is completed under the load increment of Δp, the stress conditions at any depth, at $z = 0$, $z = z$, and $z = H$, are:

$$p_{t=\infty} = p_{e_{t=\infty}} + u_{t=\infty} = p_{e_{t=\infty}} + 0 = \Delta p = \text{const.} \qquad (16\text{-}9)$$

This means that at the end of the consolidation process the hydrostatic excess pore water pressure is equal to zero: $u_{t=\infty} = 0$. The various pressure conditions for various depths and time are illustrated in a general way in Figs. 16-3 and 16-4.

From the discussion on the pressure conditions in clay upon loading, it comes distinctively to the fore that the consolidation process, as well as the mathematical function describing the consolidation process, depends upon two principal independent variables, namely the height (or depth) coordinate, z, of a point in the clay under consideration, and the time variable, t. Therefore, any differentiation of mathematical quantities involved in the linear consolidation theory of clay should be performed partially with respect to each of two independent variables: z and to t. Thus, for example, the partial differentiation of the stress equation with respect to time, t, and keeping (while differentiating after t) z constant, yields:

$$p_t = p_{e_t} + u_t = \Delta p = \text{const.} \qquad (15\text{-}8)$$

$$\frac{\partial p}{\partial t} = \frac{\partial (p_e)}{\partial t} + \frac{\partial u}{\partial t} = 0, \qquad (16\text{-}10)$$

or

$$-\frac{\partial u}{\partial t} = \frac{\partial(p_e)}{\partial t} \qquad \text{(g/cm}^2 \text{ sec)}. \qquad (16\text{-}11)$$

This partial differential equation reads as follows: the decreasing rate of change in neutral pressure is equal to the increasing rate of change in effective pressure.

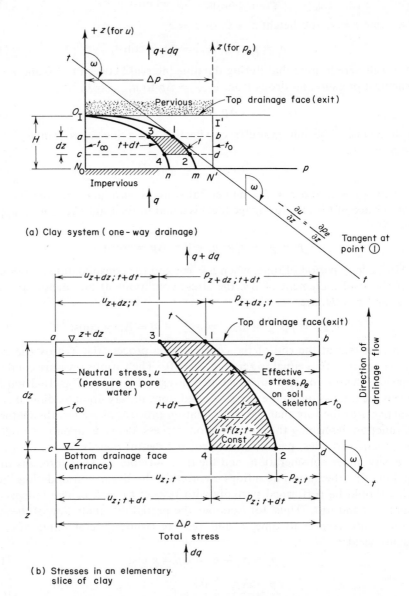

(a) Clay system (one-way drainage)

(b) Stresses in an elementary slice of clay

FIG. 16-4 Stress conditions in saturated consolidating clay.

Likewise, partial differentiation of Eq. (15-8) with respect to the depth coordinate, z, and keeping t constant, yields:

$$-\frac{\partial u}{\partial z} = \frac{\partial(p_e)}{\partial z}, \quad (g/cm^3) \quad (16\text{-}12)$$

which reads that as height, viz., depth, z, increases, the neutral stress, u, decreases. In other words, the hydraulic pressure gradient, $\partial u/\partial z$, decreases from the axis of symmetry N-N' (from the lower impermeable layer, N-N') in the direction of the top drainage exit face as the effective pressure gradient, $\partial p_e/\partial z$, increases.

16-5. The Rate of The Pore Water Flow. A flow of pore water through the voids of elementary clay prism, the thickness of which is dz, can take place only when there is a pressure gradient (or a driving force) available irrespective of its causes. In the consolidation theory, the pressure gradient is the hydrostatic pressure gradient. Because at the exit surfaces in a two-way drainage system of clay the magnitude of the hydrostatic excess pore water pressure is equal to zero, there exists a decreasing hydrostatic excess pore water pressure gradient, $-\partial u/\partial z$, directed from the horizontal plane of symmetry, N-N', towards the draining faces of exit, causing the water to flow upwards and downwards and to drain out of the clay layer into the porous material with good drainage.

Applying Darcy's law of permeability, the filtration velocity, v, is at a height, z, above the neutral plane, N-N' (or at a depth, z, below the neutral plane:

$$v = ki \quad (cm/sec), \quad (16\text{-}13)$$

where k = coefficient of permeability of the clayey soil to water, and generally, from Fig.16-5.

i = dh/dz = loss of pressure head over a distance, dz, for a certain constant isochrone.

For any isochrone in this topic under the discussion, the hydraulic gradient is then expressed in the partial derivative form as

$$i_z = \frac{\partial h}{\partial z} = -\frac{\partial u}{\gamma_w \partial z}, \quad (16\text{-}14)$$

i_z being the hydraulic gradient at a height the coordinate of which is z. Here $\partial h = \partial u/\gamma_w$ is the water pressure head, and $-\partial u/\partial z$ is the hydraulic pressure gradient in any horizontal plane, distance z above the horizontal, central axis, N-N', of the clay.

The general discharge equation for water through one square unit of area of a porous medium such as soil is

$$Q = vAt = v(1.0)t = kit \quad (cm^3), \quad (16\text{-}15)$$

where Q = total discharge of water through a horizontal unit of cross-sectional area, at depth, z, at a flow velocity, v, and during a time, t.

The rate of flow of water entering the elementary prism at its entrance face at a height coordinate, z, is $q = f(z; t)$, or

$$q = \frac{dQ}{dt} = ki(1) = -k\frac{\partial u}{\gamma_w \partial z} \qquad \text{(cm}^3/\text{sec)} \qquad (16\text{-}16)$$

The change in the hydraulic pressure gradient over a distance, dz, is

$$\frac{\partial\left(-\dfrac{\partial u}{\partial z}\right)}{\partial z}\, dz = -\frac{\partial^2 u}{\partial z^2}\, dz \qquad \text{(g/cm}^3). \qquad (16\text{-}17)$$

Hence, the hydraulic gradient at the top drainage exit face with coordinates, $z + dz$, is

$$i_{z+dz} = i_z + di_{dz} = -\frac{\partial u}{\gamma_w \partial z} + (-)\frac{\partial^2 u}{\gamma_w \partial z^2}\, dz = -\frac{1}{\gamma_w}\left(\frac{\partial u}{\partial z} + \frac{\partial^2 u}{\partial z^2}\, dz\right). \qquad (16\text{-}18)$$

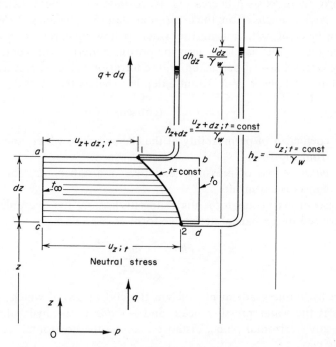

FIG. 16-5   Pressure head in an elementary prism of clay and an isochrone at $t = $ const.

The discharge through the upper face of exit of the elementary prism at height, $z + dz$, is

$$q + dq = ki_{z+dz}(1) = -\frac{k}{\gamma_w}\left(\frac{\partial u}{\partial_z} + \frac{\partial^2 u}{\partial z^2}\, dz\right) \qquad \text{(cm}^3/\text{sec)}. \qquad (16\text{-}19)$$

Obviously, the total change in flow, dq, from the entrance face to the face of exit over a distance, dz, is

$$dq = -\frac{k}{\gamma_w}\frac{\partial^2 u}{\partial z^2}\,dz. \qquad (16\text{-}20)$$

Then, the change of flow over a unit length of the height, dz. of the elementary soil prism is the specific loss of the pore water:

$$\frac{dq}{dz} = -\frac{k}{\gamma_w}\frac{\partial^2 u}{\partial z^2}. \qquad (16\text{-}21)$$

16-6. Derivation of Equation. In establishing the differential equation expressing the process of consolidation of a clayey soil, there appear, thus, two variables: the depth coordinate, z, below the top of the clay layer, and the time variable. In respect to the z-variable, the isochrone relates to the neutral stress, whereas during the time variable, the isochrone changes its shape. The shift of the isochrone from time t to time $t + dt$ is coupled with the compression of the clay, and thus with an expulsion of pore water out of the voids of the clay.

Recall first, that during a time element, dt, the clay compresses under a load, dp, and brings about a change, $-de$, in the void ratio of the clay. Second, the magnitude of the linear, confined compression, on the other hand, is equal to the amount of the expelled pore water.

Then these two conditions permit one to write:

1) by Eq. (15-31):

$$a = -\frac{\partial e}{\partial p}, \quad \text{or} \quad a\,\partial p = -\partial e \qquad (16\text{-}22)$$

and
2) by Eq. (16-21):

$$\frac{dq}{dz} = -\frac{k}{\gamma_w}\frac{\partial^2 u}{\partial z^2}. \qquad (16\text{-}21)$$

Then the change in discharge over dz must be equal to the decrease in volume:

$$\frac{dq}{dz} = -\frac{1}{1+e}\frac{\partial e}{\partial t} = +\frac{a}{1+e}\frac{\partial p_e}{\partial t} = +\frac{1}{M_v}\frac{\partial p_e}{\partial t} = -\frac{1}{M_v}\frac{\partial u}{\partial t}. \qquad (16\text{-}23)$$

Relative to equation (16-23), recall that

by Eq. (15-31), $\partial e = -a\,\partial p_e$,

by Eq. (15-43), $M_v = -\dfrac{\partial p(1+e)}{\partial e} = \dfrac{1+e}{a}$, and

by Eq. (16-11), $\partial p_e = -\partial u$.

Equating Eqs. (16-21) and (16-23), obtain

$$\frac{\partial u}{\partial t} = \frac{kM_v}{\gamma_w} \frac{\partial^2 u}{\partial z^2}, \tag{16-24}$$

or

$$\frac{\partial u}{\partial t} = \frac{k}{v_v \gamma_w} \frac{\partial^2 u}{\partial z^2}, \tag{16-25}$$

which is the partial differential equation sought for a one-dimensional consolidation process in clay involving one-dimensional drainage of variable flow of soil pore water.

Setting $(k)/(v_v \gamma_w) = c_v$, obtain finally

$$\frac{\partial u}{\partial t} = c_v \frac{\partial^2 u}{\partial z^2}, \tag{16-26}$$

where $\partial u/\partial t$ = rate of change of the hydrostatic excess pore water pressure, in $(g/cm^2/sec)$.

$$c_v = \frac{k}{v_v \gamma_w} = \frac{k}{a/(1+e)\gamma_w} = \frac{k(1+e)}{a\gamma_w} = \tag{16-27}$$

coefficient of consolidation, in cm^2/sec;

$$\frac{\partial^2 u}{\partial z^2} = \text{change in hydraulic pressure gradient } (g/cm^4),$$

and

$$c_v \frac{\partial^2 u}{\partial z^2} = \text{amount of water expelled from the voids of the clay through } 1 \text{ cm}^2 \text{ area and during a time element } dt, \text{ in } g/(cm^2 \text{ sec}).$$

This equation, Eq. 16-26, thus, is the equation of the exact shape of the isochrone. Therefore this equation must be solved for $u = f(z; t)$.

In the case of expansion of a clay, the differential equation of the swelling process is

$$\frac{\partial u}{\partial t} = c_s \frac{\partial^2 u}{\partial z^2}, \tag{16-28}$$

where

$$c_s = \frac{k}{v_s \gamma_w} \quad (cm^2/sec) \tag{16-29}$$

is the coefficient of expansion, or swelling, and

$$v_s = \frac{a}{1+e} \tag{16-30}$$

is the specific gain in pore water, or the amount of linear expansion of the clay per unit of its original thickness brought about by a decrease in pressure by one unit. The quantities, a and e, pertain here to the expansion or unloading branch of the pressure-void ratio curve.

The index, s, at c in Eq. (16-29) means coefficient of expansion, c, (swelling) in the vertical direction, c_s. The a-value must then be obtained from the expansion branch of the pressure-void ratio curve.

The derivation of the consolidation equation for clays indicates that the three topics, namely: soil investigation, pressure distribution in soil, and isochrone calculations are mutually interacting, and only as a whole complex lead to a settlement analysis of compressible soils of small permeability.

Permeability. By Eq. (16-27), the relationship between the coefficient of permeability, k, and the coefficient of consolidation, c_v, is

$$k = c_v v_v \gamma_w = c_v \frac{1}{M_v} \gamma_w = c_v \frac{a}{1+e} \gamma_w \qquad \text{(cm/sec)}. \qquad (16\text{-}31)$$

This relationship indicates that the coefficient of permeability, k, can be calculated from the experimental data obtained from the consolidation test. The coefficient of permeability, however, as seen from the above equation, and as can be inferred by the logic of the problem, is a function of the variable void ratio, e. Also, considering that $a = (-de)/(dp)$, it can be observed that k decreases with an increasing consolidation load, dp. Thus, k depends upon the degree or percent of consolidation.

SOLUTION OF THE CONSOLIDATION EQUATION

16-7. Outset. The solution of the consolidation equation

$$\frac{\partial u}{\partial t} = c_v \frac{\partial^2 u}{\partial z^2} \qquad (16\text{-}26)$$

for the neutral pressure, $u = f(z; t)$, is based on the solution of Fourier's equation in one dimension, a solution or integral which must also satisfy the given boundary conditions.

Assume that the solution of Eq. (16-26) is a product of two simpler functions, one of which is a function of depth, z, only, i.e., $F(z) = Z$, and the other a function of t only, i.e., $\Phi(t) = T$.
Then

$$u = f(z; t) = AZT, \qquad (16\text{-}32)$$

where A = a constant, known as Fourier's trigonometric coefficient, to be determined.

Partial differentiation of Eq. (16-32) results in:

$$\frac{\partial u}{\partial t} = AZ \frac{dT}{dt} \qquad (16\text{-}33)$$

$$\frac{\partial u}{\partial z} = AT \frac{dZ}{dz} \qquad (16\text{-}34)$$

$$\frac{\partial^2 u}{\partial z^2} = AT \frac{d^2 Z}{dz^2}. \qquad (16\text{-}35)$$

Substitution of Eqs. (16-33) and (16-35) into Eq. (16-26) gives

$$AZ \frac{dT}{dt} = Ac_v T \frac{d^2 Z}{dz^2}, \tag{16-36}$$

or, separating variables,

$$\frac{1}{T} \frac{dT}{dt} = \frac{c_v}{Z} \frac{d^2 Z}{dz^2}. \tag{16-37}$$

This equation is satisfied if both sides of the equation are set equal to one and the some coefficient, for example, a coefficient $(-N)$: then

$$\frac{dT}{dt} = -NT, \tag{16-38}$$

and

$$\frac{d^2 Z}{dz^2} = -N \frac{Z}{c_v}. \tag{16-39}$$

Now separate the variables in Eq. (16-38):

$$\frac{dT}{T} = -N \, dt, \tag{16-40}$$

and integrate to obtain

$$\ln T = -Nt,$$

or

$$T = e^{-Nt}. \tag{16-41}$$

Eq. (16-39) can be rewritten as

$$\frac{d^2 Z}{dz^2} + \frac{N}{c_v} Z = 0 \tag{16-42}$$

The Z-function in this equation points out that the Z-function must be such that its second derivative (save for its sign) should be proportional to Z. A function which satisfies this requirement is the sine-function:

$$(\sin y)'_z = \cos y; \qquad (\sin y)''_z = (\cos y)'_z = -\sin y. \tag{16-43}$$

Thus, the trigonometric sine-function of z is one solution of Eq. (16-42).

Referring to Fig. 16-6, z is a length varying from zero to H (thickness of half of layer). Therefore, it is practically expedient to use as the variable a ratio of z/H:

$$\text{when } z = 0, \quad \text{then} \quad z/H = 0$$

$$\text{when } z = H, \quad \text{then} \quad z/H = 1.$$

Thus a quadrant of $90°$ is indicated here, if this interval from $z/H = 0$ to $z/H = 1$ is coupled to an orthogonal quadrant of $\pi/2$. Then

$$y = \frac{\pi z}{2H}, \tag{16-44}$$

and

$$Z = \sin y = \sin\left(\frac{\pi z}{2H}\right), \tag{16-45}$$

and

$$\frac{d^2Z}{dz^2} = -\frac{\pi^2}{4H^2}\sin\left(\frac{\pi z}{2H}\right). \tag{16-46}$$

Therefore, the expression for the constant, N, in Eq. (16-42) is

$$N = \frac{\pi^2}{4}\frac{c_v}{H^2}. \tag{16-47}$$

Substitution of Eqs. (16-41) and (16-45) into Eq. (16-32) gives the particular integral of the given partial differential equation as a function of z and t:

$$u = A e^{-Nt}\sin\left(\frac{\pi z}{2H}\right). \tag{16-48}$$

Test of Integral. To verify whether this u-equation is the integral sought, differentiate partially this u-function first with respect to t, and then with respect to z:

$$\frac{\partial u}{\partial t} = -AN e^{-Nt}\sin\left(\frac{\pi z}{2H}\right) \tag{16-49}$$

$$\frac{\partial u}{\partial z} = A\frac{\pi 1}{2H} e^{-Nt}\cos\left(\frac{\pi z}{2H}\right) \tag{16-50}$$

$$\frac{\partial^2 u}{\partial z^2} = -A\frac{\pi^2}{4H^2} e^{-Nt}\sin\left(\frac{\pi z}{2H}\right). \tag{16-51}$$

Substitution of Eqs. (16-49) and (16-51) into the given partial differential equation (16-26) shows that the u-function is the integral of the partial differential equation in question.

Boundary Conditions. The next step is to test whether and how this u-function satisfies the boundary conditions governing the consolidation process.

The physical contents of the u-function are as follows:
Assume a clay system with a two-way drainage, as in Fig. 16-6. The total thickness of the clay layer is $(H + H = 2H)$. Assume further that the clay is stressed by a hydrostatic excess pressure, u, the distribution diagram of which follows a sinusoidal curve as shown in Fig. 16-6. The two half-thickness (H) systems with the origin of coordinates at the middle of the layer are in effect the same as one system of a total thickness $(2H)$ having the origin of coordinates at the top drainage surface with the positive z-axis directed downward.

Surface Boundary Conditions. At time $t = 0$, and in the middle of the clay layer, the neutral pressure is $u(z; 0) = u_0 (g/cm^2)$. At the top and bottom drainage faces the neutral pressure is zero, i.e., $u = 0$ (flow of water into atmospheric medium). The equation of the sinusoidal isochrone for these conditions is then, setting $t = 0$ in Eq. (16-48),

$$u(z; 0) = u_0 \sin \frac{\pi z}{2H}.$$ (16-52)

The test of this equation, when $t = 0$, is:
  a) when $z = 0$, then $u_{z=0} = 0$;
  b) when $z = H$, then $u_{z=H} = u_0$;
  c) when $z = 2H$, then $u_{z=2H} = 0$.
This equation satisfies the physical u-pressure conditions.

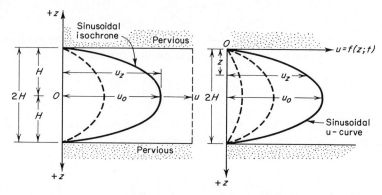

FIG. 16-6   Sinusoidal isochrones.

Interior Conditions. To test neutral pressures, u, at time $t = t$, and at various depths, z, utilize the partial differential equation (16-26). The idea here is to find a function which satisfies this partial differential equation, and has at time $t = 0$ the form of

$$u(z; 0) = u_0 \sin\left(\frac{\pi z}{2H}\right).$$

By comparison with the equation (16-48) the function for $t = t$ and $z = z$ must be

$$u(z; t) = u_0 \, e^{-Nt} \sin\left(\frac{\pi z}{2H}\right).$$ (16-53)

Test: at $t = 0$,

$$u(z; 0) = u_0 \sin \frac{\pi z}{2H},$$ (16-52)

i.e., the function tests out all right for $t = 0$.
Besides, $u(z; t) = u_0 \, e^{-Nt} \sin(\pi z/2H)$ satisfies the partial differential equation because it has already been tested for.
  End Isochrone. After a very long period of time when the consolidation has been completed, i.e., when $t = \infty$, Eq. (16-53) renders, for any value of z, the value of the neutral pressure of $u_{t=\infty} = 0$ (a vertical isochrone).

It so happens that the expression

$$u(z; t) = A_n e^{-n^2 Nt} \sin\left(n \frac{\pi z}{2H}\right) \tag{16-54}$$

also satisfies the original partial differential equation (16-26), and also the boundary conditions. Here

A_n = an arbitrary constant, and

n = an integer of the series 1, 2, 3, ...

Equation (16-54) is a more general integral of the partial differential equation (16-26). If $n = 1$, then Eq. (16-54) transforms into Eq. (16-48).

16-8. The General Isochrone Equation. If there is a series of particular solutions, u_1, u_2, u_3, ... u_n, available, and they all satisfy the partial differential equation (16-26), then it can be written:

$$\frac{\partial u_1}{\partial t} = c_v \frac{\partial^2 u_1}{\partial z^2}$$

$$\frac{\partial u_2}{\partial t} = c_v \frac{\partial^2 u_2}{\partial z^2}$$

$$\frac{\partial u_3}{\partial t} = c_v \frac{\partial^2 u_3}{\partial z^2} \tag{16-55}$$

$$\cdots \cdots \cdots \cdots$$
$$\cdots \cdots \cdots \cdots$$

$$\frac{\partial u_n}{\partial t} = c_v \frac{\partial^2 u_n}{\partial z^2}$$

Addition of Eqs. (16-55) yields:

$$\frac{\partial(u_1 + u_2 + u_3 + \cdots u_n)}{\partial t} = c_v \frac{\partial^2(u_1 + u_2 + u_3 + \cdots u_n)}{\partial z^2}. \tag{16-56}$$

The integral of the partial differential equation (16-56) is, by analogy to Eqs. (16-26) and (16-48):

$$u(z; t) = u_1 + u_2 + u_3 + \cdots u_n, \tag{16-57}$$

and can symbolically be written as

$$u(z; t) = A_1 \sin\left(\frac{1\pi z}{2H}\right) e^{-Nt} + A_2 \sin\left(\frac{2\pi z}{2H}\right) e^{-4Nt} +$$

$$+ A_3 \sin\left(\frac{3\pi z}{2H}\right) e^{-9Nt} + \cdots +$$

$$+ A_n \sin\left(\frac{n\pi z}{2H}\right) e^{-n^2 Nt} = \tag{16-58}$$

$$= \sum_{n=1}^{n=\infty} A_n e^{-n^2 Nt} \sin\left(\frac{n\pi z}{2H}\right).$$

Here A_n is an arbitrary constant.

A test of this general integral of the partial differential equation (16-48) for $z = 0$ and $z = 2H$ gives $u = 0$, which satisfies the surface boundary conditions.

Setting in Eq. (16-58) $t = 0$, one obtains an expression for the neutral pressure as a function of z in the form of a Fourier trigonometric series:

$$f(z; 0) = \sum_{n=1}^{n=\infty} A_n \sin\left(\frac{n\pi z}{2H}\right). \tag{16-59}$$

To solve for the coefficient A_n, one proceeds as follows: multiply both sides of Eq. (16-59) by $[\sin(m\pi z/2H)\, dz]$, and integrate between the limits of 0 and $(2H)$ [because z varies from 0 to $(2H)$], to obtain

$$\int_0^{2H} f(z; 0)\sin\left(\frac{m\pi z}{2H}\right) dz = \sum_{n=0}^{n=\infty} \int_0^{2H} A_n \sin\left(\frac{n\pi z}{2H}\right)\sin\left(\frac{m\pi z}{2H}\right) dz. \tag{16-60}$$

Here $m \neq n$ are unequal integers. When $n \neq m$, then the value of the definite integral is zero (14):

$$\int_0^{2H} \sin\left(\frac{n\pi z}{2H}\right)\sin\left(\frac{m\pi z}{2H}\right) dz = 0. \tag{16-61}$$

Therefore *all terms* containing this type of integral *vanish* from the equation under consideration. However, for the nth term, when $n = m$, Eq. (16-61) takes the form as in Eq. (16-62). The value of this integral is H:

$$\int_0^{2H} \sin^2\left(\frac{n\pi z}{2H}\right) dz = H. \tag{16-62}$$

Therefore, from Eqs. (16-61) and (16-62)

$$\int_0^{2H} f(z; 0)\sin\left(\frac{n\pi z}{2H}\right) dz = A_n \int_0^{2H} \sin^2\left(\frac{n\pi z}{2H}\right) dz = A_n H, \tag{16-63}$$

and

$$A_n = \frac{1}{H}\int_0^{2H} f(z; 0)\sin\left(\frac{n\pi z}{2H}\right) dz. \tag{16-64}$$

Of course, the coefficient, A_n, must be calculated for each particular function, $f(z; 0)$, a function which represents the excess pressure distribution equation for various pressure diagrams at time $t = 0$.

16-9. Solution of General Differential Equation. Substitution of A_n, Eq. (16-64), into Eq. (16-58) gives the general integral, u, as the general solution of the partial differential equation characterizing a two-way pore water flow and neutral pressures.

$$u(z; t) = \frac{1}{H}\sum_{n=1}^{n=\infty} (e^{-n^2 Nt})\left[\sin\left(\frac{n\pi z}{2H}\right)\right]\int_0^{2H} f(z; 0)\sin\left(\frac{n\pi z}{2H}\right) dz, \tag{16-65}$$

or, substituting $N = \dfrac{\pi^2 c_v}{4H^2}$,

$$u(z;t) = \frac{1}{H} \sum_{n=1}^{n=\infty} \left[\exp\left(-\frac{n^2\pi^2}{4} \frac{c_v t}{H^2} \right) \right] \left[\sin\left(\frac{n\pi z}{2H} \right) \right] \int_0^{2H} f(z;0)\sin\left(\frac{n\pi z}{2H} \right) dz. \quad (16\text{-}66)$$

Remember that $f(z;0)$ is the initial neutral pressure.

Once more, by means of this equation, the hydrostatic excess pressure, u, can be calculated in clay under any initial stress condition, $f(z;0) = u_{\text{initial}}$, and thereby at any time, t, and any depths, z, below the top drainage face of the clay.

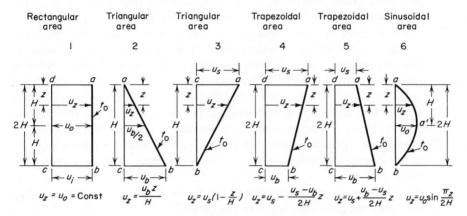

FIG. 16-7   Axial pressure distribution diagrams at time $t = 0$.

PRESSURE DISTRIBUTION DIAGRAMS

16-10. Shapes of Pressure Diagrams. Equations (16-64) and (16-66) indicate that for the evaluation of the A_n, viz., $u(z;t)$ functions there is a need to distinguish between the various possible and properly applicable shapes of the total pressure diagrams, viz., the hydrostatic excess pressure distribution diagrams with depth at time $t = 0$. In essence, these diagrams are the axial pressure distribution diagrams.

Some of the basic shapes of such pressure distribution diagrams which are commonly encountered in foundation engineering are the parallelogram, the triangle, the trapezoid, and the area under an arc (or several arcs) of a sinusoid, Fig. 16-7. In this figure, the heavy lines marked with t_0 mean the zero-time isochrones.

It can be recognized that these pressure distribution diagrams at time, $t = 0$, are isochrone diagrams at $t = 0$ at the very instant an external load, Δp, is applied on the top surface of the clay. The reader is already familiar with a parallelogram-shaped, excess pressure distribution diagram (Figs. 16-4a and 16-4b). The heavy lines of the various pressure distribution diagrams in Fig. 16-7 thus represent in each case the zero isochrone. The area in the isochrone diagram encompassed by the zero isochrone, a-b (heavy line) and the other sides of the area of the pressure distribution diagram is termed by Terzaghi the *Lastfläche*, load or pressure area, meaning the area under the zero isochrone. This area represents the pore-water pressure or neutral stress at $t = 0$.

Depending upon the soil system, the pressure distribution areas can be bounded

1) at the top and bottom with pervious material facilitating the drainage of water out of the clay (2-way drainage);
2) at the top pervious and at the bottom—impervious material; and
3) at the bottom pervious and at the top—impervious material.

16-11. Description of Diagrams.

1) The *rectangular* area of a pressure diagram means a uniform distribution of stresses of a previously completely consolidated layer of clay, i.e., $u_0 = $ const, at any depth below the top boundary surface of layer.

   Rectangular pressure distribution diagrams may apply to thin layers of clay under extensive contact areas of foundations, such as mats, for example, where the axial stress distribution can be assumed as constant throughout the thickness of the clay layer, Fig. 16-8. The consolidation test would also belong to the category of a constant pressure distribution, shaped like a parallelogram, when two drainage faces are present, and because the clay sample in the consolidometer is relatively very thin.

2) A *triangular* pressure distribution area with its apex up may apply only to the pressure distribution due to the self-weight of the soil, placed or naturally situated on an impervious layer, Fig. 16-9. The pressure increases directly in proportion with depth. As a concrete example, such a triangular pressure area may apply in the case of

   a) backfilling of quay walls with cohesive material through open water, and in the consolidation process (H);
   b) hydraulic fills on permeable base ($2H$);
   c) earth dams on impermeable base (H);
   d) sludge deposits (H), and
   e) possibly other instances of materials suspended in a liquid.

   The apex indicates the direction of drainage of the pore water out of the soil.

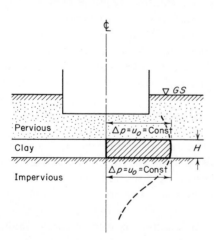

FIG. 16-8   Rectangular pressure distribution area.

3) A *triangular* pressure distribution area with its apex down is shown in Fig. 16-10.

4) This kind of *trapezoidal* pressure distribution diagram applies to foundation footings founded in sand with clay layers interspersed. Axial pressure from the foundation load is distributed on each layer approximately trapezoidally (compare with Boussinesq's vertical pressure distribution diagram), with the maximum pressure ordinate, Δp, at the top, and the minimum pressure ordinate, p_b, at the bottom of the layer of clay.

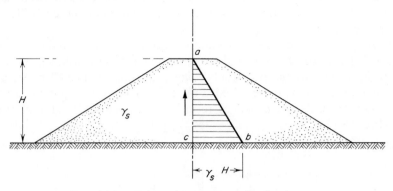

FIG. 16-9. Triangular pressure distribution area.

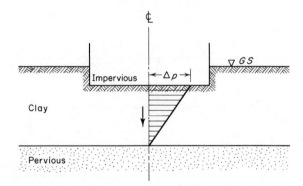

FIG. 16-10 Triangular pressure distribution area with its apex down.

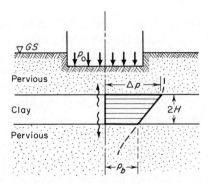

FIG. 16-11 Trapezoidal pressure distribution diagram, maximum ordinate at top.

Because at the first instant of load application on clay the load is carried fully by the excess pore-water pressure, the pressure distribution diagram is trapezoidal. A trapezoidal pressure distribution diagram is illustrated in Fig. 16-11.

5) A *trapezoidal* pressure distribution diagram with its maximum pressure ordinate at the bottom and its minimum pressure ordinate at the top results when to the trapezoidal diagram (1-2-3-4) effected by structural load (as in case 4) there is added the triangular, vertical pressure diagram (1-5-6-4) (ordinates *a* and *b*) resulting from the self-weight of the soil (Fig. 16-12.)

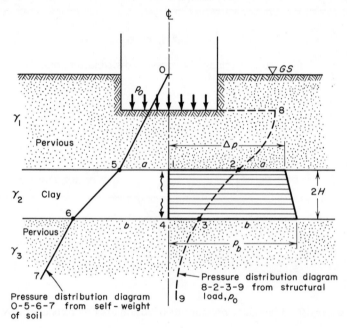

FIG. 16-12 Trapezoidal pressure distribution diagram, maximum ordinate at bottom.

6) The *sinusoidal* pressure diagram results from the rigorous solution of the partial differential equation (16-26) of the consolidation process.

Thus the pressure areas, $f(z; 0)$, to use for the integral in Eq. (16-66) can be a parallelogram, triangle, trapezoid, sinusoid, or even an arbitrary parabola. With these types of pressure area diagrams the pressure areas can be formed and expressed analytically for most common cases in foundation engineering when the clay drains up, or down, or in a two-way fashion.

SETTLEMENT CALCULATIONS
BY THE USE OF PRESSURE DISTRIBUTION AREAS

16-12. Settlement. By means of the pressure distribution diagram areas it is possible to perform at any time, *t*, settlement calculations of soil, to draw the time-settlement curve, and to express the degree or percent of consolidation of soil with time.

Rectangular Pressure Distribution Area. Now refer to Fig. 16-13, which represents a rectangular pressure distribution area, $OABCO$, or $A_o = Hu_o$, when the initial hydrodynamic excess pressure is $u_o = \Delta p$ at time $t = 0$, where Δp is the pressure increment suddenly applied on the clay. This diagram indicates a one-way drainage. At point O, where $z = 0$ and $t = 0$, the pore water pressure is $u_A = 0$ because it is assumed that the sand offers no resistance to flow of

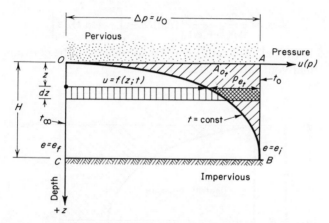

FIG. 16-13   Settlement from rectangular pressure area.

water. The initial void ratio of the clay is $e = e_i$, and the end void ratio after completion of consolidation is $e = e_f$. The zero isochrone is indicated by t_o. After some time, t, the isochrone, is indicated by $t = \text{const}$ (imagine that this isochrone is arrested for a moment; therefore, all calculations involving depth, z, and pressure, u, are performed with respect to this particular isochrone as though the isochrone were constant). The end isochrone is indicated by t_∞. All other designations are the same as before.

It should be noticed that the consolidation pressure distribution area diagrams, such as shown in Fig. 16-13, indicate that consolidation of a clay takes place with depth in the direction from the free drainage face to the interior of the clay.

Considering, from Fig. 16-13, that

$$p_{e_t} + u_t = \Delta p = \text{const} = u_o,\qquad(16\text{-}67)$$

where Δp = total pressure,

  p_{e_t} = effective pressure at time, t, and

  u_t = neutral pressure at time t,

then the compression, ds_t, of a differential slice of clay, dz thick at depth, z, below the pervious layer, at time, t, or the settlement, is, by analogy to Eq. (15-45):

$$\Delta H = v_v p_e H\qquad(\text{cm})\qquad(16\text{-}68)$$

or

$$ds_t = v_v(\Delta p - u_t)\, dz, \qquad (16\text{-}69)$$

where $v_v = a/(1 + e)$ = amount of linear compression, in (cm²/g).

Integration of Eq. (16-69) between the limits $z = 0$ and $z = H$ gives the total settlement, s_t, of the clay layer H units of length thick after elapsed time, t:

$$s_t = \frac{a}{1 + e_i} \int_0^H [\Delta p - u(z; t)]\, dz \qquad (16\text{-}70)$$

or

$$s_t = \frac{e_i - e_f}{\Delta p(1 + e_i)} \left[(\Delta p)H - \int_0^H u(z; t)\, dz \right], \qquad (16\text{-}71)$$

where a and e_i (initial void ratio) may be considered to be constant;
  e_f = final void ratio at effective pressure, p_e.

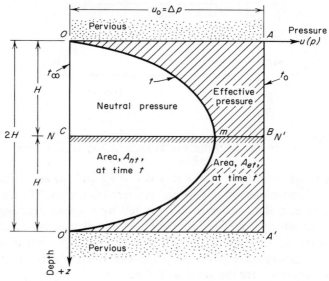

FIG. 16-14 Effective and neutral pressure areas, A_{et} and A_{nt}, respectively, for a clay system with a two-way drainage.

Note that geometrically, the quantity in the brackets, Eq. (16-71), is the hatched area, A_{et}. This area, A_{et}, is the effective pressure area, A_e, at time, t, Fig. 16-14. Again, note that at time, $t = 0$, the effective area, A_{eO}, is zero. At time $t = \infty$, the magnitude of the effective area is expressed as

$$A_{e\infty} = p_e H = \Delta p H = A_\circ, \qquad (16\text{-}72)$$

where the effective pressure area $A_\circ$ = area $OABCO$ + area $CBA'O'C$ for a two-way drainage.

Eq. (16-71), expressing settlement at any time, t, can be rewritten as

$$s_t = \frac{e_i - e_f}{1 + e_i} \frac{A_{et}}{\Delta p}. \qquad (16\text{-}73)$$

For one-way drainage, A_{et} is the effective pressure area $OABmO$. When $t = \infty$, the effective pressure area is $A_{e\infty} = A_o = OABCO$.

16-13. Degree of Consolidation. If in Eq. (16-71), the quantity $(\Delta p)H$ is taken out before the brackets, then settlement, s_t, is

$$s_t = \frac{e_i - e_f}{1 + e_i} H \left[1 - \frac{\displaystyle\int_0^H u(z;t)\, dz}{(\Delta p)H} \right] \tag{16-74}$$

or

$$s_t = \mu \frac{e_i - e_f}{1 + e_i} H = \mu v_v (\Delta p)H, \tag{16-75}$$

or

$$s_t = \mu v_v A_o, \tag{16-76}$$

where

$$\mu = 1 - \frac{\displaystyle\int_0^H u(z;t)\, dz}{(\Delta p)H} \tag{16-77}$$

is a dimensionless coefficient expressing the degree of consolidation of the clay at time, t, and thickness, H. Here thickness, H, means also the shortest drainage path in one-way drainage of the clay layer.

If $(\Delta p)H = A_o$, total pressure area at time $t = 0$, then Eq. (16-77), expressing the coefficient of the degree of consolidation, may be rewritten as

$$\mu = \frac{A_o - \displaystyle\int_0^H u(z;t)\, dz}{A_o} = \frac{A_o - A_{nt}}{A_o} = \frac{A_{et}}{A_o}, \tag{16-78}$$

where A_{nt} = neutral pressure area at time, t = the integral of the above equation.
The nominator,

$$A_o - \int_0^H u(z;t)\, dz = A_{et}, \tag{16-79}$$

expresses the effective pressure area, A_{et}, at time, t, an area which is a fraction of the total pressure area, A_o.

The effective pressure area, A_{et}, at time, t, is obtained by subtracting the neutral pressure,

$$\int_0^H u(z;t)\, dz \tag{16-80}$$

at time t, from the total pressure area A_o.

Thus, the coefficient of degree of consolidation may be defined as the ratio of the instantaneous effective pressure area, A_{et}, at time, t, to the total pressure area, A_o.

Note that here, according to Fig. 16-13, H is one-half of the thickness of the clay sample used in the consolidation test where the clay has two drainage faces:

one at the top (length of drainage path $= H$) and one at the bottom of the sample, (length of drainage path also $= H$). In effect, the term "degree of consolidation" has the same connotation as the "percent of consolidation".

If s_t is the amount of settlement brought about by an externally applied pressure during time, t, and s is the total settlement at the same pressure after a very long period of time when the consolidation process has been completed, then

$$\mu = \frac{s_t}{s} \tag{16-81}$$

expresses the degree of consolidation in decimal fractions. When s_t/s is multiplied by 100, one obtains "percent" of consolidation at time, t, of the total consolidation, viz., settlement.

After a very long time, $t \to \infty$, A_e becomes larger and at $t = \infty$, after 100% consolidation, the effective pressure area is mathematically equal in magnitude to the total pressure area A_o, i.e.,

$$A_{e\infty} = p_e H = (\Delta p)H = u_o H = A_o \tag{16-82}$$

and the degree of consolidation is

$$\mu = \frac{A_e}{A_o} = \frac{(\Delta p)H}{A_o} = \frac{A_o}{A_o} = 1.0. \tag{16-83}$$

Then, at full, or 100% consolidation, the degree of consolidation is $\mu = 1.0$, and the amount of settlement is expressed, by Eq. (16-75) as

$$s_{t=\infty} = \frac{e_i - e_f}{1 + e_i} H. \tag{16-84}$$

For 0% consolidation, the degree is $\mu = 0$, because in such a case

$$A_{nO} = \int_0^H u(z; t)\,dz = (\Delta p)H = A_o,$$

(Eq. (16-78), and

$$A_{eO} = A_o - A_o = 0.$$

The degree of consolidation (or percent of consolidation), μ, at any instant of elapsed time may also be written in an abbreviated form as

$$\mu = 1 - \frac{u}{u_i}, \tag{16-85}$$

or

$$\mu = 1 - \frac{\text{hydrostatic excess pressure at time, } t, \text{ and depth, } z}{\text{initial hydrostatic excess pressure at time, } t = 0, \text{ and depth, } z}.$$

Immediately after application of the pressure increment (Δp) on the clay, the hydrostatic excess pressure (at time, $t = 0$, and depth, $z = z$) equals the initial neutral (pore water) pressure, u_i, i.e., $(\Delta p) = u_i$.

When $u = u_i$, then $\mu = 0$ ($= 0\%$ consolidation).

When the hydrostatic excess pressure, u, decreases to zero (after time $t = \infty$), i.e., when $u = 0$, then $\mu = 1$ ($= 100\%$ consolidation).

From the foregoing discussion it can be inferred that the pressure distribution area, in a way, is a measure of the compression which the clay undergoes during the course of consolidation.

16-14. Trapezoidal Pressure Distribution Area. Assume a clay system with one-way drainage, and a layer H units thick, as in Fig. 16-15. The load increment in the trapezoidal pressure distribution diagram is Δp on top of the clay. At the bottom the pressure is p_b. At time $t = 0$, the void ratio of the clay is $e = e_i$, and the zero isochrone is indicated in the pressure distribution diagram $A_\circ = OABDO$ by $t_\circ$, or the line, AB. After a time lapse from $t = 0$ to $t = t$, the t-isochrone is represented by the curve line OfC.

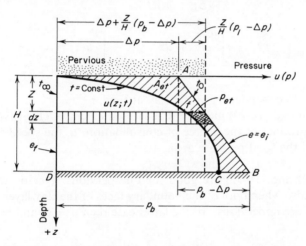

FIG. 16-15 Trapezoidal pressure distribution diagram.

The settlement, s_t, at any time, t, is calculated as before in the rectangular case, namely,

$$s_t = v_v(p_{\text{total}} - u)H, \tag{16-86}$$

or for the trapezoidal pressure distribution area,

$$ds_t = v_v\left[\Delta p + \frac{z}{H}(p_b - \Delta p) - u(z;t)\right]dz. \tag{16-87}$$

Integration of Eq. (16-87) between the limits $z_1 = 0$ and $z_2 = H$ yields the full settlement of a layer of clay H units thick;

$$s_t = \frac{a}{1+e_i}\left[(\tfrac{1}{2})(\Delta p + p_b)H - \int_0^H u(z;t)\,dz\right]. \tag{16-88}$$

Note that the quantity $(\tfrac{1}{2})(\Delta p = p_b)H = $ area $OABDO = A_\circ$, and that the quantity in brackets represents the hatched area, $OABCfO$. This area is the effective pressure area, A_{et}, at time, t.

Taking the quantity $(\frac{1}{2})(\Delta p + p_b)H$ out of the brackets, obtain

$$s_t = \frac{a(\Delta p + p_b)H}{2(1 + e_i)}\left[1 - \frac{\displaystyle\int_0^H u(z; t)\, dz}{(\frac{1}{2})(\Delta p + p_b)H}\right] = \qquad (16\text{-}89)$$

$$= \mu\, \frac{a}{1 + e_i}\, A_o = \mu v_v A_o, \qquad (16\text{-}90)$$

where

$$\mu = 1 - \frac{\displaystyle\int_0^H u(z; t)\, dz}{(\frac{1}{2})(\Delta p + p_b)H} = \qquad (16\text{-}91)$$

$$= 1 - \frac{\displaystyle\int_0^H u(z; t)\, dz}{A_o} = \frac{A_o - \displaystyle\int_0^H u(z; t)\, dz}{A_o} \qquad (16\text{-}92)$$

is the degree of consolidation of the clay at time, t.

Eqs. (16-76) and (16-90) indicate that the settlement of clay at any time, t, is equal to the product of the degree of consolidation, μ, the specific loss of pore water, v_v, and the total pressure area, A_o.

Again, at $t = \infty$, $\mu = 1$, and $s_t = v_v A_o$.

Eqs. (16-90) and (16-92) are good for one pervious layer on top, or at the bottom, and also when both of the boundary faces of the clay layer are pervious, or both faces are impervious. In the latter case then $\mu = 0$, and by Eq. (16-92),

$$A_o = \int_0^H u(z; t)\, dz, \qquad (16\text{-}93)$$

and

$$s_t = \mu v_v A_o = 0 v_v A_o = 0, \qquad (16\text{-}94)$$

which means that at an arbitrary pressure distribution of the pore water pressure, no compression of the clay can take place. Only an equalization of the u-pressures can take place until the pressure gradient at any point in the layer of clay, embedded between impermeable boundary surfaces becomes equal to zero.

Eqs. (16-90) and (16-92) can also be specialized for triangular pressure areas.

The determination of the coefficient of degree of consolidation, μ, is basically an analytical problem, because the isochrones $\int_{z_1}^{z_2} u(z; t)\, dz$ must be calculated, which, in turn, leads to calculation of the A_n-coefficients in Eqs. (16-58), (16-63), (16-64), and (16-66).

16-15. The General Isochrone Equation For $A_o = (\Delta p)(2H)$. The pressure distribution area equation $A_o = (\Delta p)(2H)$ indicates a constant total pressure (hydrostatic excess) distribution, Δp, at $t = 0$ throughout the clay layer for a clay system with two-way drainage, Fig. 16-16. In such a case the $f(z; 0)$-function in Eq. (16-64) is

$$f(z; 0) = \Delta p = \text{const,} \qquad (16\text{-}95)$$

and

$$A_n = \frac{1}{H} \int_0^{2H} f(z; 0)\sin \frac{n\pi z}{2H}\, dz = \frac{\Delta p}{H} \int_0^{2H} \sin \frac{n\pi z}{2H}\, dz. \qquad (16\text{-}96)$$

Integration yields

$$A_n = \frac{2(\Delta p)}{n}(1 = \cos n\pi). \qquad (16\text{-}97)$$

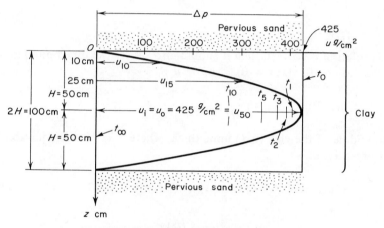

FIG. 16-16.   Sinusoidal isochrone.

For $n = 1, 2, 3, 4, 5 \ldots$, the A_n-coefficients are:

$$A_1 = \frac{4}{\pi}(\Delta p);$$

$$A_2 = 0;$$

$$A_3 = \frac{4}{3\pi}(\Delta p);$$

$$A_4 = 0;$$

$$A_5 = \frac{4}{5\pi}(\Delta p),$$

. . . .

. . . .

Upon substitution of these A_n-values into the general equation, Eq. (16-58) which is

$$u(z;t) = \sum_{n=1}^{n=\infty} A_n \, e^{-n^2Nt} \sin \frac{n\pi z}{2H}, \qquad (16\text{-}58)$$

obtain the equation of the general isochrone at depth, z, and time, t, for a clay system with a two-way drainage and for a constant initial pressure distribution, $\Delta p = u_o = $ const:

$$u(z;t) = \frac{4}{\pi}(\Delta p)\left\{ e^{-Nt} \sin \frac{\pi z}{2H} + \tfrac{1}{3} e^{-9Nt} \sin \frac{3\pi z}{2H} + \right.$$

$$\left. + \tfrac{1}{5} e^{-25Nt} \sin \frac{5\pi z}{2H} + \cdots \right\}, \qquad (16\text{-}98)$$

where $N = \dfrac{\pi^2 c_v}{4H^2}$.

If this solution is correct, then it should also satisfy the time boundary conditions when at $t = 0$, $u(z;t=0) = \Delta p = u_o$:

$$u(z;0) = \frac{4}{\pi} u_o \left\{ \sin \frac{\pi z}{2H} + \tfrac{1}{3} \sin \frac{3\pi z}{2H} + \tfrac{1}{5} \sin \frac{5\pi z}{2H} + \cdots \right\}. \qquad (16\text{-}99)$$

For the middle of the clay ($2H$) units thick, where $z = H$, the equation of the neutral pressure, u, is:

$$u(z = H; t = 0) = \frac{4}{\pi}(\Delta p)(1 - \tfrac{1}{3} + \tfrac{1}{5} - \tfrac{1}{7} + \cdots) = \qquad (16\text{-}100)$$

$$= \frac{4}{\pi}(\Delta p)\left(\frac{\pi}{4}\right) = (\Delta p) = u_o, \qquad (16\text{-}101)$$

because the series

$$1 - \tfrac{1}{3} + \tfrac{1}{5} - \tfrac{1}{7} + \cdots = \frac{\pi}{4}.$$

By Eq. (16-98), the neutral pressures at any time, t, and for the middle of the clay, where $z = H = (2H)/2$, are:

$$u(z = H; t) = \frac{4u_o}{\pi} (e^{-Nt} - \tfrac{1}{3} e^{-9Nt} + \tfrac{1}{5} e^{-25Nt} - \cdots) =$$

$$= \frac{4u_o}{\pi} (e^{-\pi^2 \tau/4} - \tfrac{1}{3} e^{-9\pi^2 \tau/4} + \tfrac{1}{5} e^{-25\pi^2 \tau/4} - \cdots) = u_o S(\tau/4).$$

where $N = \dfrac{\pi^2 c_v}{4H^2} = \dfrac{\pi^2}{4} \dfrac{\tau}{t}$, and

$$\tau = \frac{c_v t}{H^2}. \qquad (16\text{-}102)$$

Example. Given a layer of clay $(2H) = 100$ cm thick embedded between two layers of very pervious sand. The new load increment is $\Delta p = 0.425$ kg/cm². The initial, hydrostatic excess-pressure isochrone is *sinusoidally* distributed over the thickness $(2H)$. Thus the excess pressure in the clay layer at time $t = 0$ is $u_o = 0.425$ kg/cm² $= 425$ g/cm². The coefficient of consolidation is given as $c_v = 0.0005$ cm²/sec. The initial sinusoidal isochrone is shown in Fig. 16-16.

Required
1) Write the equation of the initial (zero-time) isochrone, $f(z;0) = u_i$, and test it for boundary conditions.
2) Find the integral in Eq. (16-66).
3) Calculate the depth coordinates of the zero isochrone at depths $z = 10$ cm, 25 cm, and 50 cm, and plot the zero isochrone.
4) Calculate the neutral pressure, u, at mid-thickness of the clay after a lapse of time of 1 day, 2 days, 3 days, 5 days, and 10 days.
5) After how long a time, t, is the hydrostatic excess pressure $u_{t=t} = 0$?

Solution
1) *Equation of zero isochrone*, by Eq. (16-52) (note that here $t = 0$):

$$f(z;0) = u_i = u_o \sin \frac{\pi z}{2H}. \tag{16-52}$$

Test: a) When $z = 0$, then $f(z;0) = u_i = 0$.
        b) When $z = H$, then $f(z;0) = u_i = u_i = u_o = 425$ g/cm².
        c) When $z = 2H$, then $f(z;0) = u_i = 0$.

2) *Integral of Eq.* (16-66). The integral sought is (for $n = 1$):

$$\int_0^{2H} f(z;0) \left(\sin \frac{\pi z}{2H} \right) dz \tag{16-103}$$

Because $f(z;0) = u_o \sin \frac{\pi z}{2H}$, $\tag{16-52}$

the value of that integral is

$$u_o \int_0^{2H} \sin^2 \frac{\pi z}{2H} \, dz = u_o H = \underline{(425)H}. \tag{16-104}$$

3) *Coordinates of zero isochrone*. Here $H = (2H)/2 = 100/2 = 50$ (cm).
At depth $z = 10$ cm:

$$u_{10} = f(10;0) = (425) \sin \frac{\pi}{2} \frac{10}{50} = \underline{131 \text{ (g)}}.$$

At depth $z = 25$ cm:

$$u_{25} = f(25;0) = (425) \sin \frac{\pi}{2} \frac{25}{50} = \underline{300 \text{ (g)}}.$$

At depth $z = 50$ cm:

$$u_{50} = f(50;0) = (425) \sin \frac{\pi}{2} \frac{50}{50} = \underline{425 \text{ (g)}}.$$

4) *Neutral pressure at $z = 50$ cm*. The equation to use is Eq. (16-66). Because in this equation the integral is in this case equal to $(425)(H)$, Eq. (16-66) can be written as

$$u(z;t) = \left(\frac{1}{H} \right)(u_o)(H)(e^{-\frac{\pi^2}{4} \frac{c_v t}{H^2}}) \left(\sin \frac{\pi z}{2H} \right). \tag{16-105}$$

The value of the exponent at e is:

$$\frac{\pi^2}{4} \frac{c_v t}{H^2} = \frac{(\sim 10)(0.0005)}{(4)(50^2)} (t) = (5)(10^{-7})(t). \qquad (16\text{-}106)$$

Then

$$u(z; t) = u(H; t) = u(50; t) = (425)[e^{-(5 \times 10^{-7})t}] \sin \frac{\pi}{2}, \qquad (16\text{-}107)$$

or

$$u(50; t) = (425)[e^{-(5 \times 10^{-7})t}]. \qquad (16\text{-}108)$$

The pressures, $u(50; t)$ are conveniently calculated in a tabular form.

| Time | | $(5 \times 10^{-7})t$ | $e^{-(5 \times 10^{-7})t}$ | $u(50; t)$ |
| t | | | | g/cm² |
Days	Sec.			
1	2	3	4	5
$t_1 = $ 1;	86400	0.0432	0.958	407
$t_2 = $ 2;	172800	0.0864	0.917	390
$t_3 = $ 3;	259200	0.1296	0.878	373
$t_5 = $ 5;	432000	0.2160	0.805	342
$t_{10} = $ 10;	864000	0.4320	0.649	276

These u-values indicate the positions of vertexes for isochrones t_1, t_2, t_3, t_5, and t_{10}, and are shown in Fig. 16-16.

5) *Time for* $u = 0$. In this case, $u(50; t) = 0$, and Eq. (16-66) is applicable:

$$u(50; t) = u_o e^{-(5 \times 10^{-7})t} = 0. \qquad (16\text{-}109)$$

Obviously, $u_o = 425 \neq 0$, therefore

$$e^{-(5 \times 10^{-7})t} = 0 \qquad (16\text{-}110)$$

and $t = \infty$, i.e., the $u(50; t)$ isochrone becomes zero after a very long time ($t \to \infty$). This isochrone is a vertical line through the point of origin of the coordinates, and is $2H = 100$ cm long.

16-16. Derivation of General Degree of Consolidation Equation. After familiarizing oneself with the derivation of the general isochrone equation $u(z; t)$, the study of the coefficient μ, expressing the degree of consolidation of clay with time, t, can now be resumed.

Recall from Eqs. (16-77) and (16-85) that the degree of consolidation refers to a variable thickness, z, of the clay layer.

The average value of the coefficient of consolidation, μ_{ave}, for a clay layer $2H$ units thick, at any time, t, is:

$$\mu_{av} = \frac{1}{2H} \int_0^{2H} \left(1 - \frac{u}{u_i}\right) dz = 1 - \frac{1}{2H} \int_0^{2H} \frac{u}{u_i} dz, \qquad (16\text{-}111)$$

or, with an initial pore water pressure constant throughout the thickness of the clay layer, i.e., when $u_i = u_o = \Delta p$,

$$\mu_{ave} = 1 - \frac{1}{2H} \times$$

$$\times \frac{\int_0^{2H} \frac{4}{\pi}(u_o)\left(e^{-Nt}\sin\frac{\pi z}{2H} + \frac{1}{3}e^{-9Nt}\sin\frac{3\pi z}{2H} + \frac{1}{5}e^{-25Nt}\sin\frac{5\pi z}{2H} + \cdots\right) dz}{u_o} =$$

$$= 1 - \frac{2}{\pi H}\int_0^{2H}\left(e^{-Nt}\sin\frac{\pi z}{2H} + \frac{1}{3}e^{-9Nt}\sin\frac{3\pi z}{2H} + \frac{1}{5}e^{-25Nt}\sin\frac{5\pi z}{2H} + \cdots\right) dz =$$

$$= 1 - \frac{8}{\pi^2}(e^{-Nt} + \frac{1}{9}e^{-9Nt} + \frac{1}{25}e^{-25Nt} + \cdots). \tag{16-112}$$

This equation is good for two-way drainage as it is encountered in the consolidation test, with a porous material on top and at the bottom of the clay sample in the consolidometer.

Check. At time $t = 0$, μ_{av} must be equal to zero. Inserting $t = 0$ in the μ_{ave}-equation, obtain

$$\mu_{ave_{t=0}} = 1 - \frac{8}{\pi^2}\underbrace{(1 + \frac{1}{9} + \frac{1}{25} + \frac{1}{49} + \cdots)}_{\rightarrow \pi^2/8} = 1 - \left(\frac{8}{\pi^2}\right)\left(\frac{\pi^2}{8}\right) = 0,$$

Q.E.D.

Because $N = \frac{\pi^2}{4}\frac{c_v}{H^2}$, one notes that the degree of consolidation, μ, being a function of N, t, H, and z, depends upon:

a) the coefficient of the consolidation of the soil, $c_v = k/(v_v\gamma_w)$; which, in its turn, depends upon
   i) the coefficient of permeability, k, of the soil under the instantaneous load;
   ii) the specific loss of pore water, $v_v = a/(1 + e)$, where
       $a = (-de)/dp$ = coefficient of compressibility, and
       e = initial void ratio before applying dp; and
   iii) the unit weight of water, γ_w, which is a function of temperature;
b) time, t, of consolidation;
c) thickness of the layer of clay in one-way drainage, or the length of the shortest drainage path, H;
d) whether the clay layer is bound by a drainage face at the top, or at the bottom, or at the top and bottom simultaneously, and
e) the position, z, below the top of the clay layer.

16-17. Time Factor. The coefficient $\tau = \dfrac{c_v t}{H^2}$ in one-way drainage, in the negative *e*-exponent, Eq. (16-102), is termed by Fröhlich,[2] for the sake of brevity, the *time factor*:

$$\frac{c_v t}{H^2} = \tau \qquad \left[\frac{(cm^2/sec)(sec)}{(cm)^2}\right] = (1). \qquad (16\text{-}102)$$

Here H means one-way drainage.

The time factor is dimensionless, and depends upon
   a) the coefficient of consolidation, c_v;
   b) the elapsed time, t, and
   c) the length of the shortest drainage path, H.

From the nature of the *u*-equations and from dimensional analysis it turns out that the time factor τ is dimensionless, i.e., an abstract quantity.

For two-way drainage ($H_2 = H/2$), the time factor τ_2 is

$$\tau_2 = \frac{c_v t}{H_2{}^2} = \frac{c_v t}{(H/2)^2}, \qquad (16\text{-}113)$$

i.e., the time factor, τ_2, is *four times as large* as in the case of one-way drainage (make reference to Fig. 16-17). For example, if in one-way drainage $H = 120$ cm, then in two-way drainage $H_2 = H/2 = 120/2 = 60$ (cm).

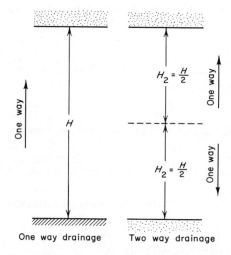

One way drainage   Two way drainage

FIG. 16-17 Length of drainage path.

16-18. Model Law. One of the important laws the theory of consolidation of clays has given to the engineering sciences is the so-called *model law of settlement*. It is here understood that the concept of consolidation is equivalent to the settlement concept. If two layers of the same clay of different thickness, say, h and H, where $h < H$, have the same number of drainage faces, and have attained the same degree of consolidation during time t and T, respectively—generally where $t \neq T$ —then their coefficients of consolidation, c_v, must theoretically be equal, and so must be their time factors, τ:

$$\tau = \frac{c_v t}{h^2}; \qquad \tau = \frac{c_v T}{H^2}. \qquad (16\text{-}114); (16\text{-}115)$$

Equating both time factors, obtain the following model law:

$$\frac{t}{T} = \frac{h^2}{H^2}. \qquad (16\text{-}116)$$

This model law of similitude of the consolidation process of a clay reads that the ratio of times, t and T, necessary to attain a certain degree of consolidation in two clay layers of the same material and the same number of drainage faces but different thicknesses, h and H, equals the ratio of the squares of the corresponding thicknesses of these layers. Thus, by the way in which t and T are related in the model law, it can be observed that, all other things being equal, to attain the same degree of consolidation of a layer of clay of twice the thickness ($H = 2h$), the time for consolidation would be four times that needed for h:

$$\frac{t}{T} = \frac{h^2}{(2h)^2},$$

or

$$T = 4t.$$

Hence, the consolidation test of soils is a model test, not a destructive test.

The model law is applicable in calculating the time, T, to attain, say a 60% consolidation of a layer, H, of clay in the field from a consolidation test performed in the laboratory on a prototype clay sample (h):

$$T = t\frac{H^2}{h^2} = \alpha H^2, \tag{16-117}$$

where $\alpha = t/h^2 =$ an experimental coefficient of proportionality. Written in this form, the model law reads: the duration, T, of a consolidation process of a layer of clay, H units thick, is proportional (α) to the square of the compressible layer (H^2). For example, if a laboratory sample, $h = 2$ cm thick, has attained in two-way drainage a 60% consolidation during $t = 6$ hours, then its prototype clay layer $H = 3$ m $= 300$ cm thick will attain a 60% consolidation in two-way drainage within a time of

$$T = 6\frac{(300)^2}{(2)^2} = 135{,}000 \text{ (hours)} = 5625 \text{ (days)} \rightleftharpoons 15.4 \text{ (years)}.$$

It is well to note that if the soil sample, h units thick, has two drainage faces, on the top and at the bottom of the sample, then the length of the drainage path of one particle of the expelled pore water is $h/2$. Therefore, Equation (16-116) is good only if the clay layer in the field, H units thick, is also bound on its top and at its bottom by pervious sand layers, i.e., the clay layer must have two-way drainage where each drainage path is $H/2$ units long.

If, however, the layer, H units thick, of the prototype clay rests on an impervious layer (real or imaginary, as in Art. 16-21), and is bounded at its top with a pervious layer of sand, then this condition represents a clay system with one-way drainage where the length of the drainage path is H units long. In such a case the model law, Eq. (16-116), transforms into the following form:

$$\frac{t}{T} = \frac{\left(\dfrac{h}{2}\right)^2}{H^2}, \tag{16-118}$$

or

$$\frac{t}{T} = \frac{h^2}{4(H)^2}. \tag{16-119}$$

In nature, intermediate sand layers between clay layers (Fig. 16-18) greatly facilitate the process of consolidation.

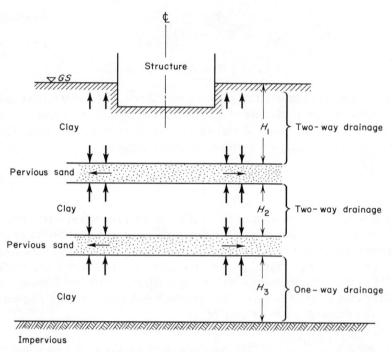

FIG. 16-18   Intermediate sand deposits facilitate the process of consolidation.

16-19. The Theoretical Time Factor-Percent Consolidation Curve.
Because $\mu_{\text{ave}} = f(Nt)$, but

$$N = \frac{\pi^2}{4} \frac{c_v}{H^2}, \tag{16-47}$$

and

$$\tau = \frac{c_v t}{H^2}, \tag{16-102}$$

it can be written that

$$Nt = \frac{\pi^2}{4} \frac{c_v}{H^2} t = \frac{\pi^2}{4} \tau, \tag{16-120}$$

where τ is the time factor. Thus, it is seen that at any time, t, the coefficient of the average degree of consolidation, μ_{av}, of a clay with two drainage faces, and initially with a constant, pore water pressure distribution, is a function of the time factor, τ, or

$$\mu_{\text{ave}} = f(\tau). \tag{16-121}$$

Of course it must be remembered that in general μ_{av}, viz., $f(\tau)$ depends upon the initial pore water pressure distribution in the clay layer, viz., the shape of the area of the initial pore water pressure diagram, $A_\circ$, and the number of free drainage faces.

Knowing the coefficient of consolidation, c_v, from testing, and the thickness of the soil sample, H, in the consolidometer, and assuming consecutive time intervals, Δt, viz., time t, the time factor, τ, can be determined, and thus the degree of the average consolidation of the clay calculated. These results can then be tabulated, or plotted in a graph showing $\mu = f(\tau)$. Therefore, it can be inferred that the degree (percent) of consolidation-time factor graph (the μ-τ graph) is indirectly merely a time-percent consolidation curve for the area of a particular shape of the pressure distribution diagram. This diagram, in soil mechanics, is referred to as the *theoretical time-consolidation curve*, which differs in its lower branch, as was discussed previously, from the experimentally obtained, time-consolidation curve. Such theoretical curves for variously shaped pressure diagrams are shown in Fig. 16-19.

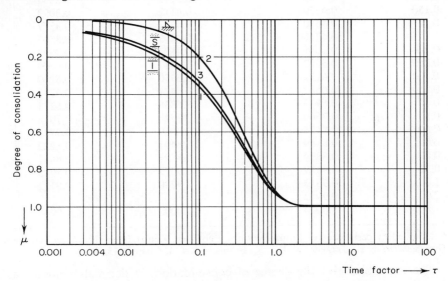

FIG. 16-19   Time factor—degree of consolidation curves.

16-20. Theoretical Time Factor-Consolidation Tables. To facilitate calculations of the coefficients of degrees of consolidation of soil as a function of the time factor, Terzaghi and Fröhlich published the μ-τ tables for various pressure distribution diagrams. These tables give for certain values, such as $\tau = 0.004$, 0.008, 0.012, the corresponding μ-values, i.e., $\mu = f(\tau)$ (see, for example, Table 16-1).

TABLE 16-1. TIME FACTOR-DEGREE OF CONSOLIDATION VALUES
FOR TWO-WAY DRAINAGE*

Time Factor, τ	Degree of Consolidation, μ		
	(column 2 diagram, $2H$)	(column 3 diagram, $2H$, 2, Sinusoid)	(column 4 diagram, $2H$, 3, Sinusoid)
1	2	3	4
0.000	0.0000	0.0000	0.0000
0.004	0.0795	0.0649	0.0098
0.008	0.1038	0.0862	0.0195
0.012	0.1248	0.1049	0.0292
0.020	0.1598	0.1367	0.0481
0.028	0.1889	0.1638	0.0667
0.036	0.2141	0.1876	0.0850
0.048	0.2464	0.2196	0.1117
0.060	0.2764	0.2481	0.1376
0.072	0.3028	0.2743	0.1628
0.083	0.3233	0.2967	0.1852
0.100	0.3562	0.3288	0.2187
0.125	0.3989	0.3719	0.2654
0.150	0.4370	0.4112	0.3093
0.167	0.4610	0.4361	0.3377
0.175	0.4718	0.4473	0.3507
0.200	0.5041	0.4809	0.3895
0.250	0.5622	0.5417	0.4603
0.300	0.6132	0.5950	0.5230
0.350	0.6582	0.6421	0.5783
0.40	0.6973	0.6836	0.6273
0.50	0.7640	0.7528	0.7088
0.60	0.8156	0.8069	0.7725
0.70	0.8559	0.8491	0.8222
0.80	0.8874	0.8821	0.8611
0.90	0.9119	0.9079	0.8915
1.00	0.9313	0.9280	0.9152
2.00	0.9942	—	—
∞	1.0000	1.0000	1.0000

* Compiled by permission of Franz Deuticke, Publisher, Vienna, from *Theorie der Setzung von Tonschichten*, by K. Terzaghi and O. K. Fröhlich, Ref. 4, Chapter 15.

The τ-μ tables give the degree of consolidation, in decimal fractions, as a function of the time factor, τ, for rectangular pressure distribution areas based on the rigorous method of solution of the time consolidation process of a layer of clay embedded between two very pervious layers of sand. The μ-values given in Column 2 of Table 16-1 are the Terzaghi-Fröhlich Table No. 12 for a rectangular area. They are also good for any other arbitrary, linear, initial distribution of the hydrostatic excess pressures, for example, triangular and trapezoidal pressure diagrams, if they have two drainage faces—one on the top and one at the bottom of the clay layer. The drainage length is $L = 2H$.

Column 3 of Table 16-1 gives μ-values for a quarter-wave, and Column 4 μ-values for a half-wave of a sinusoidal, initial pressure distribution for two-way drainage. These values are from the Terzaghi-Fröhlich Tables Nos. 13 and 14, respectively. The drainage length is $L = 2H$. The courses of the $\mu = f(\tau)$ graphs in Columns Nos. 1, 2, and 3 are illustrated in Fig. 16-19. Such graphs are convenient in laboratory work, and in calculating time of certain predetermined degrees of consolidation of given layers of clay for which the time factor, τ, is needed.

For one-way drainage the $\mu = f(\tau)$ values are based upon the following considerations.

Rectangular Pressure Diagram. At the center line, N-N', of a layer of clay $2H$ thick, embedded between two pervious sand layers, the velocity of the pore water flow, by reasons of symmetry, must be equal to zero. Therefore the boundary layer through the plane of symmetry can be considered as an impervious boundary face. Hence, in one-way drainage the height $H = (2H)/2$ is one half of that in two-way drainage. Hence, the μ-values in one-way drainage are the same as those in the two-way drainage (Table 16-1).

The $\mu_{\triangleright} = f(\tau)$ values for a *triangular pressure* area with its apex up with reference to the pervious layer, are compiled in Column 3, Table 16-2 after the Terzaghi-Fröhlich Table No. 16.

The $\mu_{\triangleright} = f(\tau)$ values for a *triangle*, whose apex rests on the impermeable layer, and whose opposite base is bounded by a pervious course, were calculated by the author after Fröhlich's equation

$$\mu_{\triangleright} = 2\mu_R - \mu_{\triangleright}, \tag{16-122}$$

and are tabulated in Column 4, Table 16-2.

The $\mu_{\triangleright} = f(\tau)$ values for a *trapezoid* in Column 5, Table 16-2 are to be calculated by Fröhlich's equation

$$\mu_T = \frac{2\mu_R + \mu_{\triangleright}(\eta - 1)}{\eta + 1}, \tag{16-123}$$

where μ_R = coefficient of degree of consolidation for a rectangular pressure distribution area,

$\eta = u_b/u_s$ = ratio of stress ordinate u_b at bottom of trapezoid to stress ordinate u_s at top (surface) of trapezoid.

One sees that for a trapezoidal pressure distribution diagram the μ-values depend upon the u_b/u_s ratio which may have infinitely many values. Therefore no tabulation of μ-values for a trapezoid were made.

16-21. Illustrative Example. The application of the τ-μ tables will now be shown by an illustrative example. Assume a layer of clay 5 m thick, the bottom of which lies on a sand deposit, and on whose top surface there is also a pervious layer of sand. After the clay has consolidated at a load of 1.3 kg/cm², the load on the surface of the clay has now been increased from 1.3 kg/cm² to 2.0 kg/cm². The unit weight of water is given as $\gamma_w = 1$ g/cm³.

TABLE 16-2. TIME FACTOR-DEGREE OF CONSOLIDATION VALUES
FOR ONE-WAY DRAINAGE*

Time Factor, τ	Degree of Consolidation, μ			
	1	2	3	4
1	2	3	4	5
0.000	0.0000	0.0000	0.0000	
0.004	0.0795	0.0085	0.1505	
0.008	0.1038	0.0162	0.1914	
0.012	0.1248	0.0241	0.2255	
0.020	0.1598	0.0400	0.2796	
0.028	0.1889	0.0560	0.3218	
0.036	0.2141	0.0720	0.3562	
0.048	0.2464	0.0950	0.3978	$\eta = \dfrac{u_b}{u_s}$;
0.060	0.2764	0.1198	0.4330	
0.072	0.3028	0.1436	0.4620	
0.083	0.3233	0.1646	0.4820	
0.100	0.3562	0.1976	0.5148	
0.125	0.3989	0.2442	0.5536	
0.150	0.4370	0.2886	0.5854	$\mu_T = \dfrac{2\mu_R + \mu_{\rightarrow}(\eta - 1)}{\eta + 1}$
0.167	0.4610	0.3174	0.6046	
0.175	0.4718	0.3306	0.6130	
0.200	0.5041	0.3704	0.6378	
0.250	0.5622	0.4432	0.6812	
0.300	0.6132	0.5078	0.7186	
0.350	0.6582	0.5649	0.7515	
0.40	0.6973	0.6154	0.7792	
0.50	0.7640	0.6994	0.8286	
0.60	0.8156	0.7652	0.8660	
0.70	0.8559	0.8165	0.8953	
0.80	0.8874	0.8566	0.9182	
0.90	0.9119	0.8880	0.9358	
1.00	0.9313	0.9125	0.9501	
2.00	0.9942	0.9930	0.9960	
∞	1.0000	1.0000	1.0000	

* Compiled by permission of Franz Deuticke, Publisher, Vienna, *Theorie der Setzung von Tonschichten*, by K. Terzaghi and O. K. Fröhlich, Ref. 4, Chapter 15.

The properties of the clay are:
coefficient of permeability: $k = (1.6)(10^{-6})$ cm/min.
The pressure-void ratio diagram of the clay is given in Fig. 16-20.
Compute:
a) the magnitude of total settlement;
b) settlement at 30%, 50%, 70%, 90% consolidation;
c) degree of consolidation after 1 year, 2 years, and 5 years;
d) settlement after 1 year, 2 years, and 5 years;
e) how long a time is required for the total settlement, and
f) how much time is needed for 30%, 50%, 70%, 90%, and 100% consolidation.

Solution

A. *Auxiliary Calculations*

i) The given clay system has two-way drainage. Hence, the *shortest drainage path* is $H = 500/2 = 250$ cm.

ii) The *settlement equation* is:

$$s_t = \mu_\square \quad v_v A_\circ \tag{16-76}$$

iii) The *pressure area* (it is a rectangle) is:

$$A_\circ = (\Delta p)(2H) \tag{15-45}$$

$$\Delta p = 2.0 - 1.3 = 0.7 \quad (\text{kg/cm}^2)$$

$$2H = \underline{500 \text{ cm.}}$$

$$A_\circ = (0.7)(500) = \underline{350 \ (\text{kg/cm})}$$

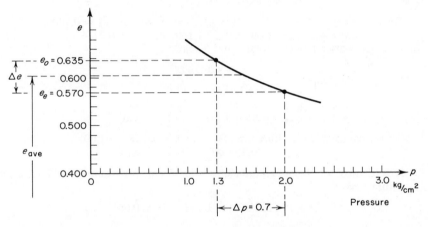

Fɪɢ. 16-20   Pressure-void ratio diagram.

iv) The *specific loss of pore water*, v_v, is:

$$v_v = \frac{a}{1 + e_{\text{ave}}} = \frac{\Delta e}{(\Delta p)(1 + e_{\text{ave}})} = \frac{e_i - e_f}{(\Delta p)(1 + e_{\text{ave}})} =$$

$$= \frac{0.635 - 0.570}{(0.7)\left(1 + \dfrac{0.635 + 0.570}{2}\right)} = \underline{0.0579 \ (\text{cm}^2/\text{kg}).}$$

v) The *coefficient of consolidation*, c_v, is:

$$c_v = \frac{k}{v_v \gamma_w} = \frac{(1.6)(10^{-6})}{(0.0579)(0.001)} = 0.02763 \quad (\text{cm}^2/\text{min}),$$

or

$$c_v = (0.02763)(60)(24)(365) = \underline{14,522 \ (\text{cm}^2/\text{year}).}$$

B. *Answers.*

a) *Total settlement* ($\mu = 1.0$):

$$s = \mu v_v A_\circ = (1.0)(0.0579)(350) = \underline{20.3 \ (\text{cm}).}$$

b) *Settlement* at 30%, 50%, 70%, and 90% consolidation:

$$s_{30} = (20.3)(0.3) = 6.1 \quad \text{(cm)}$$
$$s_{50} = (20.3)(0.5) = 10.2 \quad \text{(cm)}$$
$$s_{70} = (20.3)(0.7) = 14.2 \quad \text{(cm)}$$
$$s_{90} = (20.3)(0.9) = 18.3 \quad \text{(cm)}.$$

c) *Degree of consolidation* after $t = 1$ year, 2 years, and 5 years:
For *1 year*:

$$\text{Time factor: } \tau = \frac{c_v t}{H^2} = \frac{(14,522)(1)}{(250)^2} = 0.232.$$

The corresponding degree of consolidation, μ, from Table 16-1 by interpolation:
at $\tau = 0.200$, $\mu = 0.5041$.

$$\mu_{t=1} = 0.5041 + \frac{0.232 - 0.200}{0.250 - 0.200}(0.5622 - 0.5041) = \underline{0.5413}.$$

For 2 years: $t = 2$, $\tau_2 = 2\tau_1 = (2)(0.232) = 0.464$, and $\mu_2 = 0.7404$.
For 5 years: $t = 5$, $\tau_5 = (5)(0.232) = 1.160$, and $\mu_5 = 0.9414$.

d) *Settlement* after 1 year, 2 years, and 5 years:

$$s_t = (20.3)\mu_t.$$

$$s_{t=1} = (20.3)(0.54) = 11.0 \quad \text{(cm)}$$
$$s_{t=2} = (20.3)(0.74) = 15.0 \quad \text{(cm)}$$
$$s_{t=5} = (20.3)(0.94) = 19.1 \quad \text{(cm)}$$

Settlement after a very long time ($t \to \infty$; $\tau \to \infty$; $\mu_\infty = 1.00$):
$$s_{t \to \infty} = (20.3)(1.00) = 20.3 \quad \text{(cm)}.$$

A settlement of the magnitude of $s = 5.52$ cm, for example, will take place
within t years:

$$\mu = (5.52)/(20.3) = 0.271 \to \tau \approx 0.06,$$

and

$$t = \frac{\tau H^2}{c_v} = \frac{(0.06)(250)^2}{14,522} = 0.258 \text{ years} = 93 \text{ days}.$$

e) The total settlement of 20.3 cm will take place theoretically after a very long
time (> 8.6 years).
    If the clay sample used in the consolidation test was 2.0 cm thick, with two
drainage faces, and 100% consolidation took place within 24 hours = 0.00273
years, then the 500 cm thick prototype layer of clay would consolidate after

$$\frac{t}{T} = \frac{h^2}{H^2},$$

or

$$T = t\frac{H^2}{h^2} = 0.00273(500/2)^2 = 170.62 \quad \text{(years)},$$

which is a long period of time.

f) *Time for consolidation*:
for $\mu = 30\%$ ($\tau = 0.072$)

$$t_{30} = \frac{\tau H^2}{c_v} = \frac{(0.072)(250)^2}{14,522} = 0.31 \quad \text{(years)};$$

for $\mu = 50\%$ ($\tau = 0.200$)

$$t_{50} = \frac{(0.200)(250)^2}{14{,}522} = 0.86 \qquad \text{(years)};$$

for $\mu = 70\%$ ($\tau = 0.40$)

$$t_{70} = \frac{(0.40)(250)^2}{14{,}522} = 1.72 \qquad \text{(years)};$$

for $\mu = 90\%$ ($\tau = 0.85$)

$$t_{90} = \frac{(0.85)(250)^2}{14{,}522} = 3.66 \qquad \text{(years)};$$

for $\mu = 99.42\%$ ($\tau = 2.00$)

$$t_{99.42} = \frac{(2)(250)^2}{14{,}522} = 8.6 \qquad \text{(years)};$$

for $\mu = 1.00 \approx 0.9999$ ($\tau \approx \rightarrow \infty$)

$$t_{99.99} \rightarrow \frac{(\infty)(250)^2}{14{,}522} \rightarrow \infty \qquad \text{(a very long period of time).}$$

16-22. Illustrative Example. All data are as in the previous problem, but the clay layer, 500 cm thick, rests on an artesian aquifer from which water is flowing upwards through the clay. Because it is assumed in this problem that pore water cannot be expelled from the clay through its bottom face against the artesian pressure, then the only possibility for the pore water to escape is upwards into the sand. Therefore the contact surface between the layer of clay and the artesian aquifer may be considerey impervious at the bottom of the clay, thus presenting a clay system with one-wad drainage upward. Here $H = 500$ cm. Settlement:

$$s_t = \mu v_v A_o = (20.3).$$

a) The *total settlement* is the same as before:

$$s = (1.0)(20.3) = \underline{20.3 \text{ (cm)}}.$$

b) *Settlement* at 30%, 50%, 70%, and 90% consolidation: (same as before):

$$s_{30} = 6.1 \qquad \text{(cm)}$$
$$s_{50} = 10.2 \qquad \text{(cm)}$$
$$s_{70} = 14.2 \qquad \text{(cm)}$$
$$s_{90} = 18.3 \qquad \text{(cm)}$$

c) *Degree of Consolidation* after 1 year, 2 years, and 5 years. Because of the longer drainage path, $H = 500$ cm, the degree of consolidation in this one-way drainage system is less than in a two-way drainage system.
   For 1 year:

$$\text{Time factor } \tau_1 = \frac{c_v t}{H^2} = \frac{(14{,}522)(1)}{(500)^2} = 0.058.$$

The corresponding degree of consolidation: $\mu_1 = 0.2720$.
For 2 years:

$$\tau_2 = 2\tau_1 = (2)(0.058) = 0.116$$
$$\mu_2 = 0.3735.$$

For 5 years:

$$\tau_5 = (5)(0.058) = 0.290$$
$$\mu_5 = 0.6030.$$

d) *Settlement*

After 1 year: $s_1 = \mu_1(20.3) = (0.2720)(20.3) = \underline{5.52 \text{ (cm)}}.$
After 2 years: $s_2 = \mu_2(20.3) = (0.3735)(20.3) = \underline{7.58 \text{ (cm)}}.$
After 5 years: $s_5 = \mu_5(20.3) = (0.6030)(20.3) = \underline{12.24 \text{ (cm)}}.$

e) *Total settlement of the prototype clay layer*, for one way drainage:

$$T = t\frac{H^2}{(h/2)^2} = (0.00273)\frac{500^2}{(1)^2} = 682.5 \qquad \text{(years)}.$$

Check: in one-way drainage, the settlement takes place four times longer than in two-way drainage, i.e., $4 \times 170.62 = 682.48$ (years), which checks with the calculation above.

f) *Time for consolidation*:

for $\mu = 30\%$ ($\tau = 0.072$)

$$t_{30} = \frac{\tau H^2}{c_v} = \frac{(0.072)(500)^2}{14,522} = \underline{1.24 \text{ (years)}}$$

For $\mu = 50\%$: $t_{50} = 3.44$ (years).

Note again that in one-way drainage consolidation takes place—$(500)^2/(250^2)$ $= 4$—four times longer than in two-way drainage.

$$t_{99.42\%} = \frac{(2)(500)^2}{14,522} = 34.43 \qquad \text{(years)}.$$

As a matter of exercise, 11 cm settlement takes place within t_{11} years time:

$$11.0 = \mu(20.3),$$

or

$$\mu = (11.0)/(20.3) = 0.5418,$$

for which there is a corresponding time factor of $\tau = 0.2325$, and

$$t_{11} = \frac{\tau H^2}{c_v} = \frac{(0.2325)(500^2)}{14,522} = 4.00 \text{ (years)}.$$

16-23. Consolidation of Sludge. The early stages of settlement and consolidation of a sludge course (of sewage or any other solids in suspension in a liquid) at the bottom of a settling tank is similar to the consolidation process of soil where it is brought about by an externally applied pressure. In the case of a sludge, the hydrostatic excess pressure is caused by the self-weight of the sludge instead of by an externally applied pressure. As more sludge piles up, its weight increases. As the consolidation (and densification) process of the sludge progresses with time, more load is transferred intergranularly to the solids of the sludge (effective pressure increases).

16-24. Conclusion. Concluding the discussion on the consolidation theory of clays, it can be summarized that the consolidation process depends upon:

    a) the thickness of the clay layer (or sample, or length of the drainage path);
    b) the intensity and the manner of distribution of the externally applied pressure along the thickness of the clay layer from its top to its bottom;
    c) the number of free drainage faces of the clay layer, and

d) the coefficient of consolidation, c_v, of the clay, a coefficient which is it-self a function of the permeability of the soil, k, the unit weight of the water, γ_w, and the specific loss of pore water, v_v. Besides, the rate of con-solidation of the clay is also affected by the environmental tempera-ture, the uniformity of the soil itself, and the precision of the tests of the soil properties.

It appears that the consolidation theory of clays is good for water in bulk in the voids of the soil (this pertains to primary consolidation). The theory, how-ever, does not take into account the film moisture adsorbed to the surfaces of the soil particles (this pertains to secondary consolidation). Nor is the consoli-dation theory satisfactory for unsaturated soils (air cushions, gas, and/or vapor pressure). Only comprehensive comparison of actually measured settlements of structures with the predicted or calculated ones may permit evaluation of the usefulness of the method of settlement analysis, based on the consolidation theory of clays, where it is assumed that all voids are totally filled with water.

In the technical literature many publications on consolidations of soils and settlement of structures on such soils show that the measured magnitudes of settle-ment agree reasonably with those calculated by means of the consolidation theory. For example, it has been reported at the Second International Congress on Bridge Construction, held in 1936 in Berlin and at Munich, that, based on many settlement measurements of bridge piers and abutments, the measured, or observed magnitudes of settlement were less than the calculated ones. Of course, settlements may take place not only by consolidation, s_c, but also for other reasons, for example, lateral expulsion of soil material from underneath a foundation. Additional settlements may be caused by

1) lateral expulsion of soil particles from underneath the footing, s_L;
2) lowering the groundwater table, s_{GW};
3) increased moisture content in soil, s_M;
4) thawing of frozen soil, s_F;
5) vibrations, s_v, and
6) other possible causes.

The total settlement, s, of the soil may thus be described in a general way as

$$s = s_c + s_L + s_{GW} + s_M + s_F + s_v + \ldots \qquad (16\text{-}124)$$

Likewise, if the shear stress in a mass of soil underneath a foundation exceeds the shear strength of the soil, the soil may then fail in shear, causing large settle-ments and resulting in a tilted structure, or even in the collapse. Shear failure takes place quickly as soon as the bearing capacity of the soil is exceeded, whereas consolidation settlements continue over a long period of years after the structure has been completed.

As consolidation proceeds, more water is expelled from the soil. Thus, consolidation increases the shear strength of the soil with time.

REFERENCES

1. See Ref. 4, Chapter 15.
2. *Ibid.*

PROBLEMS

16-1. What is the "pressure distribution area"?

16-2. What is an "isochrone", and how do isochrones vary with time?

16-3. For study purposes, organize and tabulate the various pressure conditions in clay during a consolidation process in a convenient tabular form.

16-4. In which direction does the course of the consolidation process in clay proceed: from the center towards the drainage face (towards the outside), or from the drainage face in the direction of the interior of the clay? Illustrate your explanation by an appropriate sketch.

16-5. What is the fundamental, general equation governing the stress conditions in the consolidation process of a cohesive soil? Explain the physical contents this equation represents.

16-6. What is the solution of the consolidation process of a cohesive soil represented by the following equation:

$$\frac{\partial u}{\partial t} = c_v \frac{\partial^2 u}{\partial z^2} ?$$

Also, explain the physical meaning of the various terms of which this equation is composed.

16-7. Plot time-consolidation curves of the Moonachie varved clay, and determine 0% and 100% consolidation by Casagrande and Taylor methods.

Elapsed Time in Minutes	Time of initial readings and vertical dial readings					
	Oct. 2 3:00 pm	Oct. 3 3:00 pm	Oct. 4 3:00 pm	Oct. 5 3:00 pm	Oct. 6 3:00 pm	Oct. 7 3:00 pm
	Dial readings in inches					
1	2	3	4	5	6	7
0	0.9100	1.0143	1.1113	1.3143	1.6169	1.8179
0.25	0.9132	1.0180	1.1171	1.4022	1.7074	1.7151
0.50	0.9150	1.0190	1.1190	1.4056	1.7108	1.7149
1.00	0.9174	1.1005	1.2022	1.4120	1.7121	1.7140
2	1.0007	1.1025	1.2068	1.5007	1.7167	1.7129
3	1.0033	1.1036	1.2100	1.5075	1.8001	1.7111
5	1.0067	1.1053	1.2140	1.5161	1.8045	1.7095
8	1.0095	1.1065	1.2176	1.6017	1.8078	1.7070
10	1.0102	1.1070	1.2188	1.6040	1.8090	1.7050
15	1.0112	1.1077	1.3015	1.6077	1.8108	1.7035
30	1.0123	1.1087	1.3050	1.6114	1.8129	1.7019
60	1.0134	1.1093	1.3076	1.6129	1.8144	1.7000
120	1.0138	1.1098	1.3098	1.6143	1.8155	—
1440	1.0143	1.1113	1.3143	1.6169	1.8179	1.6184
Pressure on soil, kg/cm²	0.625	1.250	2.500	5.000	10.000	0.625
Temperature °F	76	78	80	80	77	76

Note. The readings of the vertical dial used in this test increased as the soil sample was compressed.

16-8. Given time-dial reading data as tabulated.

Elapsed Time in Minutes	Dial Readings in inches	Cumulative Compression h inches	Consolidation in %	Void ratio
1	2	3	4	5
0	0.24930	0.00000	0.00	0.6569
0.25	5540			
0.5	5630			
1	5776			
2	5969			
4	6245	0.01113		0.6368
8	6600			
15	6929			
30	7183			
60	7300			
120	7360			
240	7406			
480	7442			
1440	7511	0.02379	100.00	0.6103

Total pressure on soil sample, $p = 67.9$ lb/in² during a loading cycle. The soil is Raritan clay. Void ratio at time $= 0$ minutes is $e_o = 0.6596$ and at time, t_{1440}, the void ratio is $e = 0.6103$. Relative height of solids at time, t_o, is 1.000. Absolute height of solids at time, t_o, is $h = 0.448$ inches. Prepare the time-consolidation curve. Plot this data to a semi-logarithmic scale on a 5-cycle paper. Plot the dial reading (consolidation) curve. Calculate and fill in Columns 3, 4 and 5. Determine 0% and 100% consolidation.

Note. In performing this exercise, correct the compression in inches by subtracting an "equipment correction factor" of $r = 0.00202$ (in). For example, at time $t = 4$ minutes, the compression in inches is calculated as

Initial reading, R_i	0.24930
(−)	
Reading after 4 minutes, R_4	0.26245
	0.01315
(−)	
Equipment correction factor, $r =$	0.00202
Compression:	0.01113 (in).

16-9. Calculate and plot the t_1, t_2, t_3, t_5, and t_{10} isochrones in the illustrative example in Art. 16-15.

16-10. What does the following equation represent?

$$s_t = \frac{a}{1 + e_i} \int_0^H [\Delta p - u(z; t)] \, dz.$$

Explain terms and illustrate.

16-11. What does the following equation represent?

$$u(z; t) = \frac{1}{H} \sum_{n=1}^{n=\infty} \exp\left[-\left(\frac{n^2\pi^2}{4}\frac{c_v t}{H^2}\right)\right] \sin\frac{n\pi z}{2H} \int \left[f(z; 0) \sin\frac{n\pi z}{2H}\right] dz.$$

Find the value of the integral in the above equation for any initial, hydrostatic excess stress condition, $u_i = u_0 \sin\frac{\pi z}{2H}$, for the full thickness of the cohesive soil layer, $2H$, under a two-way drainage condition, when $n = 1$.

16-12. Using Eq. 16-112, calculate the value of the time factor, τ, at 90% consolidation. ($\tau = 0.848$).

16-13. Calculate the degree of consolidation, μ, for a time factor of $\tau = 0.200$ for two-way drainage and for a rectangular excess pressure distribution area. ($\mu = 0.5041$).

16-14. Prepare time factor-degree of consolidation tables for the various cases (by straight-line interpolation) from Tables 16-1 and 16-2 in 5% intervals, i.e., $\tau = f(\mu)$, arranging data as follows:

μ	τ
0.00	0.000
0.05	
0.10	
0.15	
...	
0.90	
0.95	
1.00	

16-15. After what time are the hydrostatic excess pressures on the middle line of the $2H = 100$ cm thick layer equivalent to (Art. 16-15)
  a) $u(50; t) = 300 \ (g/cm^2)$?
  b) $u(50; t) = (0.5)(u_o)$?
  c) $u(50; t) = (0.25)(u_o)$?
  d) Calculate and plot the b) and c) isochrones in full.

16-16. Report from the illustrative problem, Art. 16-15, the N and τ values.

16-17. If the coefficient of consolidation of a 3.0 m thick layer of clay is $c_v = 0.0003$ cm²/sec, what is the average consolidation of that layer of clay in one year with two-way drainage? (0.71)
  The same as above, for one-way drainage system? (0.37)

16-18. Given on the compression curve, Fig. 16-20, $p_1 = 1.5$ kg/cm² and $p_2 = 2.00$ kg/cm²; $c_v = 0.025$ (cm²/min) for a silty clay layer draining on both sides. The thickness of the clay sample in the consolidometer was 2.0 cm. The thickness of the prototype layer of the soil was 10 ft. Under the given pressure and test conditions, the clay sample gave a 50% consolidation within a period of 7.2 minutes. Experimental 100% consolidation was reached in 1.2 hours.
  Determine: a) Coefficient of compressibility.
       b) Specific loss of pore water.
       c) Permeability of clay for the given test conditions, in cm/sec, and in cm/year.
       d) How long will it take for the layer of clay 10 ft thick to reach a 50% consolidation?
       e) How large is the settlement of the clay layer at 50% consolidation?

f) What is the magnitude of the total settlement?

g) After how long a time will the 100% settlement be attained?

h) How large will be the settlement after one month, and one year?

i) What are the corresponding degrees of consolidation in h)?

j) Calculate and show all time factors involved.

16-19. Given a square footing, $6' \times 6'$, as shown in Fig. Problem 16-19, founded $4'$ below the ground surface. The footing is loaded centrally with a load of $P = 43.2$ tons. The profile of the soil is also shown. The pressure-void ratio curves are shown in Problem Figs. 16-19a, b, c and d, respectively. The four soil samples attained 100% consolidation from 0 kg/cm² to 1.2 kg/cm² in two-way drainage in the following times:

sample No. 1: thickness of sample $2H = 2.57$ cm; in 66 hr 00 min

sample No. 2: thickness of sample $2H = 2.57$ cm; in 71 hr 00 min

sample No. 3: thickness of sample $2H = 2.57$ cm; in 79 hr 06 min

sample No. 4: thickness of sample $2H = 2.57$ cm; in 125 minutes.

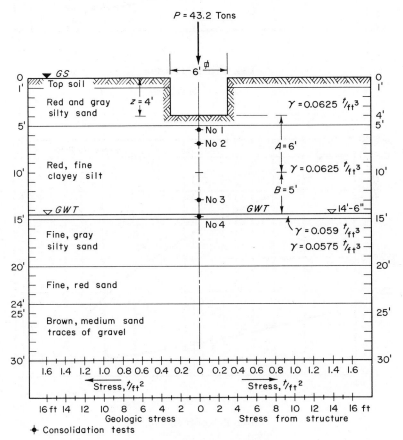

Fig. Problem 16-19.

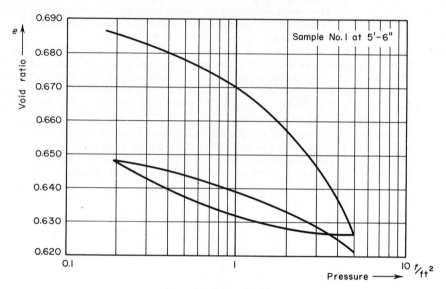

FIG. Problem 16-19a.

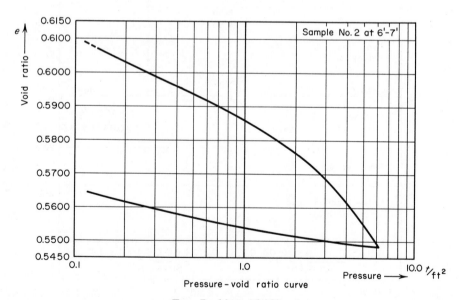

Pressure – void ratio curve

FIG. Problem 16-19b.

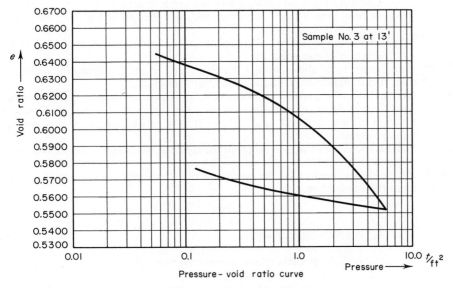

FIG. Problem 16-19c.

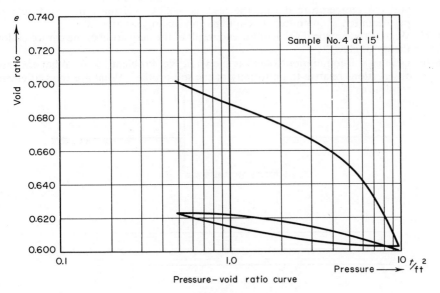

FIG. Problem 16-19d.

Required

    a) Explain the nature of the given four pressure-void ratio curves.

    b) Calculate the total settlement of the given structure

    c) In how long a time, approximately, will the soil attain 50%, 80%, and 100% consolidation?

    d) Estimate the percent of consolidation 2, 5, 10, 20, and 50 years after the erection of the structure.

16-20. Same problem as above, except that the shape of the foundation is a circular slab, 6 ft in diameter. Compare the results obtained.

16-21. Derive from the general μ_{ave}-equation, an equation expressing the average coefficient of degree of consolidation for the mid-thickness of the clay layer as a function of time, i.e., find $\mu_{ave} = f(z = H; t = t)$, when there are two drainage faces available.

16-22. What is the value of $\mu_{ave} = f(z; t)$ in the rigorous solution for a clay system with one-way drainage?

16-23. Derive the expression for the coefficient of permeability of clay, k, in cm/sec, from the consolidation test:

$$k = \frac{\gamma_u a_v \tau H^2}{(1 + e_{ave})t},$$

where γ_w = unit weight of water;

    a_v = coefficient of compressibility, cm²/kg;

    τ = dimensionless factor, termed the time factor;

    H = half the thickness of the layer of clay in one-way drainage, or the shortest path of drainage of clay;

    e_{ave} = average void ratio under a pressure increment;

    t = time in seconds.

16-24. If the coefficient of compressibility is $a_v = 0.1071$ cm²/kg, the coefficient of consolidation is $c_v = 12.960$ cm²/year, the average void ratio is $e_{ave} = 0.680$, and the temperature during the tests is $+25°C$, calculate the coefficient of permeability, k, in cm/sec, in cm/min, and in cm/year at $+20°C$.

16-25. What is the practical value of the end result of the derivation of the consolidation theory of clays?

16-26. Given a soil-foundation system as shown in Fig. Problem 16-26. What are your observations relative to uniformity of the soil profile? What are the settlement conditions?

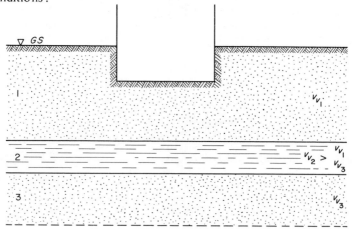

Fɪɢ. Problem 16-26.

16-27. Given a soil-foundation system as shown in Fig. Problem 16-27. What are the settlement conditions in this figure?

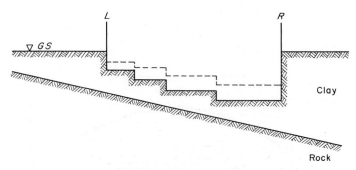

FIG. Problem 16-27.

16-28. In Fig. Problem 16-28, for the conditions shown, which end of the long, continuous structure will settle more, L or R,

if   a) if $v_{v_2} > v_{v_1}$
     b) if $v_{v_1} < v_{v_2}$
     c) if $v_{v_1} = v_{v_2}$?

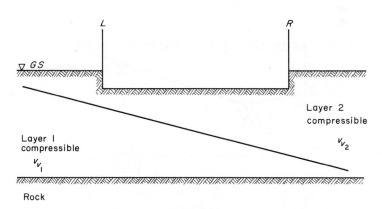

FIG. Problem 16-28.

16-29. In Fig. Problem 16-29, solid convex curve, if $v_{v_1} > v_{v_2}$, what are the settlement conditions at L, at $\mathbb{C}_L$, and at R?
If $v_{v_1} < v_{v_2}$, what are the settlement conditions?

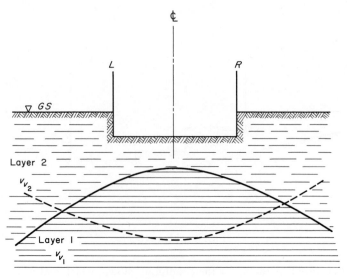

FIG. Problem 16-29.

16-30. In Fig. Problem 16-29, dotted concave curve, if $v_{v_2} > v_{v_1}$, where can most of the settlements be expected, at L, at $\mathcal{C}_L$, or at R?

If $v_{v_1} > v_{v_2}$, then what are the settlement conditions at L, $\mathcal{C}_L$, and at R?

16-31. What are your observations relative to settlement of the swimming pool structure supported at three points in Fig. Problem 16-31?

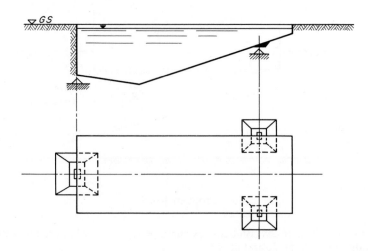

FIG. Problem 16-31.

Chapter 17

VERTICAL SAND DRAINS

17-1. Principle of Function of Sand Drains. The principle of the functioning of a sand drain is based on the consolidation theory of radially and centrally de-watered clay systems.

The normally slow process of consolidation of clays, silt, muck, and other native, compressible, saturated materials may be accelerated by means of vertical sand drains which aid in the expulsion of the pore water from the soil. Essentially, a sand drain consists of a vertical bore hole put down through the saturated, fine-particled soil, and extending to a relatively firm bottom—an impervious layer of rock, such as shale, or basalt, or any other practically impervious geological formation, and backfilled with a pervious material such as carefully graded sand Fig. 17-1.

Because, by the model law of consolidation, time varies as the square of the length of the drainage path, the distance that a particle of pore water must travel

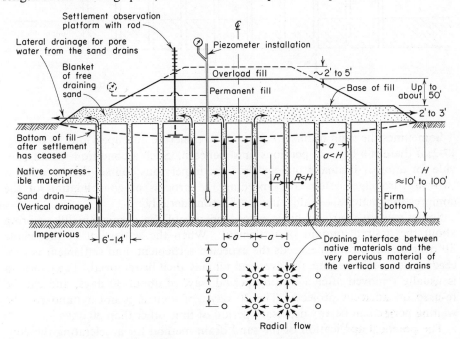

FIG. 17-1 The function of vertical sand drains.

upon expulsion from H to $H/2$, this fact increases the rate of consolidation four-fold. Thus, a vertical sand drain brings about a more than two-fold decrease in the length of the drainage path because of the radial drainage of water towards the vertical drain. The horizontal distance for drainage, in this case of sand drains, is many times shorter than the distance for draining vertically, i.e., $R < H$. Besides, the horizontal permeability of a cohesive soil is usually larger than its vertical permeability because of the shape of the clay particles.

The weight of the fill compresses the soft material, forcing the water into the sand drain and up into the lateral drainage blanket provided from the base of the fill by a layer of pervious sand, from which the pore water expelled from the sand drains, rapidly drains out laterally. The greater the load on the native, compressible material, the faster the process of consolidation.

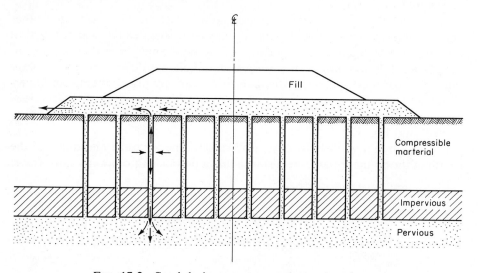

FIG. 17-2 Sand drains puncture an impervious layer.

Sometimes the sand drains are allowed to puncture an impervious layer (Fig. 17-2) if there is a layer of pervious sand beneath. Such a condition would provide for another drainage outlet below the impervious course, thus creating a two-way drainage system and speeding the process of consolidation of the compressible material—stabilizing the fill considerably.

Sometimes an overload fill is placed on top of the permanent fill to bring about the desired amount of settlement. When the settlement of the whole fill over the sand drains exceeds the expected settlement, and settlement is proceeding at a very low rate, the overload fill may then be removed. The overload is usually removed after a waiting period, say, of about 30 days, and can be re-used on adjacent projects. The 30 days, of course, is not a standard; the waiting period can be any necessary period of time other than 30 days.

The practical application of the sand drain method for accelerating the consolidation of soil in the United States is credited to O. J. Porter.[1]

17-2. Purpose of Sand Drain. The purpose of a sand drain system is to accelerate the expulsion and draining away of the pore water squeezed out of the voids of the soft soil by the earth fill, or by a structural load. This speeds up the rate of consolidation, and, thus, the settlement of the soil. Sand drains are also used, under some circumstances, to drain and to control land slides. Sand drains also relieve the hydrostatic excess pressure induced in the voids of the soil by the application of the weight of the fill material on the ground surface of the compressible soil.

Sand drains, providing supplementary outlets for the expelled pore water, also accelerate the increase in shear strength of the native soil to be consolidated.

17-3. Diameter of Drains. The diameter of sand drains varies in practice from about 18 in. in diameter to about 24 in. in diameter. Too small a diameter is not desirable because of difficulties in filling the mandrel pipe with sand, and of the danger of an arching of the sand because of the friction between the column of sand and the wall of the metal tube (mandrel). The sand drain need be only large enough to drain away the expelled quantity of pore water, and to allow for a safety margin against clogging up the drainage interface between the native material and the pervious material in the sand drain by infiltration of fine material.

17-4. Spacing of Sand Drains. The spacing of sand drains depends upon the type and permeability of the soil. For these and other possible reasons the sand drains are, in practice, spaced from 6 to 14 ft center to center. Sand drains are effective for their purpose if their spacing, a, is less than their depth, H, i.e., if $a < H$. Economy requires a study of the effect of spacing the sand drains on the rate of consolidation. Terzaghi[2] recommends choosing the spacing so that 80 % of the total consolidation is brought about during the time of construction of the fill. In practice, spacing for 20 in. diameter sand drains varies on the average from 6 to 10 ft.

17-5. Depth of Sand Drains. The depth of the sand drains is dictated by the geology, i.e., by the depth of the firm layer below the ground surface. Sand drains have been placed to a depth of from 10 ft to 60, 70, 90, and in some cases even to 100 and 135 ft. Sometimes, where "mud" depths are less than 20 ft, it is more economical to strip the "mud" before filling the embankment.

17-6. Installation of Sand Drains. A sand drain is now usually installed by means of a hollow steel pipe, called the mandrel, which acts as a casing during the filling of the sand drain. The lower end of the mandrel is provided with a flat, hinged bottom plate. The empty pipe, with the bottom plate closed, is driven vertically through the native soil material by means of a pile driver having a guide frame. At the top of the pipe there is a sand skip attached to fill the hollow plugged mandrel. The skip can slide up and down the guide frame. After the mandrel has been driven to the proper depth, the mandrel is pulled out during backfilling with sand. The sand is filled under a pressure of about 100 lb/in². The pressure is admitted into the mandrel at its top. As the mandrel is withdrawn out of the ground, the backfill sand is forced out of the mandrel through its lower end by the weight of the sand and the applied pressure (compressed air, or steam) past the now-opened and free-hanging bottom plate into the vertical hole left in the ground by driving the mandrel. The bottom plate is thus recovered and reused.

The rate of withdrawal of the mandrel and the application of pressure must, of course, be very carefully regulated. The pressure is intended to prevent developing of arching of sand in the tube, and to make a reasonably strong sand column.

Upon withdrawal of the mandrel the backfill sand is left as a vertical sand cylinder to function as a vertical sand drain.

The sand drains may also be installed by jetting a hole in the soil, or by driving an open casing into the soil, washing the soil out of the casing, and filling the hole with draining sand afterwards.

17-7. Sand for Drains. The sand used as a draining medium is usually a very carefully selected and clean material. Sometimes not more than 5% of the (-100) material is allowed. To be consistent with economy and availability of materials, no specially prepared graded sand, as applied in the construction of filters, is used. The only requirement for sand to be used in vertical drains is that it should carry away the pore water unobstructed, and not to permit the fine, native soil to be washed in. The permeability requirements are that the drain sand should be approximately 1000 times more permeable than that of the consolidating native soil. The order of magnitude of the permeability of the various consolidated soils is about between $k = 10^{-5}$ cm/sec and $k = 10^{-6}$ cm/sec.

However, the California Department of Highways, according to Stanton,[3] has used the following typical specifications on several of their vertical sand drain projects.

Grading Requirements for Sand Drains

Sieve Size	Percent Passing Sieve
$\frac{1}{2}''$	90-100
No. 8	25-100
No. 30	5- 50
No. 50	0- 20
No. 100	0- 3

17-8. Blanket. After the installation of the vertical sand drains, a blanket of free-draining sand, one to three feet in thickness, is spread over the entire sand-drain area. The blanket should extend to the outer, initial slope, or toe of the slope of the embankment. The sand blanket provides for lateral drainage at the base of the fill for pore water from the vertical sand drains. The sand and gravel used as a blanket should be clean. It is sometimes specified that the blanket material should contain not more than 5% to 10% of (-200) material $(< 0.074$ mm).

The grading of a blanket material established by the California Department of Highways for some of their projects, and also used on some New Jersey sand drain projects, is:

Grading of Blanket Material
(Clean, coarse sand or gravel)

Sieve Size	Percent Passing
$\frac{3}{8}''$	80-100
No. 8	5- 50
No. 30	0- 20
No. 50	0- 5

Permanent Fill. Permanent fill is constructed on top of the drainage blanket. Fills as high as 50 to 70 ft have been stabilized by the vertical sand drain method.

17-9. Rate of Loading. The rate of loading is one of the most important processes in making the fill. Too fast a rate of loading may cause a failure of the earthwork. Rapid loading may induce high hydrostatic excess pressures. These neutral pressures in the early stage of the consolidation process do not contribute to the shear strength of the soil. Therefore, a careful loading control must be practiced.

Control. The purpose of controlling the rate of the construction of an earth embankment is to prevent the rupture of the native soil, and the shearing off of the sand drains—deformations which result in lateral displacement or slide failures of the earth mass, and/or in the formation of "mud waves", or earth heaves.

The devices for controlling the rate of the settlement of the fill and the developed pore water pressures at various depths in the soil underneath the fill are the settlement observation platforms and the piezometers, such as described in this book under the topic on tri-axial compression of soil.

A settlement observation platform is a platform made of timber, to which a vertical rod is attached (Fig. 17-1). The platforms are installed at the base of the fill, and periodic settlement measurements of the platforms (the platforms settle as the fill settles) permit one to gain an insight into the settlement, viz., consolidation process.

The order of magnitude of induced pore water pressures while filling the embankment is up to 12 or 15 lb/in.^{2}, depending upon the type of soil and rate of loading. As time goes on, the pore water pressure indicating gauges show that pore water pressures gradually decrease to normal because the pressure of the pore water is relieved by the establishment of the drainage flow through the vertical sand drains and the lateral drainage blanket.

By correlation of the rate of consolidation of the native soil with the pore water pressures at various depths in the native soil, it is possible to estimate the rate of loading, viz., rate of application of the next safe lift of the fill material.

The amounts of settlement of soil of from 4 to 20 ft have been attained in various instances without failure in shear and without displacing the adjacent mass of soil,[4] thus proving in many instances the safe and economic value of the sand drain method for stabilizing native, compressible soil materials.

There are, however, instances known where the sand drains were not functioning successfully.[5]

17-10. Applications of Sand Drains. Sand drains have been used extensively in California, as well as on the east coast of the United States, for stabilizing compressible soils for highways; railroad yards; for airfield and port development work in the metropolitan areas of New York, N.Y. and Newark, N.J.; for highway projects in Connecticut; for the northern part of the New Jersey Turnpike and the Garden State Parkway, also in New Jersey; as well as in Europe for improving the soil properties suitable for foundation engineering purposes.

17-11. Theory of Vertical Sand Drains. The theory of the functioning of a sand drain is based on the general theory of consolidation of the soil system in space, or in three dimensions. In a spatial soil system, drainage of the expelled pore water takes place horizontally as well as vertically. The three-dimensional consolidation process is described mathematically by the following partial differential equation in the cylindrical coordinate system as

$$\frac{\partial u}{\partial t} = c_h\left(\frac{\partial^2 u}{\partial r^2} + \frac{1}{r}\frac{\partial u}{\partial r}\right) + c_v\frac{\partial^2 u}{\partial z^2}, \qquad (17\text{-}1)$$

where u = hydrostatic excess pore water pressure,
t = time,
r = radial cylindrical coordinate,
z = axial cylindrical coordinate,
c_h = coefficient of consolidation for horizontal drainage,
c_v = coefficient of consolidation for vertical drainage.

The coordinate system for a vertical sand drain is shown in Fig. 17-3.

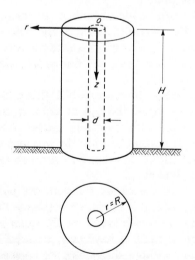

FIG. 17-3 Coordinate system for a vertical sand drain.

The pertinent mathematical solution of this three-dimensional consolidation may be found in the works of Rendulic,[5] Biot,[6] Carillo,[7] Terzaghi,[8] Barron.[9]

17-12. Summary on Vertical Sand Drains.

1) Because of the low permeability of clay, little excess pore water can be drained out of the clay during the construction period of an earth embankment.

2) Sand drains constitute supplementary outlets for the excess pore water.

3) Compressible soils with sand drains settle more rapidly than those without drains.

4) Sand drains hasten primary consolidation.
5) The horizontal permeability of the soil to pore water, a permeability which is greater than the vertical one, accounts for the effectiveness of sand drains in consolidating a soil.
6) Consolidation by means of sand drains can be brought about easily in a relatively short time, 3 to 12 months, depending upon the thickness of the consolidating layer of soil, among other conditions, and attaining most of the settlement during the construction period of the fill.
7) Sand drains are relatively weak in shear, particularly if shearing is effected by lateral displacement of the soil mass underneath the fill. Therefore, the rate of loading the fill must be such as not to cause failure in shear of the soil mass.
8) Vertical sand drains accelerate the increase in shearing resistance of the native material.
9) Sand drains are successfully applicable where soil, drainage, and geological conditions are proper and suitable for sand drains to apply.
10) The theory of the functioning of the sand drains, the pore water pressure relationships, and the solution for spacing of the vertical sand drains is based on advanced higher mathematics and requires the use of Bessel functions.

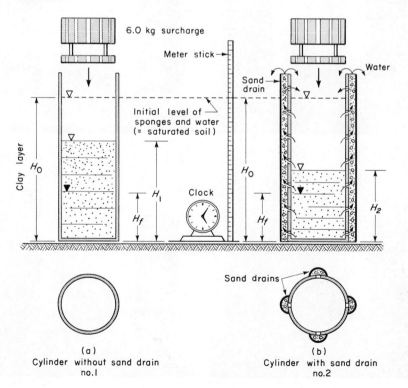

FIG. 17-4   Sand drain model.

17-13. Sand Drain Model. The effect of sand drains on the settlement, viz., consolidation process of a compressible material can most readily be studied by the following pedagogical sand drain model. Two lucite cylinders of equal size are filled to a certain height with sponges (porous material). One of the cylinders, No. 2, is provided with four sand drains (Figs. 17-4a and b). The sand drains consist of small half-cylinders spaced 90° apart around the periphery of the cylinder, filled with sand. Through the wall of cylinder No. 2 holes are drilled so that water under pressure can escape through these into the sand drains.

The sponges, representing a compressible material to be consolidated, are assumed to be identical in size, physical properties, and ability to hold water, and are snugly fitted into the cylinder ("column of soil"), and at the same initial height, H_o.

FIG. 17-5 The functioning of the sand drain model.

The experiment starts with pouring water into the cylinders just to cover the surface of the top sponge, expelling the air from the voids of the sponges. It is necessary to make sure that the water level is the same in each column of sponges. By this is meant 100% saturation of the "voids of the soil". Next, equal loads ("surcharge") of 6.0 kg (constant weight) are simultaneously placed on top of the sponges in each cylinder, and the timing and recording of the compression of the sponges is started. The weights are provided with holes to simulate a porous blanket layer on top of the "clay" layer as depicted by the sponges. At predetermined time intervals, the position of the top surface of both of the sponge columns ("consolidating soil") is noted in each cylinder. It can be observed that at time t_1 the height of the compressed sponges in cylinder No. 1 is greater than in cylinder No. 2, i.e., $H_1 > H_2$. This means that the sponges in the cylinder provided with the sand drains (cylinder No. 2) consolidate faster than those in the cylinder (No. 1) without sand drains. After some lapse of time, the heights of the sponges in both cylinders are at the same final height, H_f (indicating total or 100% consolidation under the externally applied load of 6 kg). The functioning of the sand drain model is illustrated in Figs. 17-5a, b, c, and d.

The data collected, settlement as a function of time, may be used to plot two "time-settlement" curves: one curve for a "soil" without sand drains, and one curve for the same "soil" with sand drains.

The curves would reveal that the settlement is much faster in the "soil" (cylinder No. 2) with sand drains than in the one which does not have any (cylinder No. 1).

This crude experiment shows that the time of settlement of the "compressible soil" is directly dependent on the ability of the "pore water" in bulk to escape from the "voids of the soil". It also shows that whereas in the past it was necessary to wait relatively long periods of time for settlement of the fill, today, by the proper use of sand drains, highway pavements can be laid in a much shorter period of time than without the vertical sand drains.

REFERENCES

1. O. J. Porter, "Studies of Fill Construction over Mud Flats Including a Description of Experimental Construction Using Vertical Sand Drains to Hasten Stabilization", *Proceedings*, First International Conference on Soil Mechanics and Foundation Engineering, held in June, 1936 at Cambridge, Mass., vol. 1, pp. 229-235.
2. K. Terzaghi, "Drainage of Clay Strata by Filter Wells", *Civil Engineer*, no. 10, October, 1945, p. 463.
3. F. E. Stanton, "Vertical Sand Drains as a Means of Foundation Consolidation on Accelerating Settlement of Embankment over Marsh Land", *Proceedings*, Second International Conference on Soil Mechanics and Foundation Engineering, held in 1948, in Rotterdam, vol. 5, p. 273; 278.
4. H. A. Simard, "Sand Piles Hasten Completion of California Expressway", *Roads and Streets*, December, 1947.
5. W. S. Housel, *Checking up on Vertical Sand Drains*, Highway Research Board Bulletin, no. 90, 1954, pp. 1-16.
6. L. Rendulic, *Der hydrodynamische Spannungsausgleich in zentral entwässerten Tonzylindern*, Wasserwirtschaft und Technik, 1935, vol. 2, pp. 250-253; 269-273.

7. M. A. Biot, "General Theory of Three-Dimensional Consolidation", *Journal of Applied Physics*, New York, February, 1941, vol. 12, pp. 155-164.
8. N. Carrillo, "Simple Two and Three Dimensional Cases in the Theory of Consolidation of Soils", *Journal of Mathematics and Physics*, 1942, vol. 21, pp. 1-5.
9. K. Terzaghi, *Theoretical Soil Mechanics*, New York, John Wiley and Sons, Inc., 1948, pp. 290-296.
10. R. A. Barron, "Consolidation of Fine-Grained Soils by Drain-Wells", *Proceedings*, American Society of Civil Engineers, vol. 73, 1947, vol. 113, 1948.

Chapter 18

SETTLEMENT

SETTLEMENT BY CONSOLIDATION

18-1. The Washington Monument, Washington, D.C. The Washington monument, Fig. 18-1, according to Ref. 1, affords the longest settlement record available in the United States. The monument is founded on a "sandy mound". Borings in 1931 disclosed an irregular bed of compressible clay 10 to 40 ft thick overlying rock. The size of the original footing was 80 ft square. The construction work on the monument was interrupted in 1854, when the structure was

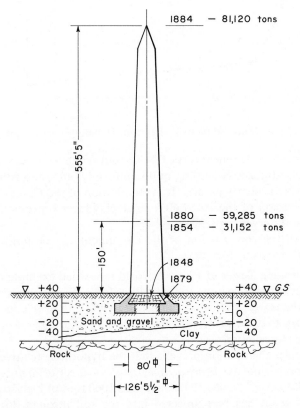

FIG. 18-1 Washington monument. Years, weights, and soil profile.

461

150 ft high, and the total weight was about 31,150 tons, giving a contact pressure on the soil of $p_o = 5$ tons/ft^2.

There are no settlement records available for this monument prior to 1879. After that year, the original foundation of the monument was underpinned to a size of 126 ft 5$\frac{1}{2}$ in. square. Then building of the monument was continued, and it attained its full height by 1884. During the process of increasing the load to

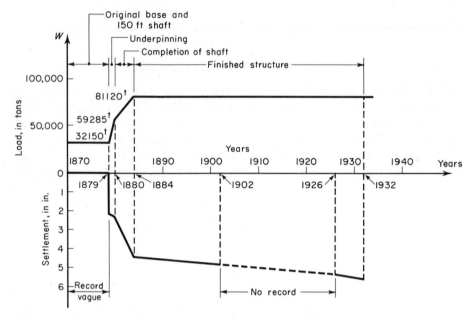

FIG. 18-2   Time-settlement diagram, Washington monument.

5 tons/ft^2 again, the monument settled 4$\frac{1}{2}$ in.; subsequent to 1885, another inch, and, is probably still slowly settling quite uniformly, and, according to the Report, the structure is nearly plumb. It is the opinion of the Committee in Ref. 1 that the compression of the 10 to 40 ft thick clay layer is probably responsible for most of the observed settlements.

The course of the construction of the monument can be followed from the time-settlement diagram, Fig. 18-2.

18-2. The Leaning Tower of Pisa. A world renowned example of differential settlement is the classical leaning tower of Pisa, Italy. Based on his studies on the settlement of the tower, Imbeaux[2] published in 1927 an article in which he put forward a theory that the principal cause of leaning of the bell tower is the subterranean water (*erosion theory*).

In Italian circles the opinion prevails that the hypothesis relative to the instability of the tower is *the low bearing capacity of the layer of sand* (see Fig. 18-3). According to Krynine,[3] "since 1932 more than 1000 tons of high strength cement in the form of grout has been injected into the soil through 361 holes, 2 in. in diameter".

In 1934, Terzaghi[4] published a stress distribution diagram in soil underneath the leaning tower, Fig. 18-3 and, based on soil mechanics considerations that the settlement and the leaning of the tower are attributed very probably and almost exclusively to the gradual consolidation of the clayey soil situated 8 m underneath the footing of the foundation of the tower, also published a time-settlement diagram for the tower, Fig. 18-4.

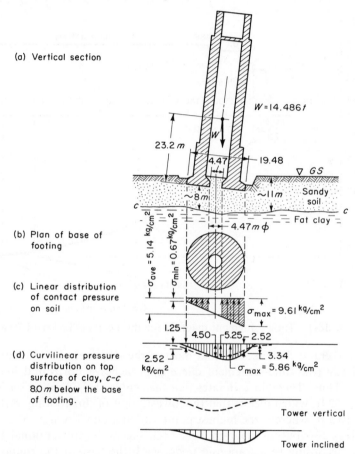

(a) Vertical section

$W = 14.486\,t$

23.2 m

4.47   19.48   ▽ GS

~8m   ~11m   Sandy soil

c $\sigma_{ave} = 5.14$ kg/cm² $\sigma_{min} = 0.67$ kg/cm²   4.47 m φ   Fat clay   c

(b) Plan of base of footing

(c) Linear distribution of contact pressure on soil

$\sigma_{max} = 9.61$ kg/cm²

1.25   4.50   5.25   2.52

(d) Curvilinear pressure distribution on top surface of clay, c–c 8.0 m below the base of footing.

2.52 kg/cm²   3.34 $\sigma_{max} = 5.86$ kg/cm²

Tower vertical

Tower inclined

FIG. 18-3   Stress distribution in soil, the Leaning Tower of Pisa.

On the horizontal time axis are plotted the years of the various construction stages and on the vertical load-axis (up) are designated the corresponding loads of the galleries erected. On the vertical settlement-axis (down) is indicated the relative settlement of the southern side of the tower. (The settlements indicated are differences in elevation between the highest and deepest point of the base of the footing). The horizontal parts in the steps of the time-load diagram indicate the years during which construction of the tower was interrupted because of the pronounced settlements which occurred during the periods of construction. The magnitude of the absolute settlement of the tower at the door is reported by Terzaghi as being 2.4 m ≈ 7.87 ft. After the intermediate settlements ceased, construction of the tower was resumed by adding one or two more galleries. The diagram also shows that the bell gallery was erected in 1350 A.D. The total load of the tower was then 14,486 metric tons, resulting in a settlement of 70 cm ≈ 27.5 in. This diagram also shows that from 1174 A.D. to 1933 A.D., a period of 759 years, the resulting settlement of the point in question

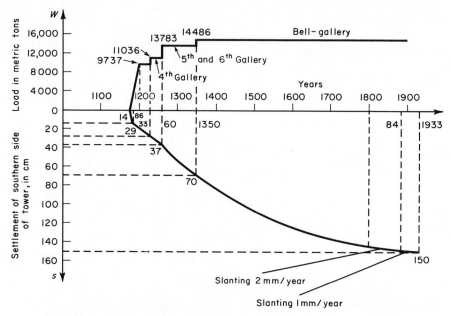

FIG. 18-4   Time-settlement diagram for the Leaning Tower of Pisa.

attained 150 cm ≈ 50.9 in., and that most of the settlement has already reached a state of rest (the time-settlement curve approaches a horizontal line asymptotically). Thus, Terzaghi estimates that the center of the footing settled about 0.8 m ≈ 2.62 ft, which means that the lowest point of this footing settled about 3.2 m ≈ 10.5 ft, whereas the highest point settled about 1.6 m ≈ 5.25 ft.

The stress distribution diagram, Fig. 18-3, shows the conventional stress distribution according to a trapezoid underneath the base of the round footing:

$$\left.\begin{array}{l}\sigma_{max} = 9.61 \text{ kg/cm}^2 \\ \sigma_{min} = 0.67 \text{ kg/cm}^2\end{array}\right\} \text{ tower in leaning position.}$$

$$\sigma_{ave} = 5.14 \text{ kg/cm}^2 \quad \text{tower in vertical position.}$$

The stress distribution diagram due to the weight of the tower at 8 m depth shows a maximum pressure of $\sigma_{max} = 5.86$ kg/cm^2 on the surface of the clay.

Terzaghi also calculates by comparison with another structure, and using the model law that 95% of the total settlement of the tower would be attained after

$$t_2 = t_1 \frac{k_1}{k_2} \frac{H_2{}^2}{H_1{}^2} = (17)(10)(2)^2 = 680 \text{ (years)}, \qquad (18\text{-}1)$$

where H_1 = 15 m thickness of clay underneath another structure used for comparison;

t_1 = 17 years to bring about 95% consolidation of the layer of clay H_1 = 15 m thick;

H_2 = 30 m = $2H_1$ = thickness of clay layer in question underneath the leaning tower of Pisa;

$k_2 = (k_1)/(10)$ = permeability relationship of clay to water between layers H_2 and H_1.

The 100% consolidation will, of course, require a very long period of time.

C. B. Spencer[5] reported in 1954 after a visit to Pisa that the tower was still leaning of some 0.04 in. per year. The question, therefore, arises whether consolidation is the only reason for the settlement of the leaning tower of Pisa.

SETTLEMENT BY LATERAL EXPULSION OF SOIL

18-3. Laterally Unconfined Settlement. In the process of consolidation the vertical settlement of the soil results solely due to the compression of the soil in a lateral confinement, and does not contain any settlement component brought about by the lateral expulsion of the soil mass from underneath the footing. The settlement accompanied by the soil lateral expulsion is, thus, another mode of settlement.

The process of the lateral expulsion of dry sand particles from underneath a loaded contact area may be observed behind the glass wall of an experimental box, as illustrated in Fig. 18-5. The foundation model is loaded centrally with no horizontal force applied to it. Note that the soil particles translocate laterally and up along a curved path, and the entire expelled wedge of soil also translocates along a curved surface. The lateral characteristic, among other

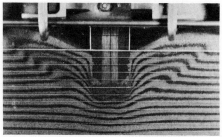

FIG. 18-5 Settlement by lateral expulsion of soil from underneath the base of the footing.

things, depends very much upon the degree of the density of the soil. From experiments performed by the author over a period of many years, it can also be observed that during the time of lateral expulsion the soil directly underneath the base of the footing generally undergoes a process of compression.

Upon the action of an external load on the soil, the latter undergoes elastic (reversible) as well as plastic (irreversible or permanent) deformations (in compression and expansion). The permanent deformations always accompany the elastic ones; the permanent ones often being greater than the elastic deformations. In this phenomenon, then, lies the principal difference in deformations in soil and deformations in the elastic body. It is here repeatedly emphasized that soils are not completely elastic materials.

18-4. Amount of Settlement by Lateral Expulsion of Soil. The present state of knowledge for evaluating the amount of settlement of a foundation due to lateral expulsion of a soil mass from underneath the base of the footing is, unfortunately, very primitive.

However, based on Kögler and Scheidig's ideas,[6] the following is a description of a method for ascertaining roughly the amount of settlement by lateral expulsion (consult Fig. 18-6).

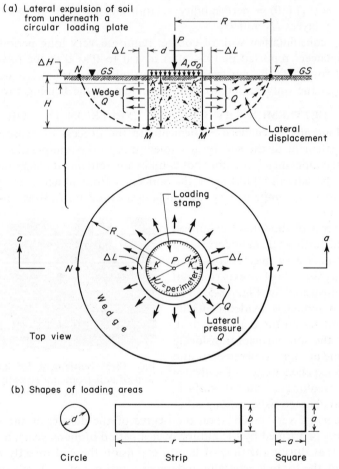

(a) Lateral expulsion of soil from underneath a circular loading plate

(b) Shapes of loading areas

Circle   Strip   Square

FIG. 18-6   System for the evaluation of settlement caused by lateral expulsion of soil (A modification after Kögler and Scheidig, Ref. 30).

Assume that load P on a circular loading or bearing plate develops in the soil a radially directed lateral pressure, Q, a pressure which, it may be said, is then a function of the contact pressure, $\sigma_o = P/A$, where A = contact area Thus the lateral pressure is a function of the contact pressure σ_o:

$$Q = f(\sigma_o). \tag{18-2}$$

This lateral pressure, Q, brings about a lateral, radial displacement, ΔL, of the soil particles around the soil cylinder k-k'-M'-M underneath the circular contact area, A, whose perimeter is U.

It is also assumed that the displacement, ΔL, is proportional to the lateral pressure, Q:

$$\Delta L = c_1 Q, \qquad (18\text{-}3)$$

where c_1 = a coefficient of proportionality.

Because of the lateral displacement, ΔL, the loading area, A, settles by an amount of ΔH. Therefore, the settled volume must be equal to the displaced volume of soil if no loosening or compaction of the displaced soil takes place:

$$(\Delta H)(A) = (B)(\Delta L), \qquad (18\text{-}4)$$

where B is the cylindrical surface of the soil cylinder k-k'-M'-M, the radius of which is $r = d/2$, and the height $= H$.

Hence, the cylindrical surface area, B, can be expressed as

$$B = UH, \qquad (18\text{-}5)$$

where U = perimeter of the circular loading area.

In this theory the depth, H, is assumed to be a function of the soil properties, for example, friction (a constant value for a particular soil). Therefore,

$$H = \Phi(\phi) = c_2 \qquad (18\text{-}6)$$

and

$$B = UH = c_2 U, \qquad (18\text{-}7)$$

where c_2 = a constant coefficient.

The displaced volume of soil, Eq. (18-4), can now be written as

$$(\Delta H)A = c_2 U \Delta L = c_2 U c_1 Q = c_2 U c_3 \sigma_o, \qquad (18\text{-}8)$$

because by Eq. (18-2), $Q = f(\sigma_o)$.

Setting $c_2 c_3 = c_4$, obtain

$$(\Delta H)(A) = c_4 \sigma_o U, \qquad (18\text{-}9)$$

or settlement, ΔH, due to lateral expulsion

$$\Delta H = c_4 \sigma_o \frac{U}{A}, \qquad (18\text{-}10)$$

where c_4 = a coefficient containing the effect of the internal friction of the soil.

18-5. Loading Radius. The quantity U/A recalls from hydraulics the expression for the hydraulic radius. In soil mechanics, this quantity is termed by the author the "loading radius", because it reflects the shape (U) and the size (A) of the loaded area to bring about settlement, ΔH, caused by the lateral expulsion of the soil from underneath the loading area.

The expressions for the most common shapes of loading areas and their perimeters, and consequently their loading radii, can now be calculated as follows:

1) *Circle*: $2r = d$ = diameter.
   Perimeter: $U = 2\pi r = \pi d$
   Area: $A = \pi r^2 = (\pi d^2)/4$
   Loading radius: $U/A = 2/r = 4/d$ (18-11)

2) *Square*: a = length of side.
   Perimeter: $u = 4a$
   Area: $A = a^2$
   Loading radius: $U/A = 4/a$ (18-12)

3) *Long strip footing*: width = b; length = a
   Perimeter: $U = 2a + 2b$
   Area: $A = ab$
   Loading radius $\quad U/A = \dfrac{2(a+b)}{ab} = \dfrac{2}{b} + \dfrac{2}{a} \approx \dfrac{4}{2b},$ (18-13)

if b is very large.

The magnitudes of settlement by lateral expulsion of soil for the above three common figures can now be expressed as

1) *Circle*:

$$\Delta H_{\text{circle}} = c_4 \sigma_o (4/d) = c(\sigma_o/d) \qquad (18\text{-}14)$$

2) *Square*:

$$\Delta H_{\text{square}} = c_4 \sigma_o (4/a) = c(\sigma_o/a) \qquad (18\text{-}15)$$

3) *Long strip*:

$$\Delta H_{\text{long strip}} = c_4 \sigma_o (4/2b) = c(\sigma_o/ab), \qquad (18\text{-}16)$$

where $c = 4c_4$ = a constant, different for different soils.

If $a = d = b$, it follows from Eqs. (18-14), (18-15), and (18-16) that loaded circular and square areas settle twice as much as a strip area of the same width as the diameter, d, of a circular area, or the side, a, of a square area. This is so because the first two area shapes (circular and square) have more possibilities for lateral displacement than the strip has.

To sum up, Eqs, (18-14), (18-15), and (18-16) show that settlement of a loaded bearing plate or area by lateral expulsion of soil at the same contact pressure, σ_o, is greater, the smaller the loaded area.

Technical literature so far furnishes very little information on the c-values, because they are very difficult to ascertain. Kögler-Scheidig give the following crude values for c:

loose sand	$c = 50 \text{ cm}^4/\text{kg}$
dense sand	$c = 6 \text{ cm}^4/\text{kg}$
very dense clay	$c = 1 \text{ cm}^4/\text{kg}.$

Thus, settlement in loose sand due to lateral expulsion is greater than in a dense sand.

A strong warning is given here that these figures are very rough and should not ordinarily be used; instead, an attempt should be made to ascertain them by tests on the particular soil material in question. Besides, this theory considers only the loading on the ground surface, but does not take into account the depth of the foundation. Nor are the rigidity of the loading plate and possibly other important factors taken into account.

A field for research on settlement by lateral expulsion of soil is open here.

REMEDIAL MEASURES AGAINST HARMFUL SETTLEMENTS

18-6. Remedy. In general, settlements of soil, as they are natural phenomena, are unavoidable. However, the engineer should make provision for keeping down large, intolerable, and non-uniform settlements.

To attain uniform settlements it is not necessary to achieve the same contact pressure intensities, σ_o, under all footings of the foundations of one structure, say $\sigma_o = W/A$, where W = weight of the structure and foundation and A = contact area. However, it is necessary to bring into accord the shape and the size of the footings so that all foundations of one and the same structure attain one and the same amount of settlement. Every non-uniform load distribution leads to unequal, or differential settlement.

The following is a list of some remedial measures against large settlements:
  a) removal of soft layers of soil, such as peat, muck, or other material, consistent with economy;
  b) the use of properly designed and constructed pile foundations;
  c) provision for lateral restraint or counterweight against lateral expulsion of a soil mass from underneath the footing of a foundation, or from underneath the base of an earth fill;
  d) reduction of the contact pressure on the soil in some instances; the problem here is more that of the proper adjustment between pressure, shape, and size of the foundation in order to attain uniform settlements underneath the structure;
  e) preconsolidation of a building site long enough for the envisioned load and tolerable settlements (dams, bridges, highway or airfield fills);
  f) building slowly on cohesive soils to avoid lateral expulsion of a soil mass, and to give time for the pore water to be expelled by the surcharge load and drained away;
  g) chemical or mechanical stabilization of soil at a building site.
To achieve uniform settlements, one would
  a) design foundations by observing the "area law" of the loaded footing;
  b) use artificial cushions of soil underneath the less settling foundation parts of the structure;
  c) build different parts of foundations of different weight and on different soil at different depths;

    d) build the heavier parts of the structure first (such as towers and spires, for example), and the lighter parts later.

To make intolerable settlements harmless, sometimes the following constructive measures are applied:

    a) structures are supported on foundations designed as statically determined structural systems;

    b) structures and their foundations are designed as a rigid, stereometric unit (for example silos on continuous slab);

    c) long structures are subdivided and built as separate units;

    d) a structure, the parts of which are non-uniformly loaded, is subdivided.

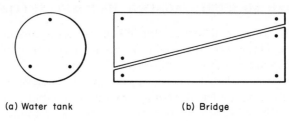

(a) Water tank   (b) Bridge

FIG. 18-7   Three-point support of structures.

Sometimes, to obviate undesirable stress at any stage of differential settlement, structures like bridges, water towers, reservoirs, and swimming pools are supported on three points,[7] Fig. 18-7. The three-point supporting system permits jacking up the structure at each individual support so that the structure may be raised and leveled as settlement takes place.

To accomplish these objectives, the need for thorough soil exploration and soil testing comes to the fore.

REFERENCES

1. "Earths and Foundations"—A Progress Report of Special Committee, presented at the Annual Meeting of the ASCE, New York, N.Y., January 18, 1933. *Proceedings,* ASCE, 1933, vol. 59, pp. 777-820, 813-814.
2. E. Imbeaux, "Les eaux souterraines, cause principale de l'inclinaison du campanil de Pise", Academie des Sciences—Comptes Rendus, Paris, Nov. 7, 1927, vol. 185, no. 19, pp. 995-998.
3. D. P. Krynine, *Soil Mechanics,* New York, 1947, McGraw-Hill Book Co., Inc., p. 410.
4. K. Terzaghi, "Die Ursachen der Schiefstellung des Turmes von Pisa", *Der Bauingenieur,* January 5, 1934, no. 1/2, pp. 1-4. Hereto, a mathematical discussion by O. K. Fröhlich on pressure distribution, consolidation and similitude; March 16, 1934, no. 11/12, pp. 112-113.
5. C. B. Spencer, "Leaning Tower of Pisa—an Engineering Absurdity", *Columbia Research News in Engineering and Science 1954 Annual,* Columbia University Engineering Center, New York, N.Y., pp. 8-9.
6. F. Kögler and A. Scheidig, *Baugrund und Bauwerk,* Wilhelm Ernst und Sohn, Berlin, 1948, p. 112.
7. P. H. Ogden, "Adjustable Water Tanks at Heanor", *Civil Engineering* (London), 1948, vol. 33, p. 131.

PROBLEMS

18-1.   Calculate settlement in dense and loose soils due to lateral expulsion of soil for the following areas, A, and contact pressures, σ_0:

σ_0 kg/cm^2	A_0 cm^2	A cm^2	A_0 cm^2	A cm^2	A_0 cm^2	A cm^2
1; 2; 5;	100	100	100	50	50	100

Formulate your observations.

18-2.   Using a value of $c = 1$ cm^4/kg, solve for settlement, considering lateral expulsion of soil from underneath the base of footings, if $A_1 = 100$ cm^2 and $A_2 = 100$ cm $\times$ 100 cm.

18-3.   Same problem as Problem 18-2, except for circular bearing areas when $d_1 = 10$ cm and $d_2 = 100$ cm.

CHAPTER 11

PROBLEMS

PART V

Strength Properties of Soil

Chapter 19

SHEER STRENGTH OF SOIL

19-1. Definition. The shear strength of soil is the resistance to deformation by continuous shear displacement of soil particles or en masse upon the action of a tangential (shear) stress.

The shear strength of a soil is basically made up of

1) the structural resistance to displacement of the soil because of the interlocking of the soil particles,
2) the frictional resistance to translocation between the individual soil particles at their contact points, and
3) cohesion (adhesion) between the surfaces of the soil particles.

19-2. Determination of Shear Strength of Soil. The shear strength of a soil is usually determined experimentally by one of the following methods:

1) direct shear test;
2) laterally confined compression test, known also as the triaxial compression test; and
3) unconfined compression test.

All shear tests of soils are essentially destructive tests in contradistinction to consolidation tests which, by their nature, are model tests.

Depending upon the type of shear test devices producing shear planes, soils can be tested in single shear, double shear, torsional shear, and punch shear, Fig. 19-1. In this book only the single type of shear will be dealt with.

19-3. Direct Shear Test. The purpose of the direct shear test of a soil is to obtain its ultimate shear resistance, τ, its angle of internal friction, ϕ, its cohesion, c, and its shear stress-deformation characteristics. This information is necessary in substructure analyses, in determining the bearing capacity of soil, in stability calculations of earth slopes, in pile driving, and other earthworks.

The shear strength of a soil can be readily determined by letting it fail in single shear in a direct shear testing apparatus (Fig. 19-2). This apparatus is of the type of controlled stress. When the shear strength is exhausted, rupture failure takes place—manifesting itself in a rupture surface of shear.

The shear strength, τ, as represented by the τ-line on the graph in Fig. 19-3, is given analytically by the following straight-line equation, known as Coulomb's shear strength equation:[1]

$$\tau = \sigma_{n_{eff}} \tan \phi + c, \quad (\text{kg/cm}^2) \qquad (19\text{-}1)$$

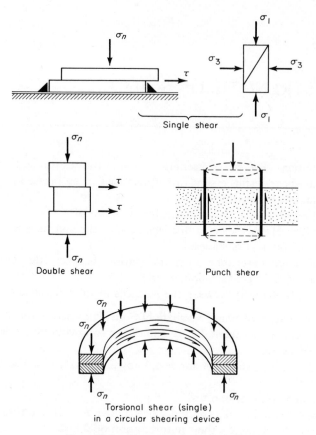

FIG. 19-1   Types of shear in soil.

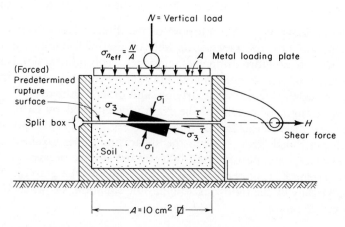

FIG. 19-2   Principle of direct soil-shear testing apparatus.

where the intercept, c, is termed the cohesion of the soil,

the slope of the τ-line, $\tan \phi$, is termed the coefficient of internal friction of that soil,

ϕ = angle of internal friction of the soil, and

$\sigma_{n_{eff}}$ = effective normal stress on the rupture plane.

Eq. (19-1) reads that the shear strength, τ, of a frictional-cohesive soil varies as a straight line function of the applied effective, normal stress, $\sigma_{n_{eff}}$. In other words, the shear strength of a soil is proportional to the normal stress on the shear plane.

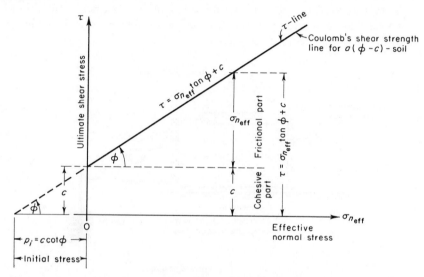

FIG. 19-3   Shear strength factors graphically.

To exclude from the shear test results the effect of apparent cohesion, the shear test must be performed under an inundated condition (surface tension of water is eliminated).

The shear strength of non-cohesive soil is

$$\tau = \sigma_{n_{eff}} \tan \phi, \qquad (19\text{-}1a)$$

because $c = 0$.

The shear strength of a pure cohesive soil whose coefficient of friction is $\tan \phi = 0$, is mathematically expressed as

$$\tau = c. \qquad (19\text{-}1b)$$

19-4. Types of Shear Tests. Among the types of testing the shear strength of soil the following are the most common:

  a) the "quick test",
  b) the "consolidated quick test", and
  c) the "consolidated slow test".

The shear test procedure to use for a soil depends upon what is considered to be the most representative behavior of the soil in the prototype. The test method should simulate natural conditions as closely as possible.

a) *The Quick Test.* A quick test is understood to be a shear test where the shear resistance of a soil sample is measured immediately after application of the normal load (perpendicular to the shear plane). In this test, no time is allowed for consolidation of the soil either before or during the shear test. To ascertain that during the test the void ratio of the soil would change as little as possible, the shear force is applied rapidly. In this method of test, one entire test can be completed till failure in about 5 to 10 minutes. In this test, the soil water has not time enough to drain fully out the voids of the soil.

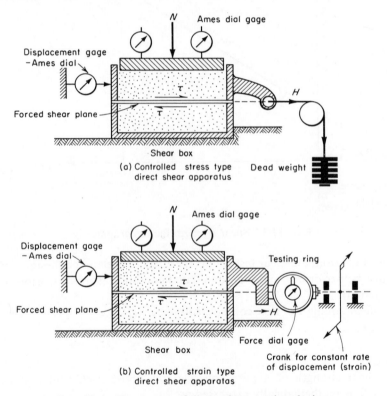

FIG. 19-4 Two types of direct shear testing devices.

In engineering practice we have mostly to deal with a relatively quick shear loading where the excess pore water has no time to escape, or there is no time to adjust or equalize the pore water pressure. Under such conditions the resistance of an earth mass to sliding under certain conditions results in smaller values than those obtained from tests. Therefore, the most unfavorable condition is to be considered—the sudden loading of a soil mass till failure. Accordingly, the shear test in the laboratory is to be performed quickly; hence the term "quick test".

b) *The Consolidated Quick Test.* This test is similar to the preceding one, except that here the drainage of soil water out of the voids is permitted, and the soil sample is allowed to consolidate fully under the applied normal load before the shear force is applied to the soil. After achieving a certain degree of consolidation, which takes place very slowly, this shear test can be accomplished in 5 to 10 minutes.

c) *The Consolidated Slow Test.* In this test, the soil sample is allowed to consolidate fully under the normal load. The consolidation in this test is performed very slowly, so that throughout the entire test there is practically no excess stress in the pore water of the soil sample. For cohesive soils, therefore, the shear force must be applied in very small increments, and with a sufficient time lapse for complete drainage before the next shear load increment is applied. It may require 4 to 6 weeks to complete a single consolidated slow test. This kind of test is almost exclusively used in research and very seldom in practical engineering on cohesive soils. Because non-cohesive sands drain and consolidate quickly, these soils are usually tested in the consolidated slow test condition.

In a way, these three methods of direct shear tests of soils reflect best the true shear properties of the soil material.

19-5. Controlled Strain Shear Testing of Soil. The shear strength of soil can also be tested by a direct shear apparatus of the controlled strain type.

The principle of the two types of direct shear test devices is illustrated in Fig. 19-4. In the controlled stress shear apparatus the shear stress is applied at a constant rate or in equal increments by means of a dead weight, for instance, till failure occurs. The shear displacement is measured by a dial gage, such as an Ames dial gage, which indicates the amount of displacement.

The controlled stress type shear test is used for most practical purposes in soil engineering. The controlled strain type shear test is primarily used in research, but can also be used for solving practical problems. The controlled strain (shear displacement) is applied to the shear box horizontally at a constant rate by means of a screw (manually operated, or motorized) and a calibrated testing ring. The constant rate of shear displacement is observed on the Ames dial gage. The testing ring with a calibrated force dial gage shows the shear resistance of the soil at any rate of horizontal strain applied to the soil, viz., shear box.

19-6. Shear Strength of Sand. The principal advantage of the shear test apparatus of the controlled strain type is that in this test of a dense sand the peak shear resistance, as well as shear resistances smaller than the peak, can be observed and plotted. Such a plot, the shear-strain diagram of a soil, is illustrated in Fig. 19-5. By this method of test, not only the magnitudes of shear resistance can be measured, but, as Fig. 19-5 illustrates, such test results plotted on a graph also indicate how the soil behaves during the process of shear, particularly as the shear process approaches failure. In this figure, the stress-strain curves for a dense sand and for a loose sand are shown, namely the shear stress τ, or the ratio of τ/σ_n, is represented as a function of unit displacement (unit deformation), or strain, ε, of soil along its forced shear plane.

At the beginning of the shear process, up to the so-called proportional limit (*P.L.*) within stage I, Fig. 19-5, the stress necessary for shearing the densely packed soil increases proportionally with the increase in strain. This can be explained by the higher density and greater pressure with which the soil particles are pressed against each other during the initial stage of shear deformation, and consequently also by the increased number of contacts between the soil particles compared with a loose structure of sand.

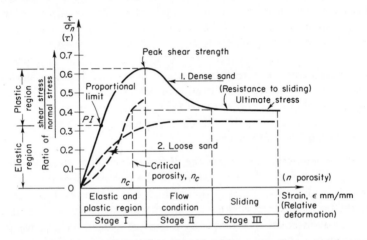

FIG. 19-5   Shear strength as a function of strain at constant normal stress, σ_n.

Point *P.L.* is also termed the critical shear stress. The region between point *P.L.* and the greatest τ-ordinate, or τ/σ_n-ordinate, in stage I depends very much upon the petrographic properties of the sand such as the shape and the surface topography of the particles.

Note, that after all of the shear strength of the dense sand is exhausted, the τ-ε curve (shear/shear displacement curve) of the dense sand has a maximum value known as the *peak shear stress*, which is the shear strength of the soil sample at that normal load in that test. Past the peak in stage II, with further continuous increase in shear displacement (strain), the resistance to shear stresses, τ, overcoming some of the cohesive forces at points of contact between soil particles, and possible distortion of individual soil particles, are dropping— attaining a continuously sliding, ultimate stress, stage III.

In the last stage (III) of the process of continuous shear displacement, the phenomenon of resistance to sliding is brought out. The resistance to sliding is less than the resistance to shear of dense sand as well as loose sand (compare with peak shear). The resistance to sliding is governed mainly by mutual friction between the translocating soil particles. The interlocking of soil particles in this stage can be considered absent.

Upon the mutual, relative translocation of a soil mass in nature, the displacing soil particles form a shear plane, the thickness or width of which may vary from a fraction of an inch to several inches, or even a couple of feet (like fault zones, for example). Such a shear zone is termed the *zone of plastic deformation* upon shear.

FIG. 19-6   Rupture surface in sand.

In soil mechanics studies, in analyzing shear processes in soil, it is assumed, for reasons of simplicity, that shear or rupture takes place along a certain idealized, thin surface called the rupture or sliding surface (Fig. 19-6).

Similar shear tests of the controlled strain type performed at other normal stresses, σ, permit one to pick out from the stress-strain graphs the peak shear stresses at the particular normal stresses, and to plot the shear strength line as a function of the effective normal stresses, as is done with the results from the controlled stress shear test.

Loose sands in the controlled strain shear test usually do not exhibit a peak shear stress on a graph as the dense sands do. Here with increase in shear strain the shear stress increases curvilinearly until an ultimate (failure) shear stress is attained. After this, a continuous, unlimited shear displacement may prevail without any change in the shear stress.

During the process of shearing of a dense sand the following phenomenon can be observed: the soil particles move over one another in the shear plane, thus showing an increase in volume under the influence of shear strains. Loose sands, on the contrary, decrease in volume upon shearing because, being in a loose state of packing, the sand particles can readily readjust their position under the applied strain. The volume change (or change in porosity, n) in the vertical direction, because of the design of the shear box, is observed by means of a vertical dial gage. An increase in volume means a decrease in the density of the packing of the soil particles. A decrease in volume means an increase in density of the packing of the soil particles.

At some intermediate state or degree of density in the process of shear, the shear strains do not bring about any change in volume, viz., density. The density of sand at which no change in volume is brought about upon the application of

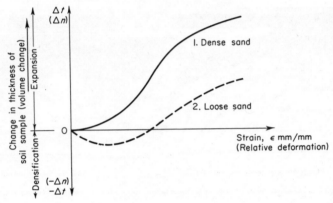

FIG. 19-7   Variation in degree of soil density upon shear.

shear strains is called the critical density. The porosity and void ratio corresponding to the critical density are called the critical porosity and the critical void ratio, respectively. The critical density, viz., porosity or void ratio, is calculated from the vertical changes in the volume of the sand in the shear box. For these quantities the corresponding shear stresses are plotted in a density-shear stress graph, or in a porosity-shear stress graph. The critical density and/or critical porosity are read and scaled off the graph at the numerical value of the ultimate shear stress (stress at continuously sliding shear deformation in Fig. 19-5).

The degree of density of a non-cohesive soil during the process of shear changes within the zone of plastic deformation, attaining a certain constant value of porosity, termed the critical porosity. Every sand has a certain critical density.[2] Sandy soils having a porosity less than critical loosen up, or expand, upon shear but loosely packed sands densify, i.e., reduce their volume, Fig. 19-7.

19-7. Shear Strength of Clay. The shear process of cohesive soils is more complicated than with sands because of the pore water present. The frictional resistance of cohesive soils is less than that of non-cohesive soils because the fine clay particles are easily deformable. The cohesion of clays is considerably larger than that of sands because in clays the sum of the surfaces of the clay particles is very large (large specific surface): this promotes the increase in true cohesion which depends upon the action of the surface forces. Also the capillary system in cohesive soils is much finer, thus contributing considerably to the magnitude of the apparent cohesion.

The shear test results of an undisturbed clay usually exhibit, too, a peak of shear strength on the deformation-shear stress graph. However, when the undisturbed clay is re-molded, the peak point in many instances no longer exists. These conditions are illustrated in Fig. 19-8.

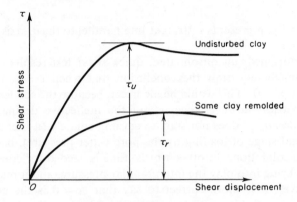

FIG. 19-8   Sensitivity of clay.

Sensitivity of Clay. The ratio of the peak shear strength of the clay, τ_u, to the maximum value of the re-molded shear strength of the same clay, τ_r, is called the *coefficient of sensitivity*, s, of that clay:

$$s = \frac{\tau_u}{\tau_r}. \tag{19-2}$$

The larger the coefficient of sensitivity, the less is the remolded shear strength of the clay, and consequently the more sensitive is that clay. The sensitivity of some clays is great, but the sensitivity of shear strength to re-molding is less great in others. Hence, the shear strength of the soil depends very much upon whether its natural structure is disturbed or not.

19-8. Unconsolidated Quick Shear Test of Clay. Clays usually contain a certain amount of free moisture. Under certain conditions the degree of saturation, S, of clays may be practically $S = 100\%$. Because clays, due to their low coefficient of permeability, drain slowly, upon the application of a normal stress to the clay in a shear box, the water has no time to drain out of the voids of the clay. Thus *the normal stress induces a balanced pore-water pressure.* This pore water, until intergranular pressure is established later after some of the water has drained out, carries the normal stress (viz., structural load on clay soil) during the initial period of time. If, at this point, a clay sample is subjected to shear, and the drainage of the water from the voids of the clay soil does not take place effectively, the shear is independent of the normal stress because of the pore water. Such a shear test is termed the undrained, or unconsolidated quick shear test. In such a test, the applied total normal stress is σ_n, and the induced pore water pressure, u, is equal in magnitude to the normal stress, i.e.,

$$\sigma_n = u. \tag{19-3}$$

Hence, the effective normal stress is

$$\sigma_{n_{eff}} = \sigma_n - u = 0, \tag{19-4}$$

and the measured shear strength of the clay in this test is

$$\tau = c, \tag{19-5}$$

which, analytically, represents a straight line parallel to the σ_n-axis and distance, c, from the latter.

From the undrained, unconsolidated, quick shear test results of a clay, one should not immediately draw the conclusion that when $\tau = c$, it should also be true that $\tan \phi = 0$. This would be incorrect, because the soil tested may have frictional properties; however, because of the ineffective drainage, the inter-granular pressure, $\sigma_{n_{eff}}$, does not start to act immediately (it is counterbalanced during the initial stage of loading by the pore water pressure), because there is no time for consolidation. In other words, time is needed for consolidating the clay sample to bring into play the intergranular pressure, and it may appear that $\phi = 0$. However, it is more correct to say that $\phi = 0$ is the angle of shear resistance because of this particular method of testing the clay under quick, undrained, and unconsolidated conditions.

The unconsolidated quick shear test of clay may in practice find its applica-tion to a stability problem of a foundation. If the foundation load is transmitted to an unconsolidated clay, the following question arises: what is the factor of safety of the clayey soil mass against shear immediately after laying the foundation?

In the course of time, as the clay consolidates more and more, the strength of the soil increases, and so does the factor of safety against shear.

19-9. Consolidated Quick Shear Test of Clay. The principle of the consoli-dated, quick shear test of a clay is that the clay sample in the shear box is sub-jected to an appropriate normal stress. Under this stress a certain amount of water will drain out of the voids of the clay, bringing about a certain degree of consolidation of the clay. The consolidation brings about a greater density, and, hence, a greater shear strength of the clay. After the appropriate degree of consolidation has been attained, the clay sample is subjected to a quick process of shear, similar to that in the unconsolidated, quick shear test. Because the permeability of clay is usually low, it is assumed that during the quick shear in the consolidated, quick shear test no drainage of water out of the voids of the clay takes place during the period of shear. Therefore, this type of test is some-times also called the consolidated, undrained shear test of soil.

The testing procedure of clay in this test is to subject a certain number of clay samples of the same type of clay to normal consolidation stress. Each consec-utive soil sample out of, say, 5 or 6 samples is subjected to a larger normal stress (or to a smaller normal stress) than the previous one until consolidation is attained, and then sheared off. During the shear, pore water pressure is built up. When each consecutive soil sample is subjected to a larger normal stress than the previous one, for example, $\sigma_1 < \sigma_2$, the attained void ratio, e, in each following soil sample consolidated is less than in the previous consolidated soil sample. The densities of each soil sample after consolidation, γ, in their turn, increase. Thus, soil samples subjected to smaller, normal consolidation stresses, contain more water in their voids than those subjected to larger, normal consolidation stresses.

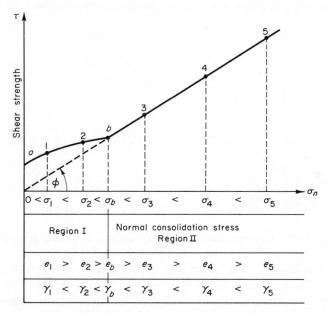

FIG. 19-9   Consolidated, quick shear test results of clay graphically.

When the shear test results of the clay at various consolidation stresses are plotted in a shear strength graph of the clay, the plot usually results in a line the first part of which (at smaller normal consolidation stresses) is curved, a-1-2-b, Fig. 19-9. The curved part of the plot is then adjoined at point b by a straight line. Over a certain range of normal, consolidation stresses, $\sigma_{n_{eff}}$, the shear strength of the clay can be approximately expressed analytically as

$$\tau = \sigma_n \tan \phi + c.$$

It can be understood, therefore, that the curved part of the shear strength curve is the effect of the amount of water, or the effect of the neutral stress in the voids of the soil.

Within region I, represented by the curved part of the shear strength diagram a-1-2-b, there is more water in the voids of the clay than within region II; in region I the effect of neutral stress is very pronounced as compared with that within region II. Within region II, the intergranular stress is more pronounced than in region I, but the pore water pressure is still present, although to a smaller magnitude than in I.

It can be understood that the angle ϕ, and the cut-off, c, on the consolidated, quick shear strength graph are parameters of these particular *test conditions*, and not the properties of the soil. The uncertain factor in this test is the magnitude of the neutral stress.

The consolidated, quick shear test is applicable, for example, for stability calculations against failure in shear of consolidated dams, slopes, and other earthworks made of cohesive soil material under conditions of rapid draw-down of water, where the water has not time to drain out of the voids.

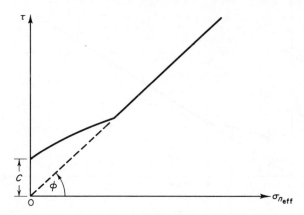

FIG. 19-10   Consolidated, slow shear test results of clay graphically.

19-10. Consolidated Slow Shear Test of Clay. The consolidated, slow shear test on clays is performed by first consolidating the various clay samples to appropriate consolidation stresses and then by shearing the consolidated soil samples very slowly. The slow process of shear affords time enough for the water to drain out of the voids of the soil under the consolidation stress. Therefore, during the shear process in this kind of test, pore water pressures do not build up to any significant degree. This means that the effective, normal stress on the soil sample during shear is equal to the applied, normal consolidation stress. The shear strength diagram obtained from the consolidated, slow shear test of clay is similar in appearance to that obtained from the consolidated, quick shear test. The difference, however, between the two curves is that in the consolidated, slow shear test of clays the ultimate shear resistances, τ, are plotted against the effective, normal stresses, $\sigma_{n_{eff}}$, Fig. 19-10.

The shear strength of the clay can be expressed analytically over a certain range of effective normal stress as

$$\tau = \sigma_{n_{eff}} \tan \phi + c.$$

In this test, the value of the parameter, ϕ, is larger than that obtained for the same soil from the consolidated, quick shear test, because the neutral stress in the slow (drained) test is practically zero, and the intergranular friction between the soil particles acts in its full magnitude.

19-11. Comments on Direct Shear Tests. The direct shear test, although simple and relatively rapid, has some inherent disadvantages, namely:

1) The stress conditions across the soil sample in the shear box are very complex, because of the change in the shear area in the split shear box with the increase in shear displacement as the test progresses, causing unequal distribution of shear stresses and normal stresses over the potential surface of sliding. The total normal load and the total shear force should, therefore, be divided by the area of the sliding surface at failure, A_f, and not by A, because at failure the upper half of the shear box has been displaced horizontally a few hundredths of an inch relative to the lower half of the shear box. In other words, the corrected area should be used in determining the values of σ_n and τ_f at failure.

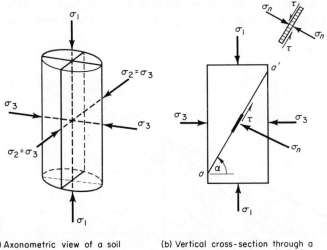

(a) Axonometric view of a soil
    sample showing principal stresses
    and principal planes

(b) Vertical cross-section through a
    soil sample showing principal
    stresses, inclined shear plane a-a',
    normal stress, σ_n, and shear
    stress, τ

FIG. 19-11   Stresses acting on a soil sample in triaxial compression test.

2) The water content of saturated samples of many types of soil changes rapidly as a result of a change in stress.
3) The imbedding of the ridges of the metal gratings or filter stones into the soil sample to be tested for shear causes distortion of the sample to a certain degree.
4) When the shear force is applied to the sample, the soil compresses against the sides of these ridges of the gratings.
5) There exists also the question of the effect of lateral restraint by the side walls of the shear box. This restraint does not act the same in the shear apparatus as it would in a foundation.

   Therefore, the value of the shear strength, obtained by dividing the shear force (H) by the rupture area (A), is only approximate.
6) Soils can also be tested in double shear, or in torsional shear, or in punch shear, for which purpose specially constructed equipment is needed.

TRIAXIAL COMPRESSION OF SOIL

19-12. Stress Conditions on the Shear Plane. The stress conditions on the shear plane a-a_1 of a cylindrically shaped soil sample, Fig. 19-11, can be determined grapho-analytically and analyzed conveniently by Mohr's[3] stress circles, Fig. 19-12.

In this method, the normal stresses (σ_1, σ_3, σ_n) acting on a soil sample subjected to a triaxial compression test, are plotted as abscissas and the shear stresses (τ) as ordinates. With the difference in major normal stresses, ($\sigma_1 - \sigma_3$), as a diameter, a circle is drawn. The radius of the stress circle is ($\sigma_1 - \sigma_3$)/2.

Remember from strength of materials that for major principal stresses, σ_1, the corresponding shear on the same plane is $\tau = 0$, and $\tau = 0$ for σ_3. Thus, the ends of the stress diameter on Mohr's stress circle have the coordinates (σ_1; 0) and (σ_3; 0).

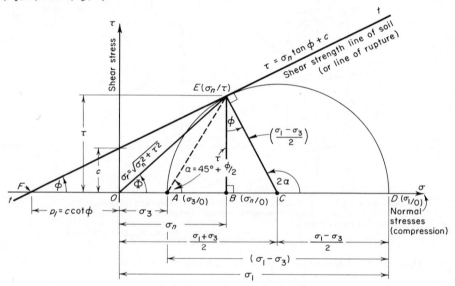

FIG. 19-12   Mohr's stress circle.

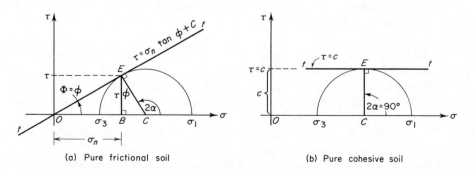

(a) Pure frictional soil   (b) Pure cohesive soil

FIG. 19-13   Stress circles for various types of soil.

The normal stress, σ_n, and the shear stress, τ, on an inclined shear plane can be geometrically demonstrated on Mohr's graph as follows:

$$\sigma_n = OB = OC + CB$$

But

$$OC = \frac{\sigma_1 + \sigma_3}{2}$$

$$CB = (CE)\cos 2\alpha,$$

and

$$CE = CA = CD = \frac{\sigma_1 - \sigma_3}{2}.$$

Therefore

$$\sigma_n = OB = \frac{\sigma_1 + \sigma_3}{2} + \frac{\sigma_1 - \sigma_3}{2} \cos 2\alpha. \tag{19-6}$$

Similarly,

$$\tau = BE = (CE)\sin 2\alpha = \frac{\sigma_1 - \sigma_3}{2} \sin 2\alpha. \tag{19-7}$$

It follows that each point on the circle gives the pair of stresses acting on a rupture plane of specific inclination, α.

A tangent, t-t, drawn to the stress circle at point E, has the equation of

$$\tau = \sigma_n \tan \phi + c, \tag{19-8}$$

an equation which characterizes the shear strength of the soil. The slope of this line, $\tan \phi$, physically means the coefficient of internal friction of the soil; ϕ is the angle of internal friction, and c is the cohesion.

For future application, ϕ and c are rather test coefficients obtained by special apparatus and by special methods of testing.

The cut-off, $OF = p_i = c \cot \phi$, Fig. 19-12, made on the normal stress axis by the tangent, t-t, indicates an initial normal stress in the cohesive soil brought about by capillary stresses.

The magnitude of the resultant stress, σ_r, can also be scaled off, or calculated from Mohr's stress diagram.

Again, as was discussed in the section on the direct shear test of soil, for non-cohesive soils $c = 0$,

$$\tau = \sigma_n \tan \phi,$$

and for pure cohesive soils, when $\phi = 0$,

$$\tau = c,$$

i.e., the tangent takes a course parallel to the σ-axis, Figs. 19-13a and b.

19-13. Discussion. At failure in shear, the stress, τ, is equal to the shear strength, $\tau = \sigma_n \tan \phi + c$, of the soil. Substitution of the normal stress, σ_n, and of the shear stress at failure, τ, into Coulomb's shear strength equation of the soil yields:

$$\sigma_n = \frac{\sigma_1 + \sigma_3}{2} + \frac{\sigma_1 - \sigma_3}{2} \cos 2\alpha \qquad (19\text{-}6)$$

$$\tau = \frac{\sigma_1 - \sigma_3}{2} \sin 2\alpha \qquad (19\text{-}7)$$

$$\tau = \sigma_n \tan \phi + c \qquad (19\text{-}8)$$

$$\sigma_1 = \sigma_3 + \frac{\sigma_3 \tan \phi + c}{(\frac{1}{2})\sin 2\alpha - \cos^2 \alpha \tan \phi}. \qquad (19\text{-}9)$$

The shear plane of least resistance to shear is caused by the least value (minimum) of the major principal stress, σ_1. But σ_1 is minimum when the term

$$(\tfrac{1}{2})\sin 2\alpha - \cos^2 \alpha \tan \phi$$

is a maximum, i.e., when

$$\frac{df}{d\alpha} = (\tfrac{1}{2} \sin 2\alpha - \cos^2 \alpha \tan \phi)' = 0 \qquad (19\text{-}10)$$

Derivation yields that

$$2\alpha = 90° + \phi \qquad (19\text{-}11)$$

or

$$\alpha = 45° + \phi/2. \qquad (19\text{-}12)$$

Substitution of this $\alpha = 45° + \phi/2$ into Eq. (19-9) yields:

$$\sigma_1 = \sigma_3 \tan^2(45° + \phi/2) + 2c \tan(45° + \phi/2). \qquad (19\text{-}13)$$

From Eq. (19-13), the magnitude of the cohesion, c, can be calculated:

$$c = \frac{\sigma_1 - \sigma_3 \tan^2(45° + \phi/2)}{2 \tan(45° + \phi/2)}. \qquad (19\text{-}14)$$

When $\phi = 0$, then in the triaxial test Eq. (19-13) transforms into

$$\sigma_1 = \sigma_3 + 2c, \qquad (19\text{-}15)$$

and

$$c = \frac{\sigma_1 - \sigma_3}{2} = \tau. \qquad (19\text{-}16)$$

When also $c = 0$, Eq. (19-15) becomes

$$\sigma_1 = \sigma_3. \qquad (19\text{-}17)$$

When $c = 0$ (in the triaxial test), Eq. (19-13) transforms into

$$\sigma_1 = \sigma_3 \tan^2(45° + \phi/2). \qquad (19\text{-}18)$$

From here the ratio of the principal stresses is

$$\frac{\sigma_1}{\sigma_3} = \tan^2(45° + \phi/2) = \cot^2(45° - \phi/2) = \quad (19\text{-}19)$$

$$= \frac{1 + \sin \phi}{1 - \sin \phi}. \quad (19\text{-}20)$$

Equation (19-18) is used in calculations of earth pressure against a vertical earth retaining wall, with a horizontal ground surface of the backfill material whose $\phi = \phi$, and $c = 0$.

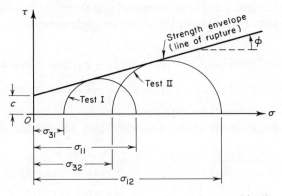

FIG. 19-14   Determination of ϕ and c graphically.

The values of ϕ and c can also be calculated from the geometry of the stress circle and its tangent from Fig. 19-12:

$$\sin \phi = \frac{\dfrac{\sigma_1 - \sigma_3}{2}}{\dfrac{\sigma_1 + \sigma_3}{2} + c \cot \phi} = \frac{\sigma_1 - \sigma_3}{\sigma_1 + \sigma_3 + 2c \cot \phi} \quad (19\text{-}21)$$

and

$$c = \frac{\sigma_1(1 - \sin \phi) - \sigma_3(1 + \sin \phi)}{2 \cos \phi}. \quad (19\text{-}22)$$

This indicates that at least two sets of triaxial tests (at different lateral or minor principal stresses, namely at σ_{31} and σ_{32}) are to be performed to determine the two unknowns, ϕ and c.

When $c = 0$ (in Eq. 19-21), then

$$\sin \phi = \frac{\sigma_1 - \sigma_3}{\sigma_1 + \sigma_3}. \quad (19\text{-}23)$$

Two sets of triaxial test. Two sets mean that two triaxial tests are performed, each at a specific minor stress, σ_{31} and σ_{32}, and at major principal stresses, σ_{11} and σ_{12}, respectively, till failure in shear. Each test is then represented by its own stress circle, denoted by test I and test II, respectively, as on Fig. 19-14.

The indexes at stresses are to be read as follows:

σ_{31} = minor principal stress (σ_3) in first set (1) of triaxial tests;

σ_{32} = minor principal stress in the second set of tests.

Thus, the second indexes, "1" and "2" mean first and second set of tests, respectively.

Generally,

$$\sigma_{11} \neq \sigma_{12},$$

and

$$\sigma_{31} \neq \sigma_{32}.$$

The values of ϕ and c can now be calculated from the results obtained from the two sets of tests by means of the shear strength equation $\tau = \sigma_n \tan \phi + c$, as follows:

$$\left.\begin{array}{l} \tfrac{1}{2}(\sigma_{11} - \sigma_{31})\sin 2\alpha = [\tfrac{1}{2}(\sigma_{11} + \sigma_{31}) + \tfrac{1}{2}(\sigma_{11} - \sigma_{31})\cos 2\alpha]\tan \phi + c \\ \tfrac{1}{2}(\sigma_{12} - \sigma_{32})\sin 2\alpha = [\tfrac{1}{2}(\sigma_{12} + \sigma_{32}) + \tfrac{1}{2}(\sigma_{12} - \sigma_{32})\cos 2\alpha]\tan \phi + c \end{array}\right\} \quad (19\text{-}24)$$

assuming that α is constant in both tests.

A simultaneous solution of the system of Eqs. (19-24) for ϕ and c yields:

$$\tan \phi = \frac{[(\sigma_{11} - \sigma_{31}) - (\sigma_{12} - \sigma_{32})]\sin 2\alpha}{[(\sigma_{11} - \sigma_{31}) - (\sigma_{12} - \sigma_{32})]\cos 2\alpha + (\sigma_{11} + \sigma_{31}) - (\sigma_{12} + \sigma_{32})}, \quad (19\text{-}25)$$

and

$$c = \frac{\sin 2\alpha}{2} \times$$

$$\times \left\{ \frac{(\sigma_{12} - \sigma_{32})(\sigma_{11} + \sigma_{31}) - (\sigma_{11} - \sigma_{31})(\sigma_{12} + \sigma_{32})}{[(\sigma_{11} - \sigma_{31}) - (\sigma_{12} - \sigma_{32})]\cos 2\alpha + (\sigma_{11} + \sigma_{31}) - (\sigma_{12} + \sigma_{32})} \right\}. \quad (19\text{-}26)$$

Example. Given the results of two sets of triaxial tests on a silty glacial outwash soil:
$\sigma_{11} = 4.0$ t/ft^2;　$\sigma_{31} = 1.0$ t/ft^2.
$\sigma_{12} = 6.8$ t/ft^2;　$\sigma_{32} = 2.0$ t/ft^2.
The angle of rupture in both tests is measured to be the same, and is:
$\alpha = \alpha_1 = \alpha_2 = 59°$.
Determine the magnitudes of ϕ and c. Draw a stress diagram.
Solution
Auxiliary quantities for Eqs. (19-25) and (19-26).
$\sigma_{11} - \sigma_{31} = 4.0 - 1.0 = 3.0$ (t/ft^2)
$\sigma_{12} - \sigma_{32} = 6.8 - 2.0 = 4.8$ (t/ft^2)
$\sin 2\alpha = \sin(2 \cdot 59°) = \sin 118° = \cos 28° = 0.883$
$\cos 2\alpha = \cos 118° = -\sin 28° = -0.470$.
$\sigma_{11} + \sigma_{31} = 4.0 + 1.0 = 5.0$ (t/ft^2)
$\sigma_{12} + \sigma_{32} = 6.8 + 2.0 = 8.8$ (t/ft^2)
The angle of internal friction, ϕ, by Eq. (19-25):
$\tan \phi = 0.504$, and $\phi = 26°45'$.
Cohesion, by Eq. (19-26):
$c = 0.36$ (t/ft^2).

Draw the stress diagram and scale off ϕ and c from the diagram after the tangent to circles I and II has been drawn.

19-14. Variation of Normal and Shear Stresses. Failure in soil occurs when in any rupture plane the shear stress attains the value of the shear strength of the soil. The general functions expressing the normal stress and the shear stress,

$$\sigma_n = \frac{\sigma_1 + \sigma_3}{2} + \frac{\sigma_1 - \sigma_3}{2} \cos 2\alpha, \qquad (19\text{-}6)$$

and

$$\tau = \frac{\sigma_1 - \sigma_3}{2} \sin 2\alpha, \qquad (19\text{-}7)$$

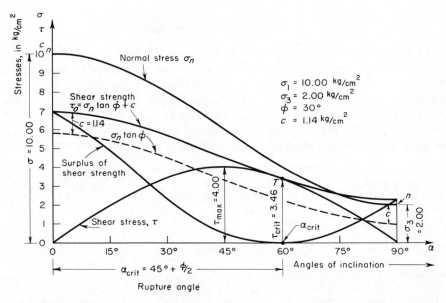

FIG. 19-15   Variation of normal and shear stresses with inclination of rupture plane.

can most readily by studied if the stresses, σ_n and τ, are plotted as functions of the rupture angle, α, Fig. 19-15. For this purpose, assume σ_1, σ_3, vary α from $0°$ to $90°$, and calculate and plot normal and shear stresses, and the shear strength line.

Assume $\sigma_1 = 10$ kg/cm^2, and $\sigma_3 = 2$ kg/cm^2. Then the σ_n-values at various α (here taken at $15°$ intervals) are:

α	$\cos 2\alpha$	σ_n
$0°$	1.000	$10.00 = \sigma_1$
$15°$	0.866	9.46
$30°$	0.500	8.00
$45°$	0.000	6.00
$60°$	-0.500	4.00
$75°$	-0.866	2.54
$90°$	-1.000	$2.00 = \sigma_3$

The plot of these σ_n-values results on Fig. 19-15 as the normal stress (σ) line. The τ-values (shear stress) are:

α	$\sin 2\alpha$	τ
0°	0.000	0.00
15°	0.500	2.00
30°	0.866	3.46
45°	1.000	4.00
60°	0.866	3.46
75°	0.500	2.00
90°	0.000	0.00

The plot of these values on Fig. 19-15 results as the shear stress (τ) curve.

If the angle of internal friction of the soil under consideration subjected to shear, is $\phi = 30°$, or the coefficient of internal friction is $\tan 30° = 0.58$, and the magnitude of cohesion is, say, $c = 1.14$ kg/cm^2, then the shear strength curve, $\tau_o = \sigma_n \tan \phi + c$, can be plotted (see Fig. 19-15).

The ordinates of the τ_o-values are tabulated as follows, where the σ_n-values are taken for the appropriate angles of α from the σ_n-tabulation.

$\alpha°$	Normal Stress σ_n kg/cm^2	$\sigma_n \tan \phi$ kg/cm^2	$c = 1.14$ kg/cm^2	Shear strength $\tau_o = \sigma_n \tan \phi + c$ kg/cm^2	Shear Stress τ kg/cm^2	Surplus of Shear strength $\tau_o - \tau$
1	2	3	4	5	6	7
0	10.00	5.80	1.14	6.94	0.00	6.94
15	9.46	5.49	1.14	6.63	2.00	4.63
30	8.00	4.64	1.14	5.78	3.46	2.32
45	6.00	3.24	1.14	4.38	4.00	0.38
60	4.00	2.32	1.14	3.46	3.46	0.00
75	2.54	1.47	1.14	2.61	2.00	0.61
90	2.00	1.16	1.14	2.30	0.00	2.30

The graph of the variation of normal and shear stresses as a function of the angle of rupture, α (with the horizontal) in Fig. 19-15 shows:

1) All σ-stresses (n-n line) are rupture stresses.
2) The τ_o stresses are the shear strength of the soil at that normal stress σ_n; these τ_o-stresses depend upon ϕ and c.
3) The maximum shear stress occurs on shear planes at $\alpha = 45°$ to the normal principal planes.
4) The τ_o-curve touches the τ-curve at point T, i.e., at their point of tangency, T; here the shear stress is equal to the shear strength of the soil which happens at a critical angle, α_{crit}, or here at $\alpha = 45° + \phi/2 = 60°$. This approximate angle can often be observed in a sharp shear failure by

measurement after the trixial compression test or an unconfined compression test is performed. Note that this angle, $\alpha = 45° + \phi/2$ is the angle of rupture of that surface in which the rupture is impending at a given stress, σ_1 and σ_3.

5) Between $\alpha = 0$ and $\alpha = 45° + \phi/2$, there is a surplus of shear strength in the soil; and so there is a surplus between the angles of $\alpha = 45° + \phi/2$ and $\alpha = 90°$ (see hatched areas).

6) At $\alpha = 0$, the normal stress is the major principal stress, σ_1.

7) At $\alpha = 90°$, the normal stress is the minor principal stress, σ_3.

19-15. Purpose of Triaxial Compression Test. The purpose of the triaxial compression test of soils is to provide basic data on:

1) the ultimate, laterally confined, compressive strength;
2) the angle of internal friction;
3) the cohesion;
4) the shear strength;
5) the so-called modulus of elasticity, and
6) the pore water pressure.

The results obtained from the triaxial compression test are used for:

1) making estimates of the probable bearing capacity of a soil;
2) stability calculations of earthworks, earth retaining structures, and foundations;
3) analyzing stress-strain relationships of loaded soils, and
4) estimating settlements of soil under load.

19-16. Types of Tests. Fundamentally, there are two types of tests which can be performed by means of the triaxial compression apparatus, namely: 1) open-system test, and 2) closed-system test.

In the open-system triaxial test, sometimes called the drained or slow test, the pore water is allowed to drain out of the soil sample.

In the closed-system test, sometimes called the undrained or quick test, no drainage is allowed. The water content of the soil sample is assumed to be constant throughout the test.

Consolidation under lateral stress in the open-system test may be allowed to any degree desired. During the process of lateral consolidation, water is allowed to drain. Then the soil sample is subjected to axial stress (σ_1). During the application of the axial stress, the system may be either open or closed. If it is closed, the shear stress develops at a constant water content which remains in the soil sample after the consolidation under the lateral stress (σ_3).

Tests may also be performed on a soil sample in which no consolidation is allowed prior to the application of the axial stress. Drainage may or may not be allowed to take place. Therefore, one distinguishes between:

1) unconsolidated-undrained, also known as unconsolidated-quick test;
2) consolidated-undrained, also known as consolidated-quick test, (Q_c);
3) unconsolidated-drained, also known as unconsolidated-slow test, and
4) consolidated-drained, also known as consolidated-slow test, (S_c). In this

test, clayey soil samples consolidate very slowly because of low permeability and long drainage path.

The unconfined compression test is an example of an unconsolidated-undrained kind of test.

19-17. Apparatus. A sketch of a triaxial compression chamber is given in Fig. 19-16. The vertical, axial stress, σ_1, can be applied to the soil sample manually by turning the gear-wheel (or by dead weights), or mechanically by means of an electric motor. For details of the triaxial testing device refer to Fig. 19-16. The soil sample of a cohesive soil is trimmed to size to fit the apparatus. The height of the soil sample, usually cylindrical in shape, is customarily 2 to 3 times its diameter.

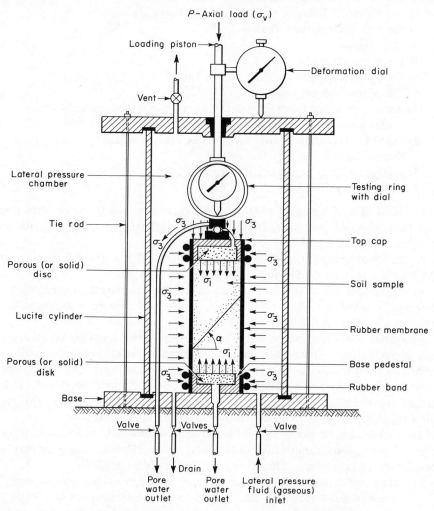

FIG. 19-16 Sketch of a triaxial compression chamber.

FIG. 19-17   Illustrating the "beam strength" of sand. *From top:* sand bag before applying partial vacuum and after removal of vacuum; sand mass subjected to a certain degree of vacuum; sand beam supports external load; collapse of "sand beam" after removal of vacuum.

19-18. Effect of Lateral Stress on Shear ("Beam") Strength of Sand. Loose, confined sand, when subjected to lateral pressure, can be densified to such a degree that it may act like a solid body. For example, consider a rubber-necked bag filled with dry, loose sand as illustrated in Figs. 19-17a, b, c, and d. This bag is connected to a vacuum system. Before being subjected to vacuum, the appearance of the sand bag is flaccid (Fig. 19-17a). Upon connecting the sand to a certain degree of vacuum, as can be read from the attached vacuum gage, a lateral stress (unbalanced excess of atmospheric pressure) is applied to the rubber-necked bag. The lateral stress is transmitted to the sand particles. Upon touching the sand mass in the bag, the mass feels as if it were a hard, solid body. During the application of such a vacuum the sand bag is placed on two supports (Fig. 19-17b), and the sand acts like a beam, capable of supporting a concentrated load of, say, two kilograms without noticeable deflection of the "sand beam", Fig. 19-17c. Upon disconnecting the vacuum from the mass of sand, the sand-filled bag collapses, losing its "beam strength" and the shear properties acquired by the sand upon applying a lateral stress to it. In the last stage after collapse the sand-filled bag again appears as it did before applying lateral pressure, Fig. 19-17d.

FIG. 19-18   Triaxial compression testing of sand.

The vacuum method is used in preparing dry sand samples for the triaxial testing. Upon applying a partial vacuum, the dry, loose sand becomes hard and supports a vertical cylinder in a rubber sleeve.

After such a "vacumized" sand cylinder has been placed in the triaxial compression chamber, a lateral compressive stress, σ_3 (gas), is gradually applied simultaneously, at approximately the same rate as the vacuum is gradually released, so that at the end of the process of the change of vacuum to lateral compression with gas (σ_3) surrounding the sand in the rubber sleeve, the dry sand cylinder in the rubber sleeve stands upright under σ_3. Then the major principal stress is applied till failure of the sand in shear. The trace of the shear plane is noticed on the rubber sleeve, Fig. 19-18.

19-19. Types of Failure. Typical kinds of compression failures observed in performing triaxial and unconfined compression tests on soils are:
   a) brittle failure with clearly expressed shear plane, Fig. 19-19a;
   b) intermediate type of failure, or semi-plastic failure, showing shear cones and some bulging, Fig. 19-19b; and
   c) plastic failure with remarkably well-expressed lateral bulging, Fig. 19-19c.

19-20. Graphs. From the triaxial test results the following graphs are plotted:

1) σ_1 vs. % axial strain, $\Delta h/h$, where h is the original height of the soil sample before test, and Δh = deformation in height of the soil sample;
2) σ_1/σ_3 vs. % axial strain, $\Delta h/h$;
3) percent volume change vs. % axial strain, $\Delta h/h$;
4) volume change vs. σ_1;

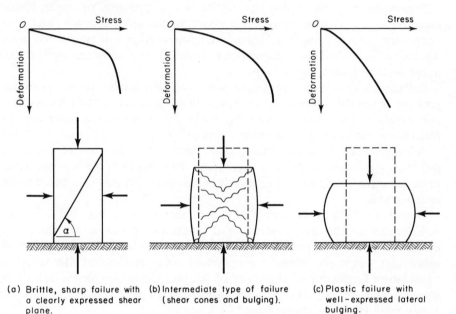

(a) Brittle, sharp failure with a clearly expressed shear plane.

(b) Intermediate type of failure (shear cones and bulging).

(c) Plastic failure with well-expressed lateral bulging.

FIG. 19-19   Types of compression failures.

5) stress circles at failure for each set of soil samples tested. From this graph, the following quantities are usually determined:
    a) ϕ
    b) c
    c) τ
    d) σ_n at the point of failure
    e) limit of proportionality and
    f) the so-called "modulus of elasticity", of the soil tested, M_v.

The graphs and other test results are analyzed, and the strength characteristics of the soil and other pertinent data are reported.

19-21. Pore Water Pressure. In triaxial compression tests, and in consolidation tests, the pore water pressure must be measured and recorded.

Generally, pore water pressure means the pressure (gage pressure) exerted by water occupying the voids of the soil. Pore water pressure is a natural force which is present not only in cohesive soils, but also in granular soils. However, in granular soils the voids are large; therefore, pore water pressure has a negligible effect on the testing process and its results. In cohesive soils the voids are minute and pore water pressure exerts an additional, all-directional pressure of considerable magnitude. This additional pressure, or pore water pressure, increases the test constant, ϕ, and thus the measured resistance against forming of rupture surfaces in the soil mass. Every rupture plane passed through the soil mass is subject to the same magnitude of pore water pressure.

Pore water pressure is also termed the neutral pressure, or the hydrostatic pressure, or the hydrostatic excess pressure, or the uplift pressure; and is also known by other designations, depending upon whether it is considered in consolidation theory, triaxial compression testing, or direct shear testing of soils, or in the construction of earth dams.

Relative to undisturbed saturated soils, Terzaghi states that the pore water pressure is termed the neutral stress, u, which "is equal to the product of the unit weight of the water, γ_w, and the height, h_w, to which the water rises in a piezometric tube at the point under consideration . . . "

Soil mechanics has demonstrated that water within the voids of a mass of a soil has a significant mechanical effect upon the strength of the soil, particularly upon its shear strength. Also, pore water pressure retards consolidation of a cohesive soil.

Pore Water Pressure Measurement in the Laboratory. A small but satisfactory contribution to the development of a laboratory device and technique for measuring pore water pressures in soils subjected to triaxial compression (viz., shear test) was made during a program of study at the Soil Mechanics and Foundation Engineering Laboratory of Rutgers University for the Joint Highway Research Project, a cooperative effort between the University and the New Jersey State Highway Department.[4]

To measure pore water pressure during undrained triaxial tests of soils, a hypodermic needle was inserted and sealed in the center of the soil specimen being subjected to test. The needle and a connecting tube leading to the exterior of the triaxial chamber were filled with de-aired water to transfer the pressure of the pore water to a pressure cell, Fig. 19-20. The pressure cell has two compartments separated by a thin metal diaphragm. One compartment was connected to the pore water needle, and the other to a manually adjusted, compressed air supply. The pore water pressure was measured by means of a standard pressure gage. Pressure equilibrium was indicated by a neutral position of the diaphragm. The diaphragm was connected by means of a pin to a contact plate which could move between two adjustable contacts. An electric circuit operating through these contacts lit a green light if the air pressure was lower than the pore water pressure. A red light went on if it was higher. Neither light operated at the point of equilibrium.

Pore Water Pressure Measurement in the Field. Pore water pressures in clay can be measured in the field by means of a device called Casagrande's pore water pressure piezometer.[5] Such a piezometer consists of a porous tube, 2 ft long, of fine grade, one end of which is plugged while the other end is connected to a piezometric standpipe. The porous tube serves as a suction cup which establishes contact between the pore water in the connecting tubing to the gage. The piezometer is installed in a bore hole drilled into the clay at a proper depth below the ground surface. The bore hole (with casing) is kept filled with clean water. Then the casing is raised, saturated clean sand is poured into the bore hole to fill the bottom to a depth of about 2 ft. When the porous cup is placed in the hole to rest on the sand, the casing is pulled up 2 ft and filled with sand around the porous cup. The hole is backfilled with more saturated sand, and tamped. Then two effective bentonite plugs, spaced 2 ft apart, are placed on top of the sand to provide a tight seal against leaks. Five 3″ layers are recommended for each plug.

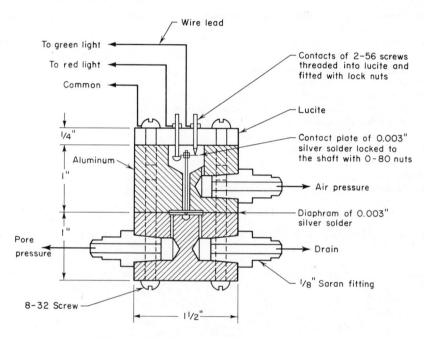

FIG. 19-20   Cross section of pressure cell.

The water level in the piezometer standpipe is measured directly and manually by a calibrated, electrical sounding device which indicates upon contact the water level in the pipe. The head of water in the piezometric pipe above the porous cup gives a measure of the magnitude of pore pressure at the location of the porous cup. If pore water pressures are so great that water is forced out of the piezometric tube above the ground surface, then pore water pressures can be measured by a Bourdon gage.

Pore water pressure measurement installations are used in the application of vertical sand drains to consolidate fills rapidly, as well as during the construction of earth dams.

In conclusion, it must be said that the greatest difficulty in applying the shear test results to practical design problems in soil engineering is the correct evaluation of the field conditions under which the soil has to perform, namely: soil type, loading, and the degree of consolidation. For the proper field evaluation the soil should be tested in an attempt to simulate conditions as they might occur in the field, and consequently the proper test values of ϕ and c should be used in stability calculations of earth masses.

19-22. Example. A triaxial compression test on a cohesive soil sample, cylindrical in shape, yielded the following effective stresses:
 a) major principal stress—1000 lb/in²,
 b) minor principal stress—200 lb/in²,
 c) the angle of inclination of the rupture plane: 60° with the horizontal.

Requirements
 a) Present all of the information pertaining to this problem in the form of Mohr's stress diagram.
 b) Determine analytically normal stress, shear stress, and resultant stress on the rupture plane through a point. Also determine the angle of obliquity of the resultant stress with the shear plane, *s-s*.
 c) What is the magnitude of the cohesion?
 d) What is the value of the coefficient of internal friction?
 e) What is the magnitude of the initial stress in the soil? ·
 f) Write the Coulomb's shear strength equation
    i) in the algebraic form, and
    ii) for the particular case of the given soil test.
 g) How is Coulomb's equation of shear strength of soil used in practice?

Answers
 a) *Mohr's stress diagram* is constructed as shown in Fig. 19-21a.

$$\sigma_1 = 1000 \text{ lb/in}^2; \quad \sigma_3 = 200 \text{ lb/in}^2; \quad \sigma_{n_{eff}} = 400 \text{ lb/in}^2;$$

$$\sigma_r = 530 \text{ lb/in}^2; \quad c = 115 \text{ lb/in}^2; \quad \phi = 30°; \quad p_i = 200 \text{ lb/in}^2.$$

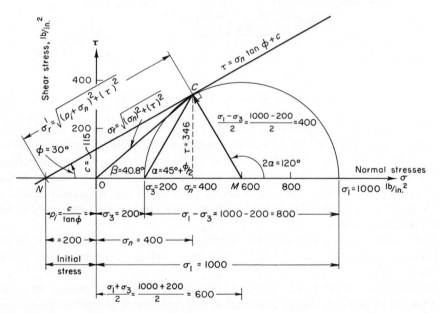

FIG. 19-21 Graphical representation of stress conditions in soil to Example 19-22.

b) i) *Normal stress*: with $\alpha = 60°$, $\cos^2 60° = 0.25$, and $\sin^2 60° = 0.75$.

$\sigma_n = \sigma_1 \cos^2 \alpha + \sigma_3 \sin^2 \alpha = (1000)(0.250) + (200)(0.750) = 400 \text{ lb/in}^2.$

ii) *Shear stress*: with $\sin 2\alpha = \sin 120° = \cos 30° = 0.866$,

$$\tau = \frac{\sigma_1 - \sigma_3}{2} \sin 2\alpha = \frac{1000 - 200}{2}(0.866) = 346.4 \text{ lb/in}^2.$$

iii) *Resultant stress*:

$$\sigma_r = \sqrt{(\sigma_n)^2 + (\tau)^2} = \sqrt{(400)^2 + (346)^2} = 530 \text{ lb/in}^2.$$

iv) *Angle of obliquity* (Fig. 19-21b):

$$\beta = \arctan \frac{\tau}{\sigma_n} = \arctan \frac{346}{400} = \arctan (0.864) = 40°50'.$$

Angle of obliquity of σ_r with shear plane:

$$90° - \beta = 90° - 40°50' = 49°10'.$$

c) $\tan \phi$: with $\alpha = 60°$, from geometry: $2\alpha = 90° + \phi$,

or $\phi = 120° - 90° = 30°$; $\tan \phi = \tan 30° = 0.577$.

d) *Cohesion*: From τ-equation: $\tau = \sigma_n \tan \phi + c$,

$$c = \tau - \sigma_n \tan \phi = 346.4 - (400)(0.577) = 115.6 \text{ lb/in}^2.$$

e) *Initial stress*:

$$p_i = \frac{c}{\tan \phi} = \frac{115.6}{0.577} = 200 \text{ lb/in}^2.$$

f) *Coulomb's shear strength equation*:
   i) algebraically:
$$\tau = \sigma_{n_{eff}} \tan \phi + c$$
   ii) for the particular case:
$$\tau = (0.577)\sigma_{n_{eff}} + 115.6$$

g) Coulomb's shear strength equation is used in practice in its modified form, namely, that the normal stress in that equation should be the effective normal stress: $\sigma_{n_{eff}} = \sigma_n - u$, where u is the neutral stress.

UNCONFINED COMPRESSION TEST

19-23. General Notes. Essentially, the unconfined compression test is a special case of the triaxial compression test of soils where the compressive and shear strengths of a soil prism, or cylinder, are measured under zero lateral stress ($\sigma_2 = \sigma_3 = 0$), see Fig. 19-22. The test is based on the assumption that there is no moisture loss during the test.

In this test, carefully prepared prisms, or cylinders, of soils are subjected to gradually increasing vertical pressure, and simultaneous measurements of the deformations of the soil samples are made. One of the features of the unconfined compression test is the ability to cause failure in a soil sample in a weak zone.

The unconfined compression test is applicable to unweathered, slightly disturbed, disturbed (remolded), and undisturbed cohesive soils. Cohesionless soils (sands and gravels) cannot be subjected to this kind of test, because they do not form unsupported prisms and cylinders.

The unconfined compression test is one of the simplest and quickest tests used for the determination of the shear strength of cohesive soils, and also a simple substitute for more cumbersome field tests.

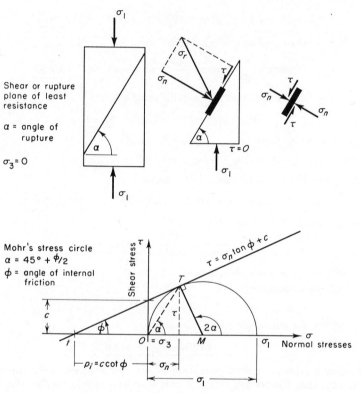

FIG. 19-22   Principle of unconfined compression test.

19-24. Purpose and Application of Unconfined Compression Test. The purpose of the unconfined compression test of cohesive soils is to determine:

1) the ultimate, unconfined compressive strength,
2) the approximate, ultimate shear strength,
3) the approximate angle of internal friction, ϕ,
4) cohesion, c (from Mohr's stress circle), and
5) the so-called Modulus of Elasticity, M_v.

The results obtained from unconfined compression tests are approximate. However,

1) they serve as a direct, quantitative measure of the consistency of cohesive soils, giving a clue as to the danger of rupture of embankment slopes or other earth masses;

2) they provide basic information on the strength properties, thus permitting us to estimate the possible bearing capacity of the soil in foundations and earthworks;

3) they give the stress-strain relationship under rapid failure conditions, and

4) they permit comparison of soil samples taken from various bore holes of approximately similar soil formation, thus saving most of the expensive and time-consuming shear tests.

19-25. Analysis. According to Coulomb's theory, the shear resistance per unit area of soils can be expressed as

$$\tau = \sigma_n \tan \phi + c,$$

where all symbols are as before.

When $\sigma_3 = 0$, as in an unconfined compression test, then the normal stress on the shear plane is:

$$\sigma_n = \sigma_1 \cos^2 \alpha. \tag{19-27}$$

The shear stress in the same shear plane is

$$\tau = \frac{\sigma_1}{2} \sin 2\alpha. \tag{19-28}$$

The resultant stress is

$$\sigma_r = \sqrt{(\sigma_n)^2 + (\tau)^2}, \tag{19-29}$$

and the angle of inclination is

$$\beta = \arctan \frac{\tau}{\sigma_n}. \tag{19-30}$$

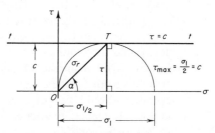

FIG. 19-23   Mohr's stress circle for cohesive, frictionless soil.

The substitution of these σ_n and τ values into the shear strength equation gives a minimum σ_1 as

$$\sigma_1 = 2c \tan^2(45° + \phi/2) \tag{19-31}$$

and from here

$$c = \frac{\sigma_1}{2 \tan^2(45° + \phi/2)}. \tag{19-32}$$

If the angle of internal friction of plastic, saturated clays can be assumed as approximately zero, then the shear strength of such a soil depends upon its cohesion (Fig. 16-23):

$$\tau = c, \quad \text{and} \quad \sigma_1 = 2c.$$

The value of c, in turn, according to theory, = half the unconfined compressive stress, i.e.,

$$c = \frac{\sigma_1}{2} = \tau_{max} \tag{19-33}$$

Note from the geometry of Fig. 19-22 that $2\alpha = 90° + \phi/2$.

19-26. Preparation of Test Samples. Because in many instances soil samples for unconfined compression tests are prepared without due precaution, the following should be noted.

1) Identify and describe the soil. Record, on the data sheet, all the necessary descriptive and qualitative information about the soil material to be tested.

2) In order to prevent the loss of moisture due to evaporation, prepare the sample in the humidity room at not less than approximately 90 % humidity, if such a room is available. If not, prepare the sample in an ordinary room. The preparation of samples should be done quickly to minimize the moisture loss by evaporation.

3) The shape of the sample to be tested may be prismatic or cylindrical. The size of the prismatic sample, in laboratory practice, usually varies from 1.5″ × 1.5″ × 3.5″ (3″) to 4″ × 4″ × 8″, but smaller or larger samples can be used. However, as a general criterion the height should be cut 2 to 3 times the width of the sample, $2\frac{1}{2}$ times the diameter or width being the usual height. Smaller or larger cylinders can be used. The dimensions of cylindrical samples usually are 1.4″ dia. × 3.5″ ht, or 2″ dia. × 5″ ht. Of course, the size of the sample depends also upon the capacity of the loading device and the volumetric size of soil material available.

4) Cut and trim from the supply of cohesive soil one or more prisms of cylinders to the desired size, and weigh them. The ends of the prisms or cylinders should be cut perpendicular to the longitudinal axis of the sample. Immediately after each prism or cylinder is cut, wrap them with sealing paper or thin plastic, or store them in an air-tight container to prevent excessive evaporation.

5) Determine the moisture content of the clay sample from the trimmings.

6) In case the prism or cylinder tends to split or crack at their ends, or if there are difficulties in trimming the ends smooth because of small scattered stones, prepare gypsum caps to provide uniform pressure distribution.

7) For area and volume, measure the free height of the clay prism or cylinder at three places by means of a steel rule or caliper. Measure to the nearest 0.01″, or 0.01 cm, and record these data.

8) For area and volume, determine the size of the prism or the diameter of the cylinder at top, middle, and bottom, to the nearest 0.01″ or 0.01 cm and record these measures. Use mean of four measurements at 90° at top, middle, and bottom. Calculate the average, initial cross-sectional area of the sample as

$$A_{av} = \frac{A_t + 2A_m + A_b}{4} \text{ (square units).} \tag{19-34}$$

9) Coat the sides of the samples to be tested with a light coating of grease or vaseline, or dip them into paraffin for a thin paraffin coating to prevent moisture loss during the test.

10) Generally, the previous comments on the preparation of the undisturbed samples apply also to disturbed (remolded) samples which are prepared at any desired density and moisture content.

11) Place the sample to be tested in the testing apparatus in an upright position, center the sample and the loading plate with the ball bearing on top, and bring down the cross-bar of the loading yoke (or piston) until it almost touches the ball bearing. Attach the deformation gage (an Ames dial) and adjust it to read zero.

19-27. Apparatus. Any compression device which permits an unconfined, axial loading and the measurement of strain is suitable for unconfined compression tests of soil. The apparatus may be of the controlled stress or controlled strain type. The axial load, σ_1, may be applied manually, or mechanically; by dead weights; pneumatically; by means of screws, or other means. A pneumatic, unconfined compression apparatus of the controlled strain type is illustrated in Fig. 19-24. The pressure is exerted on the sample and on the testing ring from below. Note in this figure the rupture plane in the tested soil cylinder.

The lower gage shows the compressed gas pressure in the gas chamber of the testing device, and the middle dial gage shows the total deformation (shortening) of the soil cylinder. The upper dial inside the testing rings indicates calibrated, total axial pressure applied on the soil cylinder.

FIG. 19-24 Unconfined compression test device.

19-28. The Vane Shear Test. If a cohesive soil is very plastic, or if it does not support a vertical cylinder or prism suitable for triaxial or unconfined compression test, or when it is difficult to extrude an undisturbed cohesive soil sample below the ground surface, the shear strength of such a material is then determined by a device called the shear vane.

The shear vane usually consists of four steel plates welded orthogonally to a steel torque rod, Fig. 19-25.

Two types of shear vanes may be distinguished, namely: laboratory and field vanes.

In Fig. 19-25 is sketched the principle of the laboratory shear vane. The field shear vane is similar in principle, but usually of larger dimensions than the laboratory one.

The vane is forced into the soil sample, or into the undisturbed soil at the bottom of a borehole (Fig. 19-26). Then a torque, T, is applied at the torque head to rotate the vane at a uniform speed, the rate usually being $1°/\text{min}$. The torque is indicated by the angle of twist, α, on a special gage. By rotating the edges of the shear vane a cylindrical surface is cut out in the soil. The applied torque is an approximate measure of the shear strength of the soil.

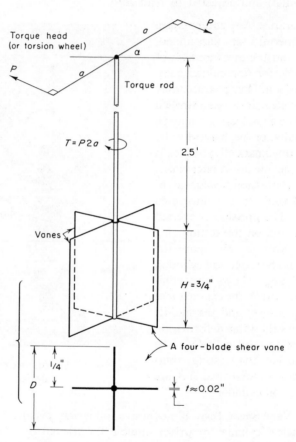

FIG. 19-25   Laboratory shear test vane.

If the two ends and the length of the vane device partake in shearing the clay, then, according to Carlson,[6] and the principle as shown in Fig. 19-26, the maximum torsional shear resistance, M_{max}, of the clay is calculated as

$$M_{max} = \tau \left(\overbrace{\pi DH \frac{D}{2}}^{\text{Mantle surface}} + \overbrace{2 \frac{\pi D^2}{4} \frac{2}{3} \frac{D}{2}}^{\text{Two ends}} \right) = \pi \tau \left(\frac{D^2 H}{2} + \frac{D^3}{6} \right), \qquad (19\text{-}35)$$

where $M_{max} = T$ = net applied torque

$\tau = c = q_u/2$ = shear strength of clay

q_u = ultimate, unconfined compressive strength of the clay

D = diameter of vane

H = vertical height of vane.

If only one end of the vane partakes in shearing the clay,[7] then

$$M_{max} = \pi c \left(\frac{D^2 H}{2} + \frac{D^3}{12} \right). \qquad (19\text{-}36)$$

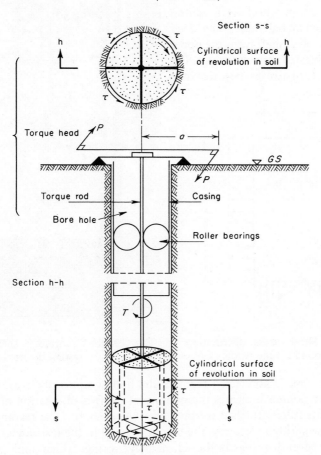

FIG. 19-26   Principle of vane shear test.

As to the shear stress distribution, Darienzo and Vey[8] assume that at failure the shear stress along the height of the blade is uniformly distributed along the surface of the circular cylinder of revolution, Fig. 19-27. The distribution of shear stresses at failure over the end shear surfaces are assumed to be triangular, varying from zero at the center of the vane device, to maximum at the edge.

A vane shear test of a cohesive soil material usually gives a value of the shear strength about 15 % greater than an unconfined compression test of clay.

Fig. 19-28 illustrates a laboratory vane shear testing device of soils manufactured by Leonard Farnell & Co. Ltd, Hatfield, England. The pillars carry the vertically adjustable torque head. The size of the vane is: $H = 13.0$ mm; $D = 12.8$ mm; $t = 0.6$ to 0.9 mm.

The rotation of the vane is brought about by means of a manually operated wheel. This wheel operates a worm gear and a worm wheel on a central shaft mounted on ball races. The lower end of this central shaft turns the upper end of a calibrated torsion spring. The spring, in its turn, causes the lower vane shaft to rotate.

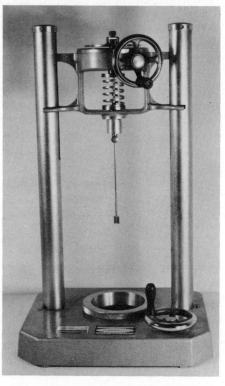

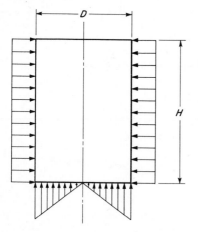

FIG. 19-27 Shear stress distribution around a vane blade.

FIG. 19-28 Laboratory shear vane testing device.

The vane shaft is connected through the hollow upper shaft to a resettable pointer. The pointer indicates the number of degrees of rotation of the spring on a graduated dial attached to the worm wheel shaft. The reading from the dial times the spring constant is the torque applied to the instrument.

There are several springs in the set, namely: springs which apply a torque of 2 in.-lb, 3 in.-lb, 4 in.-lb, and 5 in.-lb for an approximate angular movement of $\alpha = 180°$.

REFERENCES

1. C. A. Coulomb, "Essai sur une application des règles de maximis et minimis à quelques problèmes de statique relatifs à l'architecture", *Mémoires de la mathématique et de physique*, présentés à l'Académie Royale des Sciences, par divers savants, et lûs dans ses Assemblées, Paris, De L'Imprimerie Royale, 1776, vol. 7, Année 1773, pp. 347-348.

2. A. Casagrande, "Characteristics of Cohesionless Soils Affecting the Stability of Slopes and Earth Fills", *Contributions to Soil Mechanics*, 1925-1940, Boston, Boston Society of Civil Engineers, 1940, pp. 257-276.
3. O. Mohr, *Technische Mechanik*, Berlin, Wilhelm Ernst und Sohn, 1906.
4. K. A. Turner, Jr., *Design and Operation of a Pressure Cell for Measuring Pore Water Pressure* (mimeographed), New Brunswick, New Jersey, Rutgers—The State University, 1955.
5. A. Casagrande, "A Non-Metallic Piezometer for Measuring Pore Pressures in Clay", an Appendix to his paper entitled "Soil Mechanics in the Design and Construction of the Logan Airport", *Contributions to Soil Mechanics*, 1941-1953, Boston, Boston Society of Civil Engineers, 1953, pp. 198-205.
6. L. Carlson, "Determination in Situ of the Shear Strength of Undisturbed Clay by Means of a Rotating Auger", *Proceedings*, Second International Conference on Soil Mechanics and Foundation Engineering, Rotterdam, 1948, vol. 1, pp. 265-270.
7. E. Vey and L. Schlesinger, "Soil Shear Tests by Means of Rotating Vane", *Proceedings*, 29th Annual Meeting of the Highway Research Board, December 13-16, 1949, Washington, D.C., 1950, p. 547.
8. M. Darienzo and E. Vey, "Consistency Limits of Clay by the Vane Method", *Proceedings*, 34th Annual Meeting of the Highway Research Board, Washington, D.C., January 11-14, 1955, pp. 559-566.

Other Pertinent References

Procedures for Testing Soils, Philadelphia, ASTM, 1958, pp. 357-359.
K. Terzaghi, "The Shearing Resistance of Saturated Soils and the Angle Between the Planes of Shear", *Proceedings*, First International Conference on Soil Mechanics and Foundation Engineering, Cambridge, Mass., June 22-26, 1936, vol. 1, Paper no. d-7, pp. 54-56.
D. W. Taylor, "Shearing Strength Determination by Undrained Cylindrical Compression Test with Pore Pressure Measurements", *Proceedings*, Second International Conference on Soil Mechanics and Foundation Engineering, Rotterdam, June, 1948.
A. Casagrande and S. D. Wilson, *Report to Waterways Experiment Station on Triaxial Research Performed During 1950-51*, Harvard University, December, 1951.
A. Casagrande and S. D. Wilson, "Prestress Induced in Consolidated-quick Triaxial Tests", *Proceedings*, Third International Conference on Soil Mechanics and Foundation Engineering, Zürich, August, 1953.

PROBLEMS

19- 1. Prove analytically that $\alpha = 45° + \phi/2$.

19- 2. Show graphically that $\alpha = 45° + \phi/2$.

19- 3. Why do engineers need to know the shear strength of a soil?

19- 4. A direct shear test of a ϕ-soil at a normal stress of 4 kg/cm^2 resulted in a shearing stress of 3 kg/cm^2.

Determine: a) the angle of internal friction for this non-cohesive soil.

b) what will be the shearing resistance at a normal stress of 6 kg/cm^2?

c) Represent all of the stresses on a stress diagram.

19- 5. What is the physical law governing failure in shear of a soil?

19- 6. How does an effective normal stress differ from an applied total normal stress?

19- 7. Prove that

$$\frac{\sigma_1}{\sigma_3} = \frac{1 + \sin \phi}{1 - \sin \phi} = \cot^2(45° - \phi/2) = \tan^2(45° + \phi/2).$$

19- 8. Explain effective and neutral stress in soil and the significance of considering or not considering neutral stress in performing a shear test of a cohesive soil. Make illustrative sketches.

19- 9. From Mohr's rupture theory, it can be derived that in the case of a triaxial compression test of a cohesive soil (ϕ-c soil) the major principal stress, σ_1, may generally be expressed in terms of the minor principal stress, σ_3, the cohesion of soil, c, and the general angle of rupture, α, as

$$\sigma_1 = \sigma_3 + \frac{\sigma_3 \tan \phi + c}{\sin \alpha \cos \alpha - \cos^2 \alpha \tan \phi},$$

where ϕ = angle of internal friction of the given soil material.
   i) Calculate at which particular algebraic value of the critical angle of rupture, α_{crit}, the major principal stress attains a maximum value to bring about the rupture.
   ii) Develop an algebraic expression for σ_{1min} as a function of σ_3 and α_{crit}, and c.

19-10. Given the results of two sets of triaxial tests:
   $\sigma_{11} = 18.0$ kg/cm^2; $\sigma_{31} = 10.0$ kg/cm^2;
   $\sigma_{12} = 28.0$ kg/cm^2; $\sigma_{32} = 20.0$ kg/cm^2.
   Report the magnitudes of ϕ and c, and draw the stress diagram.

19-11. If the contact pressure on the soil at the base of a footing is 2 t/ft^2, what should be the least lateral restraint to prevent a lateral expulsion of s soil mass from underneath the footing?
   Given: $\phi = 30°$; $c = 200$ lb/ft^2, and the unit weight of the soil is $\gamma = 100$ lb/ft^3. How deep should the foundation pit be dug in order that the lateral restraint would just be enough to maintain equilibrium within the earth mass at the point under consideration?

19-12. Given direct shear test results on a remolded sandy soil at 13.2% moisture content and 109 lb/ft^3 dry density. The test was performed at $\sigma_n = 3.3$ lb/in^2. The testing ring dial reading constant is 33 lb per 0.0100 inch deformation of ring. The cross-sectional area of the shear area is 4.0 in^2.

Time in minutes	Testing ring dial readings in inches	Horizontal displacement dial readings in inches	Vertical displacement dial readings in inches	Remarks
1	2	3	4	5
0	0.0000	0.0000	0.0000	The minus sign
0.5	0.0024	0.0012	−0.0010	means decrease
1.0	0.0038	0.0050	−0.0010	of height of
1.5	0.0056	0.0090	−0.0005	soil sample in
2.0	0.0074	0.0120	+0.0005	the shear box
2.5	0.0090	0.0177	+0.0020	upon shearing.
3.0	0.0104	0.0225	+0.0045	
3.5	0.0114	0.0284	+0.0070	
4.0	0.0120	0.0345	+0.0100	Plus sign,
4.5	0.0116	0.0407	+0.0130	in contra-
5.0	0.0110	0.0475	+0.0170	distinction, means increase in height.

Plot and analyze the test results, showing three graphs on one drawing: shear stresses as a function of time, horizontal displacement as a function of time, and vertical displacement of soil as a function of time.

Observe the table. What kind of shear test is this? Report the ultimate shear stress. In what state of density is the sand?

19-13. Given the following test results of a remolded sandy soil with some binder at an optimum moisture content of 13% and dry density of 100 lb/ft³. The method of test is the unconsolidated, quick, direct shear test where no time was allowed for the consolidation of the specimen.

σ_n lb/in²	τ lb/in²
3.3	9.6
6.7	11.8
9.9	12.7
13.3	16.8
16.5	20.2

a) Plot the shear strength curve for this soil and for this test condition.
b) Determine the test parameters ϕ and c.
c) Establish the shear strength equation of this soil for a certain range of the strength graph.
d) Analyze and explain the obtained graph.

19-14. A consolidated, quick (undrained) (Q_c) triaxial test on a silt soil furnished the following results.

Total normal stresses σ lb/in²	Stresses on soil cylinders			
	Test numbers			
	1	2	3	4
σ_1	19.0	36.5	54.0	72.0
σ_3	10.0	19.5	30.0	40.0

The plot of these stresses gives the apparent angle of internal friction, ϕ_a.

Pore water pressure, u, in lb/in²	7.0	13.5	20.0	29.5

Effective normal stresses, $\sigma_{n_{eff}}$, in lb/in²				
$\sigma_{n_{eff}1}$		23.0		
$\sigma_{n_{eff}3}$		6.0		

The plot of these stresses gives the effective angle of internal friction, ϕ_e.

Note that the total normal stresses, as well as pore water pressures were measured in these tests.

a) Calculate the effective normal stresses for tests Nos. 1, 3, and 4, and complete the table.

b) Plot two graphs: the first representing the stress circles based on the total normal stresses, σ_n, and the second representing stress circles based on effective normal stresses, $\sigma_{n_{eff}}$.

c) Draw to the stress circles, in both graphs, Mohr's shear strength envelope as tangents according to the principle of "best fit".

Let the angle of the slope of the tangent to the total, normal stress circles (first graph) be termed the apparent angle of internal friction, ϕ_a of the silt tested, and the angle of the slope of the tangent to the effective, normal stress circles (second graph) be termed the effective angle of internal friction, ϕ_e, of same silt.

Scale off the graphs the angles ϕ_a and ϕ_e, and report their magnitudes. What is the ratio of $(\phi_e)/(\phi_a)$?

Make observations about cohesion in these two graphs.

19-15. A consolidated slow (drained) test, S_c, by method of triaxial compression on a cohesive soil gave the following results.

Effective Stresses on Soil Cylinders

normal stresses, $\sigma_{n_{eff}}$, lb/in²	Test Numbers	
	1	2
$\sigma_{n_{eff}1}$	33.0	65.0
$\sigma_{n_{eff}3}$	10.0	20.0

The plot of these stresses gives the true angle of internal friction, ϕ.

a) Plot the stress circles, and Mohr's shear strength envelope for these tests.

b) What is the magnitude of the true angle of internal friction, ϕ, in these tests?

c) Compare ϕ with ϕ_a and ϕ_e.

d) What is your observation on cohesion?

Note. Bring out the idea that ϕ_a, ϕ_e, ϕ, and c are test parameters, rather than soil constants.

19-16. Describe and illustrate how the shear strength of a soil varies with its moisture content. Discuss the deductions concerning the consequences in an earthwork when the moisture content in the soil gradually increases. Under what conditions can moisture content in soil increase in the field as applied to an earthwork?

19-17. Given the following results of five unconfined compression test results:

Axial stresses σ_1 lb/in²	Shear strength τ lb/in²
2.50	1.10
5.05	2.30
8.55	3.80
10.20	4.60
10.61	4.80

All rupture angles, α, were measured to be at $\alpha = 63°$ with the horizontal.

Present these test results in the form of stress circles on one drawing.

19-18. What means are used to increase shear strength of a soil used for fills in highway construction?

19-19. Given the following data from an unconfined compression test of a cohesive soil. The angle of rupture was measured to be $\alpha = 63°$ with the horizontal. The diameter of soil sample is 1.5". The height of the soil sample is 3 and 13/16". Type of soil: Greensand (Collington). The moisture content of the soil at its rupture was determined to be $w = 24\%$.

Point Nos. on curve	Axial load, σ_1, in lb/in²	Deformation of soil sample Δh, in inches	Remarks
0	0	0	
1	4.41	0.025	
2	9.05	0.047	
3	15.45	0.093	
4	18.80	0.148	
5	19.85	0.196	
6	17.60	0.253	
7	16.00	0.294	
8	15.40	0.348	

Required:
1) To plot the axial load as a function of deformation (i.e., $\sigma_1 = f(\Delta h)$.
2) Determine the ultimate, unconfined compressive load.
3) Plot the axial stress in lb/in² as a function of strain ($\Delta h/h$), and determine the proportional limit.
4) Plot Mohr's stress diagram, and determine σ_n, τ, ϕ and c.

19-20. Vane shear tests were performed yielding the following shear strength data on the soil tested at a 6 cm depth below the surface of the soil samples.

Plot the shear strength-moisture relationship and report your observations.

Test Nos.	Moisture Content $w\%$	Average shear strength, τ_{av}, t/ft²
1	13.4	1.50
2	13.8	1.25
3	14.0	0.90
4	20.0	0.35
5	25.0	0.20

Chapter 20

STRESS DISTRIBUTION IN SOIL

20-1. Principal Problem. One of the principal problems of soil mechanics relative to the founding of structures is the study of the relationships between the following factors: load, loading area, depth of foundation, settlement, and duration of loading.

Because of the great diversity in soil properties, and the many variables involved in the stability problems of soil and structure, the relationships between these factors are very complex indeed; and in theoretical studies one is forced in many instances to assume idealized conditions and simplifications, or to study soil mechanics problems experimentally.

20-2. Contact Stresses. Stresses in soil are caused by two principal factors, namely:

1) *self-weight of the soil,*

$$\sigma_s = \gamma H \tag{20-1}$$

where σ_s = stress in soil at depth, H, and
γ = unit weight of soil, and

2) the stress from the *structural load* applied to the soil.

20-3. Boussinesq's Theory: Assumptions. Boussinesq's stress distribution theory is based on the results given by the mathematical theory of elasticity for the simplest case of loading of a solid, homogeneous, elastic-isotropic, semi-infinite medium: namely, the case of a single, vertical, point load applied at a point on the horizontal boundary surface (ground surface).

A semi-infinite body is one bounded from one side with a horizontal boundary plane. In the case of soil, the horizontal boundary plane would be the ground surface, and semi-infinite medium is the mass of soil below the ground surface.

Point loads in soil mechanics are a) single, concentrated loads, and b) uniformly distributed loads over symmetric polygonal, or circular areas when stresses in soil are considered only at depths greater than the threefold diameter of the loaded area. In deriving his stress distribution theory for a single, concentrated load, J. V. Boussinesq[1] made the following assumptions:

1) The soil medium[2] is an elastic, homogeneous, isotropic, semi-infinite medium which extends infinitely in all directions from a level surface and which obeys Hooke's law.

2) The soil is weightless.

3) Originally, before the application of the single, concentrated load, the soil is not subjected to any other stress, i.e., the soil is stress-less, or un-stressed.

4) The stress distribution from the applied, concentrated load is independent of the type of material of which the homogeneous, elastic-isotropic body is made. Relative to soil the change in volume upon the application of stress to the soil is neglected.

5) In this medium, the law of linear stress distribution is valid.

6) There exists a continuity of stress.

7) In such a system the stresses are distributed symmetrically with respect to the z-axis.

The limitations of the theory based on the above assumptions restrict it to the proportionality between stress and deformation.

The principles of derivation of Boussinesq's equations are: there are six unknown quantities in the stress distribution problem, namely:

the normal stresses: σ_y, σ_t, σ_R;
the shear stress: τ, and
displacements: s_1 (radial component) and
s_v (vertical component).

Hence, the solution requires 6 independent equations. The equilibrium condition of an elementary material prism renders 2 equations for the axi-symmetrical stress condition. The relationship between stress and strain and the continuity conditions render the other four equations.

20-4. System. In applying Boussinesq's theory to soil, imagine the following system, Fig. 20-1: the ground surface is the ($z = 0$)-plane (plane H_o-H_o); it is

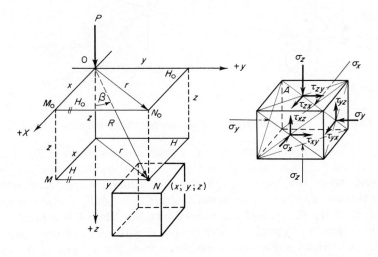

(a) Coordinate system

(b) Normal and shear stresses at point $N(x;y;z)$

FIG. 20-1 Orthogonal stresses

the horizontal boundary of a semi-infinite medium, viz., the medium of soil. A single, concentrated load, P, is acting on this plane at the point of origin of coordinates, O, along the z-axis. The positive direction of the z-axis is here, for the sake of convenience, directed downwards into the body of the semi-infinite medium to suit the contents of the matter under discussion. The positive branch of the y-axis is directed horizontally 90° counter-clockwise from the z-axis. The positive x-axis is directed orthogonally to the y- and z-axes. The $+x$ direction is then toward the viewer when viewing the $(z\text{-}y)$-plane.

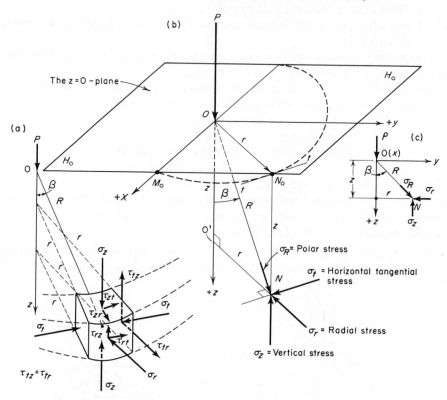

FIG. 20-2   Load and stresses in the cylindrical coordinate system.

In Fig. 20-1 are shown the orthogonal stresses at point, $N\,(x; y; z)$, which are the normal and the shear stresses. In Fig. 20-2 are shown at point $N(R; \beta)$ the polar stress, σ_R; or else, using the cylindrical coordinate system, there is shown the vertical stress, σ_z; the horizontal radial stress, σ_r; and the horizontal tangential stress, σ_t, in the R, z, r, and tangential directions. Here R is a radius-vector from O to N, making an angle, β, with the positive direction of the z-axis. The angle, β, is a directed angle, and is measured from the $+z$-axis to the radius-vector, R, connecting the stressed point, N, with the point of origin of coordinates, O. The angle, β, is positive when it is followed counterclockwise. The horizontal distance from the z-axis to an arbitrary point, N, is designated by r.

20-5. Designation of Stresses. The stressed condition of soil at any point is characterized by the stresses acting at that point along the coordinate axis. In the *orthogonal* coordinate system, the stressed condition of an elementary cube of soil, the faces of which are parallel to the planes of coordinates, is characterized by the following stresses, Fig. 20-1b:

a) normal stresses:

σ_z—vertical stress

σ_x—horizontal normal stress acting along or parallel to the *x*-axis of coordinates

σ_y—horizontal normal stress acting along or parallel to the *y*-axis of coordinates.

b) shear stresses:

τ_{xy} and τ_{yx}—shear stresses acting in the planes of a cube, planes which are parallel to the *z*-axis of coordinates. These two shear stresses are acting in mutually perpendicular directions.

τ_{yz} and τ_{zy}—shear stresses acting in planes parallel to the *x*-axis.

τ_{zx} and τ_{xz}—shear stresses acting in planes parallel to the *y*-axis.

Another mnemonic device for memorizing the shear stress designation is as follows: of the two subscripts to the shear stress symbol, τ, the first one indicates the direction of the plane in which the shear stress, τ, acts, whereas the second subscript indicates the direction in which τ acts.

In the cylindrical coordinate system, the stresses σ_z, σ_r, and σ_t are normal stresses. The shearing stresses are designated by τ. Because of symmetry of the state of stress with respect to the *z*-axis, the shear stresses in the vertical, radial planes, such as plane $ON_oNO'O$, are of zero magnitude.

Boussinesq's stress equations have been explained and summarized at various times by various authors, for example by Hertz,[3] Love,[4] Lamb,[5] Föppl,[6] Gray,[7] and others.

It is interesting to note that Love's paper had its origin in an attempt to throw some light on the important technical question of the safety of foundations. Love gives the stresses in differential forms. These forms are effectively due to H. Hertz, and the formulas are equivalent to those obtained by Boussinesq.

According to Boussinesq's theory, the various stresses caused in the semi-infinite medium by a single, concentrated load have the functions summarized as follows:

$$\sigma_z = \frac{3P}{2\pi} \frac{z^3}{R^5} = \frac{3P}{2\pi R^2} \cos^3 \beta \qquad (20\text{-}2)$$

$$\sigma_x = \frac{P}{2\pi} \left[3 \frac{x^2 z}{R^5} - \frac{m-2}{m} \left(\frac{x^2 - y^2}{Rr^2(R+z)} + \frac{y^2 z}{R^3 r^2} \right) \right] \qquad (20\text{-}3)$$

$$\sigma_y = \frac{P}{2\pi} \left[3 \frac{y^2 z}{R^5} - \frac{m-2}{m} \left(\frac{y^2 - x^2}{Rr^2(R+r)} + \frac{x^2 z}{R^3 r^2} \right) \right] \qquad (20\text{-}4)$$

$$\sigma_r = \frac{P}{2\pi} \left[3 \frac{r^2 z}{R^5} - \frac{m-2}{m} \left(\frac{R-z}{Rr^2} \right) \right] \qquad (20\text{-}5)$$

$$\sigma_t = \frac{P}{2\pi}\left[\frac{m-2}{m}\left(\frac{1}{r^2} - \frac{z}{R^3} - \frac{z}{Rr^2}\right)\right]$$ (20-6)

$$\tau_{rt} = \tau_{zt} = 0$$ (20-7)

$$\tau_{rz} = \frac{3P}{2\pi}\frac{rz^2}{R^5}$$ (20-8)

$$\tau_{zx} = \frac{3P}{2\pi}\frac{z^2 x}{R^5}$$ (20-9)

$$\tau_{zy} = \frac{3P}{2\pi}\frac{z^2 y}{R^5}$$ (20-10)

The stresses in soil at any point $N(R; \beta)$ in polar coordinates are:

$$\sigma_z = \frac{3P}{2\pi R^2}\cos^3 \beta$$ (20-11)

$$\sigma_r = \frac{P}{2\pi R^2}\left(3\sin^2 \beta \cos \beta - \frac{m-2}{m}\frac{1}{1+\cos\beta}\right)$$ (20-12)

$$\sigma_t = -\frac{m-2}{m}\frac{P}{2\pi R^2}\left(\cos \beta - \frac{1}{1+\cos\beta}\right)$$ (20-13)

For $m = 2$, $\sigma_t = 0$. (20-14)

$$\tau = \frac{3P}{2\pi R^2}\sin \beta \cos^2 \beta.$$ (20-15)

A volume-stable soil is characterized by Poisson's coefficient of $m = 2$, in which the cubal deformation is proportional to $(m - 2)$. With $m = 2$, Poisson's ratio is $\mu = 1/m = 0.5$.

Engineers are mostly interested in the vertical, normal, compressive stress, σ_z, particularly as it pertains to the bearing capacity of soil at different depths and on different types of soil layers below the ground surface, and to consolidation settlement analysis of foundation soils. For the same reasons, the derivation of the equation of the σ_z-stress for $m = 2$ will now be presented.

20-6. Derivation of σ_z-stress.

Deformation. Assume point $N(R; \beta)$ in the mass of soil, Fig. 20-3, and an elementary area $m - n$ at N, and thereby $\perp R$. The problem is to express algebraically the magnitude of the polar stress, σ_R, acting $\perp$ to the area, $m - n$, and then to find an equation for σ_z.

Consider that point, N, is now translocated at point, N_1, by an amount of dR. Through points N and N_1, two hemispheres can be drawn, the radii of which are R, and $R + dR$, respectively. The change in length of radius is, thus, dR. Note that the farther the point, N, is spaced, along the radius from the concentrated load, P, the less is its displacement. The displacement is thought to take place because of the radially distributed stress in the soil. Besides, considering point N translocating along the circle whose radius is R, note, from previous discussion on normal stress distribution in soil on a horizontal plane, that when $\ast\beta = 0$, displacement of point N is larger than at $\ast\beta > 0$. At $\beta = 90°$, displacement of point N approaches the value of zero.

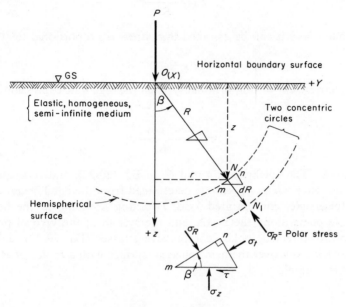

FIG. 20-3   Static system.

Designating displacement by the symbol, s, and noting from the above discussion that displacement is inversely proportional to R, and that displacement for a constant, R, is largest when $\beta = 0$, then displacement, s, can be written as

$$s = C \frac{\cos \beta}{R}, \tag{20-16}$$

where C = coefficient of proportionality.
At constant, R, when $\beta = 90°$, $s = 0$.

Assume now that point N is displaced at point N_1. Displacement, analogous to Eq. (20-16), is written as

$$s_1 = C \frac{\cos \beta}{R + dR}. \tag{20-17}$$

Strain, ε, or relative deformation, δ/dR, relative to length, dR, where δ is absolute deformation, is

$$\varepsilon = \frac{\delta}{dR} = \frac{s - s_1}{dR} = \frac{C \cos \beta}{R\, dR} - \frac{C \cos \beta}{(R + dR)\, dR}, \tag{20-18}$$

or

$$\varepsilon = \frac{C \cos \beta}{R^2 + R\, dR}. \tag{20-19}$$

Stress and Strain. Neglecting in the denominator of Eq. (20-19) the quantity $(R\,dR)$ which is small as compared with R^2, obtain radial compressive strain

$$\varepsilon = \frac{C\cos\beta}{R^2}. \tag{20-20}$$

By Hooke's law, it can be assumed that stress is proportional to strain, i.e.,

$$\sigma_R = \alpha\varepsilon, \tag{20-21}$$

where α = coefficient of proportionality, then the algebraic expression for polar stress is

$$\sigma_R = \frac{\alpha C\cos\beta}{R^2}. \tag{20-22}$$

Equilibrium. The coefficients, α and C, in Eq. (20-22), and consequently the polar compressive stress, σ_R, can be determined from the equilibrium condition between the single, concentrated load, P, acting normally to the horizontal, semi-infinite plane along the z-axis, and the system of the vertical projections of the upward-directed, polar, compressive stresses (Eq. 20-22), acting with uniform distribution over the hemispherical surface with a radius of R, through point N, for example.

$$\Sigma F_z = 0$$

$$P = \int_0^A \sigma_R\cos\beta\,dA, \tag{20-23}$$

where $\qquad dA = 2\pi R\,dh = 2\pi R(R\,d\beta)\sin\beta = 2\pi R^2\sin\beta\,d\beta \tag{20-24}$

is the curved surface of the spherical zone, $n_1 nmm_1$, bounded by two parallel planes (nn_1 and mm_1), Fig. 20-4.

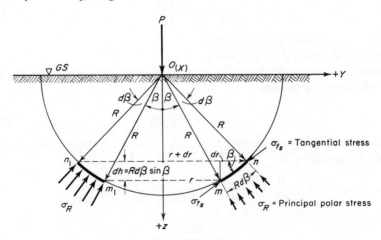

FIG. 20-4   Equilibrium: $\Sigma F_z = 0$.

Eq. (20-23) is now rewritten as

$$P = 2\pi R^2 \int_0^{\pi/2} \sigma_R \sin \beta \cos \beta \, d\beta, \qquad (20\text{-}25)$$

or, after integration,

$$P = \tfrac{2}{3}\pi\alpha C, \qquad (20\text{-}26)$$

or

$$\alpha C = \tfrac{3}{2}(P/\pi). \qquad (20\text{-}27)$$

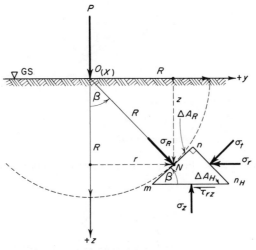

Polar Stress. Substituting Eq. (20-27) into Eq. (20-22), obtain the expression for polar stress

$$\sigma_R = \frac{3}{2}\frac{P}{\pi}\frac{\cos\beta}{R^2}. \qquad (20\text{-}28)$$

This equation reads that the polar stress, σ_R, varies inversely as the square of the distance, R^2, from the point of application of the concentrated load, P, at the ground surface.

Vertical Normal Stress. In foundation engineering engineers are interested more in the vertical, normal, compressive stress, σ_z, acting on a horizontal area rather than in the polar stress. To find the vertical, normal, compressive stress, σ_z, Fig. 20-5, use is now made of Mohr's graphical stress circle, Fig. 20-6. (Note from Eq. (20-14) that for $m = 2$ stress, $\sigma_t = 0$). By means of this graphical construction,

$$\sigma_z = \sigma_R \cos^2 \beta. \qquad (20\text{-}29)$$

Note from Fig. 20-6 that angle β determines the magnitude of σ_z; σ_R is here known from Eq. (20-28).

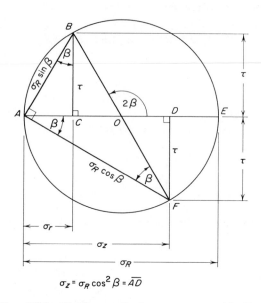

$$\sigma_z = \sigma_R \cos^2 \beta = \overline{AD}$$

FIG. 20-6   Finding vertical stress, σ_z, graphically.

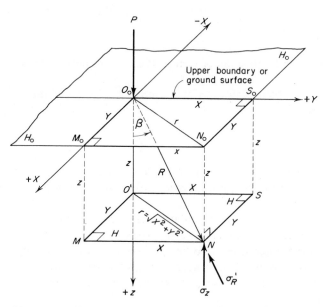

FIG. 20-7   Coordinates of point N, the point of application of σ_z.

Because $\cos \beta = z/R$, Fig. 20-7,

$$\sigma_z = \sigma_R \left(\frac{z}{R}\right)^2,$$ (20-30)

or substituting Eq. (20-28) into Eq. (20-30), obtain

$$\sigma_z = \frac{3}{2} \frac{P}{\pi} \frac{z^3}{R^5}.$$ (20-31)

With $R^2 = z^2 + r^2$, and with $r^2 = x^2 + y^2$, where x, y, and z are the coordinates of point N, Fig. 20-7, the vertical, normal, compressive stress, σ_z, is calculated as

$$\sigma_z = \frac{3P}{2\pi z^2} \frac{1}{\left[1 + \left(\frac{r}{z}\right)^2\right]^{5/2}},$$ (20-32)

or

$$\sigma_z = K \frac{P}{z^2},$$ (20-33)

where

$$K = \frac{3}{2\pi} \frac{1}{\left[1 + \left(\frac{r}{z}\right)^2\right]^{5/2}} = \frac{0.478}{\left[1 + \left(\frac{r}{z}\right)^2\right]^{5/2}},$$ (20-34)

is the Boussinesq vertical stress coefficient.

Thus, Eqs. (20-32) and (20-34) permit the calculation of the vertical, normal, compressive stress, σ_z, caused by a concentrated load, P, at any point, N, below the boundary surface, H_o-H_o of a semi-infinite medium (viz., below the ground surface).

When point N is on the z-axis, i.e., on the line of action of P, then $\beta = 0$, $r = 0$, and σ_z has a maximum value of

$$\sigma_z = \frac{3P}{2\pi z^2} = (0.478) \frac{P}{z^2},$$ (20-35)

see Eqs. (20-32) and (20-34).

Note that Boussinesq's equations give the stresses in a semi-infinite medium caused by the surface loads only (refer to the assumption that the medium is weightless, and that the load, P, is a concentrated point load.

Boussinesq's Vertical Stress Coefficients, K. To facilitate vertical stress distribution calculations of single, concentrated loads by means of Boussinesq's theory, there are tables available[8] supplying the K-values for various r/z-ratios in Boussinesq's stress distribution equation, $\sigma_z = K(P)/(z^2)$, see Table 20-1. The K-values can also be presented in a graph, Fig. 20-8.

Example. The vertical stress, σ_z, at a point the coordinates of which are $z = 15.0$ ft, and $r = 7.5$ ft away from the line of action of a single, vertical, concentrated load of $P = 400,000$ lb $= 200$ tons is calculated by means of the K-tables as follows:

$$\frac{r}{z} = \frac{7.50}{15.00} = 0.5; \qquad K_{0.5} = 0.2733 \text{ (from the } K\text{-tables)};$$

$$z^2 = (15.0)^2 = 225.0;$$

$$\sigma_z = K\frac{P}{z^2} = (0.2733)(200)/(225) = 0.24 \text{ (t/ft}^2).$$

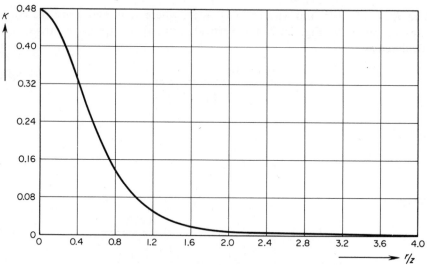

FIG. 20-8 $K = f(r/z)$

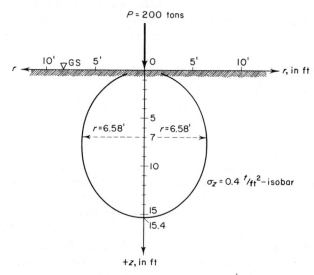

FIG. 20-9   The $\sigma_z = 0.40$ t/ft^2-isobar.

TABLE 20-1. BOUSSINESQ COEFFICIENTS $K = f(r/z)$.[8]

r/z	K	r/z	K	r/z	K	r/z	K	r/z	K	r/z	K
.00	.4775	.50	.2733	1.00	.0844	1.50	.0251	2.00	.0085	2.50	.0034
.01	.4773	.51	.2679	1.01	.0823	1.51	.0245	2.01	.0084	2.51	.0033
.02	.4770	.52	.2625	1.02	.0803	1.52	.0240	2.02	.0082	2.52	.0033
.03	.4764	.53	.2571	1.03	.0783	1.53	.0234	2.03	.0081	2.53	.0032
.04	.4765	.54	.2518	1.04	.0764	1.54	.0229	2.04	.0079	2.54	.0032
.05	.4745	.55	.2466	1.05	.0744	1.55	.0224	2.05	.0078	2.55	.0031
.06	.4723	.56	.2414	1.06	.0727	1.56	.0219	2.06	.0076	2.56	.0031
.07	.4717	.57	.2363	1.07	.0709	1.57	.0214	2.07	.0075	2.57	.0030
.08	.4699	.58	.2313	1.08	.0691	1.58	.0209	2.08	.0073	2.58	.0030
.09	.4679	.59	.2263	1.09	.0674	1.59	.0204	2.09	.0072	2.59	.0029
.10	.4657	.60	.2214	1.10	.0658	1.60	.0200	2.10	.0070	2.60	.0029
.11	.4633	.61	.2165	1.11	.0641	1.61	.0195	2.11	.0069	2.61	.0028
.12	.4607	.62	.2117	1.12	.0626	1.62	.0191	2.12	.0068	2.62	.0028
.13	.4579	.63	.2070	1.13	.0610	1.63	.0187	2.13	.0066	2.63	.0027
.14	.4548	.64	.2040	1.14	.0595	1.64	.0183	2.14	.0065	2.64	.0027
.15	.4516	.65	.1978	1.15	.0581	1.65	.0179	2.15	.0064	2.65	.0026
.16	.4482	.66	.1934	1.16	.0567	1.66	.0175	2.16	.0063	2.66	.0026
.17	.4446	.67	.1889	1.17	.0553	1.67	.0171	2.17	.0062	2.67	.0025
.18	.4409	.68	.1846	1.18	.0539	1.68	.0167	2.18	.0060	2.68	.0025
.19	.4370	.69	.1804	1.19	.0526	1.69	.0163	2.19	.0059	2.69	.0025
.20	.4329	.70	.1762	1.20	.0513	1.70	.0160	2.20	.0058	2.70	.0024
.21	.4286	.71	.1721	1.21	.0501	1.71	.0157	2.21	.0057	..	..
.22	.4242	.72	.1681	1.22	.0489	1.72	.0153	2.22	.0056	2.72	.0023
.23	.4197	.73	.1641	1.23	.0477	1.73	.0150	2.23	.0055	..	..
.24	.4151	.74	.1603	1.24	.0466	1.74	.0147	2.24	.0054	2.74	.0023
.25	.4103	.75	.1565	1.25	.0454	1.75	.0144	2.25	.0053	..	..
.26	.4054	.76	.1527	1.26	.0443	1.76	.0141	2.26	.0052	2.76	.0022
.27	.4004	.77	.1491	1.27	.0433	1.77	.0138	2.27	.0051	..	..
.28	.3954	.78	.1455	1.28	.0422	1.78	.0135	2.28	.0050	2.78	.0021
.29	.3902	.79	.1420	1.29	.0412	1.79	.0132	2.29	.0049	..	..
.30	.3849	.80	.1386	1.30	.0402	1.80	.0129	2.30	.0048	2.80	.0021
.31	.3796	.81	.1353	1.31	.0393	1.81	.0126	2.31	.0047	..	..
.32	.3742	.82	.1320	1.32	.0384	1.82	.0124	2.32	.0047	2.84	.0019
.33	.3687	.83	.1288	1.33	.0374	1.83	.0121	2.33	.0046	..	..
.34	.3632	.84	.1257	1.34	.0365	1.84	.0119	2.34	.0045	2.91	.0017
.35	.3577	.85	.1226	1.35	.0357	1.85	.0116	2.35	.0044	..	..
.36	.3521	.86	.1196	1.36	.0348	1.86	.0114	2.36	.0043	2.99	.0015
.37	.3465	.87	.1166	1.37	.0340	1.87	.0112	2.37	.0043	..	..
.38	.3408	.88	.1138	1.38	.0332	1.88	.0109	2.38	.0042	3.08	.0013
.39	.3351	.89	.1110	1.39	.0324	1.89	.0107	2.39	.0041	..	..
.40	.3294	.90	.1083	1.40	.0317	1.90	.0105	2.40	.0040	3.19	.0011
.41	.3238	.91	.1057	1.41	.0309	1.91	.0103	2.41	.0040	..	..
.42	.3181	.92	.1031	1.42	.0302	1.92	.0101	2.42	.0039	3.31	.0009
.43	.3124	.93	.1005	1.43	.0295	1.93	.0099	2.43	.0038	..	..
.44	.3068	.94	.0981	1.44	.0288	1.94	.0097	2.44	.0038	3.50	.0007
.45	.3011	.95	.0956	1.45	.0282	1.95	.0095	2.45	.0037	..	..
.46	.2955	.96	.0933	1.46	.0275	1.96	.0093	2.46	.0036	3.75	.0005
.47	.2899	.97	.0910	1.47	.0269	1.97	.0091	2.47	.0036	..	..
.48	.2843	.98	.0887	1.48	.0263	1.98	.0089	2.48	.0035	4.13	.0003
.49	.2788	.99	.0865	1.49	.0257	1.99	.0087	2.49	.0034	..	..
										4.91	.0001
										6.15	.0001

20-7. Pressure Distribution Diagrams. By means of the Boussinesq vertical stress equation, Eq. (20-32), the following diagrams can be calculated and presented graphically:

1) the stress isobar diagram;
2) the vertical stress distribution on a horizontal plane, z units below the ground surface; and
3) the vertical stress distribution vertically r units away from the line of action of the single, vertical, concentrated load, P.

The Stress Isobars. An isobar is a line which connects all points below the ground surface of equal stress, Fig. 20-9. Obviously, for any one load system many isobars can be drawn on one diagram. In other words, an isobar is a stress contour. In the literature such an isobar diagram is termed the "bulb of pressure", or simply the "pressure bulb".

A system of isobars indicates the decrease in stress intensity and reminds one of an onion bulb. Hence the term "pressure bulb". The soil mass within the boundaries of the pressure bulb, it may be said, furnishes the support for the bearing or loading plate, or for the footing of the foundation.

Example. The plotting of isobars is now illustrated by the following example.

For a single, concentrated load of $P = 200$ tons construct an isobar for $\sigma_z = 0.4$ kg/cm^2 = 0.4 t/ft^2 = 800 lb/ft^2.

The calculation is best performed in a tabular form. The problem consists of finding corresponding r-values for various depths, z. By Eq. (20-33),

$$K = \frac{\sigma_z z^2}{P},$$
(20-36)

or

$$K = \frac{(0.4)z^2}{200} = \frac{z^2}{500}.$$

Assuming various z-values, calculate their corresponding K-values for which determine from the K-tables the respective (r/z)-ratios. Knowing the (r/z)-ratios, calculate r for each of the previously assumed z-values. The σ_z-values for the same radius, r, are the same on both sides of the axis of symmetry of the pressure bulb. The $\sigma_z = 0.4$ t/ft^2 isobar calculation is compiled in Table 20-2.

When $r = 0$, then $K = 0.478$, and the isobar crosses the line of action of the load, $P = 200$ tons, at a depth of

$$z = \sqrt{500K} = \sqrt{(500)(0.478)} = 15.4 \quad \text{(ft)}.$$

below the ground surface.

The $\sigma_z = 0.4$ t/ft^2 isobar is illustrated in Fig. 20-9. It lies in the vertical plane passing through the line of action of P. Actually the isobar is a spatial, curved surface because in this case for each z the radii in all directions around the axis of symmetry are equal.

Note from Fig. 20-9 that in general isobars are not circular curves. Rather, their shapes approach the curve of lemniscate.

System of Several Concentrated Loads. If a system of several concentrated loads is given, then for plotting the resulting isobars each of the normal, compressive stresses in the system may be added at any point to obtain the total stresses at that point. Points with equal stresses are connected by a curvilinear line to give isobars (by interpolation).

TABLE 20-2. ISOBAR DATA FOR $\sigma_z = 0.4$ t/ft^2 = const.

Depth z ft	K	$\dfrac{r}{z}$	r in ft	σ_z t/ft^2
1	2	3	4	5
0.5	0.0005	3.750	1.875	0.40 = const
1	0.002	2.840	2.84	0.40
2	0.008	2.035	4.06	0.40
3	0.018	1.650	4.95	0.40
5	0.050	1.210	6.05	0.40
7	0.098	0.940	6.58	0.40
8	0.128	0.830	6.64	0.40
10	0.200	0.650	6.50	0.40
14	0.392	0.290	4.06	0.40
15	0.450	0.155	2.33	0.40
15.4	0.478	0.000	0.00	0.40

Vertical Stress Distribution Diagram on a Horizontal Plane. To plot the vertical stress distribution diagram on a horizontal plane, keep the depth, z, determining the position of that horizontal plane, below the ground surface constant, i.e., z = const. Then, using various assumed values for r, calculate the (r/z) ratios, and by means of the K-Table determine the corresponding K-values. Also, calculate the (P/z²) value which for each horizontal plane (for each z) is a constant, and compute the vertical stress, σ_z, by means of Eq. (20-33):

$$\sigma_z = K \frac{P}{z^2}$$

Example. Calculate and plot the vertical stress distribution diagram on a horizontal plane located z = 7.0 ft below the ground surface. The concentrated load is P = 200 tons.

The calculation is performed in a tabular form (see Table 20-3). The soil-force system is plotted to a *geometric scale*. The vertical stresses are plotted to a *stress scale*. The diagram is plotted in Fig. 20-10 along the line, *h-h*.

Note that the vertical stress distribution diagram due to Boussinesq is bell-shaped; that therefore the vertical stress distribution is non-uniform, and that the maximum stress ordinate (in this example σ_z = 1.94 t/ft²) is located on the line of action of the concentrated load. The stress decrease is an asymptotic one.

Note that the vertical stress distribution diagram on a horizontal plane can be obtained graphically if the isobar diagram is given, containing several isobars. By passing at a certain z a horizontal plane, *h-h*, through the pressure bulb (isobars), the intersection of the horizontal line with the particular isobar gives the vertical stress ordinate at the point of intersection (read the value of the intersected isobar).

Vertical Stress Distribution Diagram Along a Vertical Plane. Such a diagram shows the variation in magnitude of vertical stress with depth, z, at a constant distance, r, from the z-axis. In the diagram these stresses are represented by horizontal ordinates.

TABLE 20-3. VERTICAL STRESS ORDINATES FOR DEPTH $z = 7.0$ ft = const.

$$\frac{P}{z^2} = \frac{200}{7^2} = 4.081 = \text{const.}$$

Radius r ft	$\dfrac{r}{z}$	K	$\dfrac{P}{z^2}$	σ_z t/ft^2
1	2	3	4	5
0	0	0.4775	4.081	1.94
1	0.14	0.4548	4.081	1.86
2	0.28	0.3954	4.081	1.61
3	0.42	0.3181	4.081	1.30
4	0.57	0.2363	4.081	0.96
5	0.71	0.1721	4.081	0.70
6	0.85	0.1226	4.081	0.50
6.58	0.94	0.0980	4.081	0.40
7	1.00	0.0844	4.081	0.34
8	1.14	0.0595	4.081	0.24
9	1.28	0.0422	4.081	0.17
10	1.42	0.0302	4.081	0.12
12	1.71	0.0157	4.081	0.06
15	2.14	0.0065	4.081	0.03
21	3.00	0.0015	4.081	0.006

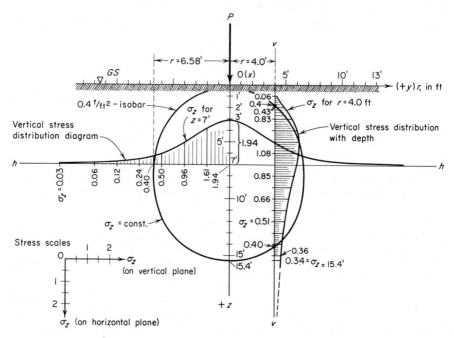

FIG. 20-10   Vertical stress distribution diagrams.

Example. For $P = 200$ tons, and with $r = 4.0$ ft $=$ const, the vertical stresses, σ_z, for various depths, z, are computed as follows. Assuming various z-values, calculate the (r/z) ratios, and determine the K-values from the K-Tables. Then calculate for each depth, z, the (P/z^2) values, and calculate the vertical stress, σ_z, by Eq. (20-33):

$$\sigma_z = K \frac{P}{z^2}$$

The calculation is performed in a tabular form (see Table 20-4). The vertical stresses

TABLE 20-4. VERTICAL STRESS ORDINATES FOR $r = 4.0$ ft $=$ const.

Depth, z (ft)	$\dfrac{r}{z}$	K	z^2	$\dfrac{P}{z^2}$	σ_z t/ft^2
1	2	3	4	5	6
0	$\to \infty$	$\to 0$	0	$\to \infty$	Indeterminate
1	4	0.0003	1	200	0.06
2	2	0.0085	4	50	0.43
3	1.33	0.0374	9	22.2	0.83
4	1.00	0.0844	16	12.5	1.06
5	0.8	0.1386	25	8.0	1.11
6	0.66	0.1934	36	5.6	1.08
6.58	0.61	0.2165	43.3	4.6	1.00
7	0.57	0.2363	49	4.08	0.96
8	0.50	0.2733	64	3.12	0.85
9	0.44	0.3068	81	2.47	0.66
10	0.4	0.3294	100	2.00	0.66
12	0.33	0.3687	144	1.39	0.51
15	0.27	0.4004	225	0.89	0.36
15.4	0.26	0.4054	235.2	0.85	0.34

are to be plotted to a stress scale. The diagram is shown in Fig. 20-10 plotted along the line, v-v.

Note from the plot that the magnitude of the vertical stress first increases, and then decreases with depth. The decrease is an asymptotic one. This diagram can also be obtained graphically if the isobar diagram is given. The ordinates are obtained by reading the isobar values at their intersection with the vertical plane, v-v.

20-8. Summary of Boussinesq's Theory.

1) Boussinesq's equations are derived for elastic, homogeneous materials—materials which completely obey Hooke's law. One of the basic underlying assumptions in this theory is that stress is proportional to deformation at pure tension or compression.

2) Boussinesq's equations are applicable to the state of elastic equilibrium of a weightless, semi-infinite, homogeneous, and isotropic medium.

3) The stresses in the semi-infinite medium under a single, concentrated load are assumed to be distributed radially in all directions and therefore uniformly. Hence the stress under a point load is larger than at points away from the line of action of the point load (center) at the same depth below the surface.

4) The size of the area upon which the single, concentrated load, P, acts does not appear at all in Boussinesq's equations.

5) The vertical stress equation for a concentrated load on a soil yields an infinitely large stress near the point of application for the concentrated load. This equation does not give real stresses at points near the point of application even in elastic materials.

6) The σ_z-equations show that the σ_z-stress on a horizontal plane is completely independent of Poisson's coefficient, m, viz., Poisson's ratio μ. Thus the stress distribution on these planes is for all elastic-isotropic materials the same—bell shaped.

7) With reference to an ideal, granular soil mass, its performance is characterized by the arrangement of the individual particles of soil. It seems, therefore, that the direction of the action of the concentrated load relative to the orientation of the soil particles is the controlling factor of stress distribution in soil. One would think that because of these conditions there should exist in a semi-infinite medium certain "favored" directions of stress distribution which would be contrary to the assumption of isotropy of the medium.

8) Soil is not a homogeneous, elastic material. It obeys Hooke's law only approximately. Because soil is more or less a non-homogeneous medium, then forces applied to the soil take a course which cannot always be controlled.

9) In soil, the so-called "modulus of elasticity" is not constant but increases with depth.

10) Although Boussinesq's equations are derived for a semi-infinite medium (elastic, homogeneous, and isotropic), they may be applied with reasonable accuracy to points near the load in a finite solid.

11) Regardless of some of the limitations attached to Boussinesq's stress equations in the application of the theory of elasticity to soil, the mathematical treatment of the stress distribution problem is, however, very useful—at least qualitatively. Until something better is suggested, Boussinesq's stress distribution theory may be, and still is, applied in estimating approximately stress conditions in soil, the soil itself usually being somewhat idealized.

12) As to the plastic region around the point of application of the single, concentrated load, the mathematical plasticity theory, which has as its goal the indication of the prevailing stress at each point in the soil medium, as well as the corresponding deformation in the plastic region, this goal so far has not yet been achieved. Temporarily, one has to be satisfied with the stability problem from the standpoint of the exact mechanics of continuity.

20-9. Stress Underneath Any Point Outside the Loaded Area. The magnitude of the vertical, normal, compressive stress, σ_z, at a point (say, point D) which is situated outside the loaded area, $AEGJ$, as in Fig. 20-11, for example, may be discovered as follows.

Complete through point D the large parallelogram, $DUGLD = (1)+(2)+(3)+(4)$. All areas, areas (1), (2), (3) and (4), should be imagined to be loaded with the same intensity as the actual parallelogram, area (1). Then add algebraically all stresses occurring at the point of interest, D:

$$\sigma_{z_D} = \sigma_{z(1+2+3+4)} + \sigma_{z(3)} - \sigma_{z(2+3)} - \sigma_{z(3+4)}, \quad (20\text{-}37)$$

$\sigma_{z(1+2+3+4)}$ meaning the stress under the corner-point of the new, or large parallelogram consisting of the small areas $(1)+(2)+(3)+(4)$. The stress $\sigma_{z(3)}$

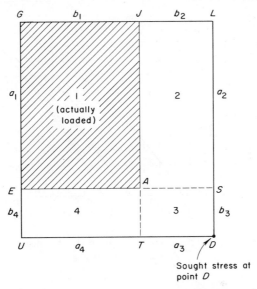

FIG. 20-11 Stress in soil underneath any point outside the actually loaded area.

under the corner-point (D) due to the small area (3) must be added because in subtracting corner stresses contributed by areas $(2+3)$ and $(3+4)$, the small area (3) is subtracted twice.

20-10. Steinbrenner's Influence Values. Uniformly loaded areas are one of the most commonly encountered conditions in foundation engineering. Therefore, attempts have been made to facilitate the calculations of vertical stresses in soil—stresses caused by uniformly distributed loads over rectangular areas—by means of graphs and charts such as those worked out by Steinbrenner[9] and Newmark,[10] for example.

Steinbrenner's diagram is prepared for uniformly loaded parallelograms based on the Boussinesq's theory. The diagram is shown and its use is explained in Figs. 20-12 and 20-13, respectively. The graph is good for $m = 2$ (elastic, isotropic medium).

From a given depth-to-width ratio, z/b as ordinate, and from a given length-to-width ratio, a/b, one obtains the influence value, $i_u = \sigma_z/\sigma_o$ on the abscissa axis, from which the stress σ_z can be calculated if σ_o is known:

$$\sigma_z = \sigma_o i_u. \quad (20\text{-}38)$$

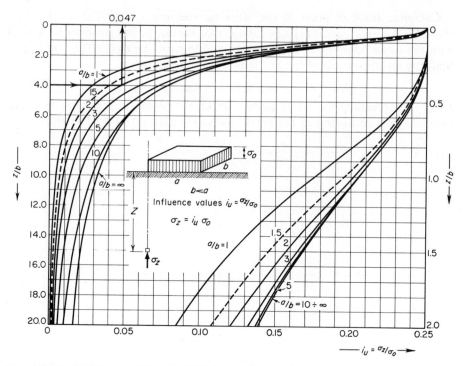

FIG. 20-12   Steinbrenner's vertical stress diagram (by permission of Dr. E. Schultze, Aachen, Germany).

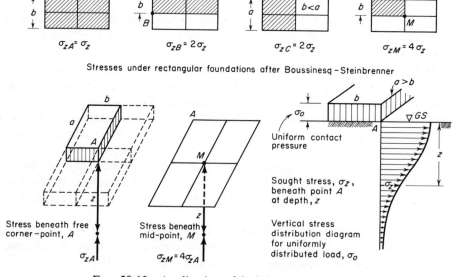

FIG. 20-13   Application of Steinbrenner's diagram.

The σ_z-stress is the one acting underneath the free corner point, A, at depth, z. The vertical compressive stress, σ_{zM}, beneath the midpoint of the loaded parallelogram is $\sigma_{zM} = 4\,\sigma_{zA}$.

Example. Given a footing the shape of which is a parallelogram. The half-dimensions of this parallelogram are:

$$a = 4.0 \text{ m} = 13.12 \text{ ft}$$

and

$$b = 2.0 \text{ m} = 6.56 \text{ ft}.$$

Hence $a/b = 4.0/2.0 = 13.12/6.56 = 2.00$.
The parallelogram area is loaded with a uniformly distributed load giving a contact pressure of $\sigma_o = 2.5 \text{ kg/cm}^2 \approx 2.5 \text{ t/ft}^2$.

Using Steinbrenner's diagram, calculate the vertical compressive stresses in kg/cm² below the midpoint of the parallelogram, M, at depths $z = 1.0, 2.0, 3.0, 4.0, 5.0$, and 8 m.

The calculation can best be carried out in a tabular form, see Table 20-5. The procedure is self-evident, and needs no additional explanations here. Form the z/b-ratios in consistent units, and read from curve, Fig. 20-12, designated $a/b = 2$, the corresponding influence values, i_u. Then calculate the σ_{zA}-values for a free corner-point (point A, for example). Multiplying these σ_{zA}-values by 4 (four corners at midpoint), find for each specified depth, z, the vertical stress, σ_{zM}.

TABLE 20-5. MIDPOINT STRESSES; $a/b = 2$; $\sigma_o = 2.5 \text{ kg/cm}^2$

Depth z, m	z/b	Influence Value $i_u = \dfrac{\sigma_z}{\sigma_o}$	Stress at Free Corner Point σ_{zA}	Midpoint Stress $\sigma_{zM} = 4\sigma_{zA}$
1	2	3	4	5
1	0.5	0.238	0.595	2.38
2	1.0	0.200	0.500	2.00
3	1.5	0.156	0.390	1.56
4	2.0	0.120	0.300	1.20
5	2.5	0.093	0.230	0.92
8	4.0	0.047	0.120	0.48

20-11. Newmark's Influence Chart. Based on equation $\sigma_z = \sigma_o i_c$, which expresses vertical, compressive stress, σ_z, underneath the center of a circular area loaded with a uniformly distributed load, σ_o (contact pressure from footing to soil), Newmark,[10, 11] devised a simple, graphical procedure for computing stresses in the interior of an elastic, homogeneous, isotropic medium bounded by a plane horizontal surface and loaded by uniformly distributed, vertical load at the surface.

The vertical stress underneath the center of uniformly loaded circular area is

$$\sigma_z = \sigma_o \left\{ 1 - \frac{1}{\left[1 + \left(\dfrac{r_o}{z}\right)^2\right]^{3/2}} \right\}, \tag{20-39}$$

or

$$\frac{\sigma_z}{\sigma_o} = f(r_o/z). \tag{20-40}$$

From this equation, the ratio r_o/z is expressed:

$$\frac{r_o}{z} = +\sqrt{\left(1 - \frac{\sigma_z}{\sigma_o}\right)^{-2/3} - 1}. \tag{20-41}$$

The quantity, r_o/z, may be interpreted as relative sizes or radii of circular-loaded bearing areas required to give particular values of the ratio of pressure to applied loading.

The substitution into this equation of various σ_z/σ_o-values, such as $\sigma_z/\sigma_o = 0.1, 0.2, 0.3, \cdots 0.9$, and 1.00 gives corresponding relative radii, for $z = 1$, for example. These radii encompass concentric circles. These areas so encompassed for a uniformly distributed loading and for c circular lines, ten in number for example, give each $(1/c)(\sigma_z)$, or in this instance $(1/10)(\sigma_z)$. The r_o/z-values necessary for the construction of the influence chart for the above-assumed σ_z/σ_o-values are tabulated for each of the $c = 10$ circles, or 1 circle and 8 rings, rather, in Table 20-6. From this table it can be seen that the widths of the concentric

TABLE 20-6. RELATIVE RADII OF INFLUENCE CHART

Circle Nos.	$\dfrac{\sigma_z}{\sigma_o}$	Relative Radii $\dfrac{r_o}{z}$	Number of Influence Mesh-Areas per Ring s
1	2	3	4
0	0.000	0.000	
			20
1	0.100	0.270	
			20
2	0.200	0.400	
			20
3	0.300	0.518	
			20
4	0.400	0.637	
			20
5	0.500	0.766	
			20
6	0.600	0.918	
			20
7	0.700	1.110	
			20
8	0.800	1.387	
			20
9	0.900	1.908	
			20
	1.000	∞	

circular slices, or rings, are wider the farther away they are from the center. The relative radii, r_o/z, are tabulated in Column 3, Table 20-6. The arc for an influence of 1.0 has an infinitely large radius.

The circles, see Fig. 20-14, may now be subdivided by rays, s in number, uniformly spaced, and emanating from the center into s sectors in number. If $s = 20$, for example, one obtains a concentric net with $s = 20$ meshes or circular elements per ring, or a total of $cs = (10)(20) = 200$ elements or influence units.

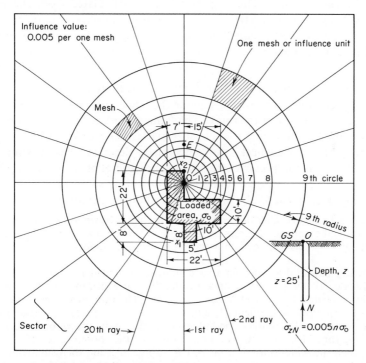

FIG. 20-14 Influence chart after Newmark for computing vertical, normal stress at depth z caused by a uniformly distributed load, σ_o, at the elevation of the base of the footing of the foundation.

In such a way each mesh area bounded by two adjacent radii and two adjacent circular arcs contribute the same influence to the vertical stress. In our case, each such mesh or element, uniformly loaded, contributes $(1/200)(\sigma_z) = (0.005)$ (σ_z) to the total vertical stress, σ_z, at a depth, z, beneath the center of the chart, because one ring, or circular slice contributes, in this example, $(1/10)(\sigma_z)$. Hence

$$\frac{\sigma_z}{c} : s = (0.1)(\sigma_z) : 20 = (0.005)(\sigma_z). \qquad (20\text{-}42)$$

One notes, therefore, that each mesh, or element, is an influence area. The influence graphs for $c = 10$ and $s = 20$, and for a Poisson's ratio of $\mu = 0.5$, or $m = 1/\mu = 2.0$ is illustrated in Fig. 20-14. The loaded area (dimensions of plan of structure) is drawn to such a scale that the length, ON, represents the magnitude of the depth, z, at which depth the stress is to be determined. Obviously, influence graphs for coarser, as well as for finer influence areas than $(0.005)(\sigma_z)$ can be established by selecting c- and s-values different from those used in the example above.

The number of rings, viz., radii can be increased above 10 by using finer σ_z/σ_o-ratios than 0.1; for example, a ratio of $(\sigma_z/\sigma_o) = 0.08$ or any other ratio up to 1.00 can be used. The total stress, σ_z, is calculated from the influence chart merely by counting on the chart the number of meshes, or circular elements, covered by a plan of the loaded area drawn to proper scale and superimposed upon the influence chart:

$$\sigma_z = 0.005n\sigma_o, \tag{20-43}$$

where n = number of meshes loaded with σ_o. Here $(0.005)(n) = i_c$ is the total influence value. Incomplete and irregular elements must be estimated and added up in each circular slice of the rings. The influence of each mesh upon one point, N, is the same for the depth, z = const, which is being dealt with.

The property of Newmark's influence chart described here permits one to determine vertical compressive stresses on a horizontal plane at any depth, z, not only for loaded circular areas, but also for any other shape of plan loaded with a uniformly distributed load. The use of the influence chart is simple and rapid.

Illustrative Example. One proceeds as follows using Newmark's influence chart to find the vertical compressive stress in soil ($\mu = 0.5$) on a horizontal plane, distance z below the ground surface, beneath a certain point on a uniformly loaded foundation area.

On tracing paper, draw the plan of a uniformly loaded foundation to a certain assumed scale. To the same scale draw the depth, z, at which the stress is computed as a segment of vertical line, say O-N, see Fig. 20-14. The radii of the influence chart are obtained by multiplying the depth length O-N by the (r_o/z) ratios (as found in Table 20-6, for example). Alternately, the influence chart may be drawn on a tracing paper by assigning for z, 1 in. = 1 ft—a value of unity for the chosen scale. If $z = 1$ ft, for example, then the scale to use is 1 in. = 1 ft. The circles are then subdivided into 20 circular sectors, giving an influence value for a single mesh of 0.005. Then the point on the plan, or outside the plan of the foundation, for which the stress in the soil is sought, is superimposed to coincide with the center, O, of the influence net. Then count the number, n, of influence meshes encompassed by the plan of the foundation, so that the meshes may be counted through the tracing paper to give the magnitude of the stress, σ_{zN}, at point N, distance, $z = (O\text{-}N)$, below the plane of the base of the footing:

$$\sigma_{zN} = 0.005n\sigma_o.$$

For any other depth, different from this $z = (O\text{-}N)$, either draw a new influence chart for the new depth $z' = (O\text{-}N')$, or draw the plan of the foundation to such a new scale that the old line O-N represents the new depth, z'. Otherwise, for any new depth, the loaded foundation area is drawn to a scale of 1 in. = new depth in feet. For 1 ft depth, the scale is 1 in. = 1 ft; for a 3 ft depth the scale is 1 in. = 3 ft; for 10 ft depth the scale is 1 in. = 10 ft. For example, if point N is $z = 25$ ft below the loaded surface under point O, the uniformly distributed load is $\sigma_o = 5000$ lb/ft^2, and the counted number of meshes is, say $n = 27$ approximately, then the stress at point N is

$$\sigma_{zN} = (0.005)n\sigma_o = (0.005)(27)(5000) = 675 \text{ lb/ft}^2 = 0.3375 \text{ t/ft}^2 \approx 0.34 \text{ kg/cm}^2.$$

The foundation is sketched here to the scale of 1 in. = 25 ft.

Note that the loading plan may be rotated through any angle about a vertical axis through the point where the vertical stress is calculated, without changing the magnitude of the stress sought. Thus the plan may be placed on the chart in a position most convenient for the particular problem.

Although remarkably simple, Newmark's chart has also some inherent deficiencies, the most important being:

a) Many loaded areas, or many influence charts have to be drawn.

b) Counting of meshes must be done repeatedly for each depth. Although simple by nature, many meshes occur which are only partially covered by the loaded area so that a considerable amount of guesswork enters into the counting result—work which in most instances cannot be left with confidence to inexperienced technical assistants. The inconvenience shows up particularly when a vertical stress distribution diagram along a vertical line is to be established.

However, the advantages of the influence chart seem to outweigh its disadvantages, particularly if it is considered that the method can be used not only for loaded circular areas, but also for loaded areas of any shape.

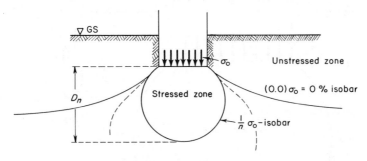

FIG. 20-15   The $(1/n)\sigma_o$-isobar.

20-12. Active Zone in Soil. In his opening discussion on settlement of structures given at the First International Conference on Soil Mechanics and Foundation Engineering (held in 1936 at Harvard University in Cambridge, Mass.), Terzaghi[12] dealt, among other things, with the subjects of the bulb of pressure and the seat of settlement. Because for any given load it is possible to obtain an infinite variety of pressure bulbs, one has to refer to a certain assumed isobar, the value of which is $(1/n)$th of the contact pressure, σ_o, see Fig. 20-15. Terzaghi pointed out that the depth, D_n, of the $(1/n)(\sigma_o)$ isobar increases in direct proportion to the width, b, of the loaded area if the shapes of these areas are similar among themselves:

$$\frac{D_n}{d_n} = \frac{B}{b} = \text{const} = f(n) \qquad (20\text{-}44)$$

For practical purposes Terzaghi recommended assuming the value of $n = 5$, for round or square footings, which means selecting an isobar characterized by

$(1/5)\sigma_o = (0.2)\sigma_o$ of the vertical contact stress. The depth of such an isobar is then denoted by $D_{n=5}$. This recommendation was supported based on Terzaghi's observation that direct stresses are considered of negligible magnitude when they are smaller than 20% of the intensity of the applied stress from structural loading, and that most of the settlement, approximately 80% of the total, takes place at a depth less than $D_{n=5}$. Therefore, the isobar marked as $(0.2)\sigma_o$ may be said to define the contour of the pressure bulb, which is a stressed zone within a homogeneous medium. The stressed zone is induced by the load from the footing. The supporting capacity of the bulb is induced by the resistance of the soil to deformation offered by the friction and cohesion of the soil.

The region within the $(0.2)\sigma_o$-isobar is termed by Terzaghi the seat of settlement.

The ratio of $D_{n=5}/B \approx 1.5$ was given as approximately good for an elastic, isotropic, semi-infinite solid. It was also mentioned that for a uniform and very thick layer of sand the value of the $D_{n=5}/B$-ratio is somewhat less than 1.5.

The two isobars of the same intensity, say of $\sigma_z = (0.2)(\sigma_o)$, in Fig. 20-16

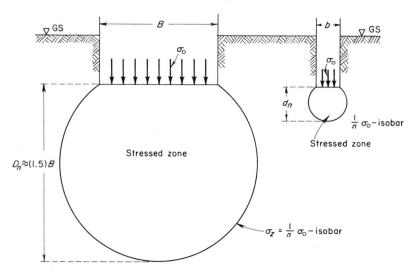

FIG. 20-16   Effect of width of footings on depth of isobars.

show that the wider the loaded area, the deeper is its effect, i.e., the deeper is the extent of this isobar. If several loaded footings are spaced closely enough, the individual isobars of each footing in question would combine and merge into one large isobar of the same intensity, Fig. 20-17, reaching about $D_{n=5} = (1.5)B$ deep below the base of the sum of the closely spaced footings.

The $(0.2)\sigma_o$-isobar and its depth, $D_{n=5} = (1.5)B$, indicates the shallowest depth to which preliminary borings for soil exploration should be put down. This is the reason for the requirement in practice that borings should penetrate the soil to a depth which is at least 1.5 times the width of the smaller dimension of the structure. Because the stressed zone is within the $(0.2)\sigma_o$-isobar, it is important to know the soil profile and the character of the soil within this stressed zone where about 80% of the total settlement takes place.

The depth, $D_{n=5}$, to which the $(0.2)\sigma_o$-isobar extends below the base of the footing of foundation, and where additional stresses are induced by the externally applied load such as the structural load—stresses which cause the soil to deform in the way of settlement—is termed the active zone. The thickness of the active zone extends, thus, from the base of the footing to that depth where the vertical stresses from the structure are 20% of the magnitude of the self-weight, or over-burden of the soil, at elevation, a-a, in Fig. 20-18 contributing to most of the settlement. All the rest of the soil layers below the active zone, a-a, are considered as being ineffective, where small stresses can be ignored.

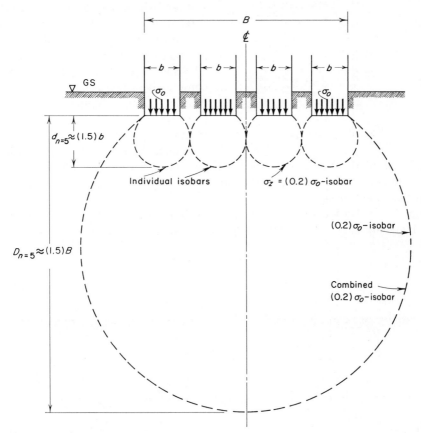

FIG. 20-17   Closely spaced isobars merge into one isobar of the same intensity, reaching far deeper than the individual isobars.

Note in Fig. 20-18 that the vertical stress diagram from self-weight of soil is of triangular shape, and that its vertex is located at the ground surface, point V. The vertical stress distribution diagram, fjv, however, starts at the base elevation, f-f, of the footing, where the structural load is transmitted to the soil.

From Fig. 20-17, it can also be deduced that the settlement of a group of closely spaced friction piles in compressible soil can be expected to be larger than the settlement of a single friction pile.

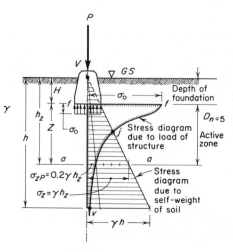

FIG. 20-18   Active zone.

Fig. 20-19. shows two widths of loaded foundations, b_1 and b_2, whereby $b_1 < b_2$. The contact pressures of both foundations are the same, namely, $\sigma_{o1} = \sigma_{o2} = \sigma_o$. This figure illustrates that the wider the loaded area, the deeper is its influence. The $(0.5)\sigma_o$-isobar underneath the narrow footing, the width of which is b_1, does not reach the soft layer of soil, whereas underneath the larger footing with a width b_2 the $(0.5)\sigma_o$-isobar intercepts the soft layer. The soft layer receives on its top a compressive stress which is larger than $(0.75)\sigma_o$. Obviously, therefore, if contact pressures are the same, the wider footing, b_2, would cause a greater settlement than footing b_1 (disregarding in this discussion the expulsion of soil laterally from underneath the base of the footing). In the latter case the narrow footing may sometimes settle more than the wide footing.

Fig. 20-19 also hints that small-scale, soil bearing tests with small loading or bearing plate areas are of very little use for settlement calculations if a wide

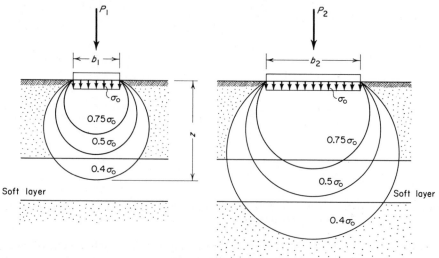

FIG. 20-19   Effect of size of footing on depth of isobar of equal intensity in a layered soil system. The larger the loaded area, the deeper is its influence.

foundation is contemplated. This is particularly true when the soil encountered is a cohesive one where expulsion of water from the voids of the soil (settlement) requires a certain amount of time, or if a seam of clay exists in the field at a certain depth. The pressure of interest (isobar) by a small plate would not reach this clay; hence the loading test results with a small loading area, applied to a wide foundation, would even be erratic. Loading tests, therefore, should be made on an area as large as practicable to reflect the combined effects of all of the soil properties to a greater depth at the site.

REFERENCES

1. J. V. Boussinesq, *Application des potentiels à l'étude de l'equilibre et du mouvement des solides élastiques*, Paris, Gauthier-Villars, 1885.
2. S. Timoshenko, *History of Strength of Materials*, New York, McGraw-Hill Book Co., Inc., 1953, p. 332.
3. H. Hertz, "Uber die Berührung fester elastischer Körper", *Journal für Mathematik* (Crelle), 1881, vol. 2.
4. A. E. H. Love, "The Stress Produced in a Semi-infinite Solid by Pressure on Part of the Boundary", *Philosophical Transactions of the Royal Society of London. Series A*, vol. 228, London, Hanison and Sons, Ltd, November, 1929, pp. 377-420.
5. H. Lamb, "On Boussinesq's Problem", *Proceedings of the London Mathematical Society*, 1902, vol. 34, p. 276.
6. A. Föppl and L. Föppl, *Drang und Zwang, Eine Höhere Festigkeitslehre für Ingeniere*, München and Berlin, R. Oldenburg, 1944, vol. 2, p. 202.
7. H. Gray, "Stress Distribution in Elastic Solids", *Proceedings*, First International Conference on Soil Mechanics and Foundation Engineering, held in June, 1936, Cambridge, Mass., Paper E-10, vol. 2, pp. 157-168.
8. Progress Report of Special Committee of the American Society of Civil Engineers, "Earths and Foundations", *Proceedings*, American Society of Civil Engineers, May, 1933, vol. 59, no. 5, p. 781.
9. W. Steinbrenner, Tafeln zur Setzungsberechnung, p. 121, no. 4, Schriftenreihe der Strasse 1, Strasse, 1934.
10. N. M. Newmark, "Influence Charts for Computation of Stresses in Elastic Foundations", *Bulletin*, University of Illinois, Urbana, Illinois, November 10, 1942, Bulletin Series no. 338, vol. 40.
11. N. M. Newmark, "Stress Distribution in Soil", *Proceedings*, Purdue Conference on Soil Mechanics and its Applications, September 2 to 6, 1940, Purdue University, Lafayette, Indiana, 1940, pp. 295-303.
12. K. Terzaghi, "Opening Discussion on Settlement of Structures", *Proceedings*, First International Conference on Soil Mechanics and Foundation Engineering, held in June, 1936, at Cambridge, Mass., vol. 3, pp. 79-87.

QUESTIONS AND PROBLEMS

20-1. Determine the vertical compressive stress caused by a soil at a depth $z = H = 10.0$ ft. The unit weight of the soil is $\gamma_s = 110$ lb/ft^3. Plot the total stress distribution diagram.

20-2. The same as in Problem 20-1. At a 4 ft depth below the ground surface there is a groundwater table ($\gamma_w = 62.4$ lb/ft^3). Plot the vertical stress distribution diagram due to the soil.

20-3. Given a layered system of soil as shown in Fig. Problem 20-3. Plot the total stress distribution diagram.

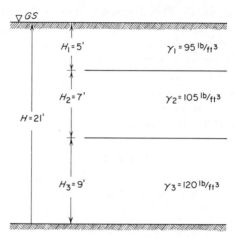

FIG. Problem 20-3.

20-4. Explain the concept of "pressure bulb", and illustrate.
20-5. What is "stressed zone"? Illustrate.
20-6. What is "active zone"? Illustrate.
20-7. The vertical stress, σ_z, at any point in a homogeneous, isotropic medium caused by a vertical concentrated load, P, is expressed as

$$\sigma_z = \frac{3}{2} \frac{P}{\pi} \frac{\cos^3\beta}{R^2}.$$

1) Calculate the angle, β, for which σ_z is a maximum in a vertical plane.
2) the same as under 1) on a horizontal plane.
3) What is the depth, z, corresponding to the angle, β, for which σ_z is a maximum?

20-8. In the example in Sect. 20-7 on isobars, determine z for which σ_z is at its maximum for $r = 0, 2, 4, 6, 8, 10,$ and 12 ft. Prepare a sketch showing a curve connecting the points where σ_z is maximum.
       Also, calculate the magnitudes of $\sigma_{z_{max}}$ for $r = 0, 2, 4, 6, 8, 10,$ and 12 ft, and plot to a stress scale, at points $(r; z)$ where $\sigma_{z_{max}}$ occurs, the values of $\sigma_{z_{max}}$.
       What is your observation as to the variation in $\sigma_{z_{max}}$? Formulate your observations.

20-9. Given a single, vertical, concentrated load of $P = 200$ tons at the ground surface. The area of the foundation is 100 sq ft. Calculate and plot isobars for 80%, 60%, 40%, 20%, 10%, 5%, 3%, 2%, and 1% of total contact pressure.
       Note. For small, symmetrical bearing areas or footings, when their contact areas may be considered small, the problem may be solved based on the single, concentrated load, P. However, when the contact area of the base of the footing is relatively large, the problem must be solved based on load from the footing uniformly distributed on the soil. In this problem, for illustrative purposes, assume that the area 100 sq ft is small.

20-10. Given two concentrated loads, $P_1 = 100$ tons and $P_2 = 300$ tons, spaced 12 ft apart. Draw the 0.5 t/ft²-isobar. Order of spacing of loads: $P_1 - P_2$.
       Hint. First plot the 0.5 t/ft²-isobars for each load separately. Then plot 0.4, 0.3, 0.2, and 0.1 t/ft²-isobars, and by the principle of superposition combine these isobar values to give intersections to result in the combined 0.5 t/ft²-isobar for the given two loads P_1 and P_2.

20-19. Plot the vertical stress distribution diagram in the example of Sect. 20-7 at a horizontal plane where $z = 1.0$.

20-20. The same problem as 20-19, but for $z = 3.0$, and for $z = 10.0$ and $z = 15.0$.

20-21. For $P_1 = 200$ tons and $P_2 = 100$ tons, spaced 8 ft apart, plot the stress distribution diagram on a horizontal plane located 7 ft below the ground surface. P_1 acts at the point of origin of coordinates.

20-22. Plot for $P = 200$ tons the vertical stress distribution diagram for $r = 0$ ft, $r = 2$ ft, and $r = 6.58$ ft.

20-23. For $P_1 = 200$ tons and $P_2 = 100$ tons, plot the vertical stress distribution diagrams on a vertical plane through P_1 and through P_2. The spacing of P_1 and P_2 is 8 ft.

20-24. Given three concentrated loads in one vertical plane, $P_1 = 100$ tons, $P_2 = 200$ tons, and $P_3 = 300$ tons. The loads are spaced in the order of P_3-P_1-P_2. Their spacing is 15 ft -12 ft. Plot the vertical stress distribution diagram on a horizontal plane at $z = 5$ ft.

20-25. Given $P_1 = 200$ tons; $P_2 = 160$ tons, and $P_3 = 100$ tons as shown in Fig.

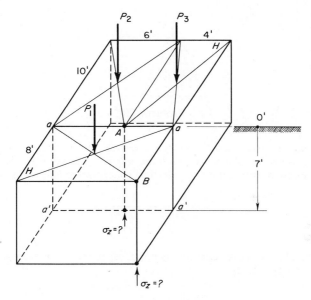

FIG. Problem 20-25.

Problem 20-25. Calculate vertical compressive stresses at points A and B, 7 ft below the ground surface.

20-26. In the above problem, plot the vertical stress distribution diagram on a horizontal plane a'-a' 7 ft below the ground surface.

20-27. Plot in the problem above a vertical stress distribution diagram on a vertical plane through a-a'.

20-28. A foundation as sketched in Fig. Problem 20-28 transmits a vertical concentrated load of $P = 200$ tons.

    a) What is the vertical stress distribution on a horizontal plane at elevation -20.00?

    Note. 1) Plot this figure to a geometric scale.

           2) Plot stresses to a stress scale.

           3) Elevations are given in feet.

           4) The unit weight of soil is $\gamma = 110$ lb/ft^3.

b) What is the vertical stress, induced by P, on the crest of the underground utility facility?

c) Plot the soil vertical stress distribution diagram along a vertical line, A-B, drawn through the crest of the underground utility facility.

d) What is the total vertical stress at point B?

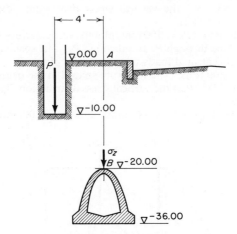

FIG. Problem 20-28.

20-29. According to Boussinesq's theory of vertical stress distribution in a homogeneous, isotropic, elastic, semi-infinite medium the vertical stress, σ_z, at any point caused in the medium by a vertical concentrated load, P, is expressed as

$$\sigma_z = \frac{3P}{2\pi z^2} \frac{1}{\left[1 + \left(\frac{r}{z}\right)^2\right]^{5/2}},$$

where r and z are coordinates of any point, say point M, for example, as sketched in Fig. Problem 20-29.

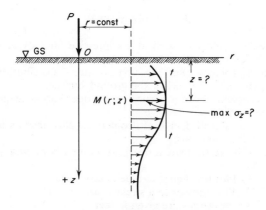

FIG. Problem 20-29.

Required.

    a) Determine algebraically the depth coordinate, z, at which the vertical stress, σ_z, becomes maximum if r is kept constant.

    b) Express algebraically $\sigma_{z_{max}}$ for z as found in a).

    c) What is the magnitude of z for $\sigma_{z_{max}}$ where $r = 0$?

    d) Find inflection points on the vertical stress distribution diagram on the vertical plane.

    e) Find inflection points on the vertical stress distribution diagram on the horizontal plane.

    f) What are the angles β_1 and β_2 for the inflection points on the vertical plane and on the horizontal plane?

20-30. The compressive strength of a silty clay at elevation $-18'00''$ is 0.4 t/ft². What is the stress at this elevation transmitted from a 200 ton concentrated load placed at an elevation of $-10'00''$ on the line of action of the concentrated load?

20-31. A long foundation 2 ft wide carries a uniform, linear load of $q = 1500$ lb/ft. Assuming that the foundation load system represents a linear load, and disregarding the weight of the foundation, calculate the vertical stress, σ_z, at a point N the coordinates of which are $x = 9$ ft, $y = 4$ ft, and $z = 5$ ft.

20-32. Given the same linear load as above. Plot in the y-z plane the vertical stress distribution diagram on a horizontal plane located a distance of $z = 7$ ft below the base of the footing.

20-33. Given the same linear load as above. Plot the vertical stress distribution diagram along a vertical line through a point on the line-load (x-axis).

20-34. For the same, as in Problem 20-33, plot along a vertical line through point $N(9, 4, 5)$.

20-35. Given: two foundation footings the sizes of which are $6' \times 6'$ and $4' \times 4'$, and carrying vertical loads of 108,000 lb and 64,000 lb, respectively. They are founded 10 ft below the ground surface. These footings are spaced 21 ft center to center.

Calculate

    a) the vertical stress in soil 10 ft below the ground surface midway between the edges of the two foundations.

    b) plot the vertical stress distribution diagram on a horizontal plane at $z = 5$ ft below the base of the footing under the $4' \times 4'$ footing.

20-36. In the example of Sect. 20-10,

    a) plot the vertical stress distribution diagram beneath the free corner point, A;

    b) plot the vertical stress distribution diagram beneath the midpoint, M, of the loaded area;

    c) plot the vertical stress distribution diagram beneath the midpoint of the long side of the parallelogram; and

    d) plot the vertical stress distribution diagram beneath the midpoint of the short side of the parallelogram.

20-37. Prepare an influence chart with an influence value of 0.02 for the same example as in Fig. 20-14. Find the stress, σ_{z_N}, at $z = 0'$, $5'$, $10'$, $15'$, and $25'$.

20-38. Prepare an influence chart with an influence value of 0.001 for the same problem as in Fig. 20-14.

20-39. Calculate σ_{z_E} at a depth of $z = 12$ ft. Point E is located 16 ft from point O, and 10 ft from point x_2 (see Fig. 20-14).

20-40. A circular ring-type foundation exerts on the soil a uniformly distributed pressure of $\sigma_o = 4000$ lb/ft² $= 2$ t/ft². The dimensions of this foundation are shown in Fig. Prob. 20-40. Plot the vertical stress distribution diagram along a vertical line through the center, O, of the circular foundation for each two feet of depth from $z = 0$ ft to $z = 12$ ft.

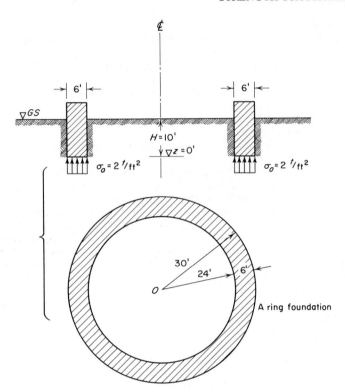

FIG. Problem 20-40.

FIG. Problem 20-40.

Chapter 21

EARTH PRESSURE THEORY

21-1. Retaining Walls. A retaining wall is a structure designed to sustain the lateral pressure of earth and other material (grain, ore, liquids, for example) and retain it in a steep-faced slope which otherwise would rupture or slide down.

Earth retaining structures are retaining walls, sheet piling, bulkheads, basement walls, and other permanent and temporary structures used in earthworks and foundation engineering that retain vertical or almost vertical slopes of earth masses.

Retaining walls are encountered and constructed in various fields of engineering such as civil, hydraulic structures, highway, railway, tunnel, mining, military (fortifications), and others.

According to their geometrical design and function retaining walls are generally classified into the following groups:

1) Massive or gravity retaining walls
2) Reinforced concrete walls ("light" walls), such as
   a) Cantilever walls,
   b) Counterforted walls,
   c) Buttressed walls, and
3) Crib walls.

The first four types of retaining walls are illustrated in Fig. 21-1. A crib wall is essentially a gravity, earth retaining structure and can quickly be erected. Crib walls are made of timber, or of precast concrete or steel sections. Such walls resemble a rock-filled log crib.

Lateral forces interacting between the earth retaining structure and the retained earth mass are caused by *lateral earth pressure.* The magnitude of the lateral earth pressure is calculated and evaluated by means of the so-called lateral earth pressure theory, or simply earth pressure theory. All earth pressure theories put forward hitherto are based on an ideal, dry soil which is endowed with hypothetical, ideal, and uniform properties. This, therefore, permits the engineer to solve earth pressure problems only approximately at the present time.

21-2. Some Possible Forces Acting on Earth Retaining Structures. Some of the most common forces acting on earth retaining structures encountered in practice are:

weight of the wall; lateral earth pressure; vertical loads on the wall; wind pressure; horizontal loads on the wall (loads attached to a puller, or pull in tie-rods, for example); hydrostatic pressure of water; hydrostatic uplift; pore water pressure; hydrodynamic water pressure (wave action upon maritime and other hydraulic structures); seepage forces; ice pressure by frozen water in front of wall, or by frozen soil moisture behind the wall; seismic forces such as earthquakes; dynamic impact (impact by ships on a quay, for example); vibrations induced by machinery, pile driving operations, transportation facilities, blasting, mining operations, military operations; reactions of soil underneath the base of the footing of the wall; thermal forces—induced by temperature, for example, stresses induced in materials by heating and cooling.

Consideration should be given to good drainage from the backfill material behind the retaining wall. This is aimed at decreasing the lateral pressure on the wall by water and ice.

In discussing the lateral earth pressure theory, however, only weight, surcharge, and soil lateral pressures will be discussed here.

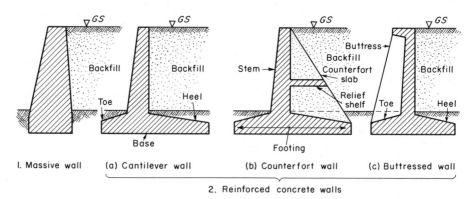

I. Massive wall   (a) Cantilever wall   (b) Counterfort wall   (c) Buttressed wall

2. Reinforced concrete walls

FIG. 21-1   Some types of retaining walls in cross section.

21-3. Lateral Earth Pressures. As already mentioned in the previous section, lateral earth pressure is the force which is exerted by the soil mass and which acts upon an earth retaining structure, for instance, a retaining wall.

The magnitude of the lateral earth pressure is known to vary considerably a) with the displacement of the retaining wall,[1] and b) with the nature of the soil.

If the wall does not translocate but is fixed rigidly, the pressure is termed *earth pressure at rest.* Its value can be ascertained only approximately.

If the wall yields or displaces away from the backfilled soil some of the retained backfill would break away from the rest of the soil mass and slide down, thereby exerting a pressure on the wall. This pressure is termed the *active earth pressure* (the soil mass is active). The value of the active earth pressure is less than the "at rest" value, and attains a limiting or minimum value, E_a. The moving away of the wall from the soil mass removes the confinement of the soil wedge. The active earth pressure is thus a force which tends by rotating and/or translation to put the retaining structure out of equilibrium. The active earth pressure indicates the magnitude of the force which can develop upon the motion of a retaining structure away from the earth mass which the structure must resist.

If the inner or back face of the retaining wall is forced against the backfill, the pressure is termed the *passive earth pressure*, or the *passive earth resistance*. Passive earth resistance is encountered, for example, when the supporting toe of an arch bridge transmits its horizontal component of the inclined force through the foundation of the bridge to the soil. One also encounters passive earth resistance in sheet-piling problems.

The magnitude of the passive earth pressure is greater than the "at rest" value, attaining a limiting or maximum value, E_p. The passive earth pressure indicates the maximum value of the force which can develop upon the motion of the retaining structure towards the earth mass—a force which the soil must resist before it ruptures. Generally, the surface upon which the broken-away or sheared-off soil slides down is termed the *rupture* or *sliding surface*.

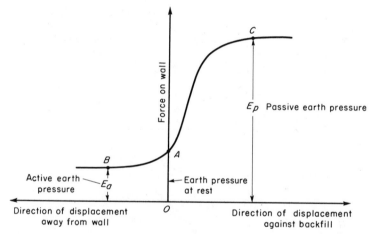

FIG. 21-2   Effect of displacement of a retaining structure on lateral earth pressure.

The effect of displacement of a retaining structure on the magnitude of the lateral earth pressure is illustrated in Fig. 21-2. Theory as well as experiments show that the passive earth pressure is always greater than the active earth pressure.

The difference in magnitude between the active and passive earth pressures may be accounted for by the following conditions. In the case of active earth pressure, the downward sliding soil wedge induces shearing resistance in such a way that it aids in supporting the soil mass. In this way the shearing resistance reduces the value of the earth pressure against the wall, resulting in a limiting value of pressure, termed the active earth pressure. In the passive earth pressure the upward-sliding soil wedge induces shearing resistance in such a way that it acts against the displacement of the earth retaining structure. Upon shearing off a soil wedge, this resistance must be overcome by the movement of the wall.

The variation in magnitude of lateral earth pressure caused by the nature of soil can be characterized by the type of soil—whether cohesive or non-cohesive (frictional and cohesive characteristics)—by porosity, by moisture conditions in soil, and by its unit weight. The magnitude of the total earth pressure also depends upon the height of the backfill.

COULOMB'S EARTH PRESSURE THEORY

Some historical notes about the period of the classical earth pressure theory have already been given in Chapter 2 of this book. Now Coulomb's earth pressure theory will be more fully discussed.

21-4. Assumptions. The basic assumptions underlying Coulomb's earth pressure theory are as follows (Fig. 21-3).

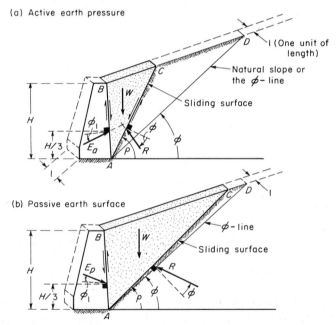

FIG. 21-3 Principal sketches of Coulomb's earth pressure-retaining wall system.

1) The soil behind the retaining wall is considered to be dry; homogeneous; isotropic; elastically un-deformable but breakable, granular material; endowed with internal friction but possessing no cohesion; capable of resisting compressive and shear stresses only. Such a soil is termed an *ideal soil.*

2) The soil, depending upon its properties, forms a natural slope angle, ϕ, with the horizontal and the soil may be filled to this angle without rupturing and sliding down. Today this angle is understood to be the angle of internal friction of the soil, ϕ. The concept of friction (a fraction of the normal load to the sliding surface) was clear to Coulomb.

3) Coulomb assumed that if the wall yields, then rupture of the backfill soil

takes place and a soil wedge is torn off from the rest of the soil mass. In the case of an active earth pressure due to its own weight, the soil wedge slides sideways and downward over the rupture surface, thus exerting a lateral pressure upon the wall. In the case of passive earth resistance, the soil wedge, due to forcing the wall against the backfilled earth mass, slides sideways and upward on the rupture surface. The pressure at rest of the wall is not considered in this theory.

4) For the sake of convenience in analysis, the rupture surface is assumed to be a plane. The rupture surface passes through the heel of the wall under a certain angle, ρ. The rupture surface actually is not a plane, but is curved. This fact was known to Coulomb.

5) The sliding wedge itself is considered as a rigid body.

6) For a rupture plane within the soil mass, as well as between the inner face of the wall and the soil, the classical Newton's law of friction is valid:

$$f = \tan \phi = \frac{T}{N}, \qquad (21\text{-}1)$$

where f in general is the coefficient of friction.

ϕ = the proper angle of friction,

T = the force tangential to the shearing surface, and

N = the force normal to the shearing surface.

At equilibrium, the resulting stresses upon any surface within the ideal soil mass may be offset from the normal to that surface by an angle which does not exceed the angle of internal friction of the soil material—an angle which depends upon the physical properties of the given ideal soil.

7) The friction is distributed uniformly on the plane sliding or rupture surface.

8) The position and direction of the earth pressure, E, is assumed to be known. The pressure, E, acts on the inner face of the wall at a point one third of the height of the wall above the base of the wall, and makes an angle, ϕ_1, with the normal of the inner (back) face of the wall. Angle ϕ_1 is the angle of friction between wall and backfill materials. Coulomb assumed the wall friction to be zero.

9) The problem of determining the earth pressure, active or passive, is solved for a two-dimensional case (in plane). This is to say that the retaining wall is assumed to be of infinite length and linear, and that the profile of the retained earth mass, its weight, and other pressure and stress conditions in soil remain constant along the length of the wall. This assumption permits the performance of earth pressure calculations for a section of soil which is one linear unit of measure long perpendicular to the drawing plane.

10) When sliding of the soil wedge is just impending, the earth pressure theory gives two limiting pressure values: the least and the greatest values (active and passive) compatible with equilibrium.

11) The magnitudes of the active and passive earth pressures are calculated from the following considerations:

Among the infinitely large number of rupture surfaces which can be passed through the heel-point, A, the most dangerous is that for which the active earth pressure, E_a, becomes a maximum (the wall must resist even the greatest pressure in the given system).

In the case of passive earth resistance, E_p, the most dangerous rupture surface is that for which E_p becomes a minimum. If the soil mass ruptures at a minimum force, it will rupture at a force larger than minimum. Or, the question can be asked: what is the minimum force necessary to tear off a soil wedge, ABC, from a soil mass when the wall is forced against the backfilled soil?

Thus, the magnitude of the earth pressure is calculated by the application of the rules of maximum and minimum from the equilibrium condition, i.e., when rupture of the soil wedge is just impending.

Note that Coulomb's theory treats the soil mass of the sliding soil wedge in its entirety.

These assumptions in Coulomb's classical earth pressure theory permit one to treat the question of earth pressure as a statically determinate problem.

21-5. Deficiencies in Coulomb's Theory.

The classical earth pressure theory by Coulomb, because of its simple application, seems hitherto to have been the only available practical method for calculating the dimensions of earth retaining structures.

Between its application and its basic meaning, however, there exists an apparent contradiction, since the nature of the backfill material does not permit its treatment scientifically and precisely. The main disadvantage of the classical earth pressure theory lies in its limitation to the ideal backfill soil material or pouring body, i.e., dry, granular, uniform soil. Also, Coulomb's theory is based on a plane sliding surface of soil rupture. Coulomb, however, as already mentioned, was aware of this deficiency in his theory and merely used it to simplify the calculation of equilibrium of the soil wedge. Besides, Coulomb knew about soil cohesion and considered it in his calculations. The friction between the wall and the backfill material did not enter into Coulomb's analysis and was introduced in calculations only some time later.

One of the main deficiencies in Coulomb's theory is that, in general, it does not satisfy the static equilibrium condition occurring in nature. The three forces (weight of the sliding wedge, its reaction, and earth pressure) acting on the sliding wedge generally do not meet in a common point when sliding surface is assumed, as in Coulomb's theory, to be planar.

Regardless of this objection and the assumptions made, Coulomb's theory usually gives quite useful results in practice. The theory is effective in proportion to the reliability of the corresponding constants (properties) to be used in the formulas. These soil constants should be determined as accurately as possible in the soil mechanics laboratory.

21-6. Principles. In order to calculate the dimensions of an earth retaining structure, or to determine the stresses occuring in it, or to perform stability analysis of such a structure, it is necessary to know the magnitude, point of application, and the direction of the lateral earth pressure.

To determine the active earth pressure, consider a retaining wall and behind it a soil wedge, ABC (Fig. 21-4). This soil wedge is subjected to the following three forces: its weight, W; reaction, R, on the sliding surface, AC; and reaction from the wall induced by the active earth pressure E_a, for example, of the sliding soil wedge upon the wall. The instant the equilibrium of these three forces is destroyed, failure occurs.

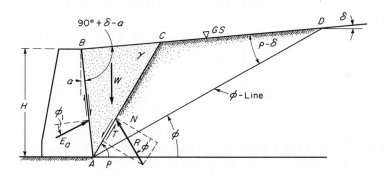

(a) Forces in the wall-soil wedge system

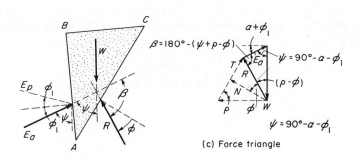

(b) Free body diagram

(c) Force triangle

FIG. 21-4   Active earth pressure.

By geometry of Fig. 21-4b, the weight of the sliding wedge, which is a function of the rupture angle, ρ, is:

$$W = \tfrac{1}{2}\gamma H^2 \left[\frac{\cos(\delta - \alpha)}{\cos^2 \alpha} \frac{\cos(\rho - \alpha)}{\sin(\rho - \delta)} \right]. \tag{21-2}$$

From the force triangle, Fig. 21-4c, the active earth pressure function, E_a, is

$$E_a = W \frac{\sin(\rho - \phi)}{\sin[180° - (\psi + \rho - \phi)]}, \tag{21-3}$$

where ρ = angle of rupture,
  ϕ = angle of internal friction of soil,
  δ = angle of slope of ground surface,
  α = angle of batter of backface of wall,
  ϕ_1 = angle of friction between backfill material and wall material, and
  $\psi = 90° - \alpha - \phi_1$.

The two unknowns, E_a and ρ, may be calculated from the following system of equations:

$$\left. \begin{array}{l} E_a = \left[W \dfrac{\sin(\rho - \phi)}{\sin(\psi + \rho - \phi)} \right]_{max} \\[2em] \dfrac{dE_a}{d\rho} = 0. \end{array} \right\} \tag{21-4}$$

The first derivative in Eq. (21-4) is based on Coulomb's presupposition that the rupture surface has a slope angle, ρ, at which the active earth pressure of a pouring body (ideal soil) upon a retaining wall is maximum.

The point of application of the earth pressure is on the back face of the wall one-third of the height of the wall above the base of the footing.

Everything that has been said about calculating analytically the magnitude of active earth pressure and the position of the most dangerous rupture surface holds also for calculating the passive earth pressure, E_p, except that the signs of the angles of friction, ϕ and ϕ_1 have to be changed to the opposite.

The system of the two equations for calculating the two unknowns, ρ and E_p, is:

$$\left. \begin{array}{l} E_p = \left[W \dfrac{\sin(\rho + \phi)}{\sin(\psi + \rho + \phi)} \right]_{min} \\[2em] \dfrac{dE_p}{d\rho} = 0. \end{array} \right\} \tag{21-5}$$

Here $\psi = 90° - \alpha + \phi_1$.

21-7. Method of Force Projections.

Active Earth Pressure. To demonstrate quickly the establishment of the E_a-function by the method of force projections, assume a retaining wall the back face of which is vertical, the ground surface horizontal, and the angle $\phi_1 = 0$, so that E_a would act horizontally and thereby parallel to the ground surface, Fig. 21-5.

On the soil wedge, ABC, the following forces act: the weight, W, of the soil wedge; the normal and tangential components of the soil reaction, R, namely

N and $T = N \tan \phi$, respectively; and the reaction E_a from the retaining wall.

The angle of rupture, ρ, is the variable, and the magnitude of the active earth pressure is obtained from such a position, ρ, of the rupture surface as results in a maximum value of E_a which the wall must resist.

The weight of the soil wedge is calculated as

$$W = \tfrac{1}{2}\gamma H^2 \tan(90° - \rho) = \tfrac{1}{2}\gamma H^2 \cot \rho = \tfrac{1}{2}\gamma H^2 / \tan \rho, \qquad (21\text{-}6)$$

where γ = unit weight of the backfill material, soil, for example.

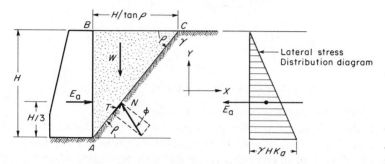

Fig. 21-5 System of active earth pressure.

The forces acting in the wall-soil system are now projected for equilibrium on horizontal and vertical axes:

$$\begin{cases} \Sigma X = E_a + T \cos \rho - N \sin \rho = 0 & (21\text{-}7) \\ \Sigma Y = -W + T \sin \rho + N \cos \rho = 0 & (21\text{-}8) \end{cases}$$

With $T = N \tan \phi$, $W = (\tfrac{1}{2}) \gamma H^2 / \tan \rho$, and eliminating N from Eqs. (21-7) and (21-8), the general E_a-function is calculated from Eq. (21-7) as

$$E_a = \tfrac{1}{2}\gamma H^2 \, \frac{\tan \rho - \tan \phi}{\tan \rho + \tan \phi \tan^2 \rho}. \qquad (21\text{-}9)$$

21-8. Derivation of the Active Earth Pressure Function, E_a When $\alpha = \delta = 0$. To find such a rupture angle, ρ, which would give a maximum of E_a, the E_a-function, Eq. (21-9) must be derived after the variable ρ, i.e., $dE_a/d\rho$, this first derivative set equal to zero, and solved for ρ.

$$\frac{dE_a}{d\rho} = \tfrac{1}{2}\gamma H^2 \times$$

$$\times \frac{(\tan \rho + \tan \phi \tan^2 \rho)\dfrac{1}{\cos^2 \rho} - (\tan \rho - \tan \phi)\left(\dfrac{1}{\cos^2 \rho} + 2 \tan \phi \tan \rho \dfrac{1}{\cos^2 \rho}\right)}{(\tan \rho + \tan \phi \tan^2 \rho)^2}$$

$$(21\text{-}10)$$

Setting the above derivative equal to zero, the rupture angle, ρ, is calculated in terms of its tangent as

$$\tan \rho = \tan \phi + \sqrt{1 + \tan^2 \phi} = \tan(45° + \phi/2), \qquad (21\text{-}11)$$

and

$$\rho = 45° + \phi/2. \qquad (21\text{-}12)$$

Substitution of the tan ρ-value into the general E_a-function Eq. (21-9) gives the maximum earth pressure, which is the active earth pressure the wall must resist:

$$E_a = \tfrac{1}{2}\gamma H^2 \frac{1 - \sin \phi}{1 + \sin \phi} = \tfrac{1}{2}\gamma H^2 \tan^2(\pi/4 - \phi/2), \qquad (21\text{-}13)$$

or

$$E_a = \frac{\gamma H^2}{2} K_a, \qquad (21\text{-}14)$$

where

$$K_a = \tan^2(\pi/4 - \phi/2) = \text{const} \qquad (21\text{-}15)$$

for the given retaining-wall system and for the given soil.

The units of E_a are in pounds per linear foot of the length of the wall, or in kips per one linear foot of wall, or in kilograms or tons per one linear meter of the length of wall, or in any other consistent unit depending upon the system of measurements used.

21-9. Lateral Earth Pressure Stress Distribution Diagram. The distribution of the lateral stress caused by the total active earth pressure on the wall is shown by the lateral stress distribution diagram in Fig. 21-5.

The point of application of E_a is the centroid of the triangular, lateral stress distribution diagram of the lateral earth pressure at a distance of one-third of the height of the triangle from its base.

With the stress ordinate at the base of the stress triangle of $\gamma H \tan^2(\pi/4 - \phi/2) = \gamma H K_a$, the total active earth pressure is the physical area of this stress diagram, namely:

$$E_a = \frac{\gamma H^2}{2} \tan^2(\pi/4 - \phi/2) = \frac{\gamma H^2}{2} K_a.$$

21-10. Passive Earth Pressure. Reasoning in a similar way as in the case of active earth pressure but letting the reaction R, act against the upward-sliding wedge of soil, one finds the expression for the total, minimum, passive earth pressure, E_p, for a vertical wall, horizontally backfilled ground surface, for $\phi_1 = 0$ and for an angle of internal friction, ϕ, is calculated as

$$E_p = \frac{\gamma H^2}{2} \frac{1 + \sin \phi}{1 - \sin \phi} = \frac{\gamma H^2}{2} \tan^2(\pi/4 + \phi/2), \qquad (21\text{-}16)$$

or, abbreviated,

$$E_p = \frac{\gamma H^2}{2} K_p, \qquad (21\text{-}17)$$

where

$$K_p = \tan^2(\pi/4 + \phi/2) = \text{const} \qquad (21\text{-}18)$$

for the given retaining wall system and for the given soil.

The point of application of E_p is through the centroid of the passive earth pressure stress distribution diagram.

SURCHARGE

21-11. Various Kinds of Surcharge. When the ground surface of the backfill behind the earth-retaining structure is superimposed in any way with some load, such as, for example, a crowd of people, goods on quays and wharves, warehouses and other buildings near the waterfront; or when the load consists of a highway or railroad, or earth-moving machinery; or, in the case of a trench or open excavation, the excavated soil and operating construction machinery (excavators, transporters, bulldozers), then such a loading is called *surcharge*. The surcharge may result in a heavy load per square foot as it would be the case in storing heavy reels of lead cables on the waterfront.

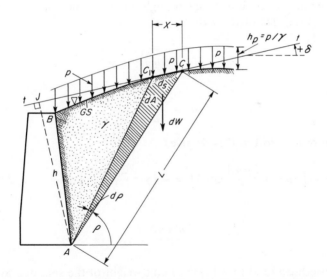

FIG. 21-6   Rebhann's rule for uniformly distributed surcharge.

The effect of surcharge on the soil below it is to increase the intensity of the lateral earth pressure. In the case the ground surface is curved and it carries a uniformly distributed surcharge, the intensity of which is p (say lb/ft^2 or kg/m^2), and the back face of the wall has a batter, Fig. 21-6, then the unit weight of the soil, because of the surcharge, is modified as follows:

$$dW = -(\gamma\, dA + p\, ds \cos \delta), \qquad (21\text{-}19)$$

where ds = differential length of curve or length on the ground surface over which the surcharge is distributed;

dW = differential modified weight of a differential soil wedge, ACC_1, the differential area of which is dA;

γ = unit weight of backfill material;

ds = C_1C = differential length of curve (or length on the ground surface), viz., a differential length, ds, on an inclined tangent, t-t, at point C;

$ds \cos \delta$ = dx = horizontal projection of ds;

δ = angle between tangent and the horizontal;

$p\, ds \cos \delta$ = differential vertical load on elementary, horizontal ground surface, dx.

The minus sign in Eq. (21-19) means this: as the weight of the sliding wedge, by adding up counter-clockwise, increases, each successive differential wedge, dA, decreases.

The tangent, t-t, at point C determines the height, $h = AJ$, of the differential triangle, $\triangle AC_1C$, the base of which is ds ($h \perp t$-t).

If the ground surface were inclined and plane, for example, BC, then the tangent is also the ground surface (straight line), and then the height, $h = AJ$, is the same for any other differential triangle between the rupture surface, AC, and the back face, AB, of the wall.

In Fig. 21-6,

$$dA = \tfrac{1}{2}h\, ds,\qquad(21\text{-}20)$$

and

$$ds = \frac{2\, dA}{h}.\qquad(21\text{-}21)$$

Substitution of ds into Eq. (21-19) gives

$$dW = -\left(\gamma\, dA + \frac{2p\, dA}{h}\cos\delta\right) = -\left(\gamma + \frac{2p\cos\delta}{h}\right)dA = -\gamma_1\, dA,\quad(21\text{-}22)$$

where

$$\gamma + \frac{2p\cos\delta}{h} = \gamma_1.\qquad(21\text{-}23)$$

This is the modified (and thus heavier) unit weight of the soil, due to surcharge to be used in Coulomb's and Rebhann's equations for calculating W and E_a when there is a uniformly distributed surcharge on the ground surface:

$$W = \tfrac{1}{2}\gamma_1 fn,\qquad(21\text{-}24)$$

and

$$E_a = \tfrac{1}{2}\gamma_1 fe.\qquad(21\text{-}25)$$

Note that γ_1 is larger than the actual unit weight of soil γ by an amount of $(2p \cos \delta)/h$.

Because γ_1 is the sum of γ and $(2p \cos \delta)/h$, the active earth pressure can also be expressed as the sum of two terms, namely: of active earth pressure caused by the backfill material and of active earth pressure caused by the uniformly distributed surcharge:

$$E_a = \tfrac{1}{2}\gamma_1 fe = \tfrac{1}{2}\left(\gamma + \frac{2p \cos \delta}{h}\right)fe = \tfrac{1}{2}\gamma fe + \frac{p \cos \delta}{h}fe = E_{aW} + E_{aP}. \quad (21\text{-}26)$$

If the back face of the wall is vertical, and the ground surface loaded with surcharge is horizontal ($\delta = 0$), then $\cos 0° = 1$, $h = H$, $p = p_o$ and $\gamma_1 = \gamma + (2 p_o)/H$, and

$$E_a = \tfrac{1}{2}\gamma_1 fe = \tfrac{1}{2}\left(\gamma + \frac{2p_o}{H}\right)H^2 K_a. \quad (21\text{-}27)$$

PONCELET GRAPHICAL METHOD

A graphical method for the direct location of Coulomb's most dangerous rupture surface and for the determination of the lateral earth pressure was given by Poncelet[2] in 1840. The method is derived for a wall with an unbroken, straight, back face and for a plane ground surface, the latter of which may be inclined, Fig. 21-7. The ground surface may or may not contain a uniformly distributed surcharge.

The method of Poncelet construction is suitable for determining active as well as passive earth pressures.

21-12. Active Earth Pressure. Poncelet graphical method is based on constructing the triangle

$$\triangle ABC(= \tfrac{1}{2}fn = \triangle ACS = W/\gamma) \text{ to find quantities } n, f, \text{ and } e.$$

The graphical construction starts with drawing the line of natural slope (ϕ-line), AD, under an angle of ϕ with the horizontal. Then the position line is drawn through heel A of the wall. The position line makes an angle of $(\phi + \phi_1)$ with the back face of the wall, AB. Through point B, another line, BK, is drawn parallel to the position line to give point K on the line of natural slope, AD. Points, B, C, and D must lie on one continuous, unbroken line. The line, BK, forms an angle, $\measuredangle AKB = \psi$, with line AD. By geometry, from $\triangle ABK$, the value of this angle is:

$$\measuredangle AKB = 180° - (\phi + \phi_1) - (90° + \alpha - \phi) = 90° - \alpha - \phi_1 = \psi, \quad (21\text{-}28)$$

which is the angle between the position line and the line of natural slope. Hence, $BK \parallel CS$. Assuming that the position of point S is known, draw also $SV \parallel AC$. The $\triangle ACD \sim \triangle SVD$ and $\triangle BDK \sim \triangle CDS$. Besides, $\triangle ACS = \triangle ACV$ because of their common base $AC = L$, and equal height, h_s. But, because $\triangle ACS = \triangle ABC$, then also $\triangle ACV = \triangle ABC$.

These latter and equal triangles have the same height, h_d, therefore their bases, BC and CV, must be of equal length, i.e.,

$$BC = CV = d \quad (21\text{-}29)$$

Let $AK = a$, and let $AD = b$. Based on the similarity of triangles, $\triangle ACD$ and $\triangle SVD$, Fig. 21-7, the following side ratios can be written:

$$\frac{b}{n} = \frac{c+d}{d} \tag{21-30}$$

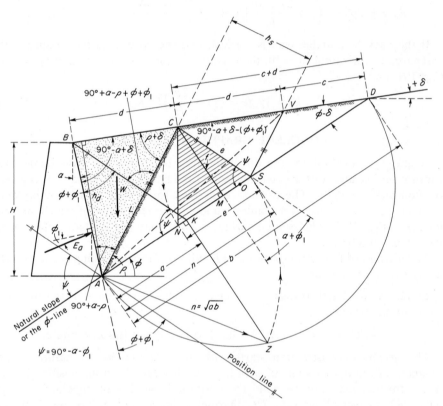

FIG. 21-7   Poncelet construction for active earth pressure.

In the similar triangles $\triangle KBD$ and $\triangle SCD$, Fig. 21-7, the side ratios are:

$$\frac{b-n}{n-a} = \frac{c+d}{d} \tag{21-31}$$

The equating of Eqs. (21-30) and (21-31) gives

$$\frac{b}{n} = \frac{b-n}{n-a}, \tag{21-32}$$

yielding

$$n^2 = ab$$

or

$$n = \sqrt{ab}. \tag{21-33}$$

Hence, if n is known, the position of point S and thus the position of the most dangerous rupture surface, AC, can be determined and the weight of the sliding soil wedge, W, and the active earth pressure, E_a, can be calculated. Thus, Eq. (21-33) is Poncelet's relationship which exists when the lateral earth pressure, E_a, is maximum. One would draw now through point S a line, CS, parallel to the position line to give point C, Fig. 21-7; CS determines the magnitude of e. Then a perpendicular is dropped from point C to AD to give point M on AD. The magnitude of $CM = f$, which is the height of the triangle, NCS, is thus determined. With e, f, and n known,

$$W = \tfrac{1}{2}\gamma f n,$$

and

$$E_a = \tfrac{1}{2}\gamma f e.$$

Note that the quantity $n = \sqrt{ab}$ represents the geometrical mean between two quantities, a and b, which can be constructed graphically. In the discipline of earth pressure theory the geometric mean, $n = \sqrt{ab}$, is termed the Poncelet rule.

Proof. From geometry, Fig. 21-7,

$$\frac{n}{a} = \frac{b}{n} \tag{21-34}$$

or

$$n = \sqrt{ab}.$$

Also,

$$n^2 = (AS)^2 = (AZ)^2 = h^2 + a^2 = a(b - a) + a^2 = a(b - a + a) = ab, \tag{21-35}$$

and

$$n = \sqrt{ab}.$$

21-13. Steps for Graphical Method. To find n and the active earth pressure, proceed by steps as follows (Fig. 21-7):

1) Draw AB to represent the back face of the wall.
2) Draw BD to represent the ground surface.
3) Draw line of natural slope, AD, at an angle, ϕ, with the horizontal.
4) At point B draw the position line, BK, at an angle of $(\phi + \phi_1)$ with the line, AB, the back face of the wall. This line cuts the line AD at K, and gives $AK = a$.
5) On $AD = b$ as a diameter, describe a semicircle, AZD.
6) From point K erect a perpendicular, KZ to AD, cutting the semicircle at the point Z.
7) With the chord, $AZ = n$, as a radius, with its center point at A, draw the arc, $\overarc{ZS}$, cutting the line, AD, at point S. Then $AS = AZ = n$. Here n is the geometric mean of a and b.
8) Draw SC parallel to the line, BK, cutting the ground surface line at point C. Then $CS = e$.

9) Join A and C. This line represents Coulomb's most dangerous rupture plane, and it defines the size of the sliding soil wedge. This wedge, ABC, sliding over the rupture plane, AC, would give the maximum value of the active earth presssure, E_a.

10) From point C erect a perpendicular to AD to give point M. Then $CM = f$. The triangular area, $\triangle ACS$, $= \frac{1}{2}fn$, which is the area of the weight of the sliding soil wedge.

11) From point S as a center, and with a radius of $SC = e$, draw the arc, $\overset{\frown}{CN}$, cutting AD at point N. Thus $NS = e$. Join points C and N to obtain the triangular area, $\triangle NCS = \frac{1}{2}fe$.

12) The triangular areas, $\frac{1}{2}fn$ and $\frac{1}{2}fe$, when multiplied by the unit weight of soil, γ, give the weight of the sliding wedge and active earth pressure, respectively:

$$W = \tfrac{1}{2}\gamma fn \tag{21-36}$$

$$E_a = \tfrac{1}{2}\gamma fe. \tag{21-37}$$

21-14. Surcharge. If the ground surface is surcharged with a uniformly distributed load the intensity of which is p, then

$$W = \tfrac{1}{2}\gamma_1 fn = \tfrac{1}{2}\left(\gamma + \frac{2p\cos\delta}{h}\right)fn, \tag{21-38}$$

and

$$E_a = \tfrac{1}{2}\gamma_1 fe = \tfrac{1}{2}\left(\gamma + \frac{2p\cos\delta}{h}\right)fe. \tag{21-39}$$

21-15. Passive Earth Pressure (Earth Resistance). The determination of Coulomb's earth pressure graphically by Poncelet's method is similar to that in the case of active earth pressure, except that the signs of the angles of friction, ϕ and ϕ_1, have to be changed to the opposite. Graphically this is accomplished by constructing the position line through points A or B under an angle of $(-)(\phi + \phi_1)$ with the line AB, of the back face of the wall, or, in other words, the angle $(-)(\phi + \phi_1)$ is constructed on the opposite side of the wall-line, AB, as compared with the active case, see Fig. 21-8. Likewise, the ϕ-line is to be drawn through point A under the angle $(-)\phi$.

21-16. Steps for Construction for Passive Earth Pressure. The steps to be followed in Poncelet's construction for passive earth pressure are shown in Fig. 21-8. These are:

1) Draw the wall, the back face of which is AB.
2) Draw the ground surface. Extend the ground surface line through point B to the left of wall.
3) Draw the $[(-)\phi]$ line, AD, through A at an angle of $(-)\phi$ with the horizontal.
4) Intersect the ground surface, AD, with the $[(-)\phi]$ line, BD, to give point D.

5) Through point B, draw the position line, BK, at an angle of $(-)(\phi + \phi_1)$ with the line AB. BK cuts AD at point K. Then $AK = a$.

6) On $AD = b$ as a diameter, describe a semicircle, AZD.

7) Draw a perpendicular KZ to AD to give point Z on the semicircle.

8) With $AZ = n = \sqrt{ab}$ as a radius whose center is at point A, draw the arc, $\widehat{ZS}$, cutting the line, AD, in point S. Then $AS = AZ = n = \sqrt{ab}$.

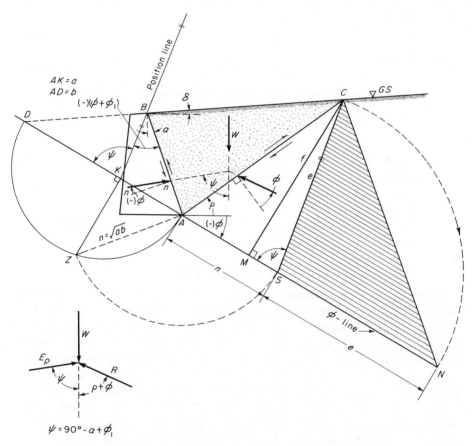

FIG. 21-8   Poncelet construction for passive earth pressure.

9) Draw SC parallel to BK: SC cuts the ground surface line, DBC, at point C. $CS = e$.

10) Join A and C. Line AC is Coulomb's most dangerous rupture surface, and it defines the size of the sliding soil wedge. This wedge, sliding over the rupture surface, AC, would give the value of the earth resistance (passive earth pressure), E_p.

11) From point C, establish a perpendicular, $CM = f$, to line AD to give point M on line AD. Then, the triangular area, $\triangle ACS = \frac{1}{2}fn$, is the

area of the weight of the sliding soil wedge, ABC. The weight of the sliding wedge is

$$W = \tfrac{1}{2}\gamma fn. \tag{21-40}$$

12) From point S as a center, and with a radius of $SC = e$ draw arc, $\overgroup{CN}$, cutting AD at point N: $NS = e$, and by joining C and N, the triangular area, $\triangle SCN = \tfrac{1}{2}fe$, is found. The magnitude of the passive earth pressure is

$$E_p = \tfrac{1}{2}\gamma fe, \tag{21-41}$$

or

$$E_p = \tfrac{1}{2}\gamma e^2 \sin \psi. \tag{21-42}$$

If the ground surface is surcharged, then instead of γ, γ_1 must be used:

$$\gamma_1 = \gamma + \frac{2p\cos\delta}{h},$$

where h is the perpendicular distance from the heel point, A, to the ground surface, BC, or its extension, BD.

Note that the magnitude of the passive pressure is greater than that in the active case.

The point of application of E_p is determined by the position of the centroid of the soil lateral stress distribution diagram.

CULMANN'S METHOD

21-17. Active Earth Pressure. Culmann's method permits one to determine graphically the magnitude of the earth pressure and to locate Coulomb's most dangerous rupture surface.[3] By rotating the shown force triangle in a clockwise direction through an angle of $90° - \phi$, Fig. 21-9, vector, W, becomes parallel to the line, AD, of the natural slope, reaction, R, is parallel to the rupture line, AC, and vector, E_a, is parallel to the position line. The position line makes an incline with the inner or back face of the wall under the angle of $(\phi + \phi_1)$.

Hence, if the weights, W_n, of the various arbitrarily assumed sliding surfaces of the sliding soil wedges are set off to a certain force scale on the line of the natural slope, AD, from point A, and if from the end points of the weights the E_n-lines are drawn under the angle ψ, which means drawn parallel to the position line, then the end points of the E_n-lines will lie on the sliding rupture surfaces. Connection of the end points of the E_n-lines results in a curve, the so-called E-curve, which is termed Culmann's curve. A tangent, t-t, drawn to the curve parallel to the line of natural slope scales off to the same force scale to which the weights were drawn a maximum value of E, i.e., E_{max}, which represents then the magnitude of the active earth pressure, E_a.

A line, $AF_1'C$ drawn through the heel-point, A, of the wall and the end point of $E_{max} = E_a$ determines the position of the most dangerous sliding surface, $AF'C$.

In case the ground surface is plane, i.e., points B, B_n, C, and D are on a line, then points ABB_1, ABB_2, ABC, ABB_n form triangles. If there is no surcharge on the ground surface, then there is no need to compute the weight of the various arbitrary soil wedges, but Culmann's construction can be carried out to a geometric scale instead of to a force scale.

Because the weight of any soil wedge is

$$W = \tfrac{1}{2}\gamma(\overline{AB})(x), \tag{21-43}$$

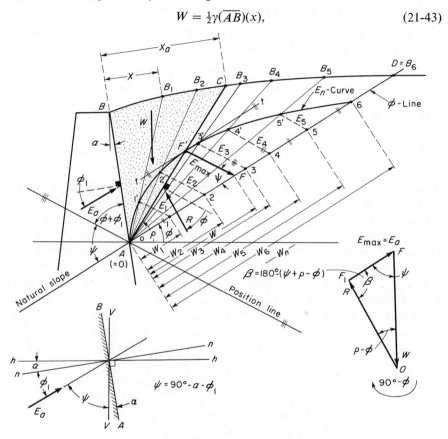

FIG. 21-9   Culmann's active earth pressure curve.

where $(\overline{AB})$ is the base of the wedge-shaped triangle, and x is the height of the triangle, the weight is proportional to x. Therefore, instead of plotting on AD the weights, W_n, of each of the soil wedges, the corresponding heights, x_n, or lengths proportional to x_n of the respective wedge can be plotted, the E_n-lines and the E_n-curve drawn, and the maximum E-ordinate, F-F', for example, scaled off. The magnitude of the active earth pressure is then calculated from the following considerations:

$$E_a = W_a \frac{\overline{FF'}}{\overline{AF}} = \tfrac{1}{2}\gamma(\overline{AB})(x_a) \frac{\overline{FF'}}{\overline{AF}}, \tag{21-44}$$

where W_a = weight of the soil wedge at $E_{max} = E_a$;

$\quad\quad\ \gamma$ = unit weight of soil;

$\quad\quad\ x_a$ = height of triangle, ABC, at E_a;

$\quad\quad\ \overline{FF'}$ = ordinate to some scale (force scale) proportional to, and representing the maximum active earth pressure, E_a;

$\quad\quad\ \overline{AF}$ = a segment of line, which is proportional to and representing to
some scale the weight of the active soil wedge.

Note that the expression $E_a = (W_a)(\overline{FF'})/(\overline{AF})$ is the same as that established
from the force triangle, in Coulomb's theory, namely:

$$E_a = W \frac{\sin(\rho - \phi)}{\sin(\psi + \rho - \phi)}.$$

If there is a uniformly distributed surcharge on the ground surface, say p
lb/ft², then

$$E_a = \tfrac{1}{2}\left[\left(\gamma + \frac{2p\cos\delta}{h}\right)(\overline{AB})\frac{x_a}{\overline{AF}}\right](\overline{FF'}), \tag{21-45}$$

where h = perpendicular distance from the heel point, A, of the wall to the
ground surface line, BD, or its extension to the left of B.

Culmann's method is more general than the Poncelet method. It is particularly applicable with good results for the case when the ground surface is curvilinear, or irregular, or when the backfill material consists of a layered system
of various densities. Also, the method is good when point D lies outside the
drawing paper. It is likewise applicable to a system where the ground surface
is superimposed with a surcharge of a uniformly distributed load of various
intensities—p_1 and p_2, for example, Fig. 21-10. In the latter case Culmann's

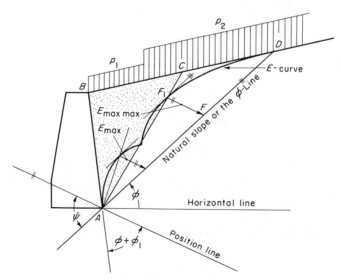

FIG. 21-10   Culmann's method for surcharge. Active earth pressure.

curve may have several maximum E-values. The maximum of the several maximum values, the so-called maximum maximorum, is then taken as the active
earth pressure: $E_a = E_{max\ max}$. This $E_{max\ max}$ also determines the position of
the most dangerous rupture surface, AC. The segment of line, AF, cut off by
$E_{max\ max}$ on the natural slope is the weight, W, of the sliding soil wedge, ABC.

21-18. Passive Earth Pressure. The determination of the passive earth pressure
by Culmann's method is pursued in a similar manner as for the active earth
pressure. The method is illustrated in Fig. 21-11.

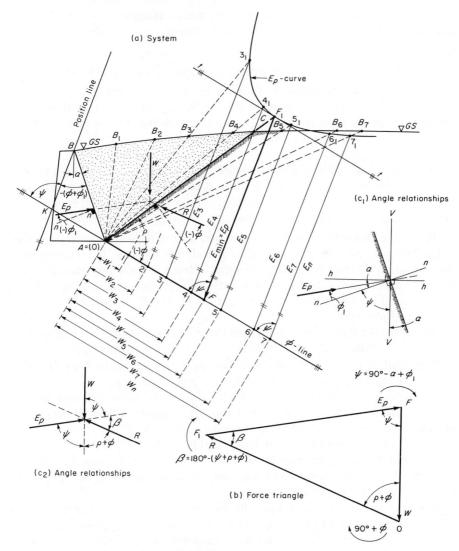

FIG. 21-11   Culmann's passive earth pressure curve.

Note that the natural slope (ϕ-line) is to be drawn through point A under an angle of $(-)\phi$, i.e., the ϕ-line must be drawn at an angle ϕ below the horizontal. On this ϕ-line, the weights, W_n, of the arbitrarily assumed sliding wedges, ABC_n, are plotted to a certain force scale. Through B, the position line, BK, is drawn at an angle of $(-)(\phi + \phi_1)$ (or to the left of the back face line, AB, of the wall). From the endpoints of the weights, W_n, draw the corresponding E_n magnitudes parallel to the position line. This means that the force triangles are rotated through an angle of $(90° + \phi)$ in the clockwise direction and placed on the ϕ-line. Connect the graphically obtained E_n-values to form Culmann's passive earth pressure curve, or the E_p-curve. The minimum ordinate, E_{min}, of the E_p-curve is determined from the ϕ-line by drawing a tangent, t-t, to the E_n-curve. This minimum E_n-ordinate represents, on the chosen scale, the magnitude of the passive earth pressure, E_p.

GENERAL EARTH PRESSURE COEFFICIENT EQUATIONS

21-19. Basis for Establishment of Equations. Earth pressures on walls can be calculated in a general form analytically. In Section 21-8 the analytical calculation is presented for a simple case when the back face of the wall is vertical and the ground surface horizontal.

Poncelet's graphical constructions permit the establishment of general equations for active and passive earth pressure coefficients, K_a and K_p, respectively, for varions inclinations, α, of the back face of the wall, for various slopes, δ, of the ground surface, and for various values of ϕ and ϕ_1. The effect of surcharge must be taken care of by modifying the unit weight of soil from γ to γ_1.

21-20. Key Figure to K_a- and K_p-Equations. The value, α, represents the design of the batter of the wall relative to the vertical, and angle, δ, the inclination of the ground surface relative to the horizontal. Hence, α and δ are relative values. When α and/or δ are negative, then α and/or δ must be introduced into the K_a and K_p functions with a negative sign, and the K_a and K_p values are then calculated out algebraically.

The key for the signs of the angles used in the K_a and K_p equations is illustrated in Fig. 21-12. When the wall has a batter, then α, by convention, is positive, and is designated as $(+)\alpha$. When the wall has an overhang on the back face side then α, by convention, is negative, and is designated as $(-)\alpha$.

The angle, δ, is, by convention, positive if the ground surface behind the wall slopes up and away from the wall, i.e., $(+)\delta$. The angle is negative if the ground surface slopes downward and away from the wall: $(-)\delta$.

The signs of ϕ_1 are likewise indicated on this figure.

Note that K_a and K_p are functions of α, δ, ϕ, and ϕ_1 only, and that they do not depend upon surcharge. The effect of surcharge can be taken care of by modifying the unit weight of the soil.

By means of these K_a- and K_p-coefficients it is possible to calculate quickly active and passive earth pressures for various angles of α, δ, ϕ, and ϕ_1.

The specialization of the K_a and K_p coefficients can be aided by the above-mentioned key figure for angles α, δ, and ϕ_1 inserting in the K_a- and K_p-equations the proper signs, as well as adjusting the sign of ϕ for the given particular condition.

21-21. Derivation of K_a- and K_p-Coefficients. The general, trigonometric, active and passive earth-pressure coefficients, K_a and K_p, will now be derived.

The K_a-Coefficient. By Eq. (21-4), the active earth pressure, E_a, is expressed as

$$E_a = W \frac{\sin(\rho - \phi)}{\sin(\psi + \rho - \phi)} \tag{21-4}$$

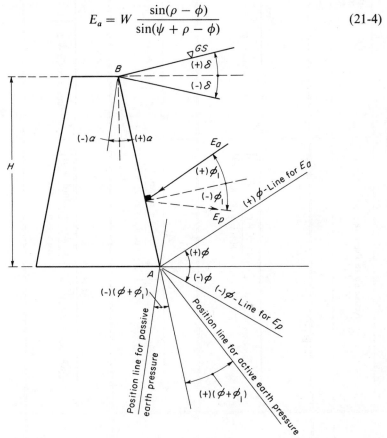

FIG. 21-12 Key figure to K_a- and K_p-equations

From Poncelet's graphical construction in Fig. 21-7, this active earth pressure for system 1, (see Fig. 21-13)[4], can be expressed as

$$E_a = \tfrac{1}{2}\gamma n f(e/n) = \tfrac{1}{2}\gamma f e = \tfrac{1}{2}\gamma e^2 \sin \psi, \tag{21-46}$$

where $W = \tfrac{1}{2}\gamma n f$ = weight of sliding wedge, $\triangle ABC$, and from sine law,

$$\frac{\sin(\rho - \phi)}{\sin(\psi + \rho - \phi)} = \frac{e}{n}, \tag{21-47}$$

where $e = \overline{SC}$; $n = \sqrt{ab}$ (the geometric mean).

Coefficients of

No. and signs of angles relative to system 1	Earth Pressure System	Active Earth Pressure K_a	Passive Earth Pressure (resistance) K_p
1.	2.	3.	4.

①

Angles:

A	P
$(+)\alpha$	$(+)\alpha$
$(+)\delta$	$(+)\delta$
$(+)\phi$	$(-)\phi$
$(\div)\phi_1$	$(-)\phi_1$

$$K_a = \dfrac{\cos^2(\phi-\alpha)}{\cos^2\alpha\,\cos(\alpha+\phi_1)\left[1+\sqrt{\dfrac{\sin(\phi+\phi_1)\sin(\phi-\delta)}{\cos(\alpha+\phi_1)\cos(\alpha-\delta)}}\right]^2}$$

$$K_p = \dfrac{\cos^2(\phi+\alpha)}{\cos^2\alpha\,\cos(\alpha-\phi_1)\left[1-\sqrt{\dfrac{\sin(\phi+\phi_1)\sin(\phi+\delta)}{\cos(\alpha-\phi_1)\cos(\alpha-\delta)}}\right]^2}$$

②

Angles:

A	P
$(+)\alpha$	$(+)\alpha$
$\delta=0$	$\delta=0$
$(+)\phi$	$(-)\phi$
$(+)\phi_1$	$(-)\phi_1$

$$K_a = \dfrac{\cos^2(\phi-\alpha)}{\cos^2\alpha\,\cos(\alpha+\phi_1)\left[1+\sqrt{\dfrac{\sin(\phi+\phi_1)\sin\phi}{\cos(\alpha+\phi_1)\cos\alpha}}\right]^2}$$

$$K_p = \dfrac{\cos^2(\phi+\alpha)}{\cos^2\alpha\,\cos(\alpha-\phi_1)\left[1-\sqrt{\dfrac{\sin(\phi+\phi_1)\sin\phi}{\cos(\alpha-\phi_1)\cos\alpha}}\right]^2}$$

③

Angles:

A	P
$(+)\alpha$	$(+)\alpha$
$(-)\delta$	$(-)\delta$
$(+)\phi$	$(-)\phi$
$(+)\phi_1$	$(-)\phi_1$

$$K_a = \dfrac{\cos^2(\phi-\alpha)}{\cos^2\alpha\,\cos(\alpha+\phi_1)\left[1+\sqrt{\dfrac{\sin(\phi+\phi_1)\sin(\phi+\delta)}{\cos(\alpha+\phi_1)\cos(\alpha+\delta)}}\right]^2}$$

$$K_p = \dfrac{\cos^2(\phi+\alpha)}{\cos^2\alpha\,\cos(\alpha-\phi_1)\left[1-\sqrt{\dfrac{\sin(\phi+\phi_1)\sin(\phi-\delta)}{\cos(\alpha-\phi_1)\cos(\alpha+\delta)}}\right]^2}$$

④

Angles:

A	P
$\alpha=0$	$\alpha=0$
$(+)\delta$	$(+)\delta$
$(+)\phi$	$(-)\phi$
$(+)\phi_1$	$(-)\phi_1$

$$K_a = \dfrac{\cos^2\phi}{\cos\phi_1\left[1+\sqrt{\dfrac{\sin(\phi+\phi_1)\sin(\phi-\delta)}{\cos\phi_1\cos\delta}}\right]^2}$$

$$K_p = \dfrac{\cos^2\phi}{\cos\phi_1\left[1-\sqrt{\dfrac{\sin(\phi+\phi_1)\sin(\phi+\delta)}{\cos\phi_1\cos\delta}}\right]^2}$$

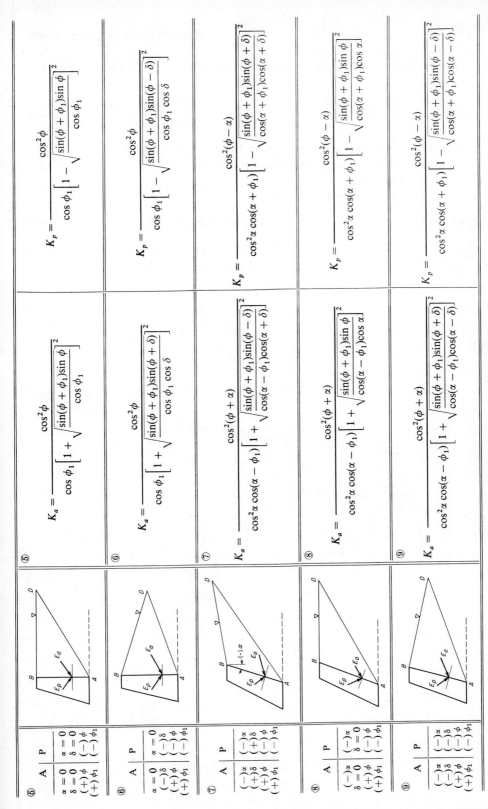

⑤

A	P
$\alpha = 0$	$\alpha = 0$
$\delta = 0$	$\delta = 0$
$(+)\phi$	$(-)\phi$
$(+)\phi_1$	$(-)\phi_1$

$$K_a = \cfrac{\cos^2\phi}{\cos\phi_1\left[1 + \sqrt{\cfrac{\sin(\phi + \phi_1)\sin\phi}{\cos\phi_1}}\right]^2}$$

$$K_p = \cfrac{\cos^2\phi}{\cos\phi_1\left[1 - \sqrt{\cfrac{\sin(\phi + \phi_1)\sin\phi}{\cos\phi_1}}\right]^2}$$

⑥

A	P
$\alpha = 0$	$\alpha = 0$
$(-)\delta$	$(-)\delta$
$(+)\phi$	$(-)\phi$
$(+)\phi_1$	$(-)\phi_1$

$$K_a = \cfrac{\cos^2\phi}{\cos\phi_1\left[1 + \sqrt{\cfrac{\sin(\phi + \phi_1)\sin(\phi + \delta)}{\cos\phi_1\cos\delta}}\right]^2}$$

$$K_p = \cfrac{\cos^2\phi}{\cos\phi_1\left[1 - \sqrt{\cfrac{\sin(\phi + \phi_1)\sin(\phi - \delta)}{\cos\phi_1\cos\delta}}\right]^2}$$

⑦

A	P
$(-)\alpha$	$(-)\alpha$
$(+)\delta$	$(+)\delta$
$(+)\phi$	$(-)\phi$
$(+)\phi_1$	$(-)\phi_1$

$$K_a = \cfrac{\cos^2(\phi + \alpha)}{\cos^2\alpha\cos(\alpha - \phi_1)\left[1 + \sqrt{\cfrac{\sin(\phi + \phi_1)\sin(\phi - \delta)}{\cos(\alpha - \phi_1)\cos(\alpha + \delta)}}\right]^2}$$

$$K_p = \cfrac{\cos^2(\phi - \alpha)}{\cos^2\alpha\cos(\alpha + \phi_1)\left[1 - \sqrt{\cfrac{\sin(\phi + \phi_1)\sin(\phi + \delta)}{\cos(\alpha + \phi_1)\cos(\alpha + \delta)}}\right]^2}$$

⑧

A	P
$(-)\alpha$	$(-)\alpha$
$\delta = 0$	$\delta = 0$
$(+)\phi$	$(-)\phi$
$(+)\phi_1$	$(-)\phi_1$

$$K_a = \cfrac{\cos^2(\phi + \alpha)}{\cos^2\alpha\cos(\alpha - \phi_1)\left[1 + \sqrt{\cfrac{\sin(\phi + \phi_1)\sin\phi}{\cos(\alpha - \phi_1)\cos\alpha}}\right]^2}$$

$$K_p = \cfrac{\cos^2(\phi - \alpha)}{\cos^2\alpha\cos(\alpha + \phi_1)\left[1 - \sqrt{\cfrac{\sin(\phi + \phi_1)\sin\phi}{\cos(\alpha + \phi_1)\cos\alpha}}\right]^2}$$

⑨

A	P
$(-)\alpha$	$(-)\alpha$
$(-)\delta$	$(-)\delta$
$(+)\phi$	$(-)\phi$
$(+)\phi_1$	$(-)\phi_1$

$$K_a = \cfrac{\cos^2(\phi + \alpha)}{\cos^2\alpha\cos(\alpha - \phi_1)\left[1 + \sqrt{\cfrac{\sin(\phi + \phi_1)\sin(\phi + \delta)}{\cos(\alpha - \phi_1)\cos(\alpha - \delta)}}\right]^2}$$

$$K_p = \cfrac{\cos^2(\phi - \alpha)}{\cos^2\alpha\cos(\alpha + \phi_1)\left[1 - \sqrt{\cfrac{\sin(\phi + \phi_1)\sin(\phi - \delta)}{\cos(\alpha + \phi_1)\cos(\alpha - \delta)}}\right]^2}$$

Fig. 21-13 Earth pressure coefficients (Ref. 4).

From other relationships, from similar triangles, $\triangle SCD$ and $\triangle KBD$, Fig. 21-14:

$$e = \overline{BK}\,\frac{b-n}{b-a} = \overline{AB}\,\frac{\sin[90° + (\alpha - \phi)]}{\sin\psi}\,\frac{b-n}{b-a} = \frac{H}{\cos\alpha}\,\frac{\cos(\phi-\alpha)}{\sin\psi}\,\frac{b-n}{b-a}, \quad (21\text{-}48)$$

where $\overline{AB} = H/\cos\alpha$ is the length of the batter of the back face of the wall,
    α = angle of batter of back face of wall,
    $a = \overline{AK}$, and
    $b = \overline{AD}$ = diameter of circle.

The ratio, $(b-n)/(b-a)$, can be transformed as follows: $\qquad\qquad$ (21-49)

$$\frac{b-n}{b-a} = \frac{b-\sqrt{ab}}{b-a} = \frac{1-\sqrt{a/b}}{1-(a/b)} = \frac{1}{1+\sqrt{a/b}} \qquad (21\text{-}50)$$

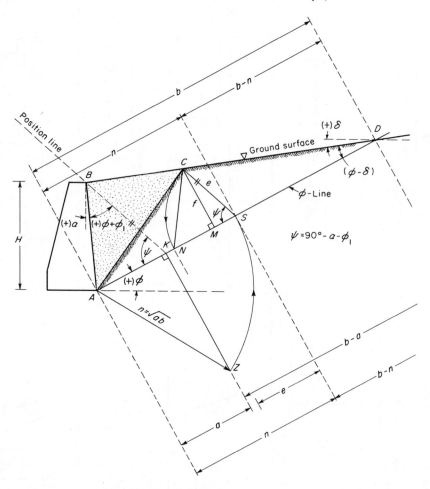

FIG. 21-14   Derivation of K_a-equations.

From triangles, $\triangle ABK$ and $\triangle ABD$, and by the application of the sine law, obtain:

$$\frac{a}{b} = \frac{a}{\overline{AB}} \frac{\overline{AB}}{b} = \frac{\sin(\phi + \phi_1)}{\sin\psi} \frac{\sin(\phi - \delta)}{\sin(90° + \delta - \alpha)}, \tag{21-51}$$

where

$$\sin\psi = \sin(90° - \alpha - \phi_1) = \cos(\alpha + \phi_1), \tag{21-52}$$

and

$$\sin(90° + \delta - \alpha) = \cos(\delta - \alpha). \tag{21-53}$$

Substituting the trigonometric values of e, $(b - n)/(b - a)$, and a/b into the E_a-equation, Eq. (21-46), obtain

$$\frac{b - n}{b - a} = \frac{1}{1 + \sqrt{\dfrac{\sin(\phi + \phi_1)\sin(\phi - \delta)}{\cos(\phi_1 + \alpha)\cos(\delta - \alpha)}}}, \tag{21-54}$$

$$e = \frac{H}{\cos\alpha} \frac{\cos(\phi - \alpha)}{\cos(\alpha + \phi_1)} \frac{1}{1 + \sqrt{\dfrac{\sin(\phi + \phi_1)\sin(\phi - \delta)}{\cos(\alpha + \phi_1)\cos(\delta - \alpha)}}}, \tag{21-55}$$

and

$$E_a = \tfrac{1}{2}\gamma e^2 \sin\psi =$$

$$= \tfrac{1}{2}\gamma H^2 \frac{\cos^2(\phi - \alpha)\cos(\alpha + \phi_1)}{\cos^2\alpha \cos^2(\alpha + \phi_1)\left[1 + \sqrt{\dfrac{\sin(\phi + \phi_1)\sin(\phi - \delta)}{\cos(\alpha + \phi_1)\cos(\delta - \alpha)}}\right]^2}, \tag{21-56}$$

or

$$E_a = \tfrac{1}{2}\gamma H^2 K_a, \tag{21-57}$$

where

$$K_a = \frac{\cos^2(\phi - \alpha)}{\cos^2\alpha \cos(\alpha + \phi_1)\left[1 + \sqrt{\dfrac{\sin(\phi + \phi_1)\sin(\phi - \delta)}{\cos(\alpha + \phi_1)\cos(\delta - \alpha)}}\right]^2} \tag{21-58}$$

is the general trigonometric active earth pressure coefficient for system 1. For other systems use angles with their appropriate signs according to sign convention as shown in Fig. 21-12.

Note for future studies that K_a pertains to the geometry of the earth pressure system and frictional coefficients of soil and between masonry and soil only. It does not involve any effects of surcharge on the ground surface.

Note that when in system 1 $\delta > \phi$, K_a is unreal.

One sees that the trigonometric pressure coefficient depends upon the combination of angles α, δ, ϕ, and ϕ_1 in the system. Therefore, for each system there is a different K_a-coefficient.

Depending upon the configuration, or geometry, the various possible simple earth pressure systems are arbitrarily grouped into nine systems, Fig. 21-13. These are:

1) positively battered wall and positively inclined ground surface,
2) positively battered wall and horizontal ground surface,
3) positively battered wall and negatively inclined ground surface,
4) vertical back face of wall and positively inclined ground surface,
5) vertical back face of wall and horizontal ground surface,
6) vertical back face of wall and negatively inclined ground surface,
7) negatively battered wall (inclined backwards) and positively inclined ground surface,
8) negatively battered wall and horizontal ground surface, and
9) negatively battered wall and negatively inclined ground surface.

The algebraic K_a- and K_p-equations for various earth pressure systems are compiled in Fig. 21-13. Some of the K_a- and K_p-coefficients in this figure are purposely left unsimplified and unreduced to enable one better to visualize the effects of the factors in each of the nine earth pressure systems shown.

Fig. 21-15 shows the derivation of the equation expressing tan ω, or tangent of the rupture angle, ω, for active earth pressure, system 1. The derivation is based on Rebhann's rule. Angle ω is to be measured counterclockwise from the ϕ-line. Angle ω permits one to draw easily the rupture line through the heel of the wall.

By similar reasoning, the tangent of the rupture angle, Ω, for passive earth pressure—system 9—can be derived.

The algebraic expressions for tan ω and tan Ω are tabulated for various systems in Figs. 21-16 and 21-17, respectively. Some of these equations can be simplified and transformed. However, to afford a visual comparison of the various factors entering into these equations, and to see their effect on the tan ω- and tan Ω-values, transformation has not been attempted.

The K_p-Coefficient. By procedure analogous to that followed in deriving the K_a-coefficient, the general trigonometric earth pressure coefficient, K_p, for system 1 is

$$K_p = \frac{\cos^2(\phi + \alpha)}{\cos^2 \alpha \cos(\alpha - \phi_1)\left[1 - \sqrt{\dfrac{\sin(\phi + \phi_1)\sin(\phi + \delta)}{\cos(\alpha - \phi_1)\cos(\delta - \alpha)}}\right]^2}. \qquad (21\text{-}59)$$

The general passive earth pressure equation is then

$$E_p = \tfrac{1}{2}\gamma H^2 K_p. \qquad (21\text{-}60)$$

Specialization of the K_a and K_p equations can be made for any combination of given set of angles governing the configuration of the given retaining wall-earth pressure system as tabulated in Fig. 21-13.

Example. Calculate the magnitude of the active earth pressure for the following conditions:

$$H = 24 \text{ ft}; \qquad \gamma = 100 \text{ lb/ft}^3; \qquad p = 0;$$
$$\alpha = -10°; \qquad \delta = 8°; \qquad \phi = 30°; \qquad \phi_1 = 20°.$$

By Eq. (21-58),

$$K_a = \frac{\cos^2[30° - (-10°)]}{\cos^2(-10°)\cos(-10° + 20°)\left[1 + \sqrt{\dfrac{\sin(30° + 20°)\sin(30° - 8°)}{\cos(-10° + 20°)\cos[8° - (-10°)]}}\right]^2} =$$

$$= \frac{\cos^2 40°}{\cos^2 10° \cos 10°\left[1 + \sqrt{\dfrac{\sin 50° \sin 22°}{\cos 10° \cos 18°}}\right]^2} = 0.255.$$

The magnitude of the active earth pressure is calculated as

$$E_a = \tfrac{1}{2}\gamma H^2 K_a = \tfrac{1}{2}(100)(24^2)(0.255) = 7344 \text{ (lb)}.$$

The horizontal stress ordinate for the tirangular stress distribution diagram at the base of the wall is

$$p_a = \gamma H K_a = (100)(24)(0.255) = 612.0 \text{ (lb/ft}^2).$$

DISCUSSION ON FACTORS
ENTERING INTO E_a- and E_p-EQUATIONS

21-22. Factors. In studying earth pressure problems one generally must be clear about the following factors involved in the lateral earth pressure coefficients:

1) unit weight of soil, γ;
2) angle of internal friction of backfill material, viz., soil, ϕ;
3) cohesion;
4) angle, ϕ_1, of friction between the surface of the back face material of the earth retaining structure and the backfill material, viz., soil;
5) angle of batter of the back face of the wall, α;
6) angle of slope of the ground surface, δ; and
7) point of application of the partial and resultant lateral earth pressures on the wall.

The range of variation of some of these factors is quite wide, and their influence upon the static effect of the lateral earth pressure is relatively large.

There are, generally, few difficulties in performing lateral earth pressure calculations. The main difficulty seems to lie in the evaluation of the possible conditions which may affect the factors involved, and consequently in the correct determination of the γ, ϕ, c (cohesion), and ϕ_1 values, as well as in the correct evaluation of the probable drainage conditions of the soil under which the wall has to perform. It must, therefore, be understood that the determination of γ, ϕ, c, and ϕ_1 values to use in earth pressure calculations, besides experience, is also a problem of test rather than assumption.

21-23. Unit Weight of Soil, γ. The unit weight of soil in lb/ft^3 or in kg/m^3, varies considerably depending upon the soil type, its texture, porosity, whether it is in a loose or dense state (hence the degree of density), the amount of moisture content present, and possibly other factors.

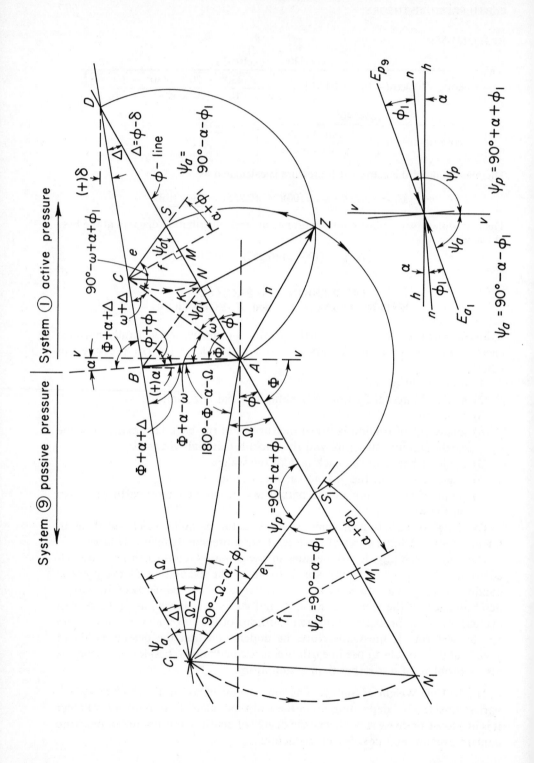

System ⑨ passive pressure | System ① active pressure

① *Rebhann's Rule*:   Area = $ABC = \triangle ACS$

System ①: *Active Earth Pressure*

∴ $\triangle ABC = \triangle ACS$.

$\triangle ABC$: $\overline{AB} = \overline{AC}\,\dfrac{\sin(\omega+\Delta)}{\sin[180° - (\Phi + \alpha + \Delta)]} = \overline{AC}\,\dfrac{\sin(\omega+\Delta)}{\sin(\Phi + \alpha + \Delta)}$

$\triangle ABC = \tfrac{1}{2}\overline{AB}\,\overline{AC}\sin(\Phi + \alpha - \omega) = \tfrac{1}{2}(\overline{AC})^2\dfrac{\sin(\omega+\Delta)\sin(\Phi + \alpha - \omega)}{\sin(\Phi + \alpha + \Delta)}$

$\triangle ACS$: $\overline{AS} = \overline{AC}\,\dfrac{\sin(90° - \omega + \alpha + \phi_1)}{\sin(90° - \alpha - \phi_1)} = \overline{AC}\,\dfrac{\cos(\omega - \alpha - \phi_1)}{\cos(\alpha + \phi_1)}$

$\triangle ACS = \tfrac{1}{2}\overline{AC}\,\overline{AS}\sin\omega = \tfrac{1}{2}(\overline{AC})^2\dfrac{\sin\omega\cos(\omega - \alpha - \phi_1)}{\cos(\alpha + \phi_1)}$

$\sin(\omega+\Delta)\sin(\Phi + \alpha - \omega)\cos(\alpha + \phi_1) = \sin\omega\cos(\omega - \alpha - \phi_1)\sin(\Phi + \alpha + \Delta)$

$\Phi - \phi = \Phi_1$ $\Phi = \Phi_1 + \phi_1$ $-(\alpha + \phi_1) = \alpha_1$ $\alpha = -(\alpha_1 + \phi_1)$ $\Phi + \alpha = \Phi_1 - \alpha_1$

$\sin(\omega + \Delta)\sin(\Phi_1 - \alpha_1 - \omega)\cos\alpha_1 = \sin\omega\cos(\omega + \alpha_1)\sin(\Phi_1 - \alpha_1 + \Delta)$

∴

$\sin(\omega + \Delta) = \cos\omega\cos\Delta[\tan\omega + \tan\Delta] = \cos\omega\cos\Delta(x + a)$

$\sin(\Phi_1 - \alpha_1 - \omega) = \cos(\Phi_1 - \alpha_1)\cos\omega[\tan(\Phi_1 - \alpha_1) - \tan\omega] = \cos(\Phi_1 - \alpha_1)\cos\omega(b - x)$

$\cos\alpha_1$

$\sin\omega$

$\cos(\omega + \alpha_1) = \sin\alpha_1\cos\omega[\cot\alpha_1 - \tan\omega] = \sin\alpha_1\cos\omega[c - x]$

$\sin(\Phi_1 - \alpha_1 + \Delta) = \cos(\Phi_1 - \alpha_1)\cos\Delta[\tan(\Phi_1 - \alpha_1) + \tan\Delta] = \cos(\Phi_1 - \alpha_1)\cos\Delta(b + a)$

$x = \tan\omega$

$a = \tan\Delta = \tan(\phi - \delta)$

$b = \tan(\Phi_1 - \alpha_1) =$
$= \tan(\Phi + \alpha) =$
$= \tan(90° - \phi + \alpha) = \cot(\phi - \alpha)$

$c = \cot\alpha_1 = -\cot(\phi_1 + \alpha)$

$c(x + a)(b - x) = x(c - x)(a + b); \quad x = \dfrac{-ac + \sqrt{ac(a+b)(c - b)}}{c - a - b}$

$x^2(c - a - b) + 2acx - abc = 0$

$\tan\omega = x = \dfrac{-\tan(\phi - \delta)\cot\alpha_1 + \sqrt{\tan(\phi - \delta)[\tan(\phi - \delta) + \cot(\phi - \alpha)]\cot\alpha_1[\cot\alpha_1 - \cot(\phi - \alpha)]}}{\cot\alpha_1 - \tan(\phi - \delta) - \cot(\phi - \alpha)}$

$= \dfrac{-\tan(\phi - \delta) + \sqrt{\tan(\phi - \delta)[\tan(\phi - \delta) + \cot(\phi - \alpha)][1 - \tan\alpha_1\cot(\phi - \alpha)]}}{1 - \tan\alpha_1[\tan(\phi - \delta) + \cot(\phi - \alpha)]}$

Active:

$$\boxed{\tan\omega = \dfrac{-\tan(\phi - \delta) + \sqrt{\tan(\phi - \delta) + \cot(\phi - \delta)[\tan(\phi - \delta) + \cot(\phi - \alpha)][1 + \tan(\phi_1 + \alpha)\cot(\phi - \alpha)]}}{1 + \tan(\phi_1 + \alpha)[\tan(\phi - \delta) + \cot(\phi - \alpha)]}}$$

$$\omega = \arctan\left[\dfrac{-(\;\;) + \sqrt{[\qquad]}}{[\qquad]}\right]$$

Passive:

$$\boxed{\tan\Omega = \dfrac{\tan(\phi + \delta) + \sqrt{\tan(\phi + \delta) + \cot(\phi + \delta)[\tan(\phi + \delta) + \cot(\phi + \alpha)][1 + \tan(\phi_1 - \alpha)\cot(\phi + \alpha)]}}{1 + \tan(\phi_1 - \alpha)[\tan(\phi + \delta) + \cot(\phi + \alpha)]}}$$

Fig. 21-15   Derivation on tan ω (see facing page).

Tangents of Rupture Angles, tan ω

No. and signs of angles relative to system 1	Active Earth Pressure System	
1.	2.	3.
① $\begin{aligned}&+\alpha\\&+\delta\\&(+\phi)\\&(+\phi_1)\end{aligned}$		$\tan \omega = \tan(\rho - \phi) = \dfrac{-\tan(\phi - \delta) + \sqrt{\tan(\phi - \delta)[\tan(\phi - \delta) + \cot(\phi - \alpha)][1 + \tan(\phi_1 + \alpha)\cot(\phi - \alpha)]}}{1 + \tan(\phi_1 + \alpha)[\tan(\phi - \delta) + \cot(\phi - \alpha)]}$
② $\begin{aligned}&+\alpha\\&\delta = 0\\&(+\phi)\\&(+\phi_1)\end{aligned}$		$\tan \omega = \tan(\rho - \phi) = \dfrac{-\tan \phi + \sqrt{\tan \phi[\tan \phi + \cot(\phi - \alpha)][1 + \tan(\phi_1 + \alpha)\cot(\phi - \alpha)]}}{1 + \tan(\phi_1 + \alpha)[\tan \phi + \cot(\phi - \alpha)]}$
③ $\begin{aligned}&+\alpha\\&-\delta\\&(+\phi)\\&(+\phi_1)\end{aligned}$		$\tan \omega = \tan(\rho - \phi) = \dfrac{-\tan(\phi + \delta) + \sqrt{\tan(\phi + \delta)[\tan(\phi + \delta) + \cot(\phi - \alpha)][1 + \tan(\phi_1 + \alpha)\cot(\phi - \alpha)]}}{1 + \tan(\phi_1 + \alpha)[\tan(\phi + \delta) + \cot(\phi - \alpha)]}$
④ $\begin{aligned}&\alpha = 0\\&+\delta\\&(+\phi)\\&(+\phi_1)\end{aligned}$		$\tan \omega = \tan(\rho - \phi) = \dfrac{-\tan(\phi - \delta) + \sqrt{\tan(\phi - \delta)[\tan(\phi - \delta) + \cot \phi][1 + \tan \phi_1 \cot \phi]}}{1 + \tan \phi_1[\tan(\phi - \delta) + \cot \phi]}$

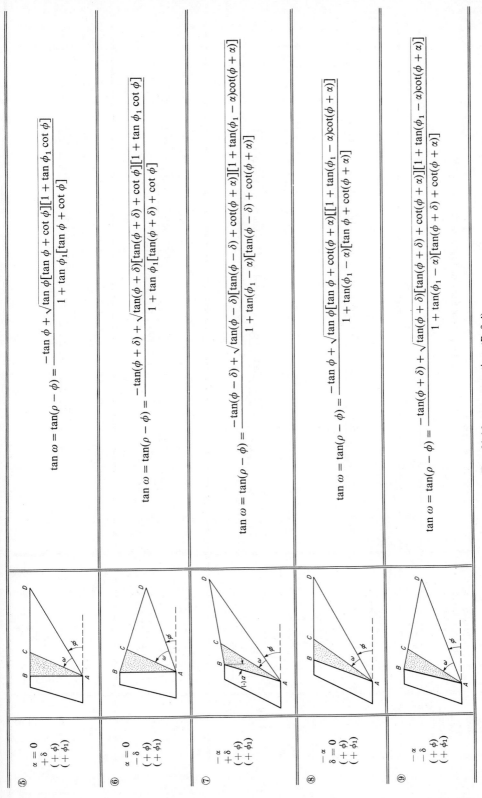

Fig. 21-16 tanω-equations (Ref. 4).

⑤
$\alpha = 0$
$+\delta$
$(+\phi)$
$(+\phi_1)$

$$\tan\omega = \tan(\rho - \phi) = \frac{-\tan\phi + \sqrt{\tan\phi[\tan\phi + \cot\phi][1 + \tan\phi_1\cot\phi]}}{1 + \tan\phi_1[\tan\phi + \cot\phi]}$$

⑥
$\alpha = 0$
$-\delta$
$(+\phi)$
$(+\phi_1)$

$$\tan\omega = \tan(\rho - \phi) = \frac{-\tan(\phi + \delta) + \sqrt{\tan(\phi + \delta)[\tan(\phi + \delta) + \cot\phi][1 + \tan\phi_1\cot\phi]}}{1 + \tan\phi_1[\tan(\phi + \delta) + \cot\phi]}$$

⑦
$-\alpha$
$+\delta$
$(+\phi)$
$(+\phi_1)$

$$\tan\omega = \tan(\rho - \phi) = \frac{-\tan(\phi - \delta) + \sqrt{\tan(\phi - \delta)[\tan(\phi - \delta) + \cot(\phi + \alpha)][1 + \tan(\phi_1 - \alpha)\cot(\phi + \alpha)]}}{1 + \tan(\phi_1 - \alpha)[\tan(\phi - \delta) + \cot(\phi + \alpha)]}$$

⑧
$-\alpha$
$\delta = 0$
$(+\phi)$
$(+\phi_1)$

$$\tan\omega = \tan(\rho - \phi) = \frac{-\tan\phi + \sqrt{\tan\phi[\tan\phi + \cot(\phi + \alpha)][[1 + \tan(\phi_1 - \alpha)\cot(\phi + \alpha)]}}{1 + \tan(\phi_1 - \alpha)[\tan\phi + \cot(\phi + \alpha)]}$$

⑨
$-\alpha$
$-\delta$
$(+\phi)$
$(+\phi_1)$

$$\tan\omega = \tan(\rho - \phi) = \frac{-\tan(\phi + \delta) + \sqrt{\tan(\phi + \delta)[\tan(\phi + \delta) + \cot(\phi + \alpha)][1 + \tan(\phi_1 - \alpha)\cot(\phi + \alpha)]}}{1 + \tan(\phi_1 - \alpha)[\tan(\phi + \delta) + \cot(\phi + \alpha)]}$$

Tangents of Rupture Angles, $\tan \Omega$

No. and signs of angles relative to system 1	Passive Earth Pressure System	Tangents of Rupture Angles, $\tan \Omega$
1.	2.	3.
① $\begin{array}{l}+\alpha \\ +\delta \\ (-\phi) \\ (-\phi_1)\end{array}$		$\tan \Omega = \dfrac{\tan(\phi+\delta) + \sqrt{\tan(\phi+\delta)[\tan(\phi+\delta)+\cot(\phi+\alpha)][1+\tan(\phi_1-\alpha)\cot(\phi+\alpha)]}}{1+\tan(\phi_1-\alpha)[\tan(\phi+\delta)+\cot(\phi+\alpha)]}$
② $\begin{array}{l}+\alpha \\ +\delta = 0 \\ (-\phi) \\ (-\phi_1)\end{array}$		$\tan \Omega = \dfrac{\tan\phi + \sqrt{\tan\phi[\tan\phi+\cot(\phi+\alpha)][1+\tan(\phi_1-\alpha)\cot(\phi+\alpha)]}}{1+\tan(\phi_1-\alpha)[\tan\phi+\cot(\phi+\alpha)]}$
③ $\begin{array}{l}+\alpha \\ -\delta \\ (-\phi) \\ (-\phi_1)\end{array}$		$\tan \Omega = \dfrac{\tan(\phi-\delta) + \sqrt{\tan(\phi-\delta)[\tan(\phi-\delta)+\cot(\phi+\alpha)][1+\tan(\phi_1-\alpha)\cot(\phi+\alpha)]}}{1+\tan(\phi_1-\alpha)[\tan(\phi-\delta)+\cot(\phi+\alpha)]}$
④ $\begin{array}{l}+\alpha = 0 \\ +\delta \\ (-\phi) \\ (-\phi_1)\end{array}$		$\tan \Omega = \dfrac{\tan(\phi+\delta) + \sqrt{\tan(\phi+\delta)[\tan(\phi+\delta)+\cot\phi][1+\tan\phi_1\cot\phi]}}{1+\tan\phi_1[\tan(\phi+\delta)+\cot\phi]}$

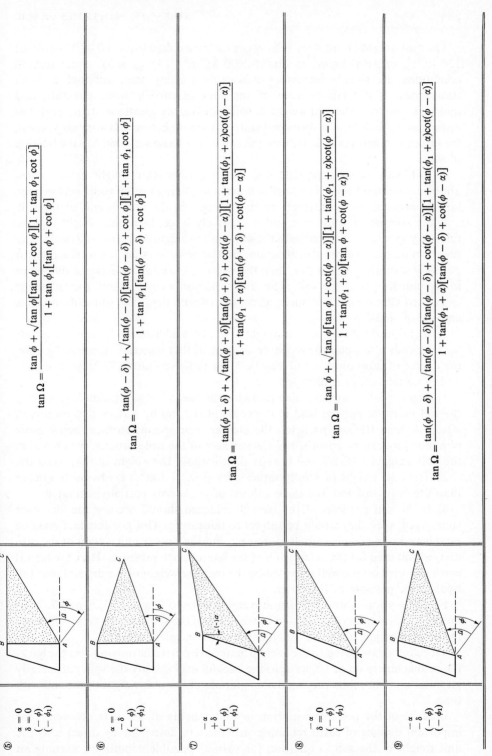

Fig. 21-17 tanΩ-equations (Ref. 4).

The unit weight of ordinary soils varies on the average from $100 \, \text{lb/ft}^3$ to about $130 \, \text{lb/ft}^3$, or $1600 \, \text{kg/m}^3$ to about $2000 \, \text{kg/m}^3$. Clayey soils, under natural conditions, are usually somewhat heavier than sandy ones, although a direct comparison is difficult because of the varying particle sizes, minerals, and moisture content. The unit weight of soil is ordinarily greater in its natural, undisturbed state than in a disturbed state. Compare before and after excavation, for instance, when in the latter case the soil is in a loose state, such as the bulking of sand.

A soil with variable particle size has a greater unit weight than a fine, uniformly textured soil. The finer soil particles, filling up the voids between the larger particles, thus contribute to the increase in the unit weight of the soil.

If the volume of voids of a soil is relatively large, then unit weight may be relatively small as compared with the same soil in a densified state and containing fewer voids than before densification. If the voids of such a soil are fully or partially saturated with water, then the degree of saturation makes a difference in the unit weight of the soil. The larger the unit weight of soil, the larger the calculated lateral earth pressures, as compared with dry, ideal soil with the same amount of voids.

As mentioned before, the unit weight of the backfill material behind a retaining wall depends also upon the moisture content of that material. Depending upon the degree of saturation, a soil may be 1) partially saturated; 2) fully saturated; and 3) inundated, or submerged.

1) In a partially saturated, fine-particled soil (degree of saturation $S < 100\%$), the soil moisture may be held in the voids of the soil by surface tension forces. Also, the finer the soil particles, the greater their specific surface; hence more film moisture can be adsorbed to the surfaces of the soil particles, which makes the unit weight of such a soil heavier than without the weight of that moisture.

2) The unit weight of a fully saturated soil ($S = 100\%$) is obviously greater than the same soil with the same volume of voids only partially saturated.

3) If the soil particles of the backfill material should become inundated or submerged, then they would be subject to buoyancy. This possible fact must be established or such a possibility foreseen, and the proper unit weight of the submerged soil used for the calculation of the lateral earth pressure. Here the lateral earth pressure on the wall is caused by the *buoyant* weight of the dry soil plus full hydrostatic pressure of the water.

For the various formulas of unit weights refer to Chapters 5, 6, and 7. One notes that the degree of saturation of the voids of the soil causes a great difference in the unit weight of soil to use in earth pressure calculations.

Vibrations transferred to the backfill material from traffic moving over the backfill, or machinery on or adjacent to the backfill may densify the soil, particularly granular material, thus varying the magnitude of the unit weight of the soil with time.

Because of the possible variation in unit weights of soil it is necessary for important designs of earth retaining structures to determine by direct tests the unit weight of the soil in question for various possible conditions, keeping an eye also on the possible variations in hydrological conditions or man's activities in the immediate neighborhood of the structure areas concerned.

Movements of earth masses setting in after a prolonged period of rainfall may also have their cause in the increased unit weight of the ruptured mass of soil. It is obvious that, depending upon conditions, there is a great variation in unit weights of soil.

21-24. Angle of Internal Friction. In performing earth pressure calculations it is essential that the shear strength of the soil, viz., angle of internal friction (and cohesion, c), be determined *by test* on the particular backfill material in question.

Soils possessing constant physical properties have, approximately, a constant angle of internal friction, ϕ. This angle is usually less for uniformly textured soils than for soils with well-graded texture, which have greater interlocking properties, and hence a larger ϕ.

The angle of internal friction for coarse-particled (permeable) soils is almost independent of moisture content. Regardless of whether wet or dry, the coefficient of internal friction of such soils varies considerably between about $\tan \phi = 0.46$ to about $\tan \phi = 0.70$. For clayey soils the $\tan \phi$-values usually range from about $\tan \phi = 0.20$ to about $\tan \phi = 0.85$.

Because the active earth pressure, E_a, is a function of ϕ, it follows that the less is ϕ, the larger is the magnitude of E_a:

$$E_a = \tfrac{1}{2}\gamma H^2 \tan^2(45° - \phi/2),$$

for a system with a vertical back face of wall and horizontal ground surface. This demonstrates clearly that the right angle of internal friction, ϕ, of the backfill material should be used.

The magnitude of angle ϕ for clean sand, as shown by Krey,[5] is practically the same above and below the groundwater table, and is unaffected by water.

The rupture surface of an ideal, granular material assumes almost the character of a plane, such as AC, Figs. 21-18 and 21-19.

21-25. Cohesion. As seen from the earth pressure equation for cohesive soils, active case,

$$E_a = \tfrac{1}{2}\gamma H^2 K_a - 2cH\sqrt{K_a}, \tag{21-61}$$

cohesion decreases the magnitude of the active earth pressure as compared with an ideal soil, and increases the magnitude of the passive earth presssure as compared with an ideal soil possessing friction only.

In practice, in earth pressure calculations, and in performing stability analysis on retaining walls by applying Coulomb's earth pressure theory, the cohesion of a cohesive, frictional, backfill material is often omitted. The omission of cohesion is often practiced under the pretense of increased degree of safety relative to the stability of the structure. This may be the case when, upon the omission of cohesion in earth pressure calculations, the true angle of internal friction, ϕ, is retained and used. Also, upon the increase in soil moisture content, cohesion may decrease considerably. However, if, as is frequently done, a larger angle of friction is used as a substitute for the true one, with the thought behind it of comprehending by this means the effect of both friction and cohesion, then such a method will result instead in a decreased degree of safety. This can particularly be noticed with frictional, cohesive soils where, as can be seen from Eq. (21-61), the frictional forces vary quadratically with H, but the cohesive forces vary only linearly with H.

FIG. 21-18   Approximate plane rupture surface in sand (after Müller-Breslau, Ref. 6).

FIG. 21-19   Surface of rupture

In dry sand, there is practically no cohesion present. It is also of small magnitude in moist and wet granular soils, the particles of which are angularly shaped, such as in the case of some sands and gravel. Cohesion of considerable magnitude is present in cohesive, plastic soils.

The value of cohesion for some soils ranges approximately from $c = 0.01$ t/ft² to about $c = 0.12$ t/ft². Admittedly, exceptions to these values are possible, and c-values are reported as high as $c = 3500$ lb/ft² $= 1.75$ t/ft² for a very stiff boulder clay with $\phi = 16°$.[7]

The magnitude of cohesion, viz., shear strength of a soil, must be determined by *test on that soil*. The test should be performed under conditions which would simulate as closely as possible those most likely to occur in nature.

Changes in moisture conditions in the backfill soil may bring about changes in the values of the apparent cohesion of a soil. Shear strength of a cohesive soil is very much affected by the soil moisture content. This phenomenon gives an idea of the possible danger of rupture of earth masses, such as laterally supported and unsupported embankment slopes.

21-26. Angle of Friction Between Wall and Backfill Material. This angle determines the direction of the soil lateral pressure. This direction (angle ϕ_1) against the wall is more difficult to evaluate than the angle of internal friction of the soil.

The magnitude of the angle of friction, ϕ_1, between the surface material of the back face of wall and the backfill material is a function of

    a) the type of wall material,

    b) the degree of smoothness of the surface of the back face of the wall,

    c) the type of soil,

    d) the density of soil,

    e) the hydrologic conditions,

    f) vibrations and shocks, and

    g) possibly other changes and variations.

It is relatively easy to understand the effect of points a to e on the magnitude of ϕ_1. The smoother the back face of the wall, and the smoother the soil particles behind the wall, the less is the angle ϕ_1. If the wall is smooth, the value of the angle ϕ_1, in calculations, is sometimes set equal to zero.

If the wall is rough, with cavities, protrusions, and other uneven spots, these may be filled with interlocking soil. Upon sliding of the wall relative to the backfill soil, the soil would not slide along the back face of the wall, but may become sheared off, and the relative sliding may thus be soil against soil. In such a case the value of the angle, ϕ_1, may attain the value of the angle of internal friction, ϕ, of the backfill soil in question, i.e., $\phi_1 \rightarrow \phi$.

Sometimes, under special conditions, the angle of friction, ϕ_1, between wall and soil may shift through zero from one extreme to the other, i.e., $\pm \phi_1$. Such a shift may be brought about when part of the backfill soil immediately behind the wall is excavated for repair purposes and the wall is braced against the remaining earth mass of the backfill. The bracing system may then transmit the active earth pressure from the unexcavated part of the backfill material to the wall under an angle of friction, ϕ_1, which may be different from that which existed before the excavation of the backfill and installation of the braces. Hence, in stability analysis of a retaining wall, this worst possible statical condition of the wall, where ϕ_1 may shift from one extreme to the other, should not be overlooked.

Settlement of a wall may also bring about a change in the magnitude of ϕ_1, viz., inclination of the earth pressure vector against the wall. The wall is stable as long as ϕ_1 is not larger than ϕ. It can generally be said that stability of a retaining wall depends more upon the direction than upon the magnitude of the earth pressure against the wall.

Methods of backfilling also influence the magnitude of the friction angle ϕ_1 between wall and soil. The backfilled soil may be rolled, tamped, or vibrated into an arbitrary stress condition of the soil, particularly as the densified backfill material grows in thickness. In such instances ϕ_1 may assume entirely arbitrary directions of inclination against the wall between $(+\phi_1)$ and $(-\phi_1)$, and may also assume a value of $\phi_1 = 0$.

The change in magnitude, viz., inclination of ϕ_1, may also result upon the yielding of an anchored bulkhead wall, where ϕ_1 may shift from $+\phi_1$ to $-\phi_1$.

Dynamic vibrations and shocks also affect the magnitude of ϕ_1. Dynamic vibrations on earth retaining structures may be induced by highway and railway rolling stock; improperly founded machinery in the adjacent factories and/or power plants; nearby pile driving operations; or shocks from blasting, explosions, earthquakes, and other possible causes.

Vibrations and shocks tend to reduce soil friction, and friction between soil and wall. The higher the frequency of vibrations, the less the friction, and the less is ϕ_1 (over-densification).

Under the densifying effect of vibrations and shocks, the active earth pressure, E_a, increases and may attain the value of the passive earth pressure, E_p. This E_p-pressure would drop again to the original E_a-value. The next shock would bring up the pressure on the wall to a higher value than E_a, so that there exists the possibility that the wall may collapse if not designed to resist such dynamic forces.

Practitioners assume $\phi_1 = 0$ if the backfill is wet, and/or the back face of the wall is smooth. Where such an increased degree of safety is not needed, ϕ_1 is assumed to be from $\phi_1 = (\frac{1}{3})\phi$ for smooth walls and with no vibration, to $\phi_1 = (\frac{2}{3})\phi$ for ordinary retaining walls, and with no vibrations. On rough walls it is set $\phi_1 = \phi$. For approximate calculations, Müller-Breslau[8] mentions in his work the following ϕ_1 values. When the back face of the wall is vertical $(\alpha = 0)$, then for active earth pressure on a concrete earth-retaining wall, and upon steel sheet piling, the ϕ_1 to use is: $\phi_1 = \phi/2$. When $\alpha \gtrless 0$, then for active earth pressure $\phi_1 = 0$ is indicated. Also, $\phi_1 = 0$ when vibrations on the backfill material may take place, and also when, as in wharves and quays, a great amplitude in water-table fluctuations occurs.

For passive earth pressure, on concrete and steel, and for a plane rupture surface assume $\phi_1 = -\phi/2$, and for steel and curved rupture surfaces $\phi_1 = -\phi$.

Müller-Breslau, based on his large-scale experimental research, says that it is appropriate for rough walls and careful drainage of the backfill material to set $\phi_1 = (\frac{3}{4})\phi$.

21-27. Effect of Wall Friction Angle ϕ_1 on K_a and K_p. It seems that the most sensitive, and thus the most important angle in earth pressure calculations is the angle of friction, ϕ_1, between the backfill material and the nature of the surface of the back face of the retaining wall. The effect of the wall-friction angle, ϕ_1, on the K-coefficients (for $\alpha = 5°$, $\alpha = 10°$, and $\alpha = 30°$), as illustrated in Fig. 21-20 by graphs, $K_a = \phi(\phi_1)$ and $K_p = \Phi(\phi_1)$, seems to be more pronounced than that of α and δ (observe particularly that the passive pressure coefficient, $K_p = \Phi(\phi_1)$, is influenced by ϕ_1 over a wide range as compared with $K_a = \phi(\phi_1)$).

It seems that the success of the earth pressure theory and the application of the earth pressure coefficients to the solution of earth pressure problems depends very much upon the *correct determination* of the friction angles, ϕ and ϕ_1, by test. Because soil properties may vary in the field from foot to foot, it is not advisable to use in earth pressure calculations an assumed value of ϕ and/or ϕ_1 from tabulations in handbooks.

The success of the theory depends also upon the proper evaluation of possible future conditions which may occur while the structure is in service, since these conditions may effect possible variations in the wall friction angle, ϕ_1.

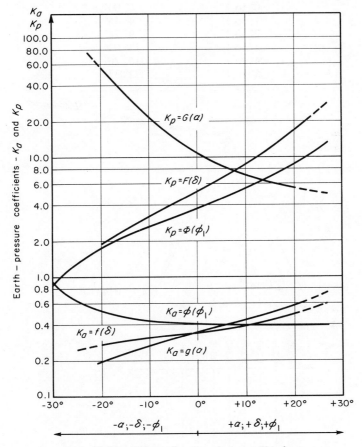

FIG. 21-20 Effect of α, δ and ϕ_1 on K values.

21-28. Effect of α and δ on K_a and K_p. The factors, α and δ, are a matter of structural design. Hence, there is not much to say about these factors, except that it should be of interest to know their effect upon K_a and K_p, viz., E_a and E_p, respectively. Once chosen, these angles, α and δ, usually do not vary during the service time of the structure (this is especially true for α).

Battered earth retaining walls are very seldom designed with the back face, AB, making an angle, α, greater than 25° with the vertical. The batter-slope and batter-angle relationships are shown in Table 21-1.

TABLE 21-1. SLOPE AND ANGLE RELATIONSHIPS
OF A BATTERED BACK FACE OF A RETAINING WALL

Batter-slope ratio (inches) : (foot)	Angle of batter α
1	2
0" to 1'	0° 00'
1" to 1'	4° 46'
2" to 1'	9° 28'
3" to 1'	14° 02'
4" to 1'	18° 26'
5" to 1'	22° 37'

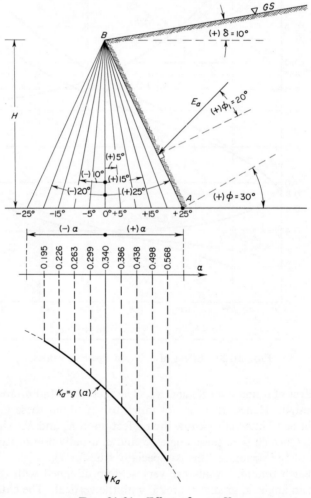

FIG. 21-21   Effect of α on K_a

The slope of the ground surface is seldom designed to a greater angle than $(\pm)\delta = 30°$ with the horizontal.

The effects of the batter angle, α, and the angle of inclination, δ, on the magnitudes of the earth pressure coefficients, K_a and K_p, for $\phi = 30°$ and $\phi_1 = (\frac{2}{3})\phi$ $= 20°$ are illustrated in Figs. 21-21 and 21-22. These illustrations pertain to an earth-pressure system with a) an inclination of ground surface, $(+)\delta = 10° =$ const, and varying α at $5°$ intervals; and b) batter angle $(+)\alpha = 5° =$ const and varying δ at $5°$ intervals, respectively.

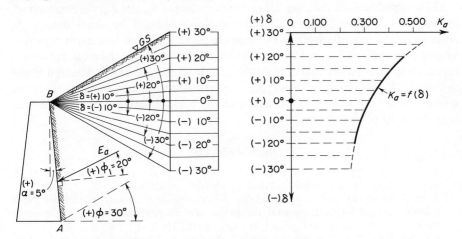

FIG. 21-22   Effect of δ on K_a

21-29. Points of Application of E. The points of application of partial and total, active and passive earth pressures on the wall are determined by the positions of the centroids of the partial and total soil lateral stress distribution diagrams. For points of application of lateral earth pressures caused by backfill materials on elastic, flexible walls and elastic bulkheads the reader is referred to Terzaghi[9] and Tschebotarioff.[10]

The many reported failures of retaining walls and bulkheads are probably not so much to be attributed to the approximate calculations of earth pressures and stability but rather to the incomplete knowledge of the soil or any other backfill material.

ACTIVE AND PASSIVE EARTH PRESSURE
COEFFICIENT TABLES

21-30. Tables. To facilitate earth pressure calculations, earth pressure coefficient tables such as given by Reference 4, for example, can be used. These tables are prepared for plane rupture surfaces, and quickly give the numerical values of the K_a and K_p coefficients for various α, δ, ϕ, and ϕ_1 at even five-degree intervals. The batter angles of the wall, α, vary in these tables between $(+)25°$ and $(-)25°$. The angles of inclination, δ, of the ground surface vary between $(+)30°$ and $(-)30°$. The angle of friction, ϕ, of the soil or any other backfill material is varied in five-degree intervals from $0°$ to $55°$. The angles of friction, ϕ_1, between the backfill material and the surface material of the back face or the earth-retaining structure is allowed to vary in five-degree intervals between $-55°$ to $+55°$. For example, if $\alpha = 5°$, $\delta = 10°$, $\phi = 30°$, and $\phi_1 = 20°$, then the earth pressure coefficient for the active earth pressure by Table A-29 is $K_a = 0.386$. Intermediate K-values for angles not given in these tables can be determined with satisfactory precision by linear interpolation from the given K-values in the tables between which the desired K-value is located.

These tables likewise indicate, for each entry value of K_a and K_p, the corresponding angles of rupture, ω and Ω. The angle designated by small omega, ω, pertains to the most dangerous soil rupture angle for the active earth pressure, whereas the angle designated by capital omega, Ω, pertains to the most dangerous rupture angle for passive earth pressure. These angles are to be measured in the counterclockwise direction from the corresponding ϕ-lines in earth pressure systems where the wall is to the left, and the backfill material behind the wall is to the right of the viewer.

REFERENCES

1. K. Terzaghi, "Large Retaining-Wall Tests", *Engineering New Record*, 1934, vol. 112, pp. 136-140, 259-262, 316-318, 403-406, 503-508.
2. J. V. Poncelet, *Mémoire sur la stabilité des revêtments et de leurs fondation.* Note additionelle sur les relations analytiques qui lient entre elles la poussée et la butée de la terre. *Memorial de l'officier du genie*, Paris, 1840, vol. 13.
3. K. Culmann, "Die Graphische Statik" (Section 8, *Theorie der Stütz und Futtermauern*), Zürich, Meyer und Zeller, 1866.
4. A. R. Jumikis, *Active and Passive Earth Pressure Coefficient Tables*, Bureau of Engineering Research, Bulletin no. 43, New Brunswick, New Jersey, Rutgers— The State University, (in preparation).
5. H. D. Krey, *Erdruck, Erdwiderstand und Tragfähigkeit des Baugrundes*, Berlin, Wilhelm Ernst und Sohn, 1936.
6. H. Müller-Breslau, *Erddruck auf Stützmauern*, Stuttgart, Alfred Kröner Verlag, 1906, 1947.
7. A. L. Bell, "Lateral Pressure and Resistance of Clay and the Supporting Power of Clay Foundations", *Minutes*, Proceedings of the Institution of Civil Engineers, London, 1915, vol. 199.
8. See Ref. 6.
9. See Ref. 1.
10. G. P. Tschebotarioff, *Large Scale Earth Pressure Tests with Model Flexible Bulkheads.* Final Report to the Bureau of Yards and Docks, U.S. Navy, Princeton, New Jersey, Princeton University Press, January, 1949.

PROBLEMS

21-1. Determine the active and passive earth pressures, without and with a surcharge of $p = 300$ lb/ft^2, exerted by a sandy, backfill soil. $H = 12$ ft, $\alpha = 0$, $\delta = 0$. The groundwater table is 4 ft below the ground surface, see Fig. Prob. 21-1.

     Unit weight of dry soil: $\gamma = 100$ lb/ft^3;

     Moisture content of soil above ground-water table: $m = 12\%$ by dry weight; $\phi = 30°$; $\phi_1 = 0°$; $G = 2.65$; $\gamma_w = 62.4$ lb/ft^3;

     Porosity $n = 30\%$.

Draw to scale, and complete the soil lateral stress distribution diagram, and calculate the magnitude of partial and total earth pressures. Also, calculate the points of applications of the partial and total earth pressures.

21-2.   Given a two-layered system of soil as shown in Fig. Prob. 21-2.

   a) *No groundwater present.*

   Plot to scale the stress distribution diagrams

      i) for $c = 0$ for both layers

      ii) for $c_1 = 0$ and $c_2 = 100$ lb/ft², and for both active and passive pressures.

   Note. Calculate active and passive earth pressures for all possible combinations.

   b) *Groundwater present.* Required same excercise as under a).

21-3.   Determine analytically the position of the rupture surface in soil so that sliding of the retaining wall out of its position would just impend due to the lateral pressure of the soil wedge, *ABC*, Fig. Prob. 21-3. The weight of the retaining wall is W pounds per linear foot of wall line. Unit weight of soil $= \gamma$; $\phi = 30°$; $\phi_1 = 0$ at the backfill; $\phi_1 = 32°$ at the base of footing.

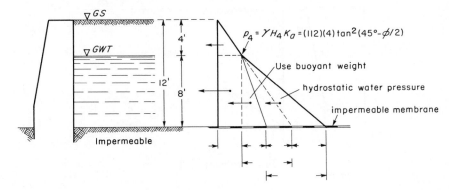

$$p_A = \gamma H_A K_a = (112)(4)\tan^2(45° - \phi/2)$$

Use buoyant weight

hydrostatic water pressure

impermeable membrane

FIG. Problem 21-1.

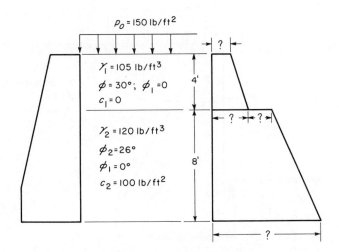

$p_0 = 150$ lb/ft²

$\gamma_1 = 105$ lb/ft³

$\phi = 30°$; $\phi_1 = 0$

$c_1 = 0$

$\gamma_2 = 120$ lb/ft³

$\phi_2 = 26°$

$\phi_1 = 0°$

$c_2 = 100$ lb/ft²

FIG. Problem 21-2.

Required:
    a) Draw soil lateral stress distribution diagram.
    b) Show algebraically stability calculations against rotation of the system
        with and without earthquake considerations.
Note: Quantities not given should be assumed. Also, note that W is not given
by a numerical value.
    If the height of the wall is $H = 12$ ft, $\gamma = 100$ lb/ft³; $\phi = 30°$; $\phi_1 = 0$;
$\phi_{c/s} = 0.60$, what should be the weight of the wall to attain an overall coefficient
of stability of $\eta = 1.5$? Use Poncelet's method and compare the results with
theoretical calculations.

21-4.   Check the stability of the earth retaining wall as shown in the Fig. Prob. 21-4.
    The upper ground surface is subjected to a surcharge of 400 lb/ft². The
backfill is a mixture of sand and gravel with some silt. The unit weight of this
backfill material is 120 lb/ft³; $\phi = 30°$. The coefficient of friction between
concrete and soil was found to be tan $\phi_1 = 0.50$. The allowable bearing capacity

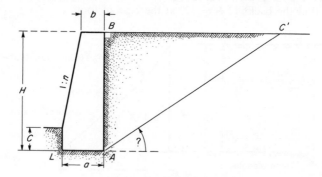

FIG. Problem 21-3.

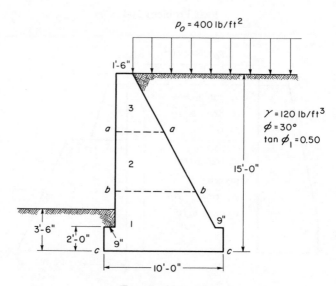

FIG. Problem 21-4.

of the soil was found to be 4 t/ft². Unit weight of concrete $= 150$ lb/ft³. The wall rests on compact soil.

    a) Determine total active earth pressure on the retaining wall
          i) analytically and
          ii) graphically (by Poncelet's and Culmann's methods).
          iii) Find the position of the resultant pressure at the base, c-c, of the retaining wall.
    b) Determine active earth pressures on parts ①, ②, and ③ of the retaining wall; determine the position of the resultant pressure at the base, c-c, of the retaining wall.
    c) Compare the positions of the resultant pressure at c-c found by the three methods as above.
    d) Check compressive stresses in concrete in sections (a-a), (b-b), and contact pressure on soil at (c-c).
    e) Check the stability of wall against overturning.
    f) Check the stability of wall against sliding.
    g) Draw force and pressure diagrams.

21-5. Given: earth retaining system as follows: $H = 10$ ft; unit weight of saturated soil $\gamma_{sat} = 115$ lb/ft³; moisture content at full saturation $= 20\%$; $\phi = 35°$; $\phi = 20°$ (angle of wall friction).

Required: Determine by means of Culmann's method the magnitude of the total, active earth pressure per foot of run of retaining wall for the following conditions:

    a) free groundwater level through top of wall (point B);
    b) free groundwater table 10 ft below the top of wall (assume that backfill is capillary saturated);
    c) the groundwater table is 10 ft below the top of the wall, and backfill is dry; $G = 2.65$.
    d) For each of the following three conditions determine the position of the rupture plane, and report it by an angle.

21-6. What are the assumptions underlying the earth pressure theory?

21-7. Specialize the general K_a- and K_p-equations, and calculate E_a and E_p for the following conditions:

    a) $\alpha = 0$; $\quad \delta = (+)\delta$; $\quad \phi = \phi$; $\quad \phi_1 = 0$
    b) $\alpha = 0$; $\quad \delta = 0$; $\quad \phi = \phi_1$
    c) $\alpha = 0$; $\quad \delta = \phi_1$; $\quad \phi = \phi$
    d) $\alpha = 0$; $\quad \delta = \phi = \phi_1$
    e) $\alpha = \delta = \phi = \phi_1$
    f) $\alpha = (-)\alpha$; $\quad \delta = (-)\delta$; $\quad \phi = \phi$; $\quad \phi_1 = 0$

21-8. List as many possible forces as you know that may be acting singly or simultaneously on an earth retaining structure.

21-9. Given a wharf as shown in Fig. Prob. 21-9. Determine the magnitude of the active earth pressure for the most disadvantageous static conditions. Use Culmann's method of analysis. Also, indicate the position of the most dangerous rupture surface in the backfill soil.

21-10. Given an earth pressure system as shown in Fig. Prob. 21-10. Determine the active earth pressure, E_a, by the Poncelet graphical method, and locate the position of the most dangerous rupture surface.

21-11. Same problem as Prob. 21-10 but for passive case.

21-12. Construct a soil lateral stress distribution diagram against the wall for conditions as shown in Fig. Prob. 21-12. Also, indicate the stress ordinates algebraically and write an algebraic expression for the total active earth pressure, E_a, calculated by means of the soil lateral stress distribution diagram. Given: γ_w, γ, K_a, $\alpha = 0$, ϕ, $\phi_1 = 0$, $c = 0$, $\delta = 0$.

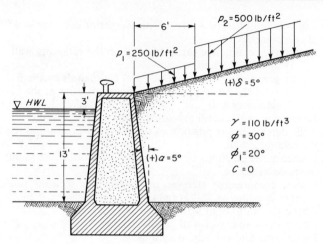

Fig. Problem 21-9.

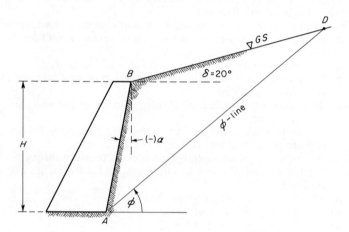

Fig. Problem 21-10.

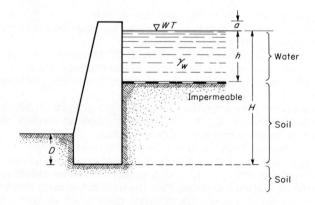

Fig. Problem 21-12.

Chapter 22

BEARING CAPACITY OF SOIL; DEPTH OF FOUNDATION

22-1. Stability Requirements of a Foundation. The stability of a foundation depends upon the safety of a soil against 1) its failure in shear (associated with plastic flow of the soil material underneath the foundation, and lateral expulsion of soil from underneath the footing of the foundation) and 2) excessive vertical displacement, or settlement, caused by the process of consolidation of the soil under the foundation (elastic and plastic deformation). Therefore, in order not to endanger the structure, these are the two independent foundation stability requirements, which must be met simultaneously: 1) there should be adequate safety against a shear failure within the soil mass, and 2) the probable differential and maximum settlements of the soil, viz., foundation, must be limited to safe, tolerable, acceptable magnitudes.

Naturally, the question arises: what is the maximum, allowable, contact pressure that can be imposed on a certain type of soil by a certain type, size, and shape of a structure without causing distress to the structure by either of these modes of failure?

This question leads to the problem of rating soils as to their bearing capacity.

22-2. Rating of Soil. A soil for supporting structural foundations is rated by expressing its ability to support load without failures or deformations within the soil mass. The rating is given in terms of *bearing capacity.*

Definitions. The contact area between the soil and the base of the footing on which the load rests is called the *loaded, or bearing area.*

Ultimate bearing capacity of a soil, σ_u, is understood to be the ultimate value of the average contact pressure, or stress, or load intensity transmitted by the base of the footing of the foundation to the soil, causing the soil mass to rupture, or fail in shear.

Naturally, the engineer has to provide for adequate safety against bearing capacity failure (in shear and/or settlement).

Safe bearing capacity, or *allowable pressure* on soil, σ_{adm}, is the ultimate bearing capacity divided by a factor of safety, η:

$$\sigma_{adm} = \frac{\sigma_u}{\eta}.$$

Depending upon the importance and kind of structure, the factor of safety used is from $\eta = 2$ to about $\eta = 5$.

Sometimes, when settlement is the governing factor in stability considerations of a foundation, bearing capacity of a soil means the load intensity or contact pressure that may be applied to the soil without causing intolerable settlement of the structure.

A limit imposed on the total settlement of any one structural element of a foundation is understood to be the *tolerable settlement*. Depending upon the type of the structure, whether statically determinate or statically indeterminate, tolerable settlements are usually set from about $\frac{1}{4}''$ to about $1.0''$. According to Terzaghi-Peck,[1] ordinary structures such as office buildings, apartment houses, or factories can withstand differential settlement between adjacent columns of $\frac{3}{4}''$. Accordingly, the safe bearing capacity of a soil is defined as the compressive stress on the soil that would bring about a predetermined amount of settlement, or tolerable settlement of the structure in question—a settlement which would not affect its function or structural integrity.

22-3. Sources of Obtaining Values of Soil Bearing Capacity. The sources for obtaining soil bearing capacity values for designing foundations are:
1) building codes, official regulations, and civil engineers' handbooks;
2) soil loading tests in place;
3) laboratory testing of soils, and
4) analytical methods of calculation.

22-4. Building Codes. When a construction job is contemplated within the jurisdiction of a building code—New York City, for example—the character of the soil at the level of the footings, and the safe bearing capacity of the soil upon which the structure is to be erected, must be ascertained by the methods directed by the code.

Building codes, official bridge and building specifications, and engineers' handbooks usually contain tables of the safe values of bearing capacities (or "presumptive" bearing capacities as termed by the building laws of the City of New York) for various types of soils and rocks. Such values are compiled in these tables based on many years of observations in practice.

Table 22-1 contains abridged excerpts from the National Building Code[2] and the Building Laws of the City of New York.[3] The values listed in this table are the maximum allowable bearing values.

Some books tabulating safe bearing values of soil include also a value for "quicksand". It should be remembered that there is no such soil type as "quicksand". Under proper hydraulic conditions any sand can be set into a "quick" condition.

Besides the tabulated safe bearing values of soils, the National Building Code, for example, provides on p. 115 that

" ... *b*) Where portions of the foundation of an entire building or structure rest directly upon, or are underlain by, medium or soft clay upon different materials, or where the layers of such softer materials vary greatly in thickness, the magnitude and distribution of the probable settlement shall be investigated, and, if necessary, the allowable loads shall be *reduced* or special provisions made in the design of the building or structure to prevent serious differential settlements which will impair the safety of the structure.

c) Where the bearing materials directly under a foundation overlie a stratum having smaller allowable bearing values, such smaller values shall not be exceeded at the level of such stratum. Computation of the vertical pressure in the bearing materials at any depth below a foundation shall be made on the assumption that the load is spread uniformly at an angle of 60° with the horizontal".

The Boston Building Code of 1944, Section 2904c, for example, permits an increase in the allowable pressure on sound rocks (shale, slate, schist) if the

TABLE 22-1. SOIL BEARING VALUES
PRESUMPTIVE CAPACITY IN TONS PER SQUARE FOOT

Clay, soft, medium	1 to 1.5
Clay, stiff, medium	2.5
Clay, compact	2
Clay, hard	5
Sand, fine, loose	2
Sand-clay soils, compact	3
Sand-clay soils, loose, saturated	1
Sand, coarse, loose;	
compact fine;	
and gravel mixture, loose	3
compact, with inorganic silt	2
Gravel, loose; and compact coarse sand	4 to 6
inorganic silt soils	4 to 6
Sand-gravel mixture, compact	6
very compact	10
Hardpan and exceptionally compacted or	
partially cemented gravels or sands	10 to 12
Rock, soft	8
medium hard	40
hard, sound	60
Sedimentary rocks:	
shale	8 to 10
hard shales	8 to 10
limestones	10 to 20
sandstones	10 to 20
chalk and coral	8
Foliated rocks:	
schist, and slate in sound condition	40
Massive bedrock (igneous rocks):	
basalt, diorite, diabase, granite, lava,	
trap rock in sound condition	20 to 40 to 100
Metamorphic rocks:	
gneiss	100
marble	10 to 20
schist	20 to 40
slate	8

depth of the base of the footing is greater than 2' below the ground surface. The increase is 20% for each foot of additional depth, but shall not exceed twice the tabulated values.[4] For example, if a footing is to be placed on a sound shale at $z = 5$ ft below the ground surface, then the allowable contact pressure σ_o on this shale is

$$\sigma_o = \sigma_{allow} + 0.20(z - 2.0)\sigma_{allow} = 10[1 + 0.20(5 - 2)] = 16\,t/ft^2, \quad (22\text{-}1)$$

where $\sigma_{allow} = 10$ t/ft^2 is the allowable contact pressure on sound shale at a 2-ft depth tabulated by the Boston Building Code.

The maximum allowable pressure, σ_{max}, from 7 ft on below the ground surface is

$$\sigma_{max} = (2)(\sigma_{allow}) = \sigma_{allow} + (0.2)(7.0 - 2.0)\sigma_{allow} = (2)(10) = 20\,(t/ft^2). \quad (22\text{-}2)$$

Provisions for increasing the bearing capacity of various soils on account of depth of foundations are also described in the Boston Building Code of 1944, Section 2904.

The allowable soil bearing capacity may also be reduced by building authorities on account of mechanical vibrations and earthquakes in localities and regions where the latter occur, or if the soil boring log indicates a possibility of consolidation in deep soft layers of soil, or where a flow of water through soil takes place.

Every application for increasing the soil bearing value must usually be supported by pertinent facts based on test, or sometimes by theoretical considerations.

22-5. Summary on Bearing Capacity of Soils as Tabulated by Building Codes. Inspection of building code tables for safe bearing capacities of soils reveals:

1) By specifying one bearing capacity value or a range of values, the concept of a bearing capacity of a certain type of soil is usually greatly oversimplified.

2) Usually the building codes tacitly assume that the allowable soil bearing capacity is based only on the general descriptive character of the soil in respect to the types concerned, such as gravel, sand, clay—stiff and/or soft.

3) The tabulated soil types neglect to report density, moisture content of soil, variation in soil type, thickness and dip of these soil layers, effect of groundwater, compressibility, or any other soil property which may affect the value of soil bearing capacity. It is known that in reality the allowable bearing capacity values for each type of soil under various circumstances may differ considerably from those compiled in the building codes.

4) The building codes usually do not indicate how and by what method the tabulated soil bearing capacity values are obtained.

5) For normal cases the building codes usually consider soil bearing capacity to be independent of the size, shape, and depth of the footing. It is known that the ultimate bearing capacity of soil depends upon the properties of the soil, the depth of foundation, the size of the footing, and the shape of the bearing area of the footing. The codes usually say nothing as to

the shape and size of loaded (bearing) areas on soil tested, i.e., whether the tabulated bearing capacity values are applicable to large or small footings, or to circular or strip footings. One must realize that it is impossible to assign to various soil types allowable soil bearing capacity values which can be used under all circumstances, for small and large footings alike, and at all depths below the ground surface. Nor do building codes usually say for what depth of foundation below the ground surface the tabulated soil bearing capacity values are valid. Some building codes, though, say that the base of the footing must be founded below the depth of frost penetration.

6) Likewise, the building code tables do not state whether the tabulated bearing capacity values of the indicated soil types are applicable to statically determinate or statically indeterminate structures, or to temporary or permanent structures.

7) Bearing capacity of soil cannot be expressed by fixed figures like those in the building codes. Bearing capacity is a variable quantity depending upon many factors.

8) Building codes are usually not up to date.

Regardless of all of these deficiencies inherent in the soil bearing capacity values as compiled in the various building codes, these soil bearing capacity values are helpful in selecting a soil bearing value to use in that locality for which the building codes are written, provided the bearing capacity values are prepared and tabulated based on actual experience with soils in that locality.

Many engineers use soil bearing capacity values, selected from building codes, in preliminary design of foundations and earthworks. However, it should be kept in mind that building codes do not protect one against failure, nor exempt one from responsibility if failure of the structure occurs due to excessive settlement or rupture of soil, or both. Therefore, it appears to be more appropriate to obtain the necessary soil bearing capacity values from field and laboratory tests of soils.

22-6. Soil Loading Tests. According to the American Standard Building Code Requirements for Excavations and Foundations,[5] whenever the allowable load on a bearing soil material is in doubt, it should be determined by field loading tests. From the code descriptions of such tests it appears that the tests are static loading tests.

A soil static loading test in the field is essentially a model test of a prototype foundation. The purpose of the soil loading test is to determine the ultimate bearing capacity of a soil, from which the safe bearing capacity of soil could be established. The loading test can also be made use of for determining the load-contact settlement characteristics of the soil in its natural condition for the purpose of predicting bearing capacity and settlement of soil under a full-scale prototype foundation. The soil loading test also gives some information about the elastic deformation of the soil in place. The results of the soil loading test are to be interpreted for a full-scale foundation, the interpretation being based on the corresponding theory.

Soil static loading tests in the field are also performed in order to check the soil bearing capacity values tabulated in building codes, or to ascertain a bearing capacity value in localities where there are no official building ordinances.

The method for performing a soil static loading test is also regulated by the various building codes. The ASCE code, for example, says that the soil shall be tested in one or more places and at such levels as the conditions may warrant. The codes usually specify that for foundations a quadratic loading plate or concrete block, 1 to 2 sq ft in size, should be used.

For the evaluation of the bearing capacity of soil for highway pavement support, loading plates 30 in. in diameter are employed.

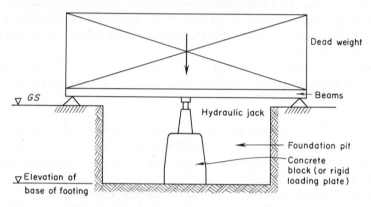

FIG. 22-1   Principle of a device for soil static loading test.

A device for performing a direct soil static loading test is illustrated in Fig. 22-1. It consists of a stiff loading or bearing plate or a concrete slab or block upon which a hydraulic jack is supported. The jack exerts pressure against the dead weight on the platform inducing a reaction, and transfers the pressure to the soil.

A direct soil static load test can also be performed without the jack. The pressure, transferred to the soil, is obtained by loading the bearing block directly with dead weight, the weight having been placed on a platform erected on top of the bearing block.

The plate and/or block must be centrally loaded by direct weight or by means of a measured pressure at the elevation of the base of the footing at the construction site.

The dead weights may be water, bags of sand, rocks, bricks, bars of pig-iron, or any other material suitable for loading purposes.

The settlements or vertical displacements of the base of the loading blocks are measured at three points by means of a leveling instrument, dial gages, or are automatically recorded continuously. Measurements should be in reference to points which remain stable during the test.

Settlements are normally measured every hour during the first 6 hours after each load increment has been applied, and at least once every 12 hours thereafter.

The ASCE Code, for example, provides that the loading under each increment shall not exceed 25% of the proposed safe load. Increments shall be added until the pressure on the soil is 50% in excess of the proposed load.

The load increment remains on the loading plate until settlement has ceased, but for not less than 24 hours. After settlement has ceased, an additional 50% load, for example, is applied, and the corresponding settlements are measured. Measurements shall be made with an accuracy to 0.01 in., and preferably to 0.001 in.

The load increment which makes the total unit load on the soil equal to the proposed safe load, and the increment which makes a 50% excess load shall be maintained until the settlement in 8 hours is less than 0.01 in. Intermediate increments of load shall be maintained until the rate of settlement is less than 0.01 in. per hour.

As to the criteria for safe loading, the proposed safe load shall be allowed if the increment of settlement obtained under the 50% overload does not exceed 60% settlement obtained under the proposed safe load. The settlement under the allowable load shall not exceed $\frac{1}{2}$ in. If, at the proposed safe load, the above conditions are not satisfied, the allowable safe load shall be determined by selecting a reduced load from the load-settlement diagram, such that the above conditions are satisfied.

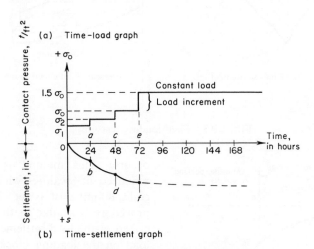

FIG. 22-2   Soil loading test graph.

To perform a direct soil static loading test, one must become familiar with the building code in question.

The data from the soil loading test, such as load, settlement, and time are conveniently presented in a graphical form as shown in Fig. 22-2. Field test results of soil loading may also be presented graphically, as shown in Fig. 22-3.

If it is desired to obtain the ultimate bearing capacity of a soil, then the direct static loading test of soil is performed till failure, i.e., till rupture of the soil

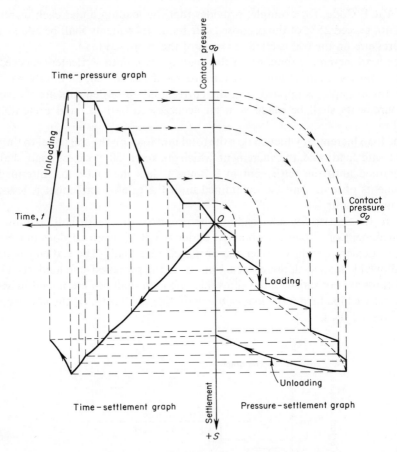

FIG. 22-3   Field loading test graphs.

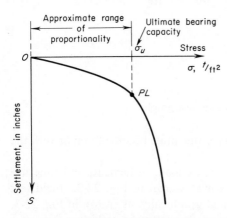

FIG. 22-4   Nature of direct soil static loading graph.

occurs. This method is sometimes practiced in localities where building codes do not exist as yet. The loading procedure is similar to that just described in the load-settlement test: the load on the loading block is applied in increments, and settlements are measured. The next load increment is applied after the settlement caused by the previous load increment has ceased. During the first stage of loading, the settlements increase almost linearly with load, Fig. 22-4. After the limit of proportionality, *P.L.*, has been exceeded at the so-called critical load, the rate of settlement rapidly increases: disproportionally under the compressive stress σ_u, the shear strength of the soil, is soon exhausted and a progressive settlement of the loaded block takes place in the soil. The block has been loaded to failure of soil. The compressive stress, σ_u, causing failure of soil is characterized as the ultimate bearing capacity of soil. The safe soil bearing capacity for design purposes is assumed to be a fraction of the ultimate bearing capacity.

The ASCE Code warns against choosing soil bearing values directly from the results of loading tests without due regard for significant factors, such as soft underlying strata or the effect of loading different-sized areas. Load tests have been denounced by many authorities, mainly because too often the results of small-scale tests have been used indiscriminately, without adequate investigation or analysis.

22-7. Summary on Field Loading Tests of Soil Bearing Materials

1) For reasons of economy direct soil static loading tests can be performed only over relatively small loading areas, 1 or 2 sq ft—because large loading areas require large dead loads, more attention, more people, and more time.

2) Because soil loading tests performed with small loading areas, whether on the ground surface or in test pits, are inevitably accompanied by lateral expulsion of soil from underneath the base of the footing, giving larger settlements than they are supposed to give, the test results do not reflect directly the actual settlement of the prototype foundation.

3) The effect of surface loading of relatively small loading areas at the elevation of the foundation does not extend deep enough where soil layers may be encountered having less bearing capacity than at the surface. Therefore, small loading plate tests have an unsatisfactory value for cohesive soils in respect to long-term consolidation, because consolidation of soil takes time, whereas the loading test allows only a fraction of the time needed for full consolidation. They may be satisfactory, however, in noncohesive soils.

4) The effects of deep foundations cannot be directly ascertained by surface loading.

5) The amount of settlement of loaded areas varies with the size of the area. Likewise the bearing capacity of soil depends upon the size of the loading area, as well as upon its shape, and whether the block is or is not constrained around by a surcharge. From this point of view, the ultimate load causing rupture in soil by surface loading is not the same for the prototype foundation. Therefore, it is well to keep in mind the scale of the soil loading test, particularly on cohesive soils, if the small scale test results are to be applied to the prototype structure.

6) Besides the size of the foundation, the elastic properties of the loading plate and of the foundation material, and the mode, type, and intensity of loading also affects the soil loading test results.

7) A careful study of bearing capacity data obtained from bearing tests in

the field on non-cohesive soils may result in reasonably accurate values of the ultimate bearing capacity.

8) The bearing capacity data obtained from bearing tests in the field on cohesive soils are of the nature of the short-period loading test. Therefore, it is very difficult to evaluate from such tests the bearing capacity for a full-scale prototype foundation which will be in position over a long period of time.

9) The cost of field loading tests on clay cannot nowadays be justified when soil borings, undisturbed soil samples, soil compression and consolidation tests can conveniently and economically be made and/or obtained.

From the foregoing discussion it seems that it will never be possible to specify exact allowable soil bearing capacity values which will be universally applicable to the design of foundations because of the many variable properties of soil and the different loading conditions of various structures.

Regardless of the aforementioned deficiencies of small-scale loading tests of soil, these tests with relatively small loading areas are also of some value, namely, the small-scale tests help one to understand what takes place in a loaded mass of soil when its shear strength is exhausted. Also, if the ground surface at the base of the elevation of the footing cannot support loads safely on the small loading areas, the soil would perform, probably, even less satisfactorily under a large, permanently applied load.

The small-scale testing method is also of some value in exploring and comparing local irregularities of the soil at a construction site. The small-scale model test results, when modeled for its prototype by means of the theory of similitude, may render a relatively satisfactory insight into the real conditions.

22-8. Housel's Bearing Capacity Method. Based on his extensive experimental research work Housel[6,7,8] proposed to determine the bearing capacity of clayey soils for a prototype foundation by two small-scale model tests, using one smaller loading area ($1' \times 1'$, for example) and one larger loading area ($2' \times 2'$, or $3' \times 3'$, or $4' \times 4'$, for example) without exceeding a certain allowable settlement, say $\frac{1}{2}''$. The method is known as the "Perimeter-Area Ratio".

Housel expresses the total allowable load, W, in lb, on a bearing area of soil to produce a predetermined settlement by a linear relationship as

$$W = \sigma A + mL = A\sigma_o \qquad (22\text{-}3)$$

where σ = developed contact pressure in lb/ft^2 under the bearing area (or an experimental constant);

   A = area, in ft^2, of the bearing area;

   m = an empirical constant with no physical contents, having a compound unit of lb/ft, to be consistent in units in Eq. (22-3);

   L = length of perimeter of the bearing area, in ft; and

   σ_o = pressure, in lb/ft^2, on any real design footing to give a certain magnitude of settlement.

Housel assumes that σ_o and m are constant for any plate loaded with the critical load to give a predetermined settlement.

A division of Eq. (22-3) by area, A, yields

$$\sigma_o = \sigma + m \frac{L}{A}, \tag{22-4}$$

where L/A = perimeter-area ratio, in $(\text{ft})^{-1}$. According to Housel, the quantity $(m)(L/A)$ in Eq. (22-4) expresses an equivalent pressure, which added to the developed contact pressure, σ, gives the total equivalent pressure, σ_o, with which the bearing area can be loaded to give a certain allowable settlement of the footing.

The two quantities, σ and m, are unknown; therefore, two equations are needed. The two equations are obtained experimentally from two different loading tests performed on the same soil on two different size bearing areas to attain under both bearing plates the same amount of settlement which would be tolerated under the prototype foundation:

$$\left.\begin{aligned} \sigma_{o1} &= \sigma + m \frac{L_1}{A_1} \\[2mm] \sigma_{o2} &= \sigma + m \frac{L_2}{A_2} \end{aligned}\right\} \tag{22-5}$$

The simultaneous solution of the system of the two equations gives the σ and m values. If the perimeter-area ratio of the prototype foundation is L_3/A_3, then the bearing capacity of the soil under the prototype foundation is calculated by Eq. (22-5):

$$\sigma_{o3} = \sigma + m \frac{L_3}{A_3} \tag{22-6}$$

One notes that the determination of W_3 (viz., σ_{o3}) is an extrapolation from the values of W_1 and W_2, or σ_{o1} and σ_{o2}, respectively.

Example. The application of the perimeter-area ratio method may be demonstrated by the following example.

Given loading areas on a clay: $A_1 = 1$ ft²; $L_1 = 4$ ft.
$$A_2 = 4 \text{ ft}^2; \quad L_2 = 8 \text{ ft.}$$

These areas were loaded with $W_1 = 7000$ lb, and
$$W_2 = 21000 \text{ lb}$$

to attain under each of the two loading plates a settlement of $\frac{1}{2}''$.

Calculate the size of the prototype foundation, square in shape, to transmit a load of $W = 260,000$ lb.

Solution. The constants, σ and m, by Eq. (22-3):

$$\left.\begin{aligned} 7000 &= (1)\sigma + (4)(m) \\ 21000 &= (4)\sigma + (8)(m) \end{aligned}\right\}$$

$$\therefore \quad \sigma = 3500 \text{ lb/ft}^2$$
$$m = 875 \text{ lb/ft}^2$$

By Eq. (22-3),

$$260000 = (3500)(a)^2 + (875)(4a),$$

where $a = 8.13$ ft = length of side of the prototype square footing to bring about $\frac{1}{2}''$ settlement.
The contact pressure, σ_{o3}, is then

$$\sigma_{o3} = \frac{W}{A} = \frac{260000}{(8.13)^2} \approx 3933 \ (\text{lb/ft})^2 \approx 1.97 \ \text{t/ft}^2 \approx 2 \ \text{kg/cm}^2.$$

This problem demonstrates that the contact pressure, 3933 lb/ft², is different from that under the small loading area $\left(= \frac{7000}{(1)^2} = 7000 \ \text{lb/ft}^2 \right)$, and also different under the

large loading area $\left(= \dfrac{21000}{4} = 5250 \ \text{lb/ft}^2 \right)$.

22-9. Summary on Housel's Perimeter-Area Ratio Method.
1) The perimeter-area ratio method, in essence, is a narrow range model test, and demonstrates that the bearing capacity on soil depends, among other things, upon the size of the quadratic loading areas.
2) In reality for full scale foundations, the perimeter-area ratio, L/A, may approach a very small quantity. Therefore the term $(m)(L/A)$ in Eq. (22-5) may be set equal to zero, resulting in $\sigma_o = \sigma$.
3) The pressure distribution in soil from a large footing, viz., the depth of the active zone in the soil, is greater than for the small test loading plates. Hence, settlement of clay can be expected to turn out to be larger than that used in the test loading to find the constants σ and m in Eq. (22-3).
4) Errors made in performing the two small-scale tests will magnify, in extrapolating from the small-scale test results a bearing capacity value or the size of footing for the actual prototype foundation, considerably relative to the actual conditions.
5) The perimeter-area ratio method gives satisfactory results for three loading areas the sizes of which vary within a very narrow range.

22-10. Laboratory Testing of Soils. The bearing capacity of a cohesive soil can also be evaluated from the unconfined compressive strength ($\sigma_3 = 0$) at failure. By Eq. (19-31), the bearing capacity of a cohesive soil is the value of the major principal stress, σ_1, at failure in shear or by bulging. This stress at failure is termed the unconfined compressive stress, or the ultimate stress, q_u:

$$\sigma_1 = q_u = 2c \tan(45° + \phi/2) \tag{22-7}$$

or

$$\sigma_1 = q_u. \tag{22-8}$$

When $\phi = 0$, then the ultimate bearing capacity of the cohesive soil is

$$q_u = 2c \tag{22-9}$$

at the ground surface where $h = 0$. The safe bearing capacity is then the ultimate bearing capacity divided by a factor of safety, η, for which 3 is usually used as a normal figure:

$$\sigma_{\text{adm}} = \frac{q_u}{\eta}. \tag{19-10}$$

According to A. Casagrande and R. Fadum,[9] the allowable soil pressures commonly specified in building codes are conservative from the standpoint of safety against rupture of the clay; therefore, the indirect check of the ultimate bearing capacity of cohesive soil by means of the soil cylinder compression test is entirely satisfactory. Besides, compression tests on undisturbed cohesive soil cylinders are usually much less expensive than loading tests performed on sufficiently large bearing areas.

ANALYTICAL METHODS FOR CALCULATING SOIL BEARING CAPACITY

The soil bearing capacity can be calculated by means of
a) the theory of elasticity
b) the classical earth pressure theory
c) the theory of plasticity and
d) experimental results.

22-11. Soil Bearing Capacity Calculations by Means of the Theory of Elasticity. In an analysis based on the theory of elasticity, and the use of Boussinesq's principle of vertical stress distribution in an elastic, isotropic medium where E and m are constant throughout and Hooke's law is valid, Schleicher[10] integrated the vertical stresses caused by a uniformly distributed surface load, and obtained an expression for the elastic settlements, s, of soil directly underneath a perfectly elastic loading or bearing slab:

$$s = \omega \frac{\sigma_o \sqrt{A}}{E} \frac{m^2 - 1}{m^2},\tag{22-11}$$

where ω = form or shape coefficient, a coefficient dependent upon the degree of the stiffness of the loaded or bearing slab, shape of the bearing area, mode of distribution of the total load, P, and position of any point on the bearing slab for which the settlement is sought;

σ_o = contact pressure from slab to soil;

A = area of bearing slab;

E = so-called modulus of elasticity of soil; and

$\mu = \varepsilon_{long}/\varepsilon_{lat} = 0.5$ = Poisson's ratio where ε_{long} = strain in the longitudinal direction;

$m = 1/\mu$, and ε_{lat} = strain in the lateral direction.

Note that the settlement is not of the same magnitude at all points under an elastic slab. Under a rigid slab, settlements are the same under all points.

If in Eq. (22-11) the following substitution is made

$$E \frac{m^2}{m^2 - 1} = \frac{E}{1 - \mu^2} = C,\tag{22-12}$$

where $\mu = 0.5$ = Poisson's ratio when $m = 2$, Schleicher's equation transforms into

$$s = \omega \frac{\sigma_o \sqrt{A}}{C}.\tag{22-13}$$

The coefficient, ω, is different for circular and for rectangular areas.

The maximum settlement occurs at the center of the circular and rectangular bearing plates. The minimum settlement occurs at the rim of the circular bearing area, or at the free corners of a rectangular bearing area. These settlements occur when the soil underneath the bearing area and in the vicinity of the influence of the bearing area is uniform. The Schleicher's shape coefficients for flexible bearing slabs are compiled in Table 22-2.

TABLE 22-2. SCHLEICHER'S SHAPE COEFFICENTS, ω

Shape of Bearing Area	Side Ratio a/b	$\omega_{max} = \omega_M$ Center Point, M	$\omega_{min} = \omega_A$ Free Corner Point A	ω_B Midpoint of Short Side, B	ω_C Midpoint of Long Side, C	ω Average
1	2	3	4	5	6	7
Circle	—	1.13	0.72	0.72	0.72	0.96
Square	1.0	1.12	0.56	0.76	0.76	0.95
Rectangle	1.5	1.11	0.55	0.73	0.79	0.94
,,	2	1.08	0.54	0.69	0.79	0.92
,,	3	1.03	0.51	0.64	0.78	0.88
,,	5	0.94	0.47	0.57	0.75	0.82
,,	10	0.80	0.40	0.47	0.67	0.71
,,	100	0.40	0.20	0.22	0.36	0.37
,,	1000	0.173	0.087	0.093	0.159	0.163
,,	10000	0.069	0.035	0.037	0.065	0.066

If in the Schleicher's elastic settlement equation (22-13) the following quantities are known:

the tolerable settlement, s

the shape coefficient, ω

the size, A, of the loading area, and

the soil properties comprehended under C,

then by Eq. (22-13) the soil bearing capacity, σ_o, can be calculated:

$$\sigma_o = \frac{s\,C}{\omega\sqrt{A}}. \qquad (22\text{-}14)$$

The elastic settlement equation also permits deriving the following rule: the settlement ratio, s_1/s_2, brought about by two bearing areas of similar shape but of different sizes, A_1 and A_2, respectively, when loaded with equal contact pressures, σ_o, equal the square root of the A_1/A_1-ratio, i.e,

$$\frac{s_1}{s_2} = \frac{\omega\,\sigma_o\sqrt{A_1}}{\omega\,\sigma_o\sqrt{A_2}} = \sqrt{\frac{A_1}{A_2}} \qquad (22\text{-}15)$$

This rule, expressing a model law, is useful in calculating the settlement of a prototype foundation, say s_1, if with a model the attained settlement under the same contact pressure σ_o was measured to be, say s_2.

This derivation helps also to clarify some of the shortcomings of the method of the field bearing capacity tests of soils. For example, according to the theory of elasticity, if in the field bearing test a bearing slab of $A_2 = 2' \times 2' = 4$ ft^2 were loaded with a contact pressure of $\sigma_o = 3$ t/ft^2 and the settlement thus attained was measured to be $s_2 = 0.75'' = 0.0625'$, then the prototype foundation the bearing area of which is $A_1 = 13' \times 13' = 169$ ft^2 will settle under the same contact pressure of $\sigma_o = 3$ t/ft^2 by an amount of

$$s_1 = s_2 \sqrt{\frac{A_1}{A_2}} = (0.0625)\sqrt{\frac{169}{4}} = 0.40625 \text{ (ft)},$$

or the large foundation will settle 6.5 times more than the small bearing slab used in the field bearing test of soil.

Example. Calculate the elastic settlement of a rectangular foundation the size of which is $(2b) = 20$ ft by $(2a) = 40$ ft. The foundation is laid on a soil which is a uniform sand having a value of $E = 200$ t/ft^2, and a value of Poisson's ratio of $\mu = 0.20$. The contact pressure is $\sigma_o = 2.0$ t/ft^2. Calculate settlements under points A, B, C, and M by means of Schleicher's formula.

Solution. The coefficient, C, in the settlement equation is calculated by Eq. (22-12) a

$$C = \frac{E}{1 - \mu^2} = \frac{200}{1 - (0.2)^2} = 208.4 \approx \underline{210 \text{ (t/ft}^2)}$$

The side ratio:

$$a/b = 20/10 = 2.$$

Area:

$$A = (2a)(2b) = (40)(20) = \underline{800 \text{ (ft}^2)}$$
$$\sqrt{A} = \sqrt{800} = 28.3 \text{ (ft)}$$

Settlement under elastic foundation:
Settlement at free corner, A:

$$s_A = \frac{\omega_A \sigma_o \sqrt{A}}{C} = \frac{(0.54)(2.0)(28.3)}{210} = \underline{0.135 \text{ ft} = 1.620 \text{ in.}}$$

Settlement at point B:

$$s_B = \frac{(0.69)(2.0)(28.3)}{210} = 0.173 \text{ ft} = \underline{2.076 \text{ in.}}$$

Settlement at point C:

$$s_C = \frac{(0.79)(2.0)(28.3)}{210} = 0.198 \text{ ft} = \underline{2.376 \text{ in.}}$$

Settlement under center point, M:

$$s_M = \frac{(1.08)(2.0)(28.3)}{210} = 0.270 \text{ ft} = \underline{3.240 \text{ in.}}$$

Settlement under rigid foundation:

$$s_{const} = \frac{\omega \sigma_o \sqrt{\overline{A}}}{C} = \frac{(0.88)(2.0)(28.3)}{210} = 0.220 \text{ ft} = \underline{2.643 \text{ in.}}$$

Again, if the tolerable settlement is $s = 3.24$ in. $= s_M$, then the bearing capacity, σ_o, can be calculated.

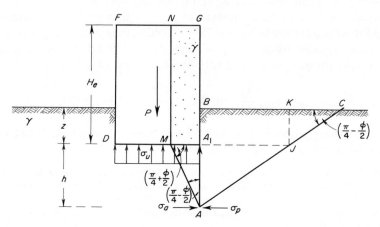

FIG. 22-5   Expulsion of soil from underneath a foundation after Pauker.

22-12. Soil Bearing Capacity Calculations by Means of the Classical Earth Pressure Theory. The classical earth pressure theory assumes that on exceeding a certain stress condition, rupture surfaces are formed in the soil mass. Thus, the stress, developing upon the formation of rupture surfaces, may be considered as the ultimate bearing capacity of the soil.

Based on the above assumption, the soil bearing capacity can be determined

a) from the relation of the principal stresses which occur upon the formation of the rupture surfaces. The pertinent theories are those by Pauker, Rankine, Ritter, Terzaghi, and possibly others;

b) from the shape of the rupture surfaces. The principal forms of rupture surfaces used in engineering practice are: broken planes, circular, circular with a tangent, logarithmically spiralled, logarithmically spiraled with a tangent, and cycloids;

c) from the mode of expulsion of the ruptured soil mass from underneath the base of the footing, i.e., one-sidedly and two-sidedly.

Hence it can be seen that the calculated bearing capacity of soil may be of different magnitude depending upon the assumptions used.

22-13. Pauker's Method. One of the oldest formulas for the determination of soil bearing capacity and depth of laying of foundations is that given by Pauker.[11,12,13] Colonel Pauker was a Russian military engineer, and derived his formula while constructing fortifications and sea-batteries in the 1850's for the Czarist naval base of Kronstadt. In his derivations Pauker operated skillfully with Coulomb's earth pressure theory.

Pauker's theory is good for sandy soils, but not for cohesive ones, although the effect of cohesion can also be considered. His theory was once very popular in the technical literature and was extensively used in the pre-revolutionary days in Czarist Russia.

The principle of Pauker's theory is the equilibrium condition of a point, say, point A, within a soil mass, Fig. 22-5. The horizontal surface, $A_1 D$, of the soil mass underneath the base of the footing, z units deep below the ground surface, is loaded with a uniformly distributed, normal, ultimate contact pressure, σ_u, from an infinitely long strip of foundation. The formula is derived based on the classical earth pressure theory of an ideal soil under the following assumptions.

1) The soil is non-cohesive. Resistance to shear in the soil mass is therefore afforded by frictional forces only.

2) The weight of the structural load, or the ultimate contact pressure, σ_u, on $A_1 D$ is replaced by an equivalent height, H_e, (or head) of soil whose unit weight, γ, is the same as that of the soil in which the foundation is laid:

$$H_e = \frac{\sigma_u}{\gamma}, \tag{22-16}$$

where H_e = equivalent height of soil, in feet

σ_u = uniformly distributed, ultimate, or critical contact pressure on soil, in t/ft^2, and

γ = unit weight of soil, in t/ft^3.

3) It is assumed that, if the ultimate bearing capacity of the soil under the footing is exhausted, and an excessive settlement of soil takes place, then an arbitrary part, for example, part $A_1 MNG$, would tear off from the equivalent layer, $A_1 DFG$, along a line, say MN. Thereupon the torn-off part can itself drop down independently of that part of the equivalent layer, $NMDF$, which remains in position.

4) Imagine a vertical section, $A_1 A$, underneath the base of the footing. Under the influence of the weight of the equivalent layer whose height is H_e, the soil particles which are to the left of the imaginary section, $A_1 A$, tend to displace to the right, inducing on $A_1 A$ an active earth pressure.

5) These soil particles which are to the right of $A_1 A$, induce to the left, on $A_1 A$, an earth resistance (passive earth pressure) against the active earth pressure from the left.

6) The equilibrium condition at point A, located h units deep below the base of the footing, tearing off an earth mass, $A_1 MNG$, from the equivalent soil layer, is determined by the equilibrium of the soil prisms, $\triangle AMA_1$, and $\square ABKJ$. The angle of friction of the soil, ϕ, on the imaginary section, AA_1, is assumed to be zero. Hence, the earth pressures from left and right act normal against AA_1, i.e., horizontally.

7) According to Pauker, the analytical expression for such a condition of the lateral stability of point A, to obviate sliding, is

$$\sigma_p \geqslant \sigma_a, \tag{22-17}$$

where σ_p = lateral stress at point A from passive earth pressure, and
σ_a = lateral stress at point A from active earth pressure.
From earth pressure theory:

$$\sigma_p = \gamma(z + h)\tan^2(45° + \phi/2) \tag{22-18}$$

$$\sigma_a = \gamma(H_e + h)\tan^2(45° - \phi/2), \tag{22-19}$$

where ϕ = angle of internal friction of soil.

Substituting Eqs. (22-18) and (22-19) into Eq. (22-17) and dividing both sides
of the expression so obtained by

$$(H_e + h)\tan^2(45° + \phi/2), \tag{22-20}$$

and noting that

$$\frac{\tan^2(45° - \phi/2)}{\tan^2(45° + \phi/2)} = \tan^4(45° - \phi/2), \tag{22-21}$$

obtain

$$\frac{z + h}{H_e + h} \geq \tan^4(45° - \phi/2). \tag{22-22}$$

According to equilibrium conditions, the most dangerous point, A, in section
AA_1 is that for which the expression

$$\frac{z + h}{H_e + h} \tag{22-23}$$

is minimum.

By inspection, the expression is at its minimum value when $h = 0$. Thus, the
most dangerous point, A, against expulsion laterally and out from underneath
the base of the footing is directly under the edge, A_1 (at $h = 0$), of the base of
the footing.

Equation (22-22) then takes the form

$$\frac{z}{H_e} \geq \tan^4(45° - \phi/2). \tag{22-24}$$

The limiting equilibrium at point A_1 is known as Pauker's equation, which
gives the necessary depth of the foundation:

$$z = H_e \tan^4(45° - \phi/2) \tag{22-25}$$

or, with $H_e = \dfrac{\sigma_u}{\gamma}$,

$$z = \frac{\sigma_u}{\gamma} \tan^4(45° - \phi/2). \tag{22-26}$$

As can be seen, Pauker's formula can be used for determining the depth of
the foundation, z, if the ultimate bearing capacity, σ_u, the unit weight of the
sandy soil, γ, and the angle of internal friction, ϕ, of that soil are known.

If the depth, z, of the foundation is known, then the ultimate bearing capacity is

$$\sigma_u = \gamma z \tan^4(45° + \phi/2). \tag{22-27}$$

The bearing capacity increases linearly with depth, z.

Pauker's formula is a simple one, but it has some limitations, namely: if $z = 0$ (as on the ground surface), then by this formula the bearing capacity is $\sigma_u = 0$. This contradicts the reality, because the soil at the ground surface has some bearing capacity to support a load. This result arises from not including in the equation the unit weight of soil of the rupturing soil wedge below the footing. Therefore Pauker's formula is valid only when $z > 0$. When $\phi = 0$, then $\sigma_u = \gamma z$, or $H_e = z$. Also, Pauker's equation does not consider the width of the foundation. Then, the two rupture surfaces in the sand are assumed to be planes which change their directions in a discontinuous way (MA and AC). The angle of internal friction at the vertical plane, AA_1, is not taken into account.

Whatever deficiencies were inherent in the reasoning in Pauker's theory, they were compensated by a factor of safety of $\eta = 1.5$ to $\eta = 3.0$, thus obtaining a safe bearing capacity of an ideal, granular soil.

Note that the derivation of Pauker's formula is based on the presupposition that no plastic deformations are permitted to develop in the soil underneath the foundation. Therefore, the allowable bearing capacity, by Pauker's equation, does not depend upon the width of the foundation. If plastic deformations in soil were permitted to develop underneath the whole width of the footing of the foundation, then the soil bearing capacity would be directly proportional to the width of the footing.

Example 1. If the depth of a foundation is $z = 8.21$ ft below the ground surface, the unit weight of soil is $\gamma = 95$ lb/ft³, and the angle of internal friction of the soil is $\phi = 28°$, calculate by means of Pauker's formula the ultimate bearing capacity of the soil and the allowable bearing capacity, using a factor of safety of $\eta = 2.0$.
Solution.

$$\tan^4(45° + \phi/2) = \tan^4(45° + 28°/2) = \tan^4(59°) = (1.664)^4 = 7.665.$$

By Eq. (22.27), the ultimate bearing capacity is

$$\sigma_u = (95)(8.21)(7.665) = 5978.7 \text{ (lb/ft}^2) \approx 3.0 \text{ (t/ft}^2).$$

The allowable bearing capacity, with $\eta = 2.0$, is

$$\sigma_{allow} = \sigma_u/\eta = 3.0/2 = 1.5 \text{ (t/ft}^2).$$

Example 2. If the ultimate bearing capacity of a sand deposit is 3.0 t/ft², the unit weight of soil is $\gamma = 95$ lb/ft², and the angle of internal friction of the sand is $\phi = 28°$, calculate by Pauker's method the depth of laying of foundation, z, using a factor of safety of $\eta = 2.0$.
Solution. By Eq. (22.26), the depth is

$$z_1 = \frac{(3.0)(2000)}{95} \tan^4(45° - 28°/2) = (63.15)(0.6)^4 \approx 8.21 \quad \text{(ft)}.$$

For $\eta = 2.0$,

$$z = z_1\eta = (8.21)(2.0) = 16.42 \text{ (ft)}.$$

22-14. Rankine's Formula.[14] Based on the theory of stress limit equilibrium conditions in an ideal soil at a point, the ratio of the major and minor principal stresses and a plane rupture surface, Rankine calculated the bearing capacity of soil as

$$\sigma_u = \gamma z \left(\frac{1 + \sin \phi}{1 - \sin \phi}\right)^2, \tag{22-28}$$

where $\sigma_u = \sigma_1$ = major principal stress = ultimate bearing capacity of soil,
  γ = unit weight of soil,
  z = critical depth for laying of foundation, and
  ϕ = angle of internal friction of the ideal soil.
    If the ultimate bearing capacity of the soil is known, then the critical depth, z, for laying of the foundation can be calculated.

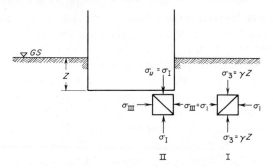

FIG. 22-6   Bell's system.

Comparing Rankine's formula, Eq. (22-28), with Pauker's equation one notes that the results are identical because

$$\frac{1 - \sin \phi}{1 + \sin \phi} = \frac{\tan(45° - \phi/2)}{\tan(45° + \phi/2)} = \tan^2(45° - \phi/2). \tag{22-29}$$

Hence, the limitations and deficiencies of the Rankine's formula are the same as in Pauker's Equation.

22-15. Bell's Equation. Pauker-Rankine's formula was modified by Bell[15,16] to be applicable for cohesive soils. In Bell's equation, both friction and cohesion are considered. His equation is also based on the classical earth pressure theory. The ultimate bearing capacity, or critical stress on a cohesive soil exerted by a footing, in the case of the active earth pressure, is

$$\sigma_u = \gamma z \tan^4(\pi/4 + \phi/2) + 2c[\tan^3(\pi/4 + \phi/2) + \tan(\pi/4 + \phi/2)]. \tag{22-30}$$

Bell considered the equilibrium of two adjacent elements of soil prisms, one just beneath the edge of a strip foundation and the other just outside, at a depth, z, below the ground surface, Fig. 22-6.
    According to the classical earth pressure theory for cohesive soils, the contact pressure $\sigma_1 (= \sigma_u$ = the ultimate bearing capacity) induces on the elementary

soil prism II a lateral active stress, σ_{III}, tending to cause prism II to rupture in shear:

$$\sigma_{III} = \sigma_1 \tan^2(\pi/4 - \phi/2) - 2c \tan(\pi/4 - \phi/2) \tag{22-31}$$

This lateral stress, σ_{III}, acting now laterally from prism II to prism I should be resisted by the passive earth resistance stress, σ_1:

$$\sigma_1 = \sigma_3 \tan^2(\pi/4 + \phi/2) + 2c \tan(\pi/4 + \phi/2), \tag{22-32}$$

where $\sigma_3 = \gamma z$. If this lateral stress, σ_1, is barely large enough to rupture prism I, then the active stress, σ_{III}, is equal to the passive stress, σ_1.

Setting $\sigma_{III} = \sigma_1$, obtain Bell's expression for the ultimate bearing capacity of a cohesive ($\phi - c$) soil, $\sigma_1 = \sigma_u$:

$$\sigma_u = \gamma z \tan^4(\pi/4 + \phi/2) + 2c \tan(\pi/4 + \phi/2)[\tan^2(\pi/4 + \phi/2) + 1] \tag{22-33}$$

When $c = 0$, then

$$\sigma_u = \gamma z \tan^4(\pi/4 + \phi/2), \tag{22-27}$$

which is the Pauker-Rankine formula for the ultimate bearing capacity of a non-cohesive soil.

When $\phi = 0$, then it follows from Eq. (22-33) that

$$\sigma_u = \gamma z + 4c \tag{22-34}$$

When $\phi = 0$, and $z = 0$, then

$$\sigma_u = 4c, \tag{22-35}$$

which is Bell's ultimate bearing capacity of a pure cohesive soil.

Example. The magnitude of cohesion, c, of a soil, has been determined in the laboratory as being $c = 600$ lb/ft². Calculate the ultimate bearing capacity, σ_u.
Solution. By Eq. (22-34),

$$\sigma_u = (4)c = (4)(600) = \underline{2400 \ (\text{lb/ft}^2) = 1.2 \ (\text{t/ft}^2)}.$$

22-16. A. Casagrande-Fadum Illustration. Reasoning along the same lines as Bell did in his treatise on the supporting power of a clay soil, by utilizing the theory of stress condition in soil at a point, A. Casagrande and R. Fadum[17] presented a lucid illustration relative to major and minor principal stress conditions in cohesive soil induced by a structural load for the purpose of calculating the ultimate bearing capacity of soil. The system underlying these calculations is illustrated in Fig. 22-7.

The ground surface is loaded through a long strip foundation by a uniformly distributed load, σ_u. The width of the strip foundation is $2b$.

In this system, the soil below the base line of the footing, as originally suggested by Terzaghi, is subdivided into three squares. The sides of each of the squares is $\alpha b = 2b$.

If the externally applied, vertical surface pressure, σ_u, is applied to the saturated cohesive soil quickly so that the clay soil has no time to consolidate, then the shear strength, τ, of the clay equals the cohesion, c, i.e., $\tau = c$, as can easily be seen from the Mohr stress diagram. The shear strength envelope of the clay appears then to be a horizontal line the equation of which is $\tau = c$ (Fig. 22-7c). In this latter figure, Mohr's stress circle, I, represents the stress conditions in the soil at rupture of the elementary soil prism in the center of the block or zone I below the ground surface. From this stress diagram, it can be seen that the magnitude of the major principal stress when failure occurs is $\sigma_1 = \gamma b + 2c$, and the minor principal stress is $\sigma_3 = \gamma b$. Relative to the elementary soil prism in the center of the block or zone II (the middle block directly underneath the base of the footing), the horizontal stress, $\sigma_{\text{III}} = \sigma_1$, is the minor principal stress causing failure in shear of the clay mass. Blocks I and II act like in a triaxial compression test failing in shear. Accordingly, $\sigma_1 = \gamma b + 4c$, which will bring about rupture.

Because γb is the pressure from the soil on the small elementary soil prism, it is deduced that to bring about failure the contact pressure, σ_u, exerted by the footing on the ground surface must be equal to $4c$, i.e.,

$$\sigma_u = 4c. \tag{22-36}$$

Hence, the ultimate bearing capacity of a saturated clay is

$$\sigma_u = 4c,$$

which is the same result as given by Bell.

If the magnitude of cohesion, c, of a clay is taken as approximately equal to one-half the unconfined compressive strength ($c = \sigma_c/2$), then the ultimate bearing capacity of clay for Bell's method of calculation is

$$\sigma_u = 4c = 4\frac{\sigma_c}{2} = 2\sigma_c. \tag{22-37}$$

Example. The unconfined compressive strength of a pure cohesive soil material has been tested to be $\sigma_c = 1000$ lb/ft². Determine the ultimate bearing capacity of this material using the Bell-Casagrande method.

Solution.

Magnitude of cohesion:

$$c \approx \frac{\sigma_c}{2} = 1000/2 = \underline{500 \ (\text{lb/ft}^2)}$$

Ultimate bearing capacity:

$$\sigma_u = 4c = (4)(500) = \underline{2000 \ (\text{lb/ft}^2)} = \underline{1 \ (\text{t/ft}^2)}$$

$$z = \frac{\sigma_u}{\gamma_f} = \frac{8750}{(120)(3)} = 24.3 \ (\text{ft}) < 25 \ (\text{ft})$$

high fill. Here $\gamma_f = 120$ lb/ft³ = unit weight of fill.

SOIL BEARING CAPACITY CALCULATIONS BY MEANS OF THEORY OF PLASTIC EQUILIBRIUM

22-17. Prandtl's Theory. Prandtl[18,19] studied the process of penetration of hard bodies, such as metal punchers, into another softer, homogeneous, isotropic material from the viewpoint of plastic equilibrium. One of his systems of study

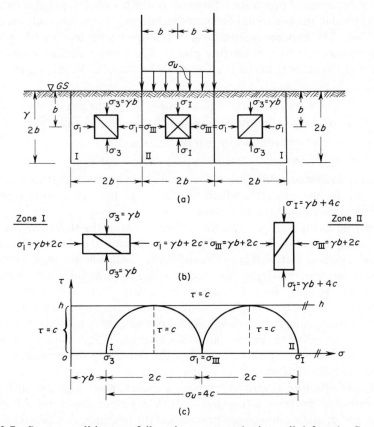

FIG. 22-7   Stress conditions at failure in a pure cohesive soil (after A. Casagrande and R. E. Fadum, Ref. 17).

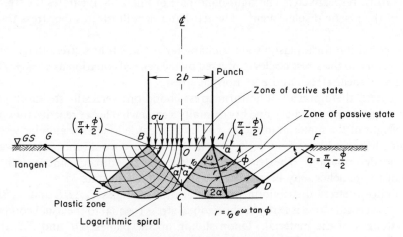

FIG. 22-8   Prandtl's system of study.

was a two-dimensional penetration problem in which a vertical puncher of width, $2b$, was applied to the horizontal surface of an infinitely extending body according to Fig. 22-8. The puncher reminds one of a surface strip loading of very long length perpendicular to the drawing plane. The contact surface between the puncher and the other material is assumed to be smooth. In this Figure,

AB = loaded region
$FDCEG$ = boundary of plastic region against the elastic one
$DF = GE$ = straight lines = tangents to curves $\widehat{CD}$ and $\widehat{CE}$
$\widehat{CD} = \widehat{CE}$ = logarithmically spiraled curves
$\alpha = \pi/4 - \phi/2$.

Interest in such studies lead Prandtl to a solution for plastic equilibrium which explains lucidly the processes which take place in the softer body (material) upon vertical punching into its surface.

In applying in his studies of plastic failure in metals the theory of plasticity, Prandtl followed the following line of reasoning. Because the elastic deformations with most common materials are extraordinarily small, whereas plastic deformations are comparatively large, for the purpose of simplification the elastic deformations are fully ignored, and the elastic part of the body is treated as a rigid body. In any case the plastic deformations can be considered so small that the geometric shape of the body would not be greatly altered. The volume change, corresponding to ignoring all elastic changes, is also assumed to be zero in the plastic region of the body so that the remaining deformations can be construed as plain slidings.

Upon application of a vertically guided puncher under high pressure to the softer horizontal material, a triangle, $\triangle ABC$, is pushed down inward into the material, and upon this downward penetration the triangles, $\triangle ADF$ and $\triangle BEG$, would be translocated obliquely and pushed out by the sectors, ACD and BCE. Through these pressures from $\triangle AOC$ and $\triangle BOC$ are transferred to $\triangle ADF$ and $\triangle BEG$, respectively. The right-hand part of Fig. 22-8 illustrates the streamlines of the plastic displacement. The left-hand part illustrates the stress trajectories.

The condition for a plastic state is characterized in Mohr's stress diagram by the envelope to the stress circles expressed by the general equation as $\tau = \pm f(\sigma)$, where τ = shear stress, and σ = normal stress.

In $\triangle ABC$ there prevails a uniform stress condition: vertically the given large pressure (from the puncher), and horizontally a somewhat lesser reactive pressure. The weight of the material in the $\triangle ABC$ is disregarded. This triangular wedge, $\triangle ABC$, behaves like a rigid body, and under pressure would move downwards with no deformation. The triangular wedge, $\triangle ABC$, directly underneath the base of the puncher may be considered a zone of active state.

A uniform stress distribution prevails also in triangles $\triangle ADF$ and $\triangle BEG$. Here the vertical stress is zero; the horizontal stress is equal to the usual compressive strength of the material. Upon sliding up the planes, DF and EG, these triangles, or wedges of the material under consideration would slide like rigid bodies. These two end-triangular wedges may be considered as the zone of passive state.

Between $\triangle ADF$ and $\triangle BEG$, and the central triangle, $\triangle ABC$, there are two sector-like elements, ACD and BCE. Curves, CD and CE, are sections of logarithmic spirals. The poles of these spirals are at points A and B. The radii in both sectors are sliding or rupture surfaces.

In the sectors, there is a system of two rupture surfaces: the fan-like radial rupture surfaces emanating from the poles, A and B, intersect the spiraled rupture surfaces under an angle of 2α, Fig. 22-8. These two sectors deform plastically. In these plastic sectors the stresses along any radius-vector, r, are constant but they vary from radius-vector to radius-vector. The plastic zone is sometimes referred to as the zone of radial shear.

In his analysis, Prandtl considers the plastic equilibrium of the plastic sectors, assuming that the major principal normal stress on the face, AC, of the triangular wedge, $\triangle ABC$, acts with the same intensity also on the face, AD, of the end prism, $\triangle ADF$, and is the ultimate compressive stress, σ_u; and that the minor principal normal stress on the same faces is zero.

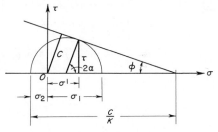

FIG. 22-9   Mohr's stress diagram as used by Prandtl.

From Mohr's stress theory, and using Airy's stress function, Prandtl obtained a differential equation of the second order, the solution of which gives the analytical expression for the ultimate compressive stress, σ_u (see Ref. 18):

$$\sigma_u = -\frac{C}{k}\left(\frac{1+k}{1-k}\,e^{\pi\tan\phi} - 1\right), \qquad (22\text{-}38)$$

where $k = \sin\phi$ (Fig. 22-9)

$\quad C = c\cos\phi =$ a constant where c is known in soil mechanics as the cohesion of the punched material, and

$\quad \phi =$ a constant (slope angle of the straight-line envelope to Mohr's stress circle).

The minus sign in Eq. (22-38) qualifies the nature of the stress, which is a compressive stress.

Omitting the minus sign, and substituting in Eq. (22-38) the k-value and the C-value, one obtains Prandtl's ultimate stress equation for the ultimate compressive stress, σ_u, at plastic equilibrium in the following form:

$$\sigma_u = \frac{c}{\tan\phi}\left(\frac{1+\sin\phi}{1-\sin\phi}\,e^{\pi\tan\phi} - 1\right) \qquad (22\text{-}39)$$

Because

$$\frac{1+\sin\phi}{1-\sin\phi} = \tan^2(\pi/4 + \phi/2), \qquad (22\text{-}40)$$

Eq. (19-40) can be rewritten as

$$\sigma_u = \frac{c}{\tan\phi}\left[\tan^2(\pi/4 + \phi/2)e^{\pi\tan\phi} - 1\right] \qquad (22\text{-}41)$$

This ultimate compressive stress, σ_u, on faces, AC and BC, thus is the ultimate bearing capacity at the surface, AB, of the punched material. Thus, this stress, σ_u, in the active zone, prism $\triangle ABC$, is assumed to be of a hydrostatic nature (it acts with the same intensity in all directions).

A useful value in calculations of bearing capacity problems is the ratio of $\dfrac{\overline{AF}}{\overline{AB}}$.

From Fig. 22-8,

$$\overline{AF} = 2(\overline{AD})\cos(\pi/4 - \phi/2) \qquad (22\text{-}42)$$

$$\overline{AD} = \overline{AC}e^{(\pi/2)\tan\phi} \qquad (22\text{-}43)$$

$$\overline{AB} = 2(\overline{AC})\sin(\pi/4 - \phi/2) \qquad (22\text{-}44)$$

and

$$\frac{\overline{AF}}{\overline{AB}} = e^{(\pi/2)\tan\phi}\cot(\pi/4 - \phi/2) \qquad (22\text{-}45)$$

Also:

$$\overline{AC} = r_o = \frac{b}{\cos(\pi/4 + \phi/2)} \qquad (22\text{-}46)$$

$$\overline{AD} = r = r_o e^{(\pi/2)\tan\phi} = \frac{b}{\cos(\pi/4 + \phi/2)}e^{(\pi/2)\tan\phi} \qquad (22\text{-}47)$$

$$\overline{AF} = 2r\cos(\pi/4 - \phi/2) = 2b\tan(\pi/4 + \phi/2)e^{(\pi/2)\tan\phi} \qquad (22\text{-}48)$$

Prandtl's theory of plastic failure in a system where a vertical puncher is applied on a horizontal surface of a metal can be applied for calculating bearing capacity of soil. In such a case, Prandtl's theory is based on an analysis of the stress condition for the ultimate plastic failure of the soil.

The puncher can be considered to be the strip foundation, usually rigid masonry, loaded with a pressure, σ_u, over the width, $2b$, of the footing.

The softer material into which the puncher penetrates would be the soil. The soil wedge immediately underneath the base of the footing is assumed to be weightless. Upon exhaustion of the shear strength of the soil, a two-sided expulsion of soil from underneath takes place according to the mode given in Prandtl's system, Fig, 22-8. This system, with some modifications as applied to soil, is illustrated in Fig. 22-10.

Because of the importance of Prandtl's ultimate bearing capacity function, σ_u, in soil mechanics, and because during the course of time several improvements were added to that function, then, for the purpose of establishing faith in Prandtl's function, σ_u, it is felt appropriate to include here an explanation of the derivation of the σ_u-function. This method of derivation of the σ_u-function as explained here is simpler than that used by Prandtl, and the method follows in general along the lines shown by Krynine.[20]

According to Prandtl's theory, the bearing pressure, σ_u, on the ground surface, AB, is transmitted through the soil wedge, $\triangle ABC$, on the face, AC, between the wedge and the plastic zone according to Pascal's law, undiminished and in

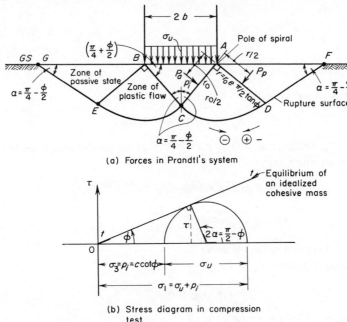

(a) Forces in Prandtl's system

(b) Stress diagram in compression test

Fig. 22-10   Prandtl's system for a (ϕ-c) soil.

all directions, Fig. 22-10a. Also, the initial stress, p_i, in the soil wedge, $\triangle ABC$, distributes hydrostatically according to Pascal's law. Hence, the pressure intensity, σ_a, from the active zone on face, AC, is

$$\sigma_a = \sigma_u + p_i \qquad (22\text{-}49)$$

where

$$p_i = c \cot \phi, \qquad (22\text{-}50)$$

see Fig. 22-10b, and where ϕ is the angle of internal friction of the (ϕ-c) soil.

Assuming that the length of the face, AC, is one unit long, or $AC = r_o = 1.00$, the total active compressive force, P_a, on this face is

$$P_a = \sigma_a A = (\sigma_u + p_i)(1)(1), \qquad (22\text{-}51)$$

where $A = 1 \times 1 =$ area of face, AC.

According to stress theory of soil, Eq. (22-29),

$$\frac{\sigma_3}{\sigma_1} = K_a = \frac{1 - \sin \phi}{1 + \sin \phi} = \tan^2(\pi/4 - \phi/2) = \frac{1}{K_p} \qquad (22\text{-}52)$$

From Fig. 22-10c,

$$\frac{\sigma_3}{\sigma_1} = \frac{p_i}{\sigma_u + p_i} = K_a, \tag{22-53}$$

and

$$\sigma_1 = \frac{\sigma_3}{K_a} = \sigma_3 K_p, \tag{22-54}$$

or

$$\sigma_u + p_i = \frac{p_i}{K_a} = p_i K_p = \sigma_p. \tag{22-55}$$

This is a passive stress, σ_p.

$$K_p = \tan^2(\pi/4 + \phi/2).$$

The force, P_p, on the face, $AD = r_o e^{(\pi/2)\tan\phi}$, of the plastic zone from the passive zone at limit equilibrium is

$$P_p = \sigma_p(r)(1) = (\sigma_u + p_i)(r_o e^{(\pi/2)\tan\phi})(1) \tag{22-56}$$

or

$$P_p = p_i K_p e^{(\pi/2)\tan\phi}, \tag{22-57}$$

because $r_o = 1$ (initial radius-vector).

For force equilibrium, $P_a = P_p$, or

$$(\sigma_u + p_i)(1) = p_i K_p e^{(\pi/2)\tan\phi} \tag{22-58}$$

For moment equilibrium about pole, A:

$$P_a \frac{r_o}{2} = P_p \frac{r}{2}, \tag{22-59}$$

or

$$(\sigma_u + p_i)(\tfrac{1}{2}) = p_i K_p e^{(\pi/2)\tan\phi}(\tfrac{1}{2})e^{(\pi/2)\tan\phi}, \tag{22-60}$$

where $r_o/2 = \tfrac{1}{2} =$ moment arm for force P_a,
and $r/2 = (\tfrac{1}{2})e^{(\pi/2)\tan\phi} =$ moment arm of force P_p.

Solving Eq. (22-60) for σ_u, obtain Prandtl's ultimate bearing capacity as applied to a (ϕ-c) soil with a factor of safety, $\eta = 1$:

$$\sigma_u = \frac{c}{\tan\phi} \left[\tan^2(\pi/4 + \phi/2)e^{\pi\tan\phi} - 1\right]. \tag{22-61}$$

22-18. Terzaghi's Correction. To prevent Prandtl's ultimate bearing capacity, σ_u, from becoming equal to zero when $c = 0$, Terzaghi suggested an improvement to account for the weight (surcharge) of the soil: to the original quantity c in Prandtl's equation a factor c' was added, where

$$c' = \gamma t \tan\phi, \tag{22-62}$$

$$t = \frac{\text{area of wedges and sector}}{\text{length } GEC} = \qquad (22\text{-}63)$$

= an equivalent height of surcharge of soil material, and

γ = unit weight of soil.

The area of wedges and a sector obviously means one half of the system. Then

$$\sigma_u = \frac{(c + c')}{\tan \phi} \{[\tan^2(\pi/4 + \phi/2)]e^{\pi \tan \phi} - 1\} \qquad (22\text{-}64)$$

Now, when $c = 0$ and thus $\sigma_u \neq 0$, as for pure frictional soil, then σ_u is

$$\sigma_u = \gamma t \{[\tan^2(\pi/4 + \phi/2)]e^{\pi \tan \phi} - 1\} \qquad (22\text{-}65)$$

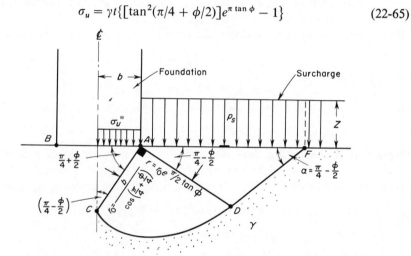

FIG. 22-11   Surcharge, p_s, added to Prandtl's system.

22-19. Taylor's Correction. In Taylor's work[21] there appears in Prandtl's equation for a half-width of footing a factor,

$$\gamma b \tan(\pi/4 + \phi/2) = \gamma b \sqrt{K_p} \qquad (22\text{-}66)$$

Then

$$\sigma_u = [c \cot \phi + \gamma b \tan(\pi/4 + \phi/2)]\{[\tan^2(\pi/4 + \phi/2)]e^{\pi \tan \phi} - 1\}, \quad (22\text{-}67)$$

where it is said that this factor, $\gamma b \tan(\pi/4 + \phi/2)$, which did not appear in the original Prandtl equation, was added later to account for strength by overburden pressure. However nothing is said in that work as to how this factor was derived.

The author of this book derives Prandtl's ultimate bearing capacity, σ_u, taking into account also the surcharge on the ground surface as follows.

The effect of surcharge, p_s, on the bearing capacity, σ_u, is visualized as follows (Fig. 22-11). Let σ''_u be the corresponding bearing capacity due to surcharge only. Reasoning similarly as in deriving Prandtl's equation, $\sigma'_u = p_i(K_p e^{\pi \tan \phi} - 1)$, balance the moments, about point A, caused by a "hydrostatic stress", σ''_u, acting on AC and the "hydrostatic stress" from surcharge, p_s, acting on AD:

$$\frac{\sigma''_u b^2}{2\cos^2(\pi/4 + \phi/2)} = p_s \frac{b^2 e^{\pi \tan \phi}}{2\cos^2(\pi/4 + \phi/2)} K_p \qquad (22\text{-}68)$$

or

$$\sigma''_u = p_s K_p e^{\pi \tan \phi}, \qquad (22\text{-}69)$$

where $p_s = \gamma z$ = stress from surcharge on ground surface,
  γ = unit weight of soil, and
  z = depth of base of footing, AB, below ground surface (height of surcharge).

By the principle of superposition, the total ultimate bearing capacity, σ_u, is

$$\sigma_u = \sigma'_u + \sigma''_u, \qquad (22\text{-}70)$$

or

$$\sigma_u = p_i(K_p e^{\pi \tan \phi} - 1) + p_s K_p e^{\pi \tan \phi}, \qquad (22\text{-}71)$$

or

$$\sigma_u = c \cot \phi \{[\tan^2(\pi/4 + \phi/2)]e^{\pi \tan \phi} - 1\} + \gamma z[\tan^2(\pi/4 + \phi/2)]e^{\pi \tan \phi}. \qquad (22\text{-}72)$$

Note that this equation does not consider the unit weight of soil below the elevation of the base of the footing. To take this weight in account, Terzaghi's factor ($c' \cot \phi$) from Eq. (22-62) may be added to the above σ_u-equation:

$$\sigma_u = (c + c')\cot \phi \{[\tan^2(\pi/4 + \phi/2)]e^{\pi \tan \phi} - 1\} +$$
$$+ \gamma z[\tan^2(\pi/4 + \phi/2)]e^{\pi \tan \phi}. \qquad (22\text{-}73)$$

22-20. Discussion of Prandtl's Theory

1) The precision of Prandtl's equation for calculating the ultimate bearing capacity of soil depends very much upon the assumed shape of the rupture surface.

2) Prandtl's rupture surface curve is a compound one, and consists of arcs of a logarithmic spiral and a tangent to the spiral.

3) Prandtl's compound rupture surface corresponds fairly well with the mode of failure along curvilinear rupture surfaces as observed from experiment.

4) Prandtl's theory is applicable to a long strip foundation.

5) Prandtl's ultimate-bearing-capacity formula is applicable to frictional-cohesive soil, (ϕ-c) soil, and to a pure cohesive soil, (c) soil loaded on its surface by a long strip foundation with a small base.

6) When $c = 0$, and $\phi > 0$, then by Prandtl's original Eq. (22-41), $\sigma_u = 0$. This result reads that the ultimate bearing capacity of an ideal, frictional sand at its ground surface is zero, which is in contradiction to common observations in reality. The contradiction originates mainly from the assumption that the soil wedge, $\triangle ABC$, directly underneath the base of

the footing is assumed to be weightless. With the introduced corrections, the bearing capacity of soil has now a real value > 0 (Eq. 22-73).

7) When $\phi = 0$, then the original Prandtl equation transforms into an indeterminate quantity, namely

$$\sigma_{u_{\phi=0}} = \infty \, 0.$$

The true value of the σ_u-function when $\phi \to 0$ is obtained by subjecting this function to L'Hospital's rule of successively differentiating independently the nominator and denominator of Prandtl's σ_u-function, first transforming it into

$$\sigma_u = c \, \frac{\{[\tan^2(\pi/4 + \phi/2)]e^{\pi \tan \phi} - 1\}}{\tan \phi} \tag{22-74}$$

$$\lim_{\phi \to 0} \sigma_u = \lim_{\phi \to 0} \frac{c \, \dfrac{d}{d\phi} \{[\tan^2(\pi/4 + \phi/2)]e^{\pi \tan \phi} - 1\}}{\dfrac{d}{d\phi} (\tan \phi)} =$$

$$= c(2 + \pi) = (5.14)c. \tag{22-75}$$

Hence the true value of Prandtl's ultimate bearing capacity of a pure, plastic, cohesive soil is

$$\sigma_u = (5.14)c \tag{22-75}$$

When $\phi = 0$, then the modified Prandtl equation, Eq. (22-73) gives

$$\sigma_u = \left(\frac{c}{0} + \gamma t\right)(0 - 0) + \gamma z,$$

or

$$\sigma_u = (c + \gamma t)(2 + \pi) + \gamma z, \tag{22-76a}$$

or

$$\sigma_u = (5.14)(c + \gamma t) + \gamma z \tag{22-76}$$

8) Prandtl's ultimate bearing capacity is independent of the width, $2b$, of the strip foundation.

9) Regardless of the analytical method of solution involved in Prandtl's ultimate-bearing-capacity function, his method relative to the real rupture surface is an approximate one only.

10) Prandtl's theory, like the other theories, says nothing about the reactive stress distribution in soil along the rupture surface at the instant rupture takes place.

Example 1. The application of Prandtl's theory of plastic equilibrium to a soil mechanics problem is now illustrated by a concrete example.

Determine the bearing capacity (resistance to soil lateral expulsion from underneath a highway fill) of a fill supporting soil which has a low cohesive strength. The system in question is illustrated in Fig. 22-12. The groundwater table coincides with the ground surface. The properties of the soil material in question are:

I. *Fill supporting soil:*
   angle of internal friction: $\phi = 10°$
   cohesion: $c = 180$ lb/ft²
   unit weight of soil: $\gamma = 100$ lb/ft³
   effective unit weight of soil because of inundation: $\gamma_b = 100 - 62.4 = 37.6$ (lb/ft³)
II. *Fill material:*
   angle of internal friction: $\phi = 20°$
   cohesion: $c = 700$ lb/ft²
   unit weight of soil: $\gamma = 120$ lb/ft³

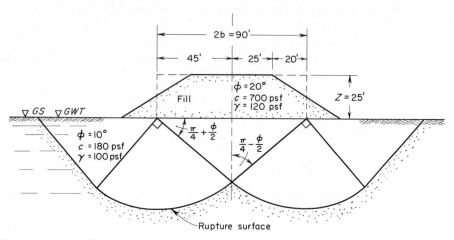

FIG. 22-12   Application of Prandtl's theory of plasticity for determining the bearing
capacity of soil.

Solution. To perform the required analysis, first convert the trapezoidal, cross-sectional area of the fill into an equivalent rectangular cross section of the same height (25 ft). Then the width of the base of the fill is $2b = 90$ ft.
   Prandtl's equation, modified by Taylor, Eq. (22-67) will be used:

$$\sigma_u = [c \cot \phi + \gamma b \tan(\pi/4 + \phi/2)]\{[\tan^2(\pi/4 + \phi/2)]e^{\pi \tan \phi} - 1\}$$

Auxiliary calculations for fill supporting soil:

$$c \cot \phi = (180)(\cot 10°) = (180)(5.671) = 1020.78 \ (\text{lb/ft}^2) \approx 1021 \qquad (\text{lb/ft}^2)$$

$$\gamma b \tan(\pi/4 + \phi/2) = (37.6)(45.0)\tan\left(45° + \frac{10°}{2}\right) = (1692)(1.192) = 2017.9 \qquad (\text{lb/ft}^2)$$

$$\tan^2 50° = (1.192)^2 = 1.421$$

$$e^{\pi \tan \phi} = e^{(3.14)\tan 10°} = e^{(3.14)(0.1763)} = e^{0.554} = 1.740$$

Ultimate bearing capacity of fill-supporting soil:

$$\sigma_u = (1021 + 2018)[(1.421)(1.740) - 1] = (3039)(2.473) - 1) =$$
$$= 4476.4 \ (\text{lb/ft}^2) \approx 2.2 \qquad (\text{t/ft}^2)$$

Pressure caused by fill on fill-supporting soil.

$$\sigma = \gamma z = (120)(25) = 3000 \ (\text{lb/ft}^2) \approx 1.5 \qquad (\text{t/ft}^2).$$

Factor of safety, η, against breaking of the fill into the fill-supporting soil:

$$\eta = \frac{\sigma_u}{\sigma} = \frac{2.2}{1.5} \approx 1.46.$$

Should the factor of safety be required to be $\eta = 3$, then

$$\eta = \frac{\sigma_u}{\sigma} = \frac{2.2}{\left(\dfrac{120}{2000}\right)(z)} = 3.0,$$

and the height of the fill should be

$$z = \frac{\sigma_u}{\gamma_f \eta} = \frac{2.2}{\left(\dfrac{120}{2000}\right)(3.0)} = \frac{4400}{360} \approx 12.2 \ \text{(ft)}$$

Here γ_f = unit weight of fill = 120 (lb/ft³).

Example 2. If in the previous example the fill-supporting soil is a pure clay with cohesion, $c = 500$ lb/ft², and a unit weight of 105 lb/ft³, then the ultimate bearing capacity of the clay (here surface loading) is calculated by Eq. (22-75) as

$$\sigma_u = (5.14)c = (5.14)(500) = \underline{2570 \ \text{(lb/ft²)}} \approx 1.28 \ \text{(t/ft²)}.$$

Neither the unit weight of the clay nor the width of the fill enter into these calculations.

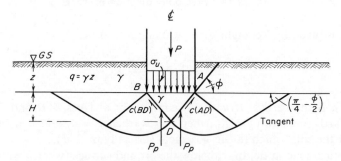

FIG. 22-13   Prandtl-Terzaghi's system.

22-21. Terzaghi's Contribution. Based on Prandtl's theory of plastic failure (in soil) Terzaghi[22] presented a modified system as illustrated in Fig. 22-13. The system is devised for a shallow strip footing ($z < 2b$), founded z units of length below the ground surface. Or else the ground surface at the base line of the footing is loaded with a uniformly distributed load, $q = \gamma z$.

The width of the footing is $2b$. The footing exerts on the soil a constant pressure of σ_u. The soil wedge, $\triangle ABD$, underneath the base of the footing is considered an elastic medium, and is assigned by Terzaghi a unit weight, γ. The base of the footing is assumed to be rough.

The critical load, $Q_{\text{crit}} = \sigma_u \, (2b)(1)$ on the soil is calculated based on the principle of static equilibrium of the soil wedge, $\triangle ABC$, the free body diagram of which is shown in Fig. 22-14.

At the critical load, Q_{crit}, the soil fails in shear. For equilibrium, the sum of all forces acting on the free body must be equal to zero:

$$\Sigma V = 0$$

$$Q_{crit} + \underbrace{\gamma b^2 \tan \phi}_{\substack{\text{weight of} \\ \text{soil wedge}}} - \underbrace{2P_p}_{\substack{\text{soil} \\ \text{reaction}}} - \underbrace{2bc \tan \phi}_{\substack{\text{force of} \\ \text{cohesion}}} = 0 \qquad (22\text{-}77)$$

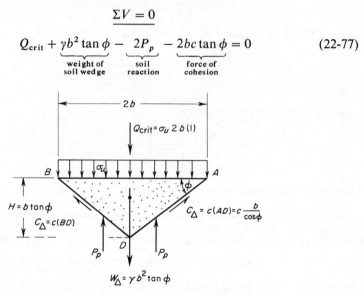

FIG. 22-14   Free body diagram of wedge.

where P_p is given by Terzaghi for $c = 0$ and $q = 0$ as

$$P_p = \tfrac{1}{2}\gamma b^2 \frac{\tan \phi}{\cos^2 \phi} K_p \qquad (22\text{-}78)$$

and which is the vertical (frictional) component at faces, AD and BD, of the passive earth pressure ($\tfrac{1}{2}\gamma b^2 K_p$ when $q = 0$, then $z = 0$, and $c = 0$) from the weight of the soil, which in this case acts vertically ($\delta = \phi$).

The critical load at depth, z, below the ground surface (when $q = 0$) is

$$Q_{z\,crit} = 2P_p + 2bc \tan \phi - \gamma b^2 \tan \phi. \qquad (22\text{-}79)$$

Because $P_p(K_p)$ is given for $c = 0$, Eq. (22-79) transforms into

$$Q_{\text{o crit}} = Q_\gamma = 2\tfrac{1}{2}\gamma b^2 \tan \phi \left(\frac{K_p}{\cos^2 \phi} - 1 \right) = (2b)(\gamma b N_\gamma) \qquad (22\text{-}80)$$

expressing the critical load on the ground surface of a non-cohesive soil. Here

$$N_\gamma = \tfrac{1}{2} \tan \phi \left(\frac{K_p}{\cos^2 \phi} - 1 \right) \qquad (22\text{-}81)$$

is called the bearing-capacity factor expressing the effect of the weight of the soil wedge, $\triangle ABD$, of a non-cohesive soil.

For the calculation of the ultimate bearing capacity of a cohesive soil Terzaghi presents the following equation of a simplified analysis for the critical load Q_{crit}:

$$Q_{crit} = \underbrace{2bc\left(\frac{K_{pc}}{\cos^2\phi} + \tan\phi\right)}_{\substack{\text{Effect of} \\ \text{cohesion}}} + \underbrace{2bq\,\frac{K_{pq}}{\cos^2\phi}}_{\substack{\text{Effect of} \\ \text{surcharge}}} + \underbrace{\gamma b^2\tan\phi\left(\frac{K_{p\gamma}}{\cos^2\phi} - 1\right)}_{\substack{\text{Effect of} \\ \text{weight of wedge }\triangle ABD}} \quad (22\text{-}82)$$

where K_{pc}, K_{pq} and $K_{p\gamma}$ are dimensionless quantities entering into the following P_p equation for a cohesive soil, $(\phi\text{-}c)$ soil:

$$P_p = \frac{b}{\cos^2\phi}(cK_{pc} + qK_{pq}) + \tfrac{1}{2}\gamma b^2\,\frac{\tan\phi}{\cos^2\phi}\,K_{p\gamma} \quad (22\text{-}83)$$

where $(cK_{pc} + qK_{pq}) = p_{pn}$ is the normal component of the passive earth pressure comprehending the effect of cohesion, c, and surcharge, q. Combining Eqs. (22-83) and (22-79) gives the above Eq. (22-82).

Dividing Eq. (22-82) by $(2b)$ obtain the ultimate bearing capacity of the cohesive soil for a footing with a rough base.

If the soil wedge, $\triangle ABD$, is assumed to be weightless $(\gamma = 0)$ then Eq. (22-82) takes the form

$$Q_c + Q_q = 2bc\left(\frac{K_{pc}}{\cos^2\phi} + \tan\phi\right) + 2bq\,\frac{K_{pq}}{\cos^2\phi} = 2bcN_c + 2bqN_q \quad (22\text{-}84)$$

The total critical load considering cohesion, c, surcharge, q, and the unit weight, γ, of the soil wedge, $\triangle ABD$, can be written as

$$Q_{crit} = Q_c + Q_q + Q_\gamma = 2bcN_c + 2bqN_q + 2b^2\gamma N_\gamma \quad (22\text{-}85)$$

With $q = \gamma z$, obtain

$$Q_{crit} = Q_c + Q_q + Q_\gamma = 2b(cN_c + \gamma zN_q + \gamma bN_\gamma) \quad (22\text{-}86)$$

The coefficients N_c, N_q, and N_γ are the bearing-capacity factors for shallow strip footings

The N_γ values are calculated by Eq. (22-81)

$$N_\gamma = \tfrac{1}{2}\tan\phi\left(\frac{K_{p\gamma}}{\cos^2\phi} - 1\right), \quad (22\text{-}87)$$

and the $K_{p\gamma}$-values are determined by the method of spiral or by the method of the friction circle (Chapter 25), or Section 22-22.

The N_c- and N_q-values Terzaghi calculates as

$$N_c = \cot\phi\left(\frac{a_w^2}{2\cos^2(\pi/4 + \phi/2)} - 1\right) \quad (22\text{-}88)$$

and

$$N_q = \frac{a_w^2}{2\cos^2(\pi/4 + \phi/2)}, \quad (22\text{-}89)$$

where

$$a_w = \exp\left(\tfrac{3}{4}\pi - \frac{\phi}{2}\right)\tan\phi. \tag{22-90}$$

When $\phi = 0$ as with pure cohesive soils, then

$N_c = (3/2)\pi + 1 = 5.71$ (obtained by applying L'Hospital's law to the
$\qquad\qquad N_c$-function, because with $\phi = 0$ the $N_c = \infty 0$) (22-91)

$N_q = 1$, and   (22-92)

$N_\gamma = 0.$ (22-93)

Setting $z = 0$ and substituting these values into Eq. (22-86) obtain critical load

$$Q_{crit} = (2b)(5.7)(c) \tag{22-94}$$

or the ultimate bearing capacity $\sigma_u = (Q_{crit})/(2b)$ at $z = 0$:

$$\sigma_u = (5.7)c. \tag{22-95}$$

For a smooth base of a footing Terzaghi obtains an expression for the ultimate bearing capacity of soil which is

$$\sigma_u = (5.14)c. \tag{22-75}$$

This expression is the same as that which can be found from Prandtl's analysis.

The critical load for a *circular footing* with a radius, r, is given as

$$Q_{crit} = \pi r^2(1.3cN_c + \gamma z N_q + 0.6\gamma r N_\gamma) \tag{22-96}$$

where the N-coefficients are bearing-capacity factors for a strip footing, supported by the same soil.

When $\phi = 0$,

$$\sigma_{ou} = (1.3)\sigma_u = (1.3)(5.7)(c) = (7.4)(c). \tag{22-97}$$

For a *square footing*, the critical load is

$$Q_{crit} = 4b^2(1.3cN_c + \gamma z N_q + 0.8\gamma b N_\gamma). \tag{22-98}$$

When $\phi = 0$,

$$\sigma_u = (7.4)c. \tag{22-99}$$

Terzaghi's method of analysis of the bearing capacity of a cohesive soil shows again that the ultimate bearing capacity of a pure cohesive soil is independent of the width of the footing. The settlement, however, of a cohesive soil is inversely proportional to the width, b, of the footing (pressure bulb).

The allowable bearing capacity, σ_{allow}, of a cohesive soil is obtained by dividing the ultimate bearing capacity, σ_u, by a factor of safety, η. For example, if the ultimate bearing capacity at a depth z feet below the ground surface is

$$\sigma_{uz} = \sigma_{uo} + \gamma z = (5.7)c + \gamma z, \tag{22-100}$$

then the allowable bearing capacity is

$$\sigma_{allow} = \frac{\sigma_{uo}}{\eta} + \gamma z = \frac{(5.7)c}{\eta} + \gamma z \qquad (22\text{-}101)$$

22-22. Krey's Method

The System for Frictional Soil. Realizing that the rupture surface in soil is not a compound, broken plane, Krey[23] suggested a grapho-analytical method for determining the bearing capacity of a cohesive soil (ϕ-c soil, or c soil) based on a circular sliding surface. Actually, his method consists of determining the safety against rupture of a soil mass loaded with a structural load. The rupture surface in soil is assumed to be a part of a circular cylinder in shape passing through one edge of the footing of the foundation, Fig. 22-15. The circular arc, $\widehat{BD}$, is coupled by a straight tangent, DG, making an angle of $\alpha = \pi/4 - \phi/2$ with the horizontal. The Krey's system analysis consists of an active zone, $ABDJKA$, and a passive zone, $DGJD$. Upon the exhaustion of the shear strength of the soil, the active zone would exert a lateral pressure, E, on the vertical plane, DJ, and tend to expel the passive zone laterally and thus to destroy it.

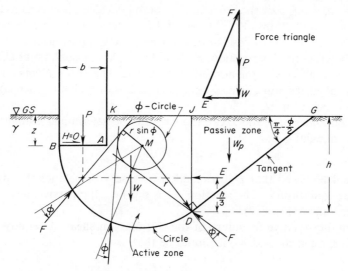

FIG. 22-15 Krey's system.

This assumption by Krey, using a circular sliding surface with a tangent, corresponds more nearly with reality when observing the soil particles in motion. To arrive at a solution certain assumptions also had to be made in this method. In his original work Krey shows a system with two-sided expulsion of soil from underneath the base of the footing. For analysis, however, because of the symmetry of the system, Krey uses only one half of the width of the loaded foundation.

The position of the center of the circle, M, is arbitrarily chosen, and it is assumed to be located on the line of the base of the footing. Then a circular arc,

$\widehat{BD}$, is drawn with the radius, $MB = r$, and a tangent, DG, is drawn to the circle. The system shown pertains to one-sided expulsion of the ruptured soil wedge from underneath the base of the footing.

At the instant of impending rupture, the following forces act:

1) Structural load, P, transmitted by the foundation to soil (magnitude and direction of action known).

2) The weight, W, of the soil mass, $ABDGJKA$ (magnitude and direction of action known). The points of application of P and W are known, or can be determined.

3) Soil reaction, F, acting up and to the right along the circular part of the rupture surface, BD (magnitude, position, and direction of action unknown).

4) Soil reaction, E, acting horizontally on plane, DJ. The point of application of E is $h/3$ above point D.

5) A horizontal frictional force, H, which is omitted from calculations because of negligible magnitude.

The active zone over the curved rupture surface exerts a pressure on the passive zone, DGJ, over the tangent. The stability calculation is as follows.

Combine P and W into a resultant, and find the point of intersection, O, of this resultant, and E. In case of equilibrium, three forces meet in a common point. Therefore the soil reaction, F, should also pass through point O. Besides, F makes an angle ϕ with the normal to the circle. Therefore, F acts tangentially to the so-called friction circle (ϕ circle) the radius of which is ($r \sin \phi$), and the center of which is at M.

The magnitudes of F and E can most readily be determined graphically from the force triangle:

$$\bar{F} = (\bar{P} + \bar{W}) + \bar{E}. \tag{22-102}$$

It should be noted that E is a reaction necessary to balance the given force system for equilibrium. The reaction, E, is not here the passive earth pressure, $E_p = \frac{1}{2}\gamma h^2 \tan^2(\pi/4 + \phi/2)$.

For stability relative to failure of the soil mass in shear along any arbitrary rupture surface such as BDG, it should be that

$$E_p > E. \tag{22-103}$$

The factor of safety, η, is

$$\eta = \frac{E_p}{E} \geqslant 1.5. \tag{22-104}$$

The magnitude of the resultant passive earth pressure, E_p, can be figured out from the equilibrium of the free body diagram of the soil wedge, DGJ, Fig. 22-16a, and from the corresponding force triangle, Fig. 22-16b.

The factor of safety is determined in the following way. Assuming various positions of centers, M, viz., various r's for the circular sliding surfaces, determine the corresponding values of E_p and E. Plot a graph, Fig. 22-17, where E_p and E are presented as functions of r. The point on the abscissa (r) axis for which the difference, $E_p - E$, is a minimum, furnishes that r_o of the rupture surface which gives the minimum factor of safety, η: $\eta = E_p/E$, whereby the minimum difference between the E_p and E curves should be such as to give a factor of safety $\eta \geqslant 1.5$. If both curves in Fig. 22-17 should intersect, then $\eta < 1$, and the structure is unstable.

If the requirement for a predetermined factor of safety is not met by several trials, then in order to increase the factor of safety the footing should be made wider, or else the depth of the foundation should be made greater, and the stability calculations should be repeated until the minimum factor of safety is attained.

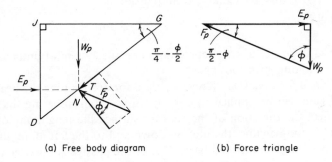

(a) Free body diagram   (b) Force triangle

FIG. 22-16   Determination of E_p.

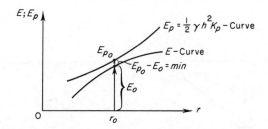

FIG. 22-17   Determination of the most dangerous rupture surface.

Krey's method also applies to the problem conversely to that described above, namely: the soil-foundation system is subjected to grapho-analysis in order to determine the load which the soil can safely bear with a predetermined factor of safety.

To do this, a desired factor of safety, η, is applied to the passive earth resistance, E_p, in the following way. An arbitrary circular-tangent rupture surface is drawn and the passive earth pressure, E_p, is determined as described before. Then the magnitude of this E_p is divided by a factor of safety, η: E_p/η. The latter expression is then the magnitude of the horizontal thrust, viz., reaction, E:

$$E = \frac{E_p}{\eta}. \qquad (22\text{-}105)$$

This E, the magnitude of which is E_p/η, should not be exceeded.

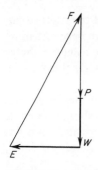

Knowing the magnitude of E, the next step is to determine the magnitude of the load, P, to be allowed to be transmitted from the foundation to the soil. This can best be accomplished from the force triangle, Fig. 22-18, by plotting the known E-vector, and the known directions of actions of F and P. The force triangle then gives the value of P, which is the allowable load of the foundation for the used rupture surface representing a factor of safety, η, against lateral expulsion of the soil mass, viz., against failure in shear.

The contact pressure, σ_o, or the safe bearing capacity of this particular soil in question is

FIG. 22-18 Determination of P.

$$\sigma_o = P/b, \qquad (22\text{-}106)$$

in tons per sq ft, or in kg/cm^2, depending upon the system of units used, where b = width of a long strip footing.

Krey's System for Cohesion. Krey's method for determining the bearing capacity of soil can also be applied to cohesive soils. Remembering that cohesion does not affect the direction of the rupture surface the magnitude of the total cohesion, C_t, acting against the motion down and to the left along the tangent, toward D, or along the inclined base, DG, of the passive soil wedge is

$$C_t = cL_t(1); \qquad (22\text{-}107)$$

see Fig. 22-19,

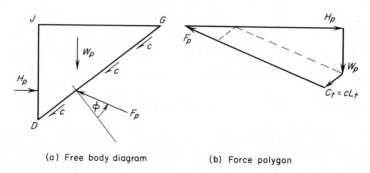

(a) Free body diagram   (b) Force polygon

FIG. 22-19   Cohesion in the passive zone.

where c = unit cohesion, and
$L_t = DG$ is the length of the tangent to the circle.

The moment arm, d, of the resultant cohesion, C_c, along the circular part of the rupture surface can be calculated from the following considerations. Resolve the cohesive forces acting along a unit length of the arc, ΔL_c, for example parallel and perpendicular to the chord, BD. Note from Fig. 22-20a that the parallel components are additive, whereas the perpendicular components cancel out each other. Thus, the direction of the resultant cohesive forces, C_c, is parallel to the chord, BD, and the magnitude of the resultant cohesive force can be expressed as $C_c = cL_{ch}$, where L_{ch} = length of the chord, BD. Accordingly, the moments of the cohesive forces must be equal:

$$cL_{ch}\, d = \sum_0^{L_c} (c\Delta L_c r) = cr \sum_0^{L_c} \Delta L_c = crL_c, \qquad (22\text{-}108)$$

and consequently, the moment arm, d, of the resultant cohesive force relative to the center of rotation, point M, is

$$d = r\, \frac{L_c}{L_{ch}} \qquad (22\text{-}109)$$

or

$$d = \frac{\alpha r r}{2r \sin \dfrac{\alpha}{2}} = \frac{\alpha r}{2 \sin \dfrac{\alpha}{2}}, \qquad (22\text{-}110)$$

where $r\alpha$ = length of arc = $\overparen{BD}/2$, and
 α = central angle resting on chord, BD.
Note that the ratio $L_c/L_{ch} > 1$; therefore $d > r$.

When $\phi = 0$, then moments taken about the center, M, of the circular rupture surface lead to an equation in P. Several trial circles facilitate the computation of the minimum factor of safety, η.

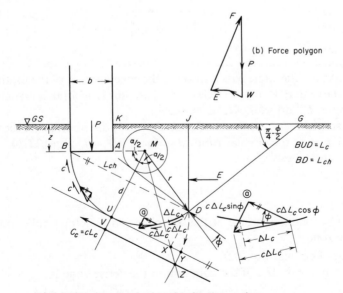

(b) Force polygon

$BUD = L_c$
$BD = L_{ch}$

(a) Cohesion along the circular part of rupture surface

FIG. 22-20   Cohesion in the active zone.

The arm, d, from Eq. (22-110), can also be determined *graphically* as follows: draw through point U a line parallel to BD. On this line scale off one half of the length of the chord so that

$$\overline{UX} = \frac{L_{ch}}{2} = \frac{\overline{BD}}{2} = r \sin \frac{\alpha}{2}$$

and

$$\overline{UY} = \frac{L_c}{2} = \frac{\overparen{BD}}{2} = \frac{\alpha r}{2}.$$

Then draw through Y a line parallel to MU, and from point M draw line MX, to obtain point Z by drawing $YZ \| MU$. The resultant cohesive force, C_c, passes then through point Z, and is $\perp$ to MU at point V. Then $\overline{MV} = d$ is the arm of the moment of the resultant cohesion, C_c.

From triangles, MVZ and MUX, obtain

$$\frac{\overline{MV}}{\overline{MU}} = \frac{\overline{VZ}}{\overline{UX}}, \tag{22-111}$$

or

$$\frac{d}{r} = \frac{\dfrac{L_c}{2}}{\dfrac{L_{ch}}{2}} = \frac{\dfrac{\alpha r}{2}}{r \sin \dfrac{\alpha}{2}} = \frac{\alpha}{2 \sin \dfrac{\alpha}{2}}, \tag{22-112}$$

or

$$d = r \frac{L_c}{L_{ch}} = \frac{\alpha r}{2 \sin \dfrac{\alpha}{2}}. \tag{22-113}$$

To determine the bearing capacity of a cohesive soil (ϕ-c soil) one proceeds as follows. Again, the circle passes through the edgepoint, B, of the footing. The position of the center, M, of the circle on the base-line is arbitrarily assumed. The active pressure, E_a, on wall, AK, is neglected.

The cohesive forces, c, are assumed to be uniformly distributed over the tangent, DG, as well as over the circular rupture surface, $BD = L_c$, Fig. 22-20.

The resultant cohesive force is

$$\sum_0^{L_c} (c\Delta L_c) = cL_c = C_c \tag{22-114}$$

$C_c = cL_c(1)$ = total magnitude of the soil cohesion (resultant cohesion) in the active zone

L_c = length of circular arc, $\overparen{BD}$.

The static moment, M_c, of the cohesion in the active zone is

$$M_c = cL_c(1)r, \tag{22-115}$$

where r = moment arm = radius of rupture surface.

The magnitude and direction of action of the resultant cohesion, C_c, can be found from the force polygon in Fig. 22-20b.

The line of the direction of action of the soil reaction, F, is determined as follows: find the line of action, S, of the resultant of E (horizontal soil reaction) and W (weight of soil of active zone). From the point of intersection of line S with vector C_c, draw line Z (along the resultant of S and C_c). Through the point of intersection of the line of action of Z and the line of action of the yet unknown structural load, P, draw line F as the tangent to the ϕ-circle.

Knowing now the magnitudes and the directions of W, E (E_p/η), C_c, and the direction of F, the magnitudes of F and P, the sought structural load, can now be determined from the force polygon, Fig. 22-21.

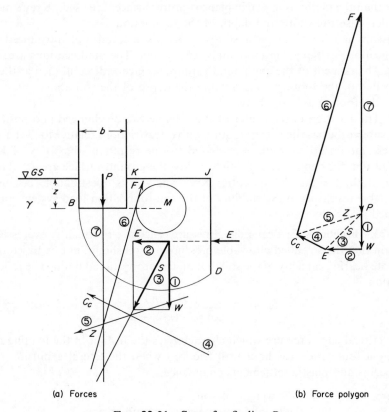

(a) Forces   (b) Force polygon

FIG. 22-21   Steps for finding P.

The Krey grapho-analytical method shows that the bearing capacity of soil depends upon

1) the type of soil, particularly γ, ϕ, and c, and its shear strength;
2) the width of the foundation, b (note $P = \sigma_o b 1$)—a wider footing is more stable than a narrow one;

3) the depth of the foundation, z, reflected in h, in greater horizontal resistance, E, and larger surcharge above the line through the base of the footing.

Although the grapho-analytical method by Krey is one of trial and error, and hence somewhat tedious, Krey's method of analyzing the stability of a structure by assuming circular-cylindrical rupture surfaces is simpler than those where broken plane rupture surfaces are used. Besides, in the Krey method, the coefficient, K_p, of the passive earth pressure of the Coulomb method can be picked out directly from the earth pressure tables, thus facilitating the work of calculation considerably. Also, the general course of the combined circle-tangent rupture surface resembles fairly closely the actual curvilinear rupture surfaces observed in nature and in the laboratory.[24]

This method, notwithstanding every possible scientific critique, is somewhat better than the methods in which plane rupture surfaces are used. Krey's method considers also the width and depth of the foundation.

Hasson and Vey[25] made a study of Krey's method and introduced some modifications of Krey's grapho-analytical system. The modifications are:

1) The tangent of the compound rupture surface is discontinued at the base line of the footing, thus treating the depth of the soil above the base of the footing as a surcharge.

2) The location of the center of the ϕ-circle can be changed and positioned above the base line of the footing with no restrictions relative to the base line.

These modifications were necessitated by the results of the study of Krey's method that for depths, z, of footings below the ground surface greater than the width of the footing, b, the entire Krey analysis is questionable because no reasonable results as to the stability of the soil-foundation-load system could be attained at $z > b$.

22-23. Fröhlich's Critical Edge Pressure Theory. Fröhlich[26] expressed the opinion that the so-called allowable pressure on soil should not be based on the ultimate bearing capacity of the soil, but on the proportional limit. The following equation

$$p_{crit} = \frac{\pi(\gamma H + p_i)}{\cot \phi - (\pi/2 - \phi)} \qquad (22\text{-}116)$$

is the critical edge pressure which characterizes the instant in the loading of the soil by a foundation (without wall friction) when the lateral expulsion of the soil begins and plastic settlements commence.

Here, γ = unit weight of soil;
   H = depth of footing below ground surface;
   $p_i = c \cot \phi$ = initial stress;
   c = cohesion;
   ϕ = angle of internal friction of soil.

For cohesive soils the general valid equation represents, therefore, nothing else but the proportional limit and should be considered a suitable basis for the evaluation of the allowable pressure on soil.

According to Fröhlich, the critical edge pressure = proportional limit, $q_{t,R}$ in kg/cm^2, for non-cohesive soil is

$$q_{t,R} = \frac{\pi(\gamma_k - \gamma_F)(1 - n)t}{\cot \phi_r - (\pi/2 - \phi_r)}, \tag{22-117}$$

where γ_k = true specific weight of soil particles, in g/cm^3;

γ_F = unit weight of water in the voids of soil;

n = porosity;

$\gamma = (\gamma_k - \gamma_F)(1 - n)$ = effective unit weight of soil;

t = depth of foundation, in cm;

ϕ_r = angle of internal friction of soil.

For a water-bearing sand and for dry sand the above typical values are, respectively:

$\gamma_k = 0.00265$	0.00265
$\gamma_F = 0.001$	0
$n = 0.394$	0.434 (assumed)
$\gamma = (\gamma_k - \gamma_F)(1 - n) = 0.001$	0.0015

The angle, ϕ_r, depends upon the density of the material, and its texture.

When $t = 0$, then Eq. (22-117) transforms into zero. It is to be understood that in the case of a surface loading there occur flow phenomena of non-cohesive soil even at the least pressure (the proportional limit is exceeded).

That the allowable soil pressure on non-cohesive soils for $t = 0$ cannot be derived from the ultimate bearing capacity of soil is demonstrated by Fröhlich by the following example.

The ultimate bearing capacity on a non-cohesive soil with $\gamma = 0.0015$ (dry sand) and $\phi_r = 35°$, loaded with a circular bearing area of 30 m in diameter is

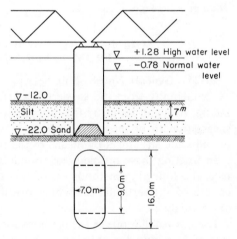

FIG. 22-22   Bridge pier.

$$\sigma_{ou} = 3000 \times 0.0015\left(\frac{1 + 0.574}{1 - 0.574}\right)^2 = 61.4 \quad (\text{kg/cm}^2).$$

If the proportional limit could be assumed to be ¼ of the ultimate, this method would still give allowable bearing capacity of about 15 kg/cm^2 which, for practical applications, is probably out of the question. Hence, according to Fröhlich, this example demonstrates that the concept of ultimate bearing capacity is unsuitable for the derivation of the allowable bearing capacity.

Example. Determine after Fröhlich the critical pressure for the bridge pier shown in Fig. 22-22.

1) For $\phi_r = 33°$. By Eq. (22-117),
$$q_{t,R} = 10.0 \times 0.576 = 5.76 \qquad \text{(kg/cm}^2\text{)}$$

2) For $\phi_r = 35°$:
$$q_{t,R} = 10.0 \times 0.671 = 6.71 \qquad \text{(kg/cm}^2\text{)}$$

The actual load of the pier is calculated as follows:

Weight of pier	5500 tons (metric)
Weight from bridge	500 ,,
Moving loads	700 ,,
	6700 tons

Area of base of footing:
$$(16.0 - 7.0)(7.0) + \frac{(7.0)^2 \pi}{4} = 101.5 \text{ m}^2$$

Pressure on soil from vertical loads:
$$\frac{6700}{101.5} = 66 \text{ t/m}^2 = 6.6 \text{ kg/cm}^2$$

Wind and flow pressure on the downstream side, approximately 1.0 kg/cm².
Uplift at normal water level $(22.0 - 0.78)$ t/m² $= 2.12$ kg/cm².
Total pressure: $6.6 + 1.0 - 2.12 = 5.48$ kg/cm².

SOIL BEARING CAPACITY DETERMINATIONS FROM EXPERIMENTAL RESULTS

22-24. General Notes. Soil bearing capacity problems can also be studied experimentally from the shape of the rupture surface developed in the soil at failure, brought about by the ultimate load of a structure upon exhausting the shear strength of the soil. Experimental results may be translated to natural, or full-scale structures by means of the theory of similitude (by modeling).

In treating these problems of foundations supported on a level ground surface, the following methods of loading the foundation footing are usually encountered: a) vertically and concentrically, b) vertically and eccentrically, and c) obliquely.

It is known that one of the methods for the determination of the bearing capacity of soils and for stability calculations of the integral foundation system, "soil-footing-load", is based on failure considerations, by introducing a so-called "coefficient of safety" to avoid failure of the soil by shear.

For this purpose, it is necessary to know, besides the physical properties of the soil, how the shear failure or rupture surface in the foundation-supporting soil takes place and what is the shape of the rupture or sliding surface.

To learn this, researchers and engineers have suggested that assumed shapes of failure surfaces be used in such calculations. As seen in the previous discussion in this book, it is the practice to use various assumed shapes of rupture surfaces rather than to determine them by experiment, or to base calculations on experimentally observed rupture surfaces. The reason for this is that it is difficult to determine the direction of the principal stresses in a fragmental medium such as a mass of soil. Because soil is an indeterminate and therefore a difficult material to study and work with, researchers usually perform their investigations relative to this subject on a small scale and with a cohesionless material: namely, dry sand. This permits excluding from their studies the effects of moisture and apparent, or transitional, cohesion associated with it. A further factor to be considered is moisture and its migration with temperature changes.

FIG. 22-23 Two-sided rupture surface from a vertical centrically applied load. Raritan sand.

22-25. Shapes of Rupture Surfaces. Every civil engineer encounters obliquely loaded foundations in his daily work, for example, wherever in addition to vertical loads, horizontal forces also act on a foundation. Such cases are foundations of vaults, arch-type bridges without ties, anchor blocks of suspension bridges, retaining walls, frameworks with horizontal reaction-components, dams, and hydraulic structures.

In order to perform calculations for the bearing capacity of a soil, for the depth of a foundation, or over-all stability of a foundation acted upon by oblique loads, it is necessary to know the mode of failure in shear of the soil underneath the foundation. Once the equation of the experimental rupture curve has been established, the length of the curve, the differential sector-areas, and the areas of the segments of the ruptured earth mass can be calculated, and stability analyses of the soil-foundation-load system performed.

The shape of the rupture surface in dry sand caused by vertically concentric and eccentric loads, as well as obliquely applied loads was studied, among others, by A. R. Jumikis from 1933 to date.[27,28,29,30,31] Figs. 22-23 through 26 illustrate

FIG. 22-24   One-sided rupture surface from a vertical, eccentrical load.

FIG. 22-25   Apparatus.

some examples of the author's experiments of two-sided and one-sided expulsion of a soil wedge from underneath the base of the footing of a foundation model.

The rupture surfaces were photographed, analyzed, mathematically and grapho-analytically treated; and polar equations for these rupture surfaces, viz., rupture curves were determined.

FIG. 22-26   One-sided rupture surface in Raritan sand under an obliquely loaded foundation model.

It revealed that the cylindrical rupture surface curve coincides remarkably well with the curve of a logarithmic spiral, the general equation of which is

$$r = r_o e^{-\omega \tan \phi}, \tag{22-118}$$

where r = radius-vector,

r_o = reference vector, or a segment on the polar axis from the pole of the spiral cut off by the spiral at $\omega = 0$,

e = base of natural logarithms,

ω = amplitude, or angle between r_o and r, and

$\tan \phi = \tan(\pi/2 - \psi)$:

$\tan \phi$ = coefficient of internal friction of sand. For the sand used in this study $\tan \phi = 0.580$;

$(\pi/2 - \psi)$ = angle between a radius-vector and its corresponding normal of the spiral.

The minus sign at ω denotes that as the amplitude, ω, increases, the radius-vector decreases. This method was adapted for the convenience of analyses of experimental data.

Or else,

$$r = r_o e^{\omega \tan \phi} \tag{22-119}$$

in which case the radius-vector, r, increases as the amplitude, ω increases.[32]

The physical, or experimental equation is obtained expressing r_o as a function of the applied resultant load, width of model, and other experimental parameters. The equilibrium condition of the soil-foundation-load system is expressed by comparing the driving and resisting moments, M_D and M_R, respectively.

A logarithmic spiral is a polar curve which intersects at a constant angle, $\psi = \pi/2 - \phi$, with all radius-vectors emanating from one point (the pole), Fig. 22-27.

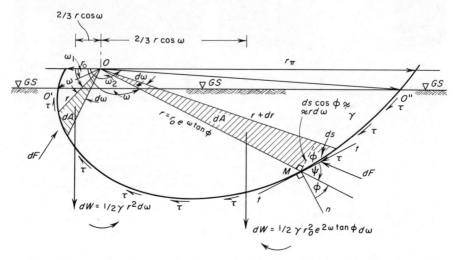

FIG. 22-27 Driving and resisting moments of weight of a spiraled soil wedge.

STATIC MOMENTS

22-26. Resisting Moments. The total resisting moment, M_R, to rotational motion about the pole of the spiral may be composed of

 a) the resultant resisting moment, M'_R, produced about the pole by the weight, W, of the soil wedge. The term "resultant resisting moment" here means the following: part of the left-hand side of the weight of the soil wedge (Fig. 22-28) contributes a driving moment (counterclockwise), and part—the right-hand side—contributes to the resisting moment (clockwise). The magnitude of the amplitude, ω, and the signs of the cosine of ω (in the expression of the arm of the differential weight of the differential sector), however, automatically take care of the resultant effect of the counter-clockwise and clockwise acting moments. Hence the concept of the resultant resisting moment, M'_R, from the weight of the soil wedge. This moment, M'_R, counterbalances, in part, the driving moment, M_D;

 b) a resisting moment, M_q, of an eventual surcharge, q, uniformly distributed over r_π, and

 c) a resisting moment, M_c, from the uniformly distributed shear resistance, $\tau = \sigma_e \tan \phi + c$, of the sand along the sliding surface. Here σ_e is the effective normal stress, and c = cohesion.

22-27. Calculation of the Resisting Moment, M'_R. The resisting moment, M'_R, produced by the soil wedge, may be calculated as follows (see Fig. 22-27):

$$M'_R = Wa = \int_0^{M'_R} dM'_R = \tfrac{2}{3} \int_0^W r\cos\omega\, dW \tag{22-120}$$

where $a = \tfrac{2}{3}r\cos\omega$ = moment arm of dW,

$$dW = \gamma dA = \tfrac{1}{2}\gamma r^2\, d\omega \tag{22-121}$$

$r = r_o e^{\omega\tan\phi}$, and

γ = unit weight of soil.

$$\therefore\ M'_R = \tfrac{1}{3}\gamma r_o^3 \int_0^\pi (e^{3\omega\tan\phi})\cos\omega\, d\omega, \tag{22-122}$$

if the ground surface coincides with a horizontal plane through the pole, O. After integration

$$M'_R = \frac{\gamma r_o^3\tan\phi}{1 + 9\tan\phi}(1 + e^{3\pi\tan\phi}). \tag{22-123}$$

All reactions, dF, pass through the pole of rotation, O, with their moment arms of the dF's equal to zero. Hence in the case when the rupture surface is a logarithmic spiral, the reactions do not contribute to the stability of the soil-foundation-load system.

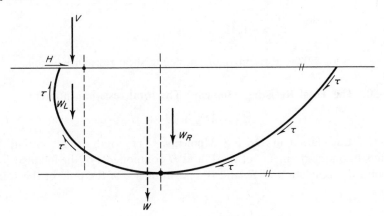

FIG. 22-28 Force system.

Note: If the ground surface is below the elevation of the pole, then the effect of the resisting moment pertaining to the soil triangle, $\triangle(O'\text{-}O\text{-}O'')$ must be taken into account accordingly. Integration of Eq. (22-122) must then be performed between $\omega = \omega_1$ and $\omega = \omega_2$, and the result of the integration should then be adjusted for the moment of $\triangle(O'\text{-}O\text{-}O'')$.

22-28. The Surcharge Moment. The surcharge moment is

$$M_q = \tfrac{1}{2}qr_\pi^2. \tag{22-124}$$

22-29. The Resisting Moment from Shear Resistance. The resisting moment, M_τ, due to the shear resistance of the soil is expressed as follows (Fig. 22-29):

$$dM_\tau = r\tau \, ds \cos = \tau r^2 \, d\omega. \tag{22-125}$$

Integration between ω_1 and ω_2 yields:

$$M_\tau = \tau \int_{\omega_1}^{\omega_2} r^2 \, d\omega = \tau r_o^2 \int_{\omega_1}^{\omega_2} (e^{2\omega \tan \phi}) \, d\omega = \frac{\tau}{2 \tan \phi} (r_{\omega_2}^2 - r_{\omega_1}^2) \tag{22-126}$$

When $\omega_1 = 0$ and $\omega_2 = \pi$, then

$$M_\tau = \frac{\tau}{2 \tan \phi} (r_\pi^2 - r_o^2) = \frac{\sigma_e \tan \phi + c}{2 \tan \phi} (r_\pi^2 - r_o^2). \tag{22-127}$$

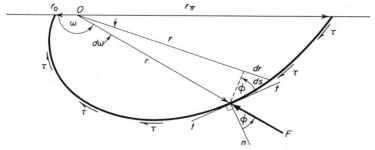

Moment: $dM_\tau = \tau ds \cos \phi \, r = \tau r^2 d\omega$
$M_\tau = \tau \int_{\omega_1}^{\omega_2} r^2 d\omega = \frac{\tau}{2 \tan \phi} \left(r_{\omega_2}^2 - r_{\omega_1}^2 \right)$

FIG. 22-29   Resisting moment due to shear resistance of soil.

22-30. The Total Resisting Moment. The total resisting moment is

$$M_R = M'_R + M_q + M_\tau. \tag{22-128}$$

22-31. Calculation of Driving Moments. The total driving moment, M_D, depends upon the moments of the V and H components of the inclined load, R; the point of application of R, and the position, y_o, of the pole of the spiral:

$$M_D = V\xi + Hy_o = M_V + M_H \tag{22-129}$$

where ξ = moment arm of V (Fig. 22-30).

If pertinent, the driving effect of the soil triangle, $\triangle(O'\text{-}O\text{-}O'')$, should not be forgotten. When $y_o = 0$, then $MH = 0$, and $MD = M_V$.

22-32. Comparison of Resisting and Driving Moments. The structure is stable when

$$\eta = \frac{M_R}{M_D} \geqslant 1.00, \tag{22-130}$$

η being, depending upon the importance of the structure and the judgment of the engineer, from $\eta = 1.5$ to about $\eta = 3$ and $\eta = 4$. Here η = factor of safety.

If $M_R < M_D$, then M_R can be increased by setting the foundation deeper. In doing so, a surcharge, q, is created on both sides of the foundation. This also means that the surcharge is distributed on the ground surface over an area $O\text{-}S$, from the front of the foundation to the end of the spiral, or even eventually over the radius-vector, r_π, if the latter would coincide with the real ground surface. Otherwise changes in R and b may be made to decrease the magnitude of the total driving moment. Here b is the width of the foundation.

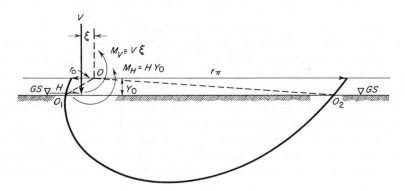

FIG. 22-30   Driving moments.

The properties of the logarithmic spiral were used for studying the experimentally obtained rupture curves, for determining the position of the poles of the experimentally found spirals, and for setting up the physical equation for the observed spiraled rupture curve.

22-33. Conclusions

1) Experiments with vertically and obliquely loaded foundation models provide clear evidence of the nature of the shape of a rupture surface in dry sand.
2) The failure of the sand mass takes place in shear.
3) The failure depends upon a) the magnitude of the resultant inclined load, R, and its point of application; b) the angle of internal friction, ϕ, of the sand; and c) the width of the model, b. Any other element of the spiral, such as r_o, r_π, and others, depends likewise upon R, ϕ, and b.
4) Upon rupture, from underneath an obliquely loaded foundation model a sand wedge is sheared off and expelled as an almost solid body laterally and one-sidedly along a curved rupture surface.
5) The shearing off of the sand wedge upon exhaustion of its shear strength takes place suddenly.
6) The study of the experimentally obtained rupture, viz., sliding surface in dry sand, corroborates that its surface-forming curve coincides very closely with the arc of the mathematical curve of a logarithmic spiral.
7) The experimental spirals are similar within the limits of the range of a particular type of experiment.

8) The angle of internal friction, ϕ, has a paramount influence upon the size of the experimental spiral.

9) The mode of loading—statically or dynamically—affects the size of the spiral greatly.

10) Generally, the larger R is, the larger is the size of the spiral.

11) The general polar equation of the experimental spiral curve for an obliquely loaded foundation model is

$$r = AR^a e^{\omega \tan \phi}, \tag{22-131}$$

where A and a are experimental parameters.

12) The horizontal load, H, necessary to produce a rupture surface, depends upon the vertical load, V, as well as upon the height of application, h, of the horizontal load.

13) The lower the height of application, h, of the horizontal load, H, is, and the larger V is, the more clearly pronounced are the rupture surfaces; at a certain high value of h, the overturning phenomenon of the model starts and no rupture surface can be observed. Here, for each vertical load, V, it is possible to find height, h, at which a horizontal load of very small magnitude (nearly zero) is sufficient to cause a condition impending to tilt.

14) In the case where the sand soil contains also some cohesion, it is possible by means of a simple integral to perform stability calculations (see Fig. 22-29). The moment of cohesion relative to the pole of the spiral is:

$$M_c = \frac{c}{2 \tan \phi} (r_\pi^{\,2} - r_\circ^{\,2}). \tag{22-132}$$

15) Theoretical considerations indicate that when $\tan \phi = 0$, i.e., if we have to deal with a pure cohesive soil, the spiral equation (22-118) transforms into a circle:

$$r = r_\circ = \text{const.} \tag{22-133}$$

16) By means of similarity or model law, the logarithmically spiralled rupture surface can also be used for stability calculations of large scale foundations.

17) There are no difficulties in drawing spirals, particularly when spiral tables or spiral templets are applied, or the rules for the construction of spirals are employed.

18) The application of a logarithmically spiraled rupture surface to stability calculations possesses a great advantage over the other assumed surfaces; namely, that it is not necessary to assume nor to be concerned as to how the reactions in sand soil along the sliding surface are distributed or what their magnitudes are. This is because the logarithmic spiral possesses an important property: all radii-vectors pass through the pole of the spiral (moment arm for reactions is 0). Hence all soil reaction moments are automatically excluded from our stability calculations by comparing active (driving) and reactive (resisting) moments.

19) The results of this experimental research are useful in studying the ultimate bearing capacity of sand soil at or below the ground surface, and the nature of the rupture surface. The experimental research results are also of significance in checking published theoretical information, and in analyzing the limits of its application.

REFERENCES

1. K. Terzaghi and R. B. Peck, *Soil Mechanics in Engineering Practice*, New York, John Wiley and Sons, Inc., 1948.
2. "Soil Bearing Values—Presumptive Capacity", *National Building Code*, Recommended by the National Board of Fire Underwriters, New York, 1955, Section 906.2, p. 115.
3. *Building Laws of the City of New York*, vol. 1, 1959, Sub-Article 5, p. 173.
4. *The Boston Building Code*, 1944, sect. 2904c.
5. *American Standard Building Code Requirements for Excavations and Foundations*, ASCE, Manual of Engineering Practice, approved by the American Standards Association in 1952, no. 32, New York, 1953.
6. W. S. Housel, *A Practical Method for Selection of Foundations based on Fundamental Research in Soil Mechanics*, University of Michigan Engineering Research Bulletin, no. 13, October, 1929.
7. W. S. Housel, "Bearing Power of Clay is Determinable", *Eng. News-Record*, February, 23, 1933.
8. W. S. Housel, *A Generalized Theory of Soil Resistance*. Papers on Soils. Presented at the Second Pacific Area National Conference at Los Angeles, California, September 17, 1956. ASTM Special Technical Publication no. 206, Philadelphia, 1957.
9. A. Casagrande and R. E. Fadum, "Application of Soil Mechanics in Designing Building Foundations", *Trans.* ASCE, 1944, vol. 109.
10. F. Schleicher, "Zur Theory des Baugrundes", *Der Bauingenieur*, no. 48, November 19, 1926, no. 49, December 3, 1926.
11. H. E. Pauker, "An explanatory report on the project of a sea-battery" (in Russian), *Journal of the Ministry of Ways and Communications*, St. Petersburg, September, 1889.
12. S. Timoshenko, *History of Strength of Materials*, New York, McGraw-Hill Book Company, Inc., 1953.
13. V. J. Kurdjümoff, "Zur Frage des Widerstandes der Gründungen auf natürlichem Boden", *Der Civilingenieur*, 1892, pp. 263-311.
14. W. J. M. Rankine, *A Manual of Applied Mechanics*, London, Charles Griffin and Co., 1885, pp. 219-220.
15. A. L. Bell, "The Lateral Pressure and Resistance of Clay, and the Supporting Power of Clay Foundation", *Minutes* of Proceedings of the Institution of Civil Engineers, London, 1915, Paper no. 4131.
16. A. W. Skempton, "Arthur Langtry Bell (1874-1956) and his Contribution to Soil Mechanics", *Geotechnique*, vol. 8, no. 4, 1958.
17. A. Casagrande and R. E. Fadum, "Application of Soil Mechanics in Designing Building Foundations", *Trans.* ASCE, 1944, vol. 109, pp. 383-419.
18. L. Prandtl, *Über die Härte plastischer Körper*, Nachrichten von der Königlichen Gesellschaft der Wissenschaften zu Göttingen (Mathematisch-physikalische Klasse aus dem Jahre 1920, 1920, Berlin, pp. 74-85.
19. L. Prandtl, "Über die Eindringungsfestigkeit (Härte) plastischer Baustoffe und die Festigkeit von Schneiden", *Zeitschrift für angewandte Mathematik und Mechanik*, vol. 1, no. 1, February, 1921, pp. 15-20.

20. D. P. Krynine, *Soil Mechanics*, New York, McGraw-Hill Book company, Inc., 1947, pp. 207-209.

21. D. W. Taylor, *Fundamentals of Soil Mechanics*, New York, John Wiley and Sons, Inc., 1948, p. 573.

22. K. Terzaghi, *Theoretical Soil Mechanics*, New York, John Wiley and Sons, Inc., 1943, pp. 118-143.

23. H. D. Krey, *Erddruck, Erdwiderstand und Tragfähigkeit des Baugrundes*, Berlin, Wilhelm Ernst und Sohn, 1936, pp. 143-148; 197-201.

24. A. R. Jumikis, "Rupture Surface in Dry Sand Under Oblique Loads", Paper no. 861, *Journal of Soil Mechanics and Foundations Division, Proceedings*, ASCE, January, 1956, vol. 82, no. SM.1.

25. R. H. Hasson and E. Vey, *An Investigation of Krey's Method for Bearing Capacity*, a paper submitted to the First Pan American Congress on Soil Mechanics and Foundation Engineering. held at the University City, Mexico, September 11-16, 1959, *Proceedings*, vol. I, pp. 97-130.

26. O. K. Fröhlich, *Druckverteilung im Baugrunde*, Wien, Springer Verlag, 1934, 1. 142.

27. A. R. Jumikis, *Experimental Research Concerning the Form of the Rupture Surface in Dry Sand Caused by an Obliquely Loaded Foundation Model* (typewritten), Riga, 1944.

28. A. R. Jumikis, "Rupture Surfaces in Sand Under Oblique Loads", *Proceedings*, ASCE, January, 1956, vol. 82, no. SM.1.

29. A. R. Jumikis, Discussion by A. R. Jumikis on "Earth Pressures and Bearing Capacity Calculations by Generalized Procedures of Slices", by N. Janbu, *Proceedings*, Fourth International Conference on Soil Mechanics and Foundation Engineering, held August, 1957, in London, London. Butterworths Scientific Publications, 1958, vol. 3, pp. 235-238.

30. A. R. Jumikis, Discussion by A. R. Jumikis on "An Investigation of Krey's Method for Bearing Capacity", by R. E. Hasson and E. Vey, *Proceedings*, First Pan American Congress on Soil Mechanics and Foundation Engineering, held September 7-12, 1959, at University City, Mexico, *Proceedings*, vol. I, pp. 131-137.

31. A. R. Jumikis, "The Shape of Rupture Surface in Dry Sand", *Proceedings*, 5th International Conference on Soil Mechanics and Foundation Engineering, held in Paris, France, July 17-22, 1961, Paper 3A, pp. 693-698.

32. A. R. Jumikis, *Some Properties of a Logarithmic Spiral* (mimeographed), New Brunswick, New Jersey, 1960 (23 pages and 14 illustrations).

PROBLEMS

22-1. A foundation is to be placed on a shale formation. Exploration indicates that the shale is in a sound condition. If the base of the footing is to be placed on the shale 5 ft below the ground surface, establish the allowable pressure on this shale. Use the Boston Building Code. Determine also the maximum allowable pressure which this code permits.

22-2. Determine the dimensions of a square footing to transmit on a clayey soil a total load of $W = 250$ tons (USA) for an allowable settlement of $\frac{1}{2}''$. The test loading areas are: $A_1 = 1' \times 1'$, and $A_2 = 3' \times 3'$, loaded with 5 tons and 15 tons, respectively at which $\frac{1}{2}''$ settlement for each loading area has been attained.

22-3. Calculate ω-values as in Table 22-2 for side ratios of $a/b = 4, 6, 7, 8, 9, 15, 20, 200, 400, 500, 600, 800,$ and 5000.

22-4. Questions pertaining to bearing capacity of foundation soils.
  a) What are the stability requirements of a foundation?
  b) Define ultimate bearing capacity of soil.
  c) Define safe (or allowable) bearing capacity of soil.

     d) Describe methods of obtaining bearing capacity of soil.

     e) What are the deficiencies of bearing capacity values given by some building codes?

22- 5. A footing exerts edge pressures as shown in Fig. Problem 22-5. Considering a factor of safety of $\eta = 3$, is this foundation safe against failure of soil in shear? Assume and use other necessary engineering values.

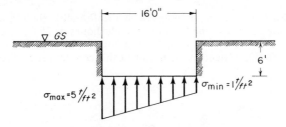

FIG. Problem 22-5.

22- 6. If the vertical contact pressure on the soil exerted by the foundation is $\sigma_o = 1.0$ t/ft²; if the allowable bearing capacity of a sand deposit is $\sigma_{adm} = 1.5$ t/ft² at a factor of safety of $\eta = 2.0$; if the unit weight of the soil is $\gamma = 95$ lb/ft³, and the angle of internal friction of the sand is $\phi = 28°$, calculate and decide upon the depth of laying of foundation. Use Pauker's and Rankine's theories. What is the difference between these two theories?

22- 7. What can be done using the Pauker-Rankine ultimate bearing capacity formula for a non-cohesive soil in order to compute a bearing capacity value which is greater than zero, if the foundation is placed on the ground surface?

22- 8. Given: $\gamma = 110$ lb/ft³; $\phi = 20°$; $c = 600$ lb/ft². Calculate the minimum depth of foundation in this ϕ-c soil, as well as for the ϕ-soil ($c = 0$) when $\phi = 20°$, for a factor of safety of $\eta = 1$ and $\eta = 3$ in both cases. Use Bell's method for the system shown in Fig. Problem 22-8.

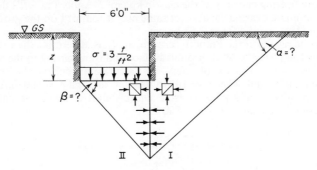

FIG. Problem 22-8.

22- 9. A foundation footing the width of which is $B = 2b = 8$ ft rests on the ground surface of a clay. The unconfined compressive strength of this clay has been tested to be $\sigma_c = 2.0$ kg/cm². Calculate by the Bell-Casagrande method the ultimate bearing capacity of this clay.

22-10. In Prandtl's equation there appears a factor $K_p e^{\pi \tan \phi}$. Prepare a graph showing $K_p e^{\phi \tan \pi} = f(\phi)$. Vary ϕ from 0° to 50° in five-degree increments. Discuss results. In particular, evaluate the magnitude of the surcharge stress, p_s, relative to the total bearing capacity of soil, σ_u.

22-11. For the purpose of graphical comparison, plot $\sigma_u = f(\phi)$ of Prandtl's formula and all its modifications.

22-12. Determine by Prandtl's method the magnitude of the pressure from a strip foundation at the ground surface and 3 ft below the ground surface which would bring about failure in a cohesive soil material. Given: specific gravity of soil: $G = 2.67$, porosity: $n = 30\%$, angle of internal friction: $\phi = 30°$, cohesion, $c = 0.4$ kg/cm².

22-13. In the illustrative example as given in the Prandtl's theory, assume that for maintaining the grade, the height of the fill should be 25 ft. A counterweight is to be placed on the soil on both sides adjacent to the slopes of the fill (Fig. Problem 22-13). Calculate the height of this counterweight necessary to attain

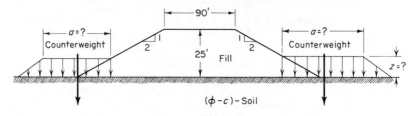

FIG. Problem 22-13.

a factor of safety of $\eta = 3.0$ against breaking of the fill into the fill-supporting soil and thus preventing the lateral expulsion of soil out from underneath the fill.

22-14. Check factor of safety, η, for the example given in Prandtl's theory using Prandtl's original equation and its modifications, and tabulate the results obtained.

22-15. A pure clay has an unconfined compressive strength of $\sigma_c = 1$ kg/cm². If an 8 ft wide strip footing is founded 5 ft below the ground surface, what is the ultimate bearing capacity of the clay in kg/cm²? Apply Prandtl's theory. What is the ultimate bearing capacity of same clay if founded on the ground surface? ($c = \sigma_c/2$; $\sigma_u = (5.14)c = 2.57$ kg/cm².)

22-16. Using the results of the Prandtl-Terzaghi analysis, determine the size of a square footing founded 8 ft below ground surface and transmitting to the soil a load of 100 tons. Select a factor of safety, η. Calculate dimensions 1) for the footing placed on a ϕ-c soil, when $\gamma = 105$ lb/ft³, $\phi = 28°$, and $c = 600$ lb/ft², and 2) for a footing placed on a pure cohesive soil (c-soil) if $\gamma = 112$ lb/ft³ and the shear strength of this material is $\tau = 800$ lb/ft².

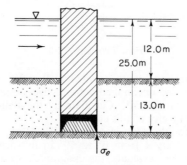

FIG. Problem 22-18.

22-17. Calculate by Prandtl-Terzaghi formulas the ultimate load per foot of length of a strip foundation, the width of which is $B = 2b = 8$ ft. The base of the footing is 8 ft below the ground surface. The soil physical properties are the same as those given in the previous problem.

22-18. The edge pressure, σ_e, is reported to be for the structure as sketched in Fig. Problem 22-18 equal to 8.9 kg/cm². Check this value by calculating the allowable soil pressure after Fröhlich for $\phi_r = 33°$ and $\phi_r = 35°$.

$$(\phi_r = 33°: q_{t.R} = 13.0 \times 0.576 = 7.5 \text{ kg/cm}^2.$$

$$\phi_r = 35°: q_{t.R} = 13.0 \times 0.671 = 8.7 \text{ kg/cm}^2.)$$

22-19. Given for a water-bearing sand: $(\gamma_k - \gamma_F)(1 - n) = \gamma_w = 0.001$ kg/cm³ and for a dry sand: $(\gamma_k - \gamma_F)(1 - n) = \gamma_d = 0.0015$ kg/cm³.

1) Assuming angles ϕ_r to vary from 28° to 40° in 2-degree intervals, prepare a table for Fröhlich's proportional limits, $q_{t.R}$ in kg/cm² for these two types of soils for a $t = 1.0$ m depth of base of footing below the ground surface.

2) Make your observations as to the effect of the groundwater on the proportional limit.

3) For $\phi = 34°$, and $t = 3.00$ m, how large an effect has the groundwater upon the critical edge pressure as compared with dry sand? (From 2.796 kg/cm² to 1.863 kg/cm³.)

4) What is the effect of hydrostatic uplift of the two soils under discussion in (3)? (Reduction in pressure by 0.311 kg/cm².)

5) What is the allowable bearing capacity of the two soils under discussion at $t = 3.0$ m? (2.796 kg/cm² for dry sand; 2.174 kg/cm² for water-bearing sand.)

Chapter 23

PILES

23-1. Introduction. In foundation engineering a pile is a construction element —a column of wood, steel, or reinforced concrete—driven into soil to support vertical and inclined structural loads and to transmit these loads into the deeper layers of firm soil below the ground surface at an economical and practical depth, in such a way that these layers of soil or rock can sustain the loads.

Pile foundations are usually used where soil properties are inferior for shallow foundations.

Functions of Piles. The functions of piles are:
1) to support superimposed loads;
2) to densify the soil;
3) to form a wall against water, dry pouring and/or plastic soil (sheet piling), and
4) to resist lateral pressures of water and soil.

Use of Piles. Piles are used in river deltas (Venice), reclaimed land (Holland), for hydraulic and waterfront structures, bridges, and heavy industrial and civilian structures. Piles are made of timber, steel, reinforced concrete, or combined of these materials. At times, where necessary, sand piles are installed in silty and clayey soils.

23-2. Types of Piles. Piles are commonly classed into 1) bearing piles and 2) sheet piles.

1) Any pile carrying a superimposed load is termed a bearing pile. Piles may bear directly on a firm layer of soil, and/or support structural loads by frictional forces distributed over their mantle surface by so-called skin friction = mantle friction—friction between the soil and the pile material.

In the first case, when piles derive their support from the underlying firm layer of soil and transmit their loads through their bottom tips, they are termed *end-bearing piles.* In the second case, when piles derive their support from mantle friction, they are termed *friction piles.* Piles which are driven at an inclination to resist lateral forces are termed *batter piles.*

End-bearing piles resting on rock can support heavier loads than those resting on a firm, geologically unconsolidated bearing material of soil. The soil below the elevation of the tips of the piles must be able to support the loads transmitted by piles into these layers.

2) Sheet piles form a diaphragm made of interlocking members of wood, steel, and reinforced concrete, driven individually to form an obstruction to filtrating

water. They are used for cofferdams, for stabilizing foundations, and to support loads.

It is obvious that the interpretation of pile-loading test results and pile-driving data for the design of piles and piled foundations depends greatly upon the proper insight into the geologic, hydrologic, and soil conditions at the construction site and upon the study and intelligent interpretation of soil boring results. Hence the soil environment must be carefully investigated to ascertain existing conditions to enable the engineer to decide upon a certain type of pile to use, and type of foundation to construct. The various types of piles are schematically illustrated in Figs. 23-1 and 23-2.

23-3. Negative Mantle Friction. The bearing capacity of a pile driven into a soil may decrease during the course of time. The decrease may be brought about by the so-called negative mantle friction. This happens when a pile is driven through cohesive and moderately compressible soils which are in a continuous process of consolidation under their own self-weight. The downward settlement of the soil by consolidation induces an oppositely directed mantle friction relative to the pile. In soil mechanics this friction is termed the negative mantle friction. This friction tends to pull the pile out of the ground.

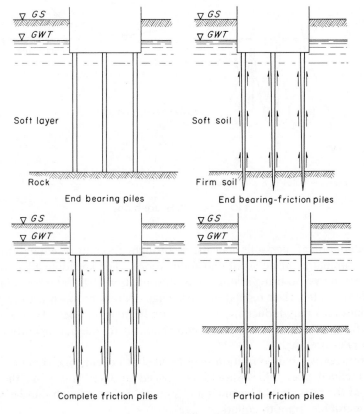

FIG. 23-1   Pile types.

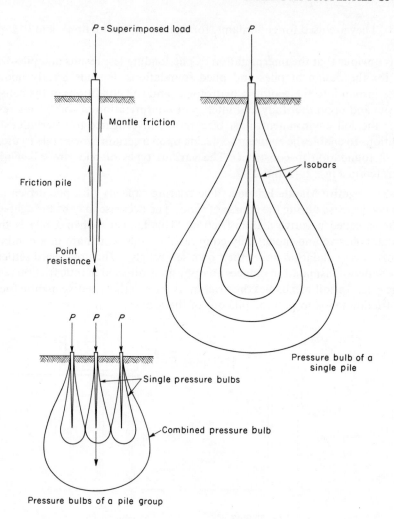

FIG. 23-2   Pressure bulbs.

Consolidation of such soils may also be brought about by recent natural and/or artificial surcharge, or adjacent mat foundations. The kneading effect of a pile-driven clay may also bring about some consolidation. The later lowering of the groundwater table, river regulations, drainage operations in an area, and other such conditions may induce negative mantle friction on piles. Hence, negative mantle friction is an undesirable phenomenon in foundation operations where friction piles are used.

Where negative mantle friction may be likely to occur, one should avoid the use of inclined piles. Piles should be spaced at large intervals; the mantle surface of the piles should be small and smooth, or the piles should be provided with discardable, smooth collars.

23-4. Bearing Capacity of Piles. The *Manual of Engineering Practice No. 27* published by the American Society of Civil Engineers[1] defines the term bearing capacity as follows:

"Bearing capacity may be defined as that load which can be sustained by a pile foundation without producing objectionable settlement or material movement—initial or progressive—resulting in damage to the structure or interfering with its use."

The bearing capacity of piled foundations is estimated based either on the bearing capacity of a *single pile*, or on that of a *group of piles*.

A pile group or cluster of piles is a pile foundation where the heads of all piles are joined together by a grillage, slabs, or caps to form a unit of piles— a pile group. By this means it is hoped that all piles will settle uniformly provided the pile-supporting soil is uniform.

The pile bearing capacity may be determined

1) by means of dynamic pile-driving formulas using data obtained from dynamic pile-driving tests from the impact on the head of the pile, i.e., from the resistance of the pile to driving it into the soil;
2) from static load tests of piles,
3) by means of static bearing capacity formulas, and
4) by empirical rules.

DYNAMIC PILE-DRIVING FORMULAS

20-5. Formulas. A dynamic pile-driving formula is an equation which is thought to predict the ultimate bearing capacity or the safe bearing capacity of a pile, depending upon what equations and factors of safety are used, to support a static load.

Such an equation, then, expresses the relationship between the dynamic resistance of the soil to rapid penetration and the static resistance of the soil.

Most of the dynamic, pile-driving formulas are derived theoretically by means of mathematics and theoretical mechanics. Such formulas serve to evaluate the static bearing capacity of piles.

All dynamic, pile-driving formulas can be broadly classed into two groups: 1) those derived from the work-energy relationships, and 2) those derived from the impact-momentum theory.

23-6. Principle of Pile Driving. The principle of pile driving is illustrated in Fig. 23-3. The pile penetrates into the soil by a succession of blows brought about by striking the pile on its head with a pile-driving hammer. During the fall of the hammer its velocity increases to a maximum the instant it strikes the pile.

Upon striking the pile, the kinetic energy of the hammer is

$$(Wh) - \Sigma \text{ (energy losses)}, \tag{23-1}$$

where W = weight of the falling hammer, and
h = height of fall.

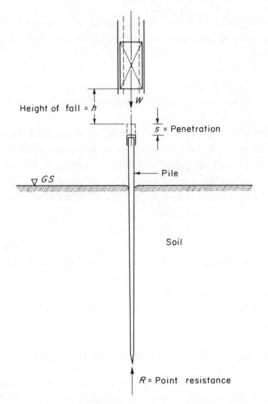

FIG. 23-3   Principle of pile driving.

The energy losses are attributed mainly to friction, rebound of hammer, dissipation of heat in the system, brooming of the head of the pile, and other losses.

Note that the kinetic energy of the falling hammer upon the striking the pile is equal to the potential energy of the uplifted hammer.

Upon impact between hammer and pile, part of the energy is lost in heating the head of the pile; compressing the hammer, the pile and the pile protective driving cap; or brooming the head of the pile. Part of the energy is dissipated in elastic compression of the pile and the soil; and by vibration of hammer, pile, and soil. The residual kinetic energy of the hammer is then transferred to the pile and soil and thus consumed for penetrating the pile into the soil against the resistance of the soil. For effective work, the weight of the hammer should be larger than the weight of the pile.

The penetration of the pile into the soil meets some resistance at the lower end, or tip of the pile, and the axial component of the lateral pressure of the soil on the mantle surface of the pile, causing mantle friction between the pile material and the soil. These resistances to penetration bring to the fore the concept that soil resistance is one of the factors upon which the bearing capacity of the pile depends.

To overcome the soil resistance to penetration of the pile, mechanical work must be performed in driving the pile into the soil (Rs), where R = average value of a variable resistance with depth to dynamic penetration, and s = distance the pile travels upon penetration.

The soil resistance to rapid penetration to be overcome depends upon the nature and depth of the soil. A pile may be driven into the soil two or three inches upon each blow. But the less the magnitude of penetration of the pile upon each blow, the greater is the actual pressure with which the blow forces the pile downwards.

In forcing the pile to penetrate into the ground, energy is expended. A pile intended to carry a heavy load permanently must be driven until it penetrates but little with each blow.

23-7. Work-Energy Relationship. The pile is driven into the soil by a hammer the weight of which is W. The hammer is so mounted that it may have a free fall from rest upon the pile. The pile is driven until it penetrates only a certain fraction of an inch, s, under each of the last blows. Under these conditions, the safe bearing capacity of a pile, P, is the resistance, R, of the soil to penetration divided by a factor of safety, η:

$$P = \frac{R}{\eta}. \tag{23-2}$$

Assuming the hammer to be a free falling body, that the hammer and pile are rigid bodies, that R for the last few blows is constant, and that the final kinetic energy is zero, then the work-energy relationship can be written as

$$\tfrac{1}{2}Mv_o^2 = \int_0^s R \, ds = Rs, \tag{23-3}$$

where M = mass of hammer, and

$$v_o = \sqrt{2gh} = \tag{23-4}$$

$$= \text{fall velocity, in consistent units.}$$

Setting

$$\tfrac{1}{2}Mv_o^2 = Wh, \tag{23-5}$$

the resistance of the soil or the bearing capacity of the pile is then, by Eq. (23-3)

$$R = \frac{Wh}{s}. \tag{23-6}$$

The safe bearing capacity of the pile is usually taken as one-sixth or one-eighth of R.

There are many work-energy relationship equations for calculating the bearing capacity of piles.

Note that if in Eq. (23-6) $s = 0$, then $R = \infty$, a very large force. To avoid this inconsistency Wellington added to s in the denominator of Eq. (23-6) a unity if working with a drop hammer, reasoning that R can never be greater than the total energy of the hammer (Wh):

$$R = \frac{Wh}{s + 1.0}.$$ (23-7)

Because of the many and various elastic conditions in the dynamic pile-driving system, and because of the many varying properties of soil, engineers have come to believe that it is impossible to arrive at a universal equation that will give absolutely dependable information relative to the bearing capacity of piles.

23-8. Rational Pile-Driving Formula. The assumptions underlying the rational pile-driving formula are that the kinetic energy induced by the falling hammer is consumed 1) in driving the pile into the soil, 2) in bringing about elastic deformations of the pile, and 3) in bringing about plastic deformations.

The bearing capacity in this theory is expressed as

$$R = \frac{Wh}{s + k} \frac{W + we^2}{W + w},$$ (23-8)

where e = coefficient of restitution;
for timber, $e \approx 0.2$,
for metal piles, $e \geqslant 0.5$,
for perfect elastic blow, $e = 1.0$, and
for perfect inelastic blow, $e = 0$;
s = penetration of pile into the soil upon one blow of hammer;
k = hammer coefficient.
The units of h, s, and k are those of length,
W = weight of hammer, and
w = weight of piles.

23-9. *Engineering News* Formulas. Based on his experience, the so-called *Engineering News* pile bearing capacity formulas were proposed by A. M. Wellington, editor of the *Engineering News*, in 1888. These equations are obtained from the rational pile-driving formula (weightless pile), and are extensively used in the U.S.A.

Safe Bearing Capacity of Pile
1) For drop hammers:

$$P = \frac{Wh}{\eta(s + 1.0)}$$ (23-9)

2) For single-acting steam hammers:

$$P = \frac{Wh}{\eta(s + 0.1)}$$ (23-10)

3) For double-acting steam hammers

$$P = \frac{(W + ap)h}{\eta(s + 0.1)} \qquad (23\text{-}11)$$

where P = safe load in pound;

$\eta = 6$ = factor of safety for piles driven to practical refusal to any material;

h = fall of hammer or length of stroke of piston, in feet;

s = average penetration of pile into soil, in inches per blow, for the last 5 blows of a drop hammer, or 20 blows of a steam hammer;

a = effective area of piston, in square inches, and

p = mean effective steam pressure, lb/in^2.

Example. Given $W = 3000$ lb; $h = 12$ ft; $s = 0.5$ in. Calculate the safe bearing capacity of a pile if a drop hammer is used.
Solution.

$$P = \frac{Wh}{\eta(s + 1.0)} = \frac{(12)(3000)(12)}{6(0.5 + 1.0)} = \underline{48,000 \text{ (lb)}}$$

Example. Given $W = 5000$ lb; $h = 4.0$ ft; $s = 0.3$ in. Calculate the safe bearing capacity of a pile if a single-acting steam hammer is used.
Solution.

$$P = \frac{(2)(5000)(4.0)}{0.3 + 0.1} = \underline{100,000 \text{ (lb)}}$$

23-10. The Pure, Classical, Complete Pile-Driving Formula. Redtenbacher's[2] classical pile-driving formula (1859) attempts to comprehend the applied effective energy on one hand and the useful work and losses on the other hand upon the application of one single blow:

$$\eta_e Wh = R_d s + \left[\eta_e Wh \frac{w(1 - e^2)}{W + w} \right] + \left[\frac{(R_d)^2 L'}{2A'E'} + \frac{(R_d)^2 L}{2AE} + CR_d \right] \quad (23\text{-}12)$$

Total applied energy	Useful work: energy used to move the pile a distance s	Loss in impact	Energy losses		
			Loss in cap	Loss in pile	Loss in soil due to elastic compression + other losses
			due to elastic compression		

The symbols in Eq. (23-12) have the following meanings:

W = weight of striking hammer;

w = weight of pile;

η_e = efficiency of hammer, usually < 1.0;

R_d = dynamic resistance of soil (ultimate load or bearing capacity of pile);

h = height of fall of hammer;

s = penetration of pile per one blow of hammer;

e = Newtonian coefficient of restitution;

L' = axial length of pile cap or cushion block;

A' = cross-sectional area of the pile cap or cushion block;

E' = modulus of elasticity of the pile cap or cushion block;

L = full length of pile as driven;

A = cross-sectional area of pile as driven;

E = modulus of elasticity of pile.

For use in pile driving, this quadratic equation must be solved for R_d.

All other dynamic, pile-driving formulas, insofar as known, may be derived from this classical formula by making various simplifications.

The safe bearing capacity, P, of the driven pile is obtained by dividing R_d by a suitable factor of safety, η:

$$P = \frac{R_d}{\eta} \tag{23-13}$$

For a complete, inelastic impact ($e = 0$) Redtenbacher's classical formula transforms into

$$R = \frac{AE}{L}\left[-s + \sqrt{s^2 + \frac{L}{A}\frac{2W^2h}{E(W + w)}}\right] \tag{23-14}$$

23-11. Stern's Formula. Stern's formula (1908)[3] may also be considered as one of the most complete. It is based on the theoretical equality between the mechanical work of the fall of the hammer minus the impact losses, and the mechanical work performed by penetration of the pile into the soil and the work of deformation:

$$Wh - \frac{Ww}{W + w}h(1 - e^2) = (R - W - w)s + \frac{R^2L}{2AE}, \tag{23-15}$$

where the symbols are as before.

From here, the ultimate bearing capacity of the pile for semi-elastic impact is

$$R = \frac{AE}{L}\left\{-s + \sqrt{s^2 + \frac{2LWh(W + we^2) + s(W + w)^2}{AE(W + w)}}\right\}. \tag{23-16}$$

The greatest difficulty in the use of this equation lies in the proper evaluation of the coefficient of restitution, e, viz., the degree of elasticity.

When $e = 0$, then Stern's equation transforms into

$$R = \frac{AE}{L}\left\{-s + \sqrt{s^2 + \frac{2LW^2h + s(W + w)^2}{AE(W + w)}}\right\}. \tag{23-17}$$

23-12. Weisbach's Formula (~1850): Pile ultimate bearing capacity:

$$R = -\frac{sAE}{L} + \sqrt{\frac{2WhAE}{L} + \left(\frac{sAE}{L}\right)^2}. \tag{23-18}$$

Here the impact loss is entirely neglected.

23-13. Other Formulas. In the following energy equation,

$$Rs = Wh \frac{W + e^2 w}{W + w}, \tag{23-19}$$

assuming a perfectly inelastic impact ($e = 0$), Eytelwein (~ 1820) obtained his dynamic pile-driving formula for ultimate pile bearing capacity;

$$R = \frac{Wh}{s\left(1 + \dfrac{w}{W}\right)} \tag{23-20}$$

and the safe pile bearing capacity is

$$P = R/\eta,$$

where $\eta = 6$.

The McKay (U.S. Navy Bureau of Yards and Docks) safe bearing capacity formula is

$$P = \frac{2Wh}{s\left[1 + (0.3)\dfrac{w}{W}\right]}. \tag{23-21}$$

23-14. Brix Equation. This equation[4] is based on the impact theory, and gives the safe static load, P, which the pile will support:

$$P = \frac{W^2 wh}{\eta(W + w)^2 s}, \tag{23-22}$$

where $\eta > 3$ is the factor of safety. The Brix equation is extensively used in continental Europe for sandy soils, and applies to drop hammers only. It is not satisfactory for small s, small h, or for dense soils.

As can be observed, all of the special dynamic pile-driving formulas can be obtained from a variation of Redtenbacher's or Stern's "complete" formulas.

In the book *Pile Foundations* by R. D. Chellis[5] there are many pile bearing capacity formulas listed, domestic as well as foreign.

23-15. Discussion. During the course of time, engineers learned that dynamic pile-driving formulas are of limited value in piled foundation work mainly because the dynamic resistance of soil does not represent its static resistance, and because often the results obtained from the use of dynamic equations are of questionable dependability.

In treating pile bearing capacity problems it is necessary to have complete information concerning the surrounding soil. In cohesive soils, the resistance to driving increases through the sudden increase in stress in the pore water, and, decreases because of the decreased value of the internal friction between soil and pile because of the pore water. These oppositely directed forces do not lend themselves to an analytical treatment; hence, they show clearly that the dynamic penetration resistance of soil to pile driving has no relationship to static bearing capacity. Besides, pile driving in cohesive soils changes the structure of the soil. The kneading effect decreases the strength of the clay many fold, but the original strength may never be regained, although it has been observed in practice in some instances that after interruption of pile-driving operations, the dynamic resistance to driving after resumption of pile-driving operations is much greater than before the interruption of work.

This is explained by the film water which is expelled from the voids of the soil upon driving the pile, decreasing the driving resistance. After a recess when the film water has had time enough to be absorbed by the soil, full static friction develops again between pile and soil.

STATIC LOAD TESTS OF PILES

23-16. Description of Test. Because theories of dynamic resistance to penetration are now considered to be crude, an effort has been made to evaluate the static bearing capacity of a pile by considerations which are based on the theory of statics.

The principal difference in the performance of piles under dynamic and static loading conditions is seen in the time effect of the various soils. Expulsion of the pore water from the voids of a cohesive soil takes a far longer period of time than from that of a non-cohesive soil. This fact alone signifies the great difference between dynamic and static loading. In addition, thixotropic effects of certain clay soils are not considered by the dynamic, pile-driving formulas.

The principle of the static load test of a single pile may be described as follows (refer to Fig. 23-4).

A pile in place is loaded at its top through a platform by dead load or by means of a hydraulic jack. The initial load on the test pile is usually taken equal to 100% of the design load of the pile. For dead load, water, sand, bricks, pig iron, or any other heavy material whose weight can be measured may be used. The initial load is then increased, say after 12 hours by 25%, and after 24 hours again by 25% of the initial load, so that after 24 hours the pile is now loaded with 150% of the design load.

This load remains on the pile for at least 48 hours. During the loading test, settlement readings of the pile before and after adding new load increments should be taken, and every 12 hours after adding the final load increment. After the loading test is over rebound readings of the soil should be taken. In practice it is considered that the resulting settlement after the removal of the test loads should not exceed a value greater than 0.01 in. per ton of the total test load. Such a requirement is set, for example, by the Building Code of the City of New York. Other building codes spell out testing specifications somewhat differently from those here described.

It should be kept in mind that the bearing capacity of piles derived from the test of one single pile may not always be the bearing capacity if the water regimen and other soil conditions should change during the course of time.

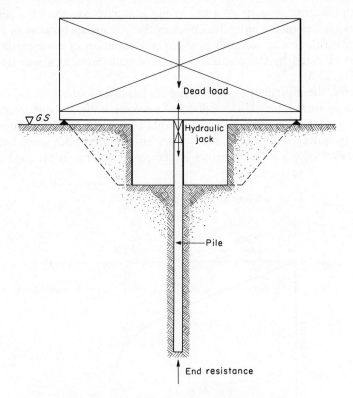

FIG. 23-4   Principle of single pile static load test.

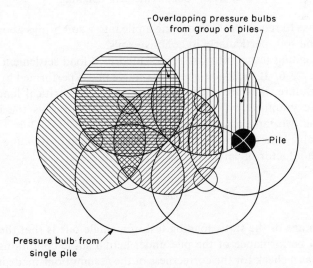

FIG. 23-5   Overlapping of pressure bulbs.

Also, the bearing capacity of a pile group is usually less than the sum of the bearing capacities of the individual piles in the pile group because of the effect of stress distribution in soil and possible consolidation of compressible layers of soil, as reflected by the combined pressure bulb brought about by the pile group (Fig. 23-5).

Of course, the mutual spacing of the piles has a lot to do with the size of the combined pressure bulb. If the individual pressure bulbs do not overlap, then the bearing capacity of the group may be that of the sum of the bearing capacity of the single piles. H. Press[6] deduced from his tests that piles spaced at a minimum distance of 6.5 to 8 diameters of the piles perform under load as single piles.

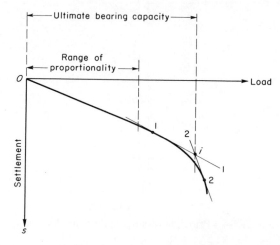

FIG. 23-6   Load-settlement diagram.

One also has to remember that driving a pile into a soil brings about structural changes in the soil, particularly in cohesive soils.

The pile loading test results are represented in a load-settlement diagram as shown in Fig. 23-6. If the loading test of a single pile is performed by continuous loading till failure, then the ultimate bearing capacity (critical load) of a pile is determined graphically from the load-settlement curve as the intersection, point i, of the two tangents, 1-1, and 2-2, as shown in Fig. 23-6.

The allowable load of the pile, P_{adm}, is then determined by dividing the ultimate load, R, with a factor of safety of $\eta = 3$ to 4:

$$P_{adm} = \frac{R}{\eta}. \tag{23-23}$$

The advantage of the static loading test of a single pile is that the test results reflect actual performance of the pile under actual static conditions. Such test results serve as a check for the correctness of the assumptions made in the design of pile foundations.

Some of the disadvantages of a single pile loading test are:

1) The performance of a single pile does not correspond to actual conditions of performance underneath the structure within the entire group of the piles.
2) The loading test must be performed at the actual construction site and under real conditions of the blueprint—conditions which are often difficult to fulfill and to execute.
3) This method of test requires specially heavy, sturdy equipment and platforms, precise settlement measuring devices, large quantities of dead loads, or powerful hydraulic jacks.
4) The aforementioned conditions and factors make this kind of pile bearing capacity test very expensive.

23-17. Pulling Tests. Pulling tests of piles out of the ground serve the purpose of determining the coefficient of mantle friction between the sides of the pile material and the soil. The pulling force is measured by strong dynamometers, and the friction coefficients are used for bearing capacity calculations of piles.

Of course, there is a great difference between the total bearing capacity of the pile and the resistance of the soil to pulling the pile out.

PILE STATIC BEARING CAPACITY FORMULAS

23-18. Assumptions. The pile static bearing capacity formulas are based on the assumption that the total resistance, R, offered to a pile by a soil system at the critical load is equal to the sum of the resistance at the tip of the pile, R_t, and to the resistance of friction, R_f, offered by the soil about the mantle surface of the pile; Fig. 23-7:

$$R = R_t + R_s \qquad (23\text{-}24)$$

Figs. 23-8 and 23-9 illustrate the nature of deformation in dry sand caused by a penetrating model pile in the author's study of deformations in soil.

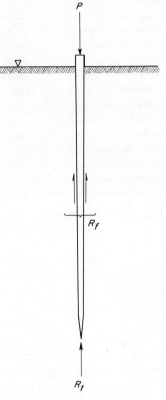

FIG. 23-7 Total resistance on pile.

23-19. Vierendeel's Formula. Vierendeel's pile static bearing capacity formula (1927) is based on the earth pressure theory:

$$p = \gamma H \tan^2(\pi/4 + \phi/2). \qquad (23\text{-}25)$$

This formula reads that at any depth, H, there is a passive earth resistance, p, on the pile. Here ϕ = angle of internal friction of soil.

The total resistance is obtained by integrating the unit resistance, p, over the total mantle surface, A, along the entire length, L, of the pile:

$$\gamma \pi D \tan^2(\pi/4 + \phi/2) \int_{H=0}^{H=L} H\, dH, \qquad (23\text{-}26)$$

where D = diameter of pile.

If P is the total superimposed load on the pile, and if under static loading conditions the pile settles by an increment of Δs, then the mechanical work done

FIG. 23-8 Deformation in dry sand caused by a penetrating model pile.

FIG. 23-9 Deformation in dry sand caused by an obtuse model pile.

is $\downarrow P(\Delta s)$. The work done oppositely to $P(\Delta s)$ by the lateral passive earth pressure is

$$\uparrow \gamma(\Delta s)\mu \pi D \tan^2(\pi/4 + \phi/2) \int_0^H H\, dH, \qquad (23\text{-}27)$$

where $\mu = \tan \phi$ = coefficient of friction between soil and pile material and
γ = unit weight of soil.

Equating both work expressions, Vierendeel's formula is obtained:

$$P(\Delta s) = \mu(\Delta s)\gamma \pi D \tan^2(\pi/4 + \phi/2) \int_0^H H\, dH, \qquad (23\text{-}28)$$

and the pile bearing capacity is:

$$P = \tfrac{1}{2}\mu \gamma \pi D L^2 \tan^2(\pi/4 + \phi/2). \qquad (23\text{-}29)$$

The values of μ are recommended by Vierendeel as follows: for cast-in-place piles, and driven timber and concrete piles with rough surfaces $\mu = 0.33$; for all other piles driven in wet and plastic soils, $\mu = 0.25$.

The nature of the static analysis underlying Vierendeel's pile bearing capacity equations implies that the equation is good for all kinds of piles, and that the pile in question is a friction pile, where $R_t = 0$.

23-20. Benebencq's Static Formula. The ultimate bearing capacity, R_d, derived theoretically by Benebencq (see Ref. 1) is:

$$R_d = \frac{md^2\gamma L}{8\sin\alpha}\tan^4(\pi/4 + \phi/2) + \frac{md\gamma L^2}{2}(\tan\phi)\tan^2(\pi/4 + \phi/2), \quad (23\text{-}30)$$

where m = ratio of perimeter of pile to radius of pile,
    d = diameter of pile,
    γ = unit weight of soil,
    L = embedded length of pile,
    α = half the angle of the pile point,
    ϕ = angle of internal friction of soil.

The assumption underlying this formula is that friction along the sides of the pile increases in simple proportion to the depth. The formula is applicable to non-cohesive soil with no difference in the strata of the deposits.

23-21. Dörr's Formula. The safe bearing capacity, P, worked out by Dörr (1922) for vertical-sided piles is made up of two terms:

$$P = R_t + R_f, \quad (23\text{-}31)$$

where

$$R_t = a\gamma L_o \tan^2(\pi/4 + \phi/2) \quad (23\text{-}32)$$

is the point bearing of the pile, and
    a = cross-sectional area of the pile. All other symbols are as before;
L_o = computation length of pile.

$$R_f = \frac{U}{2}\gamma L_o^2(1 + \tan^2\phi), \quad (23\text{-}33)$$

is the side friction, where

$$\tfrac{1}{2}\gamma L_o^2(1 + \tan^2\phi) \quad (23\text{-}34)$$

is the normal pressure of soil on the mantle surface, and
U = perimeter of pile;
μ = 0.1 to 0.55 = coefficient of friction between soil and pile.

Dörr's equation is mostly used for determining the computation length, L_o, of the pile. Written in terms of L_o, Dörr's equation appears as

$$P = R_t + R_f = \underbrace{a\gamma\tan^2(\pi/4 + \phi/2)L_o}_{B} + \underbrace{\tfrac{1}{2}\gamma U(1 + \tan^2\phi)\mu L_o^2}_{A}$$

or

$$AL_o^2 + BL_o - P = 0 \quad (23\text{-}35)$$

and

$$L_o = \frac{-B + \sqrt{B^2 + 2AP}}{2A}. \quad (23\text{-}36)$$

Working with the Dörr's pile bearing capacity is, then, as follows: if there is a layered soil system, assume an L_o, a factor of safety η, calculate A and B, and solve for L_o. Repeat this operation until the calculated L_o equals the assumed L_o.

Dörr's Equation for tapered piles:

$$P = \tfrac{1}{12}\pi\gamma \tan^2(\pi/4 + \phi/2)L_1(d_o^2 + d_o d_1 + d_1^2 + 2\mu d_o L_1 + 4\mu d_1 L_1) \quad (23\text{-}37)$$

where d_o = diameter of pile at level of ground surface,
  d_1 = diameter at base,
  L_1 = length of pile in soil.

23-22. Krey's Pile Static Bearing Capacity Formula. Krey's formula[7], too, is based on earth pressure theory. According to Krey, the total bearing capacity of a pile, P, is made up of two parts, namely resistance at the tip of the pile, R_t, and mantle friction, R_f:

$$P = \underbrace{\gamma a H K_p}_{\substack{\text{Tip} \\ \text{resistance,} \\ R_t}} + \underbrace{\tfrac{1}{2}\gamma\mu U K_p}_{\substack{\text{Mantle} \\ \text{friction} \\ R_f}} \quad (23\text{-}38)$$

Here γ = unit weight of soil
  a = cross-sectional area of pile
  H = length of pile
  ϕ = angle of internal friction of soil in $K_p = (\pi/4 + \phi/2)$, where K_p = coefficient of passive earth pressure
  μ = coefficient of friction between soil and pile material
  U = perimeter of pile

23-23. Summary.
  1) The *Engineering News* formulas are accepted
      a) when the hammer has a free fall,
      b) when the head of the pile is not broomed or crushed,
      c) when the penetration of the pile into soil is uniform and reasonably quick, and
      d) when there is no perceptible rebound of the pile after the blow.
  2) The *Engineering News* formulas are extensively used in the United States because they agree closely with practical results.
  3) The structural and physical properties of the soil are usually known from borings before the pile-driving operations are started. However, vibrations, remolding of soil, change in soil void ratio, compression, compaction, lateral displacement of soil, and pore-water pressure conditions in soil during and after driving operations bring about changes in the original soil properties. Remolding of cohesive soils, it is known, brings about a decrease in strength of these materials.
  4) Cummings[8] studied critically the available dynamic pile-driving formulas and concluded, among other things, that several formulas are based on questionable assumptions; that the customary methods of evaluating the energy losses are erroneous, the defects being that the temporary elastic

compression in a dynamic process is taken from static theory and that these elastic deformations under static conditions are not the same as under impact; that the Newtonian theory of impact does not apply to pile-driving, and that in some equations some energy losses are deducted twice. Cummings also points out that the dynamic pile-driving formula is primarily a yardstick to help the engineer to get reasonably safe and uniform results over the entire job. At the present time, the installation of a satisfactory pile foundation is largely a matter of experience and good judgment combined with a careful soil investigation.

5) Since 1948 the Building Codes of the City of New York have restricted the use of dynamic pile-driving equations, and recommend static loading tests of piles for the evaluation of static bearing capacity of piles.

6) It is interesting to note that because the dynamic penetration resistance has no relationship to pile static bearing capacity, the German Industrial Norms, DIN 1054 (§ 5.11), too, do not permit dynamic pile-driving formulas for cohesive soils. In non-cohesive soils, according to these Norms, dynamic pile-driving formulas are permitted only when their validity is verified by means of loading tests.

7) Dynamic pile-driving formulas, however, are of value when driving operations take place on a site with reasonably uniform soil conditions. In such a case the pile-driving logs may render useful comparative results for the guidance of work.

8) The German Industrial Norms, DIN 1054, of June 1953 forbid determination of the allowable load on piles by friction with values obtained from handbooks. The frictional properties used in calculating the bearing capacity of a pile must be determined by test.

REFERENCES

1. ASCE, "Pile Foundations and Pile Structures"; *Manual of Engineering Practice*, New York, 1946, no. 27, p. 2.
2. J. F. Redtenbacher, *Prinzipien der Mechanik und des Maschinenbaues*, cited from Ref. 1.
3. O. Stern, *Das Problem der Pfahlbelastung*, Berlin, Wilhelm Ernst und Sohn, 1908, p. 161.
4. K. Zimmermann, "Die Rammwirkung im Erdreich". Versuche auf neuer Grundlage. *Forschungsarbeiten auf dem Gebiete des Eisenbetons*. Heft no. 25. Berlin, Wilhelm Ernst und Sohn, 1915.
5. R. D. Chellis, *Pile Foundations*, New York, McGraw-Hill Book Co., Inc., 1951, pp. 525-538.
6. H. Press, *Druckverteilung am Einzelphahl und Einfluss benachbarter Pfähle*, Die Bautechnik, 1941, p. 45.
7. H. D. Krey, *Erddruck, Erdwiderstand und Tragfähigkeit des Baugrundes*, Berlin, Wilhelm Ernst und Sohn, 1936, p. 152.
8. A. E. Cummings, "Dynamic Pile Driving Formulas". Published in *Contributions to Soil Mechanics* 1925-1940, by the Boston Society of Civil Engineers, Boston, Mass., 1940, pp. 392-413.

QUESTIONS AND PROBLEMS

23-1. Prepare an abstract on piles and pile-driving formulas. Pay special attention to
    a) the function of bearing piles under foundations,
    b) the types of bearing piles ⎫
    c) the types of friction piles ⎬ prepare a classification diagram
    d) batter piles
    e) why it is necessary to drive timber piles below the lowest elevation of the groundwater table
    f) pile-driving hammers and their action
    g) the advantages and disadvantages of timber, concrete, steel, and composite piles
    h) basic energy relationship in pile-driving theory
    i) determination of bearing capacity of point and friction piles.

23-2. Determine by means of the *Engineering News* formula the bearing capacity of a pile.
Data: Drop hammer—2,000 lb. Height of drop—7 ft. Average penetration of pile under the last 25 blows—0.05 in.

23-3. Determine the bearing capacity of a pile by means of the *Engineering News* formula. Data: the single-acting steam hammer weighs 1,500 lb. Its fall is 3 ft. The average penetration of the pile under the last few blows is 0.02 in.

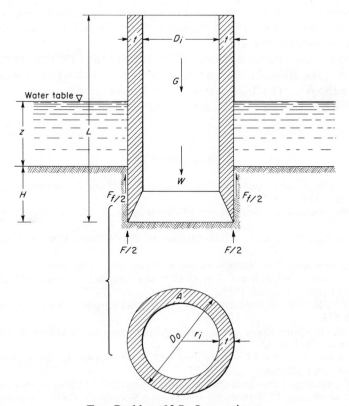

FIG. Problem 23-7. Open caisson.

23-4. Assume consistent data and calculate by means of all of the dynamic and static formula given in this book the safe bearing capacity of a timber pile for a factor of safety of $\eta = 6$.

23-5. Describe the effect of pile driving on the properties of a thixotropic soil.

23-6. What is the purpose of pile driving?

23-7. Given an open, round, reinforced caisson as shown in Fig. Problem 23-7. Calculate the necessary weight, W, viz., optimum supporting area, A, for a successful sinking of the caisson. What is the safe bearing capacity, P, of the caisson? $t \approx (0.1)D_o$.

Hint for Solution.

$$\Sigma V: G + W - F - F_f = 0$$

$\quad W \approx \gamma_c A H \quad \gamma_c$ = unit weight of concrete.

$\quad F_f = \mu U h \quad (U$ = perimeter of caisson, h = penetration depth of caisson)

$\quad F = \sigma_{adm} A \quad (\sigma_{adm}$ = safe bearing capacity of soil).

Consider buoyant weight where necessary. For a round caisson, solve the resulting quadratic equation.

Chapter 24

SHEETING AND BRACING OF TRENCHES

24-1. Application of Coulomb's Theory. Although sheeting and bracing of soil banks are temporary operations in foundation engineering, sheeting and bracing of vertical slopes and trenches and other open cuts against caving in can seldom be omitted. Even if of temporary nature (trenches, pits, etc), the problem of safety in construction work requires careful investigation of the forces involved in the earth retaining systems. This is true the more so as the insurance companies require it, to prevent injuries to workmen and damage to, or loss of, material and construction equipment.

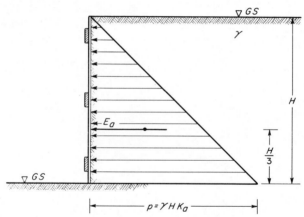

FIG. 24-1 Coulomb's triangular stress distribution diagram.

The lateral earth pressure on sheeting may be calculated, among other methods, by means of Coulomb's earth pressure theory. According to this theory the magnitude of the lateral earth pressure on timbering in a cut of a homogeneous soil increases like a hydrostatic pressure—linearly in simple proportion to depth as illustrated in Fig. 24-1. For example, if $\gamma = 116$ lb/ft^3, $h = 7.0$ ft, $\phi = 30°$, then the lateral, total, active earth pressure, E_a, on the sheeting is

$$E_a = \tfrac{1}{2}\gamma h^2 K_a.$$

With $K_a = \tan^2(\pi/4 - \phi/2) = 0.334$, and $p = \gamma h K_a = (116)(7.0)(0.334) = 272$ (lb/ft^2), the total active earth pressure is

$$E_a = \tfrac{1}{2}(7.0)(272) = 950 \text{ (lb/ft)}.$$

676

24-2. Earth Pressure Distribution in Reality. The method of sheeting and bracing of vertical banks and the magnitude of the lateral earth pressure on the wall depend primarily upon the soil type encountered.

Because the bracing system is usually somewhat elastic, the soil pressure distribution actually does not follow Coulomb's idealized straight-line rule mainly because of pressure redistribution and arching effect.

The problem as to how the lateral earth pressure distributes with depth over a shoring has been considerably discussed in the past. During the course of time several engineers have expressed the opinion that, based on observations, earth pressure does not follow the same laws everywhere, and that its point of application and distribution of its intensity depend to a great extent on the displacement of the shoring structure during construction periods, and upon the type of the soil.

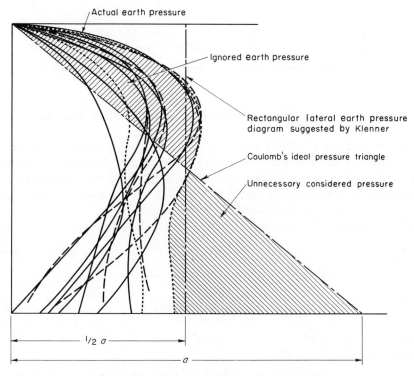

FIG. 24-2 Comparative earth pressure diagrams obtained from measurements (curvilinear) and from calculations (linear) (after Klenner, Ref. 11).

Fig. 24-2 represents an earth-pressure diagram by Klenner.[1] The earth pressures were measured during the construction of the Berlin subway, and with earthwork sheetings in Munich. The comparison of the measured earth pressure diagram with Coulomb's earth pressure triangle lead Klenner to suggest the use of a rectangular, lateral earth pressure diagram, the base of which is one half the base of the triangle. Although this rectangular diagram does not represent the true pressure distribution condition, it points out clearly that on flexible walls Coulomb's ideal linear pressure distribution is in error. The upper part of the actually measured existing pressure is usually ignored using triangular pressure distribution, but the lower part of the pressure triangle is unnecessarily estimated and introduced in calculations.

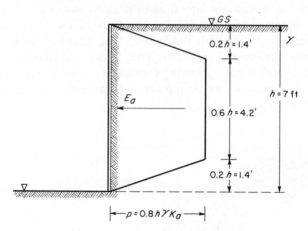

FIG. 24-3   Earth pressure diagram for dense and medium dense sand.

Terzaghi and Peck write[2] that since the construction procedure used in the Berlin subways did not differ in any essential respect from that commonly used in excavating and bracing open cuts in sand, the design procedure, viz., earth pressure diagram as illustrated in Fig. 24-3, may be used with confidence for open excavations in dense sand in any other locality.

In this diagram, the pressure ordinate, p, is set equal to

$$p = (0.8)\gamma h K_a \tag{24-1}$$

The active earth pressure, E_a, is then calculated as

$$E_a = \frac{h + 0.6h}{2} (0.8)\gamma h K_a. \tag{24-2}$$

Example. If $G = 2.65$, $\gamma_w = 62.4$ lb/ft³, $e = 0.428$, $K_a = 0.334$, and $h = 7.0$ ft, then the unit weight of the soil is

$$\gamma = \frac{G}{1 + e} \gamma_w = \frac{2.65}{1 + 0.428} (62.5) = 116 \text{ (lb/ft}^3\text{)},$$

$$p = (0.8)(116)(0.334) \approx 216 \text{ (lb/ft}^2\text{)}, \text{ and}$$

$$E_a = \frac{7.0 + 4.2}{2} (216) = \underline{1210 \text{ (lb)}}$$

per 1 ft run of wall.

For loose sand Terzaghi and Peck recommend the active earth pressure diagram as shown in Fig. 24-4.

Example. With $\gamma = 116$ lb/ft²; $h = 7.0$ ft; $K_a = 0.334$, $p = 216$ lb/ft², the active earth pressure is

$$E_a = \frac{7.0 + 5.6}{2}(216) = \underline{1361 \ (\text{lb/ft})}.$$

The point of application of E_a is the centroid of the asymmetrical trapezoid.

It may be seen from these calculations that the loose sand earth pressure diagram yields the largest active earth pressure among the given modified earth pressure diagrams, while the relatively undisturbed sands give a slightly lower lateral pressure (1210 lb). Klenner's pressure diagram seems to give the least conservative values of earth pressure.

The earth pressure on a sheeted wall in soft and medium clay is calculated according to Terzaghi and Peck based on the earth pressure diagram as illustrated in Fig. 24-5.

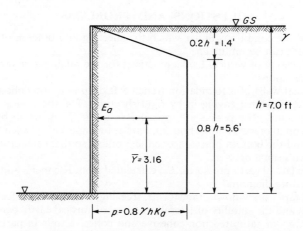

FIG. 24-4   Earth pressure diagram for loose sand.

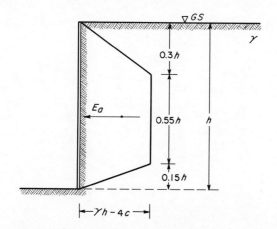

FIG. 24-5   Earth pressure diagram for soft and medium clay.

This pressure diagram is based on results of measurements of lateral earth pressure against bracing of an open cut in medium clay in Chicago.

The pressure ordinate, p, of the trapezoidal pressure distribution diagram contains the quantity c = cohesion = τ = $q_u/2$, or

$$p = \gamma h - q_u, \tag{24-3}$$

where q_u = ultimate, unconfined, compressive strength of the clay.

REFERENCES

1. C. Klenner, "Versuche über die Verteilung des Erddruckes über die Wände ausgesteifter Baugruben", *Die Bautechnik*, July 4, 1941, no. 29, pp. 316-319.
2. K. Terzaghi and R. B. Peck, *Soil Mechanics in Engineering Practice*, New York, John Wiley and Sons, Inc., 1948, p. 348.

QUESTIONS AND PROBLEMS

24-1. What are the conditions under which the sheeting and bracing of trenches and excavations can be omitted?

24-2. Why is sheeting of vertical banks practiced for the retaining of vertical banks in open excavations?

24-3. The vertical walls of a foundation trench 8 ft deep in a non-cohesive soil are to be protected against caving in by rigid sheeting. The sheeting is supported by vertical planks. The planks are spaced 3 ft apart. They are to be braced with five horizontal braces, 1 at the bottom, 1 at the top, and 3 in between. Disregarding the top and the bottom braces, space the 3 braces so that each of them would be loaded with same pressure.

24-4. Compare lateral earth pressures, E_a, calculated from Klenner's and Terzaghi and Peck pressure diagrams.

24-5. How do rapid draw-down, rainstorms, freezing, and thawing affect lateral earth pressures and the stability of laterally supported vertical earth banks in general, and in cases of saturated non-cohesive and cohesive soils in particular?

Chapter 25

STABILITY ANALYSIS OF SLOPES

25-1. Definitions. A slope is an inclined boundary surface between air and the body of an earthwork such as a dam, or highway cut, and/or fill, for example.

If the shear stress exceeds the shear strength of the soil, or, in other words when the driving forces are larger than those resisting the motion of the soil mass, then rupture (failure in shear) of the soil material located beneath the slope of the earthwork takes place. Such a failure in shear is termed a slide. After rupture the overlying mass of soil can move by gravity; until rupture occurs motion is opposed by the shear resistance of the soil. When this is overcome, resistance is diminished and the soil mass slides down. The outward manifestation of a slide of an earthwork slope is the perceptible translational or rotational movement of the ruptured soil wedge downward and outward from the embankment, depending upon the set of combinations of the various factors partaking in the shear deformation of the soil. The rupture of a slope may set in in almost every conceivable manner: slowly or suddenly, and the perceptible movement of the ruptured soil mass may be characterized in most instances as rapid. The failure of a slope-forming soil constitutes the loss of its stability.

As said before, the stability of any slope made of or in a soil material depends upon the shear strength of the soil. The shear strength, in its turn, is a function of friction and cohesion of the soil. Here friction is proportional to the effective normal stress on the rupture surface at the instant of failure.

In soil mechanics, the topic "stability of slopes" is dealt with from two engineering viewpoints, namely:

1) the design of slopes of cuts and fills in advance of new earthwork construction in accordance with prescribed safety requirements, and
2) the study of stability of existing slopes of earthworks, slopes which are potentially unstable, or which have failed, or which have to be redesigned.

In the first instance above, the position of the toe-point of the slope is known; whereas in the second instance the position of the toe-point is not always known because of the destruction of the designed slope by its rupture, and slumping down.

In soil engineering, stability analysis of a slope of an earthwork is concerned with the computing of the degree of stability relative to a sudden rupture of slope characterized by the so-called factor of safety, η, of the soil-slope-load system relative to the most dangerous, or disadvantageous stability condition of the slope—a sudden, deep-seated gravity slide.

The concept of the "stability" of a slope is an indeterminate one because no slopes made in or of soil can be regarded as fully guaranteed for their stability during their exploitation over a period of many years. Climatic and hydrologic conditions, and man's activities in the immediate and/or adjacent area of the dam or other earthwork, may bring about, years later, changes affecting the stability of man-made and natural slopes. In particular, one should not over-look the possibility of the soil becoming saturated by water with time. Besides, cases are known of stable slopes whose factor of safety, η, with respect to failure in shear has been calculated to be less than a unity, i.e., $\eta < 1.0$. For slopes of new earthworks it is advisable to maintain the factor of safety at $\eta = 1.5$ at least.

In earthworks, shear failures of soil materials are common phenomena, and result from inadequate stability analysis, or from incompletely assessing the properties of the soil materials and possible variations in their properties with time, or both. They can also result from overloading the earthwork by various kinds of loads, such as externally applied loads; by water in the voids of the soil; by flow pressure, and other possible factors. In most cases it is the water in its various modes of occurrance which in part, directly, and in part, indirectly, is the cause of rupture of soil, and hence failure of slopes.

25-2. Factors Contributing to Slope Failures. The stability of slopes depends upon the following factors:
1) the type of soil of which or in which the slope is made;
2) the geometry of the cross section of the slope (height, slope, for example);
3) weight and loads, and weight and load distribution (gravity is one of the principal causes of all slides);
4) increase in moisture content of the soil material. Water is the principal factor in promoting slides because it adds weight to the unit weight of soil; water decreases the magnitude of cohesion in soil, thus decreasing its shear strength. Water from atmospheric precipitation and the melt-waters of snow, upon entering into the soil, decrease the factor of safety, η, of the slopes in question. Water is the most aggressive factor contri-buting to many slides, particularly in unconsolidated soils;
5) decrease in shear strength of soil for reasons other than water;
6) vibrations and earthquakes.

Thus one possibility of reducing the degree of stability in slopes comes more to the fore: stability varies principally with the variation in the water regimen in the soil. Therefore, stability analysis of slopes of earthworks should be performed for the most dangerous conditions of the slope.

25-3. Slides in the Panama Canal. Some of the most conspicuous examples in soil engineering on extensive slides due to rupture of soil in shear are those which occurred during the construction of the Panama Canal.[1,2] For the sea-level canal, cuts more than 600 ft deep were made. The most disastrous slides were the great East and West Culebra slides,[3] Fig. 25-1. The Culebra slides were of the gravity type, and were brought about by groundwater and unfavorable geologic conditions. The Cucaracha slide was the most troublesome one related to the use of drainage of slope as a remedial measure. In January, 1916, the acreage of the three great slides was 191.7 acres in contrast to 122.7 acres of all other slides.[4] The amount of slide material removed up to December, 1916, was 47.5 million cubic yards. The total excavation from all other slides to January 1, 1916, amounted to 4.7 million cubic yards, or about one-tenth the amount removed from the slides of the Culebra District.

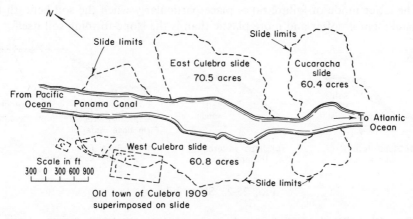

FIG. 25-1   Sketch of Panama Canal location of major slide areas (after Binger and Thompson, Ref. 5).

25-4. Classification. Slides may be classified from various veiw-points. From the point of view of analysis of stability of slopes, slides may be subjected to the following rough classification.

1) Slides over plane rupture surfaces.
2) Slides over curved rupture surfaces.

A plane rupture surface may develop along a predetermined plane of contact. This plane may have been formed a) naturally, in dipped geologic formations of harder or more dense material, such as rock or clay, which are overlain by unconsolidated soil material, or b) artificially, by man's activities.

The curved rupture surfaces are of the form of circular cylinders, spiraled cylinders, cycloidally formed cylinders, and other possibly formed surfaces.

Further, slides may be classified by the type of the sliding soil material, such as
   a) slides in pure cohesive soils (c-soils),
   b) slides in pure non-cohesive or frictional soils (ϕ-soils), and
   c) slides in cohesive-frictional soils (ϕ-c soils).

Also, the slides may take place in
   a) homogeneous soils, and in
   b) non-homogeneous soils (irregular texture, irregular density, layered soil systems, partly submerged slopes, seepage through soil and out of it through the slopes, and other possible conditions).

25-5. Mode of Rupture. As to the mode of rupture, the slope may fail basically in the following two ways:

a) the rupture surface sets in above the toe of the slope (Fig. 25-2), and the rupture surface passes through the toe of the slope. Such failures are known as slope failures.

b) the rupture surface is deep-seated and passes through the embankment supporting soil below the toe of the slope. This mode of slope failure is known as the base failure.

The latter mode of failure takes place particularly when the soil beneath the embankment is softer and more plastic than is the slope-forming soil itself.

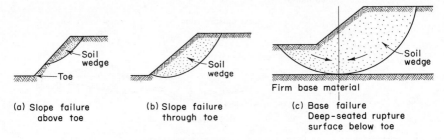

(a) Slope failure above toe

(b) Slope failure through toe

(c) Base failure Deep-seated rupture surface below toe

FIG. 25-2 Slope failures.

25-6. Plane Rupture Surfaces. In order that an analysis of a slope can be made one must know the shape of the rupture surface (plane, or curvilinear), or it should be assumed—the assumption being then based on a thorough analysis of all natural and artificial conditions at the site of the slope.

In stability analyses of slopes of earthworks over plane rupture surfaces two principal cases are to be distinguished, namely:

1) slides of unconsolidated material over a pre-existing inclined sliding plane of firm surface (Fig. 25-3), and

2) slides taking place over a plane rupture surface sheared by the driving forces within the mass of an unconsolidated soil material (Fig. 25-5).

25-7. Stability of Mass of Soil on an Inclined Plane. To start out with the stability analysis of the triangular, homogeneous soil mass, ABC, Fig. 25-3, assume that it rests upon a firm, inclined surface, AC, inclined at an angle ρ, with the horizontal. In this problem two kinds of stabilities must be checked, namely,

1) the overall stability of the entire soil mass against sliding down the incline, and

2) the stability of the slope, AB, proper against rupture in shear if the overall stability of the earth mass against sliding down is satisfactory.

The principle underlying stability calculation of the triangular soil mass is the failure in shear along the inclined plane, AC, when the driving forces exceed the resisting forces. In such a calculation, it is assumed that the shear stress, s, is distributed uniformly over the plane sliding surface, AC. The calculations of the stability of slopes here and throughout this book pertains to earthworks the lengths (or shore line) of which are one unit of length perpendicular to the drawing plane.

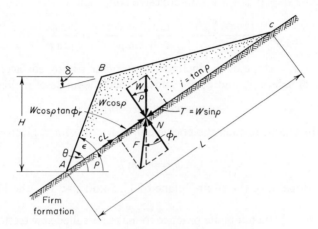

FIG. 25-3   Soil mass on an incline.

The driving force (tangential force), T, is:

$$T = W \sin \rho, \tag{25-1}$$

where W = weight of soil wedge = $\gamma \triangle (ABC)$.
The resisting force, R, is:

$$R = F \sin \phi_r + cL = (N/\cos \phi_r)\sin \phi_r + cL = N \tan \phi_r + cL = \tag{25-2}$$

$$= W \cos \rho \tan \phi_r + cL, \tag{25-2a}$$

where ϕ_r = angle of frictional resistance in plane, AC, between the soil material
and the firm surface of the inclined sliding plane;
$\tan \phi_r$ = coefficient of friction;
c = cohesion in plane, AC, and
L = length of triangular soil wedge resting on incline, AC.
The ϕ_r and c values must be ascertained by test in the laboratory.
In a stable system driving forces, $\sum F_D$, should constitute only a fraction of the resisting forces, $\sum F_R$. The factor of safety, η, of the system, characterizing the degree of stability of the soil mass on the incline is expressed as

$$\eta = \frac{\sum F_R}{\sum F_D} = \frac{\tan \phi_r \sum N + cL}{\sum T} \tag{25-3}$$

where $\sum N = W \cos \rho$ = the sum of all effective normal forces to the sliding
plane, and
$\sum T$ = the sum of all shear forces.

If $\eta > 1$, the soil mass on the incline may be considered as stable.
If $\eta = 1$, the system is at equilibrium.
If $\eta < 1$, the system should be regarded as instable as concerns pure static cal-
culations. The factor of safety, η, is usually required to be $\eta \geq 1.5$.
    If in Eq. 25-3 $c = 0$ as for a non-cohesive soil, then

$$\eta = \frac{\tan \phi_r \sum N}{\sum T} = \frac{\tan \phi_r W \cos \rho}{W \sin \rho} = \frac{\tan \phi_r}{\tan \rho}, \tag{25-4}$$

where $\tan \rho = i$ = slope of the inclined, firm, plane sliding surface.
    If a factor of safety, η, and ϕ_r are known, then the angle of incline should be

$$\rho = \arctan(\tan \phi_r / \eta) \tag{25-5}$$

If ρ cannot be changed, then the coefficient of friction for a given η should be
at least

$$\tan \phi_r = \eta \tan \rho. \tag{25-6}$$

    Up to the slope, i, of the sliding plane of $1 : 5$ and $\varepsilon < 10°$, the fill is usually
stable.
    When $\tan \rho > \frac{1}{5}$, then it is the practice to make so-called saw teeth in the firm,
inclined surface, or steps to provide for support against the sliding down of the
unconsolidated mass of soil, Fig. 25-4. The steps are bulldozed out 3 ft and more
in length, and with a back-slope of 1% to 2%. To cope with the water problem
here, drainage should be arranged.

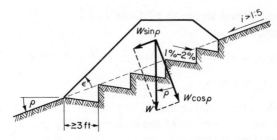

FIG. 25-4   Steps for stability against sliding down of the unconsolidated mass of soil.

25-8. Stability of Slopes With a Plane Rupture Surface. In a homogeneous soil
failure in shear along a plane rupture surface may be assumed to take place in a
surface such that the acting shear stresses are greater than the shear strength of
the soil. The stability calculation is thus based on a shear plane, AC, through
the toe-line (A), and finding the so-called critical angle of the slope, $\measuredangle \omega$, which
corresponds to the most dangerous rupture surface (Fig. 25-5), at its maximum
stressed surface.
    The weight of the ruptured soil wedge, $\triangle ABC$, is:

$$W = \tfrac{1}{2}\gamma(AC)h = \tfrac{1}{2}\gamma H^2 \frac{\sin(\theta - \delta)\sin(\theta - \omega)}{\sin^2 \theta \sin(\omega - \delta)}. \tag{25-7}$$

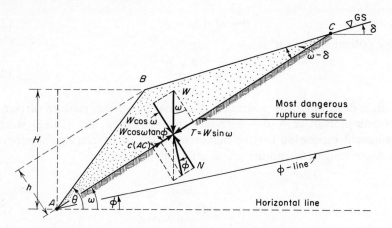

FIG. 25-5 Slope system with plane rupture surface.

The force equilibrium on plane AC:

$$c(AC) + N \tan \phi - T = 0. \qquad (25\text{-}8)$$

Here $c(AC)$ is the so-called acting cohesive force, and $N \tan \phi$ is the acting frictional force, not to be confused with the soil resistance forces.
But

$$AC = \frac{H}{\sin \theta} \frac{\sin(\theta - \delta)}{\sin(\omega - \delta)} \qquad (25\text{-}9)$$

$$N = W \cos \omega = \tfrac{1}{2}\gamma H^2 \frac{\sin(\theta - \delta)\sin(\theta - \omega)}{\sin^2 \theta \sin(\omega - \delta)} \cos \omega, \qquad (25\text{-}10)$$

$$T = W \sin \omega = \tfrac{1}{2}\gamma H^2 \frac{\sin(\theta - \delta)\sin(\theta - \omega)}{\sin^2 \theta \sin(\omega - \delta)} \sin \omega. \qquad (25\text{-}11)$$

With the aforementioned expressions, the acting cohesion from Equation (25-8) is:

$$c = \frac{T - N \tan \phi}{(AC)} = \frac{(W \sin \omega - W \cos \omega \tan \phi)\sin \theta \sin(\omega - \delta)}{H \sin(\theta - \delta)} =$$

$$= \tfrac{1}{2}\gamma H \frac{\sin(\theta - \omega)(\sin \omega - \cos \omega \tan \phi)}{\sin \theta}. \qquad (25\text{-}12)$$

In the most dangerous rupture surface the induced, acting cohesion attains a maximum value, i.e., the trigonometric nominator should be

$$\sin(\theta - \omega)(\sin \omega - \cos \omega \tan \phi) = \text{maximum}.$$

$$\frac{d}{d\omega}\left[\sin(\theta - \omega)(\sin \omega - \cos \omega \tan \phi)\right] = 0$$

$$\tan(\theta - \omega) = \frac{\sin \omega - \cos \omega \tan \phi}{\cos \omega + \sin \omega \tan \phi} = \tan(\omega - \phi) \qquad (25\text{-}13)$$

$$\theta - \omega = \omega - \phi, \tag{25-14}$$

and the critical angle ω is

$$\omega = \frac{\theta + \phi}{2}. \tag{25-15}$$

This angle determines the position of the most dangerous rupture surface, AC. The substitution of $\omega = (\theta + \phi)/2$ into the c-equation, Eq. (25-12) yields the mathematical expression for the maximum value of developed cohesion, c_{max}, in the most dangerous rupture plane, AC, upon rupture:

$$c_{max} = \tfrac{1}{2}\gamma H \frac{\sin^2 \dfrac{\theta - \phi}{2}}{\sin \theta \cos \phi}. \tag{25-16}$$

In other words, c_{max} is the necessary value a soil material with an angle of internal friction, ϕ, should possess in order that the slope, AB, with a slope angle of θ still stays at a height, H:

$$H = \frac{2c}{\gamma} \frac{\sin \theta \cos \phi}{\sin^2 \dfrac{\theta - \phi}{2}}. \tag{25-17}$$

Note that c as well as H are independent of the slope, δ, of the ground surface.
   When $\phi = 0$, then Eqs. (25-16) and (25-17) transform into

$$c_{max} = \tfrac{1}{4}\gamma H \tan \frac{\theta}{2}, \tag{25-18}$$

and

$$H = 4(c/\gamma)\cot \frac{\theta}{2}. \tag{25-19}$$

This equation shows that the greater the slope angle θ, the smaller the height of the slope,
   The overall factor of safety, η, for the critical plane is

$$\eta = \frac{\sum \text{Resisting forces}}{\sum \text{Driving forces}} = \frac{c(AC) + N \tan \phi}{T} \tag{25-20}$$

If $c = 0$, then $T = N \tan \phi$, and $\tan \omega = \tan \phi$, or $\omega = \phi$.
For a factor of safety η,

$$\eta = \frac{\tan \phi}{\tan \omega}, \tag{25-21}$$

or

$$\tan \phi = \eta \tan \omega. \tag{25-22}$$

It should be mentioned that stability analyses of slopes on plane rupture surfaces were studied by Coulomb,[6] Résal,[7] Français,[8] and others.

STABILITY OF SLOPES
CONSIDERING CURVED RUPTURE SURFACES

25-9. General Notes. There are several theories available for analyzing the stability of earthwork slopes, for example:

theory applying circular rupture surfaces;

theory applying circular rupture surfaces with the so-called friction, or ϕ-circle;

theory applying logarithmically spiraled rupture surfaces;

theory using cycloids, logoids and possibly other kinds of rupture surfaces.

The existence of so many theories merely points out just how complex the soil stability problems are. Besides, there is no satisfactory theory available for calculating the stability of slopes made in non-homogeneous soils.

25-10. Collin's Work on Landslides in Clays. The French engineer Alexandre Collin published in 1846,[9] a book on landslides in clays in which he describes his experiences with many ruptures of slopes made in clay, gained from building canals. Collin observed that ruptures of slopes occur at all seasons of the year, and in several instances even long after the earthworks were completed, mainly because of increased moisture content in these soils with time. The mode of rupture in clay masses were observed to be by deep-seated, rotational movements over a curved rupture surface. Collin suggested that the ruptured mass of soil slides down on a definite type of sliding surface, which is more or less of the type of a cycloid.

The reason for rupture of soil is given as the inadequate shear strength of the soil. Collin was also one of the early researchers who performed shear tests on clays, and showed that moisture affects greatly the shear strength of cohesive soils.

It is because of his clear understanding of the nature of the shear strength of cohesive soils that Collin's work should be regarded as a model on the subject of landslides in clays.

Stability analyses of slopes on cycloidal rupture surfaces were studied also by Frontard.[10]

25-11. Circular Sliding Surface. Nowadays one of the most commonly used types of curved rupture surfaces in stability analyses of slopes is the circular, cylindrical rupture surface. The circular, cylindrical rupture surface is, of course, merely a conventional one in order to simplify mathematical computations involved in the stability analysis. The use of the circular rupture surface may probably be justified for the three following reasons:

1) it approximately coincides with the real shape of the rupture surfaces observed in nature,

2) it is necessary to make a number of other assumptions for the mathematical analyses anyway, and

3) the circular rupture surface is easy to draw by using a compass.

Because of the early extensive studies of ruptures of slopes of earthworks made by Swedish engineers, the circular rupture surface is often referred to as the Swedish circle method.

The stability analysis of slopes on circular rupture surfaces is actually a grapho-analytical method as suggested in 1916 by Petterson,[11,12] Hultin,[13] and Fellenius.[14,15]

One distinguishes between the grapho-analytical methods with circular sliding surfaces: one, as applied to homogeneous, pure cohesive soils; and the other as applied for frictional-cohesive soils (the so-called ϕ-circle method).

The method applied to pure cohesive soils, in its turn, can be divided into two methods: stability analysis of slopes en masse, and stability analysis of slopes by the method of slices.

Besides, the analyses may be performed on circular sliding surfaces passing through the toe of the slope, and on circular sliding surfaces passing through the base of the dam.

25-12. Pure Cohesive Soils—Stability En Masse—Slope Failure. The principle of stability analysis of a slope en masse, as explained by Fellenius, [16,17] is now

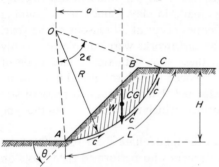

described as follows, Fig. 25-6. In his works Fellenius expressly states that stability calculations of earth masses have for their object the determination of the properties of soil (cohesion and friction) *necessary for equilibrium* in different, assumed, circular sliding surfaces. The method of analysis is based on the consideration that *that sliding surface which requires the greatest amount of cohesion, c, and the greatest angle of internal friction, ϕ, for equilibrium of the earth slope is the most dangerous one of all*, and that the degree

FIG. 25-6   W. Fellenius' system for pure cohesive soils.

of stability of the slope is expressed as the ratio of the shear strength of the soil, τ, to needed strength of the soil.

In pure, homogeneous, cohesive soils the stability analysis of slopes is relatively simple. The required amount of cohesion is calculated from the equilibrium condition of the driving moment, $M_D = Wa$ and the resisting moment, $M_R = c\widehat{L}R$ about the axis of rotation, O, which is the axis of the circular cylindrical rupture surface, AC, i.e.,

$$M_D = M_R \tag{25-23}$$

or

$$Wa = c\widehat{L}R, \tag{25-24}$$

where W = weight of sliding soil wedge, $ABCA$;

a = moment arm of W about O;

c = necessary amount of cohesion per unit area in the rupture (sliding) surface;

$\widehat{L} = R(2\varepsilon)$ = length AC of circular arc of the rupture surface.

The coordinates of the point of application, CG, of the weight, W, are determined by the rules of statics for finding the position of the centroid of irregular geometric figures analytically, graphically, or experimentally.

The necessary amount of cohesion for equilibrium, from Eq. (25-24) is

$$c = \frac{Wa}{\widehat{LR}} \qquad (25\text{-}25)$$

Factor of safety, η:

$$\eta = \tau/c, \qquad (25\text{-}26)$$

where τ = shear strength of soil.

When $M_D > M_R$, the slope-forming soil mass ruptures and slides down.

In these stability calculations of slopes it is tacitly assumed that the ruptured soil wedge, ABC, does not deform upon its sliding down the circular rupture surface, and that the cohesion is uniformly distributed throughout the entire area of the rupture surface.

If the circular arc, $\widehat{AC}$, represents the most dangerous rupture surface, then the factor of safety, η, can also be formulated as

$$\eta = M_R/M_D = \frac{\tau \widehat{LR}}{Wa} = \frac{\tau(2\varepsilon)R^2}{Wa}. \qquad (25\text{-}27)$$

When $\eta = 1$, rupture is just impending.

When $\eta > \eta_{\text{required}} \geqslant 1.5$, the slope is usually considered as stable.

When $\eta < 1$, the slope is considered as instable.

The position of the most dangerous rupture surface is found by the method of trial and error. This method consists of drawing several arcs through the toe of the slope by assuming different positions of the centers of the rupture circles. Each of the rupture circles thus assumed should be analyzed about each center chosen for the factor of safety. That circle which gives the least factor of safety among the circles analyzed is the *critical rupture surface*. The slope is considered to be stable if the least factor of safety, η, for the most dangerous rupture surface is $\eta \geqslant 1.5$.

Note that the "factor of safety" is an arbitrary quantity because the center of rotation, O, and likewise the most dangerous rupture surface forming the circular arc, $\widehat{AC}$, are chosen by trial and error. This random procedure is the reason why several rupture surfaces and not merely one surface should be analyzed in order to obtain the position of the most probably dangerous rupture surface resulting in the least acceptable factor of safety. Obviously, the trial-and-error method requires a certain amount of time. Fellenius' graphs,[17] however, decrease this deficiency of the grapho-analytical method considerably.

Using the system as shown in Fig. 25-7, Fellenius calculated the necessary cohesion for equilibrium as a function of the slope angle, θ, the central half-angle, ε, and the angle, ω, of the chord subtending the most dangerous rupture surface, AC:

$$c_o = \tfrac{1}{4}\gamma H f(\theta, \varepsilon, \omega), \qquad (25\text{-}28)$$

where $f(\theta, \varepsilon, \omega) = [(2 \sin^2 \varepsilon \sin^2 \omega)/\varepsilon] \times$

$$\times [\cot \varepsilon \cot \omega - \cot \varepsilon \cot \theta + \cot \theta \cot \omega - \tfrac{2}{3} \cot^2 \theta + \tfrac{1}{3}]. \quad (25\text{-}29)$$

The converse: if c is known, then at equilibrium with a slope angle of θ would support itself to a height of H:

$$H = \frac{4c}{\gamma} \frac{1}{f(\theta, \varepsilon, \omega)}. \quad (25\text{-}30)$$

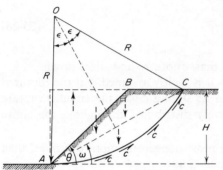

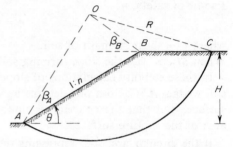

FIG. 25-7 System for calculating cohesion (after W. Fellenius).

FIG. 25-8 Locating the center of the most dangerous rupture surface in pure cohesive soils for slope failure.

TABLE 25-1. DIRECTIONAL ANGLES FOR LOCATING CENTER OF
CRITICAL RUPTURE CIRCLE THROUGH THE TOE OF A SLOPE IN PURE C-SOIL*

Slope $\diagdown$ 1 / n / 1 : n	Slope angle $\theta°$	Directional angles		System of slope
		β_A	β_B	
1	2	3	4	5
$\sqrt{3}$: 1	60°	~29°	~40°	
1 : 1	45°	~28°	~38°	
1 : 1.5	33°41′	~26°	~35°	
1 : 2	25°34′	~25°	~35°	
1 : 3	18°26′	~25°	~35°	
1 : 5	11°19′	~25°	~37°	

* Compiled from Fellenius data, Reference (17).

Table 25-1 contains for various slope angles θ, auxiliary directional angles, β_A and β_B, for finding the position of the center of the most dangerous rupture surface through the toe of the slope made in a homogeneous, pure, cohesive soil. The method of finding the center, O, is illustrated in Fig. 25-8, by plotting the angles, β_A and β_B, as shown. Should θ be different from those given in Table 25-1, then β_A and β_B may be interpolated for the angle, θ, in question from Table 25-1. To facilitate interpolation, β_A and β_B graphs based on values as shown in Table 25-1, can be plotted as functions of θ.

25-13. Tension Cracks. If there are tension cracks present in the cohesive soil, then below the depth, z, of the crack, rupture would occur along a curved rupture surface after the shear strength of the cohesive soil is exhausted. The finding of the most dangerous rupture surface is accomplished by the method of trial and error.

The most dangerous condition in the case of tension cracks would occur during rainy seasons when the tension cracks fill up with water and exert a hydro- static pressure horizontally of the mag- nitude of

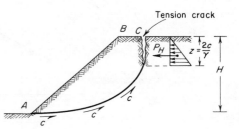

FIG. 25-9   Tension crack.

$$P_H = \tfrac{1}{2}\gamma z^2 = \frac{2c^2}{\gamma}. \qquad (25\text{-}31)$$

This pressure contributes to the total driving moment, see Fig. 25-9. In a (ϕ-c) soil,

$$z = \frac{2c}{\gamma} \tan(\pi/4 + \phi/2). \qquad (25\text{-}32)$$

Frost, evaporation, and shrinkage affect the development of tension cracks and their depth.

25-14. Pure Cohesive Soils—Stability En Masse—Base Failure. If the slope- supporting soil below the toe line of the slope is the same material and has the same properties as the slope-forming material, then there may occur more dangerous rupture surfaces than that passing through the toe of the slope. The "more dangerous" rupture surfaces are deep-seated and are termed base failures (Fig. 25-10).

When AB is a slope of a straight line, then, according to Fellenius, the center, O, of the rupture surface, $\overparen{AC}$, is situated on a vertical line drawn through the midpoint, M, of the slope, AB, so that $a = a$, where $2a = $ horizontal projection of the slope.

When AB is a vertical wall, then the center, O, of rupture surface is located on a vertical line drawn through the vertical wall. The stability analysis is performed by trial and error.

Fellenius did find that for pure cohesive soils the position of the most danger- ous rupture surface associated with deep-seated base failure is located very deep (theoretically infinitely deep), and has the value of the central angle of the circular rupture surface of $2\varepsilon = 133°34'$. However, the cohesion, c_{nec}, needed in the most dangerous rupture surface through a point a little under the toe of the slope, is only slightly less than that needed in the infinitely deep-seated rupture surface:

$$c_{\text{nec}} = \tfrac{1}{4}\gamma H \sin 133°34' = (0.181)\gamma H. \qquad (25\text{-}33)$$

If the value of the cohesion, c, of a cohesive soil is known, then the critical height, H_{crit}, of the slope can be calculated by Eq. 25-33 as

$$H_{\text{crit}} = \frac{c}{(0.181)\gamma}. \qquad (25\text{-}34)$$

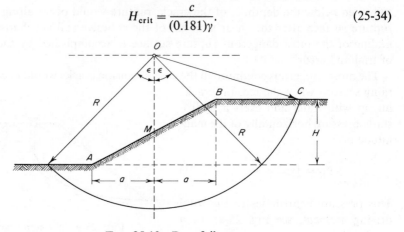

FIG. 25-10 Base failure.

25-15. Stability Number. To facilitate calculations, Ehrenberg,[18] uses for the cohesion a factor of safety, η_c, and calculates an auxiliary value

$$\frac{c}{\eta_c \gamma H} \qquad (25\text{-}35)$$

and, using Krey's $c/(\gamma H)$ graphs,[19] determines the height of the fill, or the angle of the slope, θ, whichever the case is.

To obviate the cumbersome method of trial and error of the grapho-analytical procedure for evaluating the stability of slopes, Taylor,[20] used a simplified method of analysis similar to that given by Ehrenberg, namely:

$$s = \frac{c}{\eta \gamma H}, \qquad (25\text{-}36)$$

where s is termed by Taylor the "stability number". By means of graphs the various problems connected with stability determinations of regular, uniform slopes in homogeneous soil materials can be solved.

It appears, however, that the method of trial and error for fixing the center point of the most dangerous rupture surface is more profitable than the stability number method because most of the soils encountered in earthworks are not homogeneous.

25-16.   Frictional-Cohesive   Soils,   (ϕ-c)-Soils—Stability   En   Masse—Slope Failure. If the slope-forming soil is a (ϕ-c)-soil, one proceeds, in principle, similarly as described for pure c-soils (cf. Fig. 25-11).

Upon rupture, a frictional force, $N \tan \phi$, and a cohesive force, $c\widehat{L}$, are acting in the circular rupture surface. The driving force is $T = W \sin \theta$, and the resisting force is $P = N \tan \phi + c\widehat{L}$. Again, the approximate degree of stability of a (ϕ-c)-slope can be judged from the factor of safety, η, which is calculated based on the position of the most dangerous rupture surface:

$$\eta = M_R/M_D = \frac{PR}{TR} = \frac{(N \tan \phi + c\widehat{L})R}{TR} = \qquad (25\text{-}37\text{a})$$

$$= \frac{N \tan \phi + c\widehat{L}}{T} = \qquad (25\text{-}37\text{b})$$

$$= \frac{W \cos \theta \tan \phi + c\widehat{L}}{W \sin \theta} = \qquad (25\text{-}37\text{c})$$

$$= \cot \theta \tan \phi + \frac{c\widehat{L}}{W \sin \theta} = \qquad (25\text{-}37\text{d})$$

$$= \frac{\tan \phi}{\tan \theta} + \frac{c\widehat{L}}{W \sin \theta}. \qquad (25\text{-}37\text{e})$$

Or else,

$$\eta = M_R/M_D = \frac{\tau \widehat{L} R}{Wa} \qquad (25\text{-}37)$$

where $\tau = \sigma_e \tan \phi + c$ is the general equation for the shear strength of the soil, and

σ_e = effective normal stress on the rupture surface.

Simple as the foregoing equation, Eq. (25-37) appears to be, in reality the stability calculations of slopes with circular rupture surfaces are very complex indeed. For this reason, and in order to obtain a clear insight into the partaking force system in the analysis, the calculations are best to be carried out graphically. The equilibrium equation of moments, $Wa \approx [(\tan \phi)N + c\widehat{L}]R$ when $\eta = 1$ in the case of ϕ and c being simultaneously present, holds only approximately, particularly for small angles of slopes, θ, and, hence, may be used only for rough, preliminary calculations.

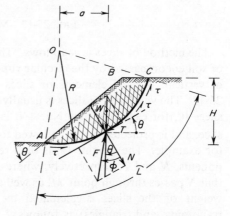

FIG. 25-11   Stability system for a (ϕ—c) soil.

25-17. Pure Cohesive Soils—(ϕ-c)-Soils—Stability Calculations by Method of Slices. If the cross section of a slope-forming body of soil is composed of pure cohesive soil layers, each layer of which has different shear strength properties; if a homogeneous slope is partially submerged; if through a homogeneous dam seepage takes place, or if the earthwork-forming slope is a broken one with steps and berms, then stability calculations of slopes over circular rupture surfaces can be more conveniently performed by the method of slices as originally shown by Petterson (cf. Refs. 11, 12).

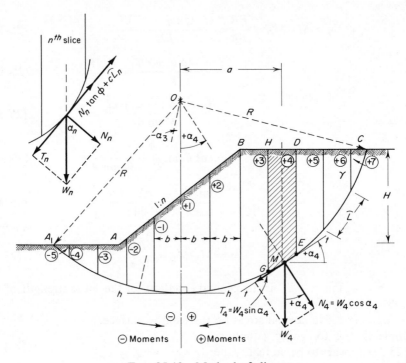

FIG. 25-12   Method of slices.

The method of slices is as follows. The cross section of the slope-forming mass of soil encompassed by the circular rupture surface is subdivided into a number of vertical, parallel elements or slices of equal width, such as shown in Fig. 25-12. The width of the slices is usually taken as $b \approx (0.1)R$. The weight of each slice, W, for example, slice No. +4, is applied at the center of gravity of the slice, and is projected on and allowed to act on the circular arc, $\widehat{GE}$, at point, M, for example. The weight, W, is then resolved into normal and tangential components, N and T, respectively, where $N = W \cos \alpha$ and $T = W \sin \alpha$. Note that N passes through point M, as well as through O, the center of rotation. The weight of the slices is calculated by simplified geometric areas (rectangles, trapezoids, and triangles) as follows:

$$W_n = A_n(1)\gamma, \tag{25-38}$$

where $A(1) = V$ = volume of slice, and
$\qquad \gamma$ = unit weight of soil.

The algebraic sum of the tangential forces of all slices, $\sum T$, tends to shear the soil wedges along the impending circular rupture surface, and is resisted by the total resistance of the soil, $\tan \phi \sum N = c\widehat{L}$, whereby the normal force, $\sum N$, must be the effective normal force.

The advantage of the method of slices lies in the convenience of evaluation of the magnitude of the normal weight component, N, of each slice which permits summing them up as $\sum N$ to be used in stability calculations. Note that the weights of the slices to the right of the vertical through the center of rotation, point O, contribute to driving moments, whereas the slices to the left of the vertical contribute to resisting moments.

The degree of the stability of slope is evaluated by comparing driving moments with resisting moments about the center, O, of rotation:

$$\eta = M_R/M_D = \frac{(\tan \phi \sum N + \sum c\widehat{L})R}{R \sum T}. \tag{25-39}$$

The factor of safety, η, should satisfy in each case the prescribed requirements for η, a magnitude of which should be at least $\eta \geqslant 1.5$.

When $\phi = 0$, then

$$\eta = \frac{\sum (c\widehat{L})}{\sum T}. \tag{25-40}$$

Several circles must be analyzed, and for each circle the factor of safety, η, computed. The least factor of safety among them indicates the most dangerous rupture surface.

The approximate coordinates of the center of rotation, O_c, of the most dangerous circular sliding surfaces through the toe of the slope for (ϕ-c)-soils, for which the factor of safety is a minimum, may be found by trial and error, starting out with Fellenius' directional angles, β_A and β_B, for pure cohesive soils, Fig. 25-13, for which $\phi = 0$. The center O_o of such a circular sliding surface, $\widehat{AC}$, having its center at point O_o, is also shown in Fig. 25-13. In order to find the critical center, O_c for a (ϕ-c)-soil, one may proceed as follows. From Fellenius' graphs it can be noted that the line on which all of the centers $O_o, O_1, O_2, O_3, \ldots O_c \ldots O_n$ line up passes through point O_o and a point K, Fig. 25-13. Point K has the approximate coordinates of $x = (4.5)H$ and $z = H$. Hence, in order to establish the position line O_o-K, find point O_o by means of directional angles, β_A and β_B. Then plot point K with the coordinates $x = (4.5)H$, and $z = H$ as indicated on Fig. 25-13. Then draw through points O_o and K the *position line* on which the centers, $O_1, O_2, O_3, \ldots O_n \ldots$ of the trial circles lie.

Fellenius' graphs show that as the value of ϕ increases, the center O_n of the circular rupture surface moves up from point $O_o (\phi = 0)$ along the position line O_o-K.

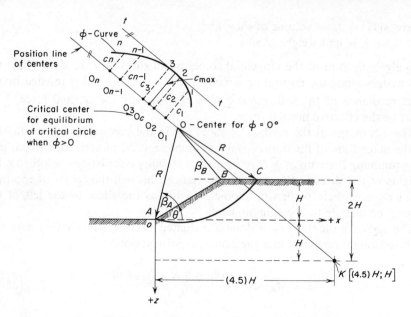

FIG. 25-13   Locating center, O_c, for critical circle.

The stability computation may now be performed as follows. Select on the position line (above O_o) several, say equally spaced, centers, $O_1, O_2, O_3, \ldots O_{n-1}$, O_n, and draw n circles through the toe-point, A. Calculate for each circle the amount of cohesion required to maintain equilibrium for the given value of ϕ of the soil:

$$\sum T = \tan \phi \sum N + c\widehat{L}, \qquad (25\text{-}41)$$

or

$$c = \frac{\sum T - \tan \phi \sum N}{\widehat{L}}. \qquad (25\text{-}42)$$

Then plot these calculated c-values as ordinates to a certain scale on the position line at points of centers for which these c-values were found. For example, plot c_1 at point O_1, c_2 at point O_2, ... and c_n at O_n. Connect the c-ordinates with a curvilinear line 1-2-3-$(n-1)$-n, the so-called ϕ-curve, and draw a tangent, t-t, to the curve and parallel to the position line O_o-K. The tangent to the ϕ-curve then scales off the maximum ordinate $= c_{max}$. This is the maximum value of the cohesion for maintaining equilibrium of the slope for a given ϕ. This maximum c-ordinate gives on the position line $(O_o\text{-}K)$ a point O_c which is the critical center of the critical rupture surface for ϕ and for which the factor of safety, η, is a minimum. With a radius of $R = (O_c - A)$ draw the critical rupture surface, $\widehat{AC_c}$, along which the rupture would most probably take place, divide the slope-forming mass of soil on this circle into slices, determine $\sum T$, $\tan \phi \sum N$ and $c\widehat{L}$

(use ϕ and c obtained from tests of this particular soil), and calculate the factor of safety, η:

$$\eta = \frac{\tan \phi \sum N + c\widehat{L}}{\sum T}. \qquad (25\text{-}43)$$

If this factor of safety is $\eta \geqslant 1.5$, the slope may be considered as stable, If $\eta < 1.5$, the slope, or the height of the slope have to be redesigned.

The calculations can best be performed in a tabular form.

25-18. Example. A slope 1 : 2, the height of which is $H = 45$ ft, is to be made in a $(\phi\text{-}c)$ soil the unit weight of which is $\gamma = 110$ lb/ft^3, the angle of internal friction, $\phi = 7°$, and the cohesive strength is found to be $c = 1200$ lb/ft^2. Compute the factor of safety, η, against rupture of slope. The minimum factor of safety should be $\eta = 2.00$. (Use slide rule).

Solution. (Refer to Fig. 25-14). The critical circle for a pure cohesive soil ($\phi = 0$) is drawn from the corresponding critical center, O_o, ($\eta = 1$). Center O_o is found by means of directional angles $\beta_A = 25°$ and $\beta_B = 35°$. Draw circle C_o, with point O_o as the center. Establish point K, and draw position line $O_o\text{-}K$, extending it beyond point O_o. The critical center, C_c, for the ($\phi\text{-}c$) soil, when $\phi = 7°$, must be found by the method of trial and error. Assume, therefore, on the position line five points, O_1, O_2, O_3, O_4, and O_5, arbitrarily spaced at equal distances from each other. Draw curves C_1, C_2, C_3, C_4, and C_5. Slice up the soil mass above the curves with slices of equal width, $b = 10$ ft to scale, for example. For each curve, determine the weight, W, of each slice, and resolve it into normal and tangential components, n and t, respectively. Because weight is proportional to area, i.e., $w = a\gamma$, where $w =$ weight of slice, and $a =$ area of slice, calculate the area of each slice, and find

$$n = a \cos \alpha \qquad (25\text{-}44)$$

and

$$t = a \sin \alpha, \qquad (25\text{-}45)$$

or find the values of the a-components graphically. The sum of the normal and tangential components of the areas of all slices on one circle is then $\sum n$ and $\sum t$, Table 25-2. The normal and vertical forces, $\sum N$ and $\sum T$, respectively, resulting from the weight of the rupturing soil wedge, ABC, are:

$$N = \gamma \sum n, \qquad (25\text{-}46)$$

and

$$T = \gamma \sum t. \qquad (25\text{-}47)$$

For circles C_1, C_2, C_3, C_4, and C_5, calculate the maximum necessary cohesion c_1, c_2, c_3, c_4, and c_5, plot them at points O_1, O_2, O_3, O_4, and O_5 as ordinates and draw the $\phi = 7°$ line connecting these c_n-ordinates. For example, by Eq. (25-42), the necessary maximum cohesions for $\eta = 1.0$ were found to be

$$c_1 = 397 \text{ lb/ft}^2$$

$$c_2 = 471.5 \text{ lb/ft}^2$$

$$c_3 = 435.0 \text{ lb/ft}^2$$

$$c_4 = 387.0 \text{ lb/ft}^2, \text{ Fig. 25-14.}$$

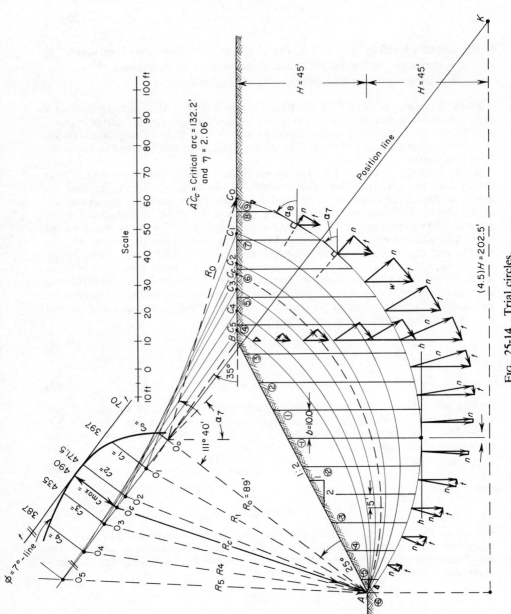

Fig. 25-14 Trial circles.

TABLE 25-2 NORMAL AND TANGENTIAL FORCES

$c = 1200 \text{ lb/ft}^2;\ \phi = 7°;\ \gamma = 110 \text{ lb/ft}^3$

Center of Curve	O_o		O_1		O_2		O_3		O_4		O_c	
Length of Arc	171.0'		153.5'		139.0'		126.0'		116.0'		132.0'	
Forces	n	t	n	t	n	t	n	t	n	t	n	t
Slice Numbers	2		3		4		5		6		7	
-6	12.9	-10.5	6.9	-4.0	7.0	-3.1	7.8	-2.1	5.0	-1.0	9.2	-3.2
-5	107.2	-63.0	88.0	-39.1	69.5	-20.6	59.6	-9.5	54.8	-2.8	71.5	-16.2
-4	206.0	-88.5	168.0	-48.8	145.0	-24.6	124.0	-6.6	114.9	+5.0	140.0	-15.6
-3	{285.0	-84.6	256.0	-43.1	224.0	-12.4	174.0	+9.2	149.0	22.5	{94.8 / 109.0	-2.6 / +3.0
-2	364.0	-63.4	322.0	-18.1	276.0	+15.1	224.0	35.6	175.0	45.0	242.0	27.0
-1	423.0	-24.2	368.0	+20.7	307.0	50.8	244.0	65.7	183.0	68.3	271.0	61.5
1	468.0	+27.8	404.0	68.9	324.0	91.8	248.0	97.5	184.8	92.1	287.0	97.9
2	510.0	88.7	423.0	123.0	324.0	134.4	250.0	120.6	169.5	110.0	284.0	134.8
3	522.0	155.0	396.4	176.0	309.0	173.1	223.0	150.5	127.0	113.8	259.0	165.5
4	508.5	218.5	394.0	228.0	268.0	202.0	169.0	157.0	92.5	102.0	212.0	179.6
5	447.0	263.0	298.0	234.0	177.0	178.0	75.0	94.6	5.9	8.2	187.0	151.2
6	334.1	273.0	195.0	210.0	71.5	103.0	3.8	5.6	—	—	107.7	49.6
7	236.4	256.0	86.3	50.3	8.3	16.5	—	—	—	—	—	—
8	111.5	186.0	4.1	13.8	—	—	—	—	—	—	—	—
9	8.5	23.2	—	—	—	—	—	—	—	—	—	—
Σn and Σt	4544.1	1187.0	3409.9	971.6	2510.3	904.0	1802.2	718.1	1261.4	563.1	2274.2	832.5
η	1.63		2.15		2.11		2.22		3.46		2.06	
2ϵ	111°40'		99°00'		86°00'		76°00'		66°00'		$2\epsilon_c = 82°00'$	
c_{nec}	69.8		397.0		471.5		435.0		387.0		$c_{max} = 490.0$	

Because from O_2 the cohesion drops from $c_2 = 471.5$ lb/ft² to $c_3 = 435$ lb/ft² at point O_3, the analysis of the fifth planned circle was omitted, since the maximum c_c-ordinate must be between points O_1 and O_3. The necessary maximum cohesion, c_{max}, for a soil with $\phi = 7°$ is found to be located at point, O_c, as shown in Fig. 25-14. The value of $c_{max} = 490$ lb/ft² was scaled off the drawing. Through point A is now drawn the critical circle, C_c, with point O_c as the center. This critical circle, with $c = 1200$ lb/ft² (given) is analyzed, and its factor of safety, as well as the factors of safety for the other circles is computed by Eq. (25-43). The critical rupture surface (for $\phi = 7°$ and $c = 1200$ lb/ft²) is revealed to have the least factor of safety, namely, $\eta_c = 2.06 \approx 2.00$. All other factors are >2.00. This indicates that the slope satisfies the prescribed value of factor of safety of 2.0. Therefore, with respect to $\eta = 2.0$, the slope for the given conditions may be considered safe.

The factor of safety for the pure cohesive soil, shown in Column 2, Table 25-2 is $\eta = 1.63$, but such a soil was not given for the analysis. The $\eta = 1.63$ is here shown only for comparison: note that, theoretically, friction adds to the factor of safety.

The slide-rule calculations in this problem are now given to elucidate some of the details involved in the foregoing analysis, and to illustrate the technique of the routine.

Necessary maximum cohesion for equilibrium when $\eta = 1.00$. By Eqs. (25-28) and (25-29),

$$c_o = \tfrac{1}{4}\gamma H f(\theta, \varepsilon, \omega) \tag{25-28}$$

$\theta = 22°; \varepsilon = 55°50'; \omega = 18°30'; \gamma = 110$ lb/ft³; $H = 45$ ft.

$$f(\theta, \varepsilon, \omega) = \frac{2 \sin^2 \varepsilon \sin^2 \omega}{\varepsilon} \cdot$$

$$\cdot [\cot \varepsilon \cot \omega - \cot \varepsilon \cot \theta + \cot \theta \cot \omega - \tfrac{2}{3}\cot^2 \theta + \tfrac{1}{3}] = \tag{25-29}$$

$$= \frac{(2)(0.827)^2(0.317)^2}{0.973} \cdot$$

$$\cdot [(0.679)(2.989) - (0.679)(2.475) + (2.475)(2.989) - \tfrac{2}{3}(2.475)^2 + \tfrac{1}{3}] =$$

$$= 0.564,$$

and

$$c_o = \tfrac{1}{4}(110)(45)(0.564) = 69.8 \approx 70 \text{ (lb/ft}^2).$$

The various angles may be calculated analytically from the geometry of the problem, or, if the drawing is made to a large scale, the angles may be scaled off by means of the protractor. Likewise, the radii, R, of the circles may be established, The lengths of the arcs, $\widehat{L}$, are obtained by calculation. By Eq. (25-42), and with $\tan \phi = \tan 7° = 0.1228$, and $\widehat{L}$ as given in Table 25-2 for the corresponding circles,

$$c = \frac{\sum T - \tan \phi \sum N}{\widehat{L}}, \tag{25-42}$$

$$c_1 = \frac{(971.6)(110) - (0.1228)(3409.9)(110)}{153.5} \approx 397.0 \text{ (lb/ft}^2)$$

$$c_2 = \frac{(904.0)(110) - (0.1228)(2510.3)(110)}{139.0} \approx 471.5 \text{ (lb/ft}^2)$$

$$c_3 = \frac{(718.1)(110) - (0.1228)(1802.2)(110)}{126.0} \approx 435.0 \ (\text{lb/ft}^2)$$

$$c_4 = \frac{(563.1)(110) - (0.1228)(1261.4)(110)}{116.0} \approx 387.0 \ (\text{lb/ft}^2)$$

The maximum necessary cohesion, c_c, for the critical circle, C_c, is scaled off the drawing as $c_{\max} = 490 \ (\text{lb/ft}^2)$.

The factors of safety, η, for circles C_1 through C_4, as well as for C_c, are calculated by Eq. (25-43) as

$$\eta = \frac{\tan \phi \sum N + c\widehat{L}}{\sum T} \tag{25-43}$$

$$\eta_1 = \frac{(0.1228)(3409.9)(110) + (1200)(153.5)}{(971.6)(110)} = 2.15$$

$$\eta_2 = \frac{(0.1288)(2510.3)(110) + (1200)(139.0)}{(904.0)(110)} = 2.11$$

$$\eta_3 = \frac{(0.1288)(1802.2)(110) + (1200)(126.0)}{(718.1)(110)} = 2.22$$

$$\eta_4 = \frac{(0.1288)(1261.4)(110) + (1200)(116.0)}{(563.1)(110)} = 3.46$$

$$\eta_c = \frac{(0.1288)(2274.2)(110) + (1200)(132.0)}{(832.5)(110)} = 2.06,$$

where $c = 1200 \ \text{lb/ft}^2$ is the actual, tested shear strength of the soil.

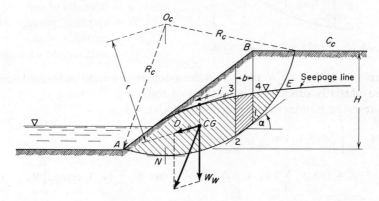

FIG. 25-15 Seepage force, D.

25-19. Seepage Force. In analyzing stability of slopes and the seepage which takes place through the soil, one should not forget to consider in the stability equations the seepage force, D (Fig. 25-15):

$$D = \gamma_w i A(1), \tag{25-48}$$

where γ_w = unit weight of water,
    i = hydraulic gradient,
    A = area $AMDNA$ = cross-sectional area of the dam below the seepage line, AMD.

This hydrodynamic force, D, is applied through the centroid of the soil mass below the seepage line, and is directed parallel to the tangent to the seepage line at a point on the seepage line above the centroid.

The factor of safety in the case of the seepage force present is calculated for the critical circle as

$$\eta = \frac{\tan \phi \sum N + c\widehat{L}}{\sum T + D(r/R)},\qquad (25\text{-}49)$$

where r = moment arm of seepage force, D, with respect to point of rotation, O_c.

Because part of the slices are below water and part above water, the weight of slices, W, is calculated as

$$W = \sum_1^s w = b \sum_1^s (\gamma_d h_1 + \gamma_{\text{subm}} h_2),\qquad (25\text{-}50)$$

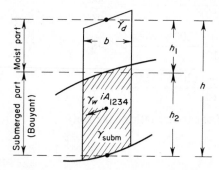

Fig. 25-16,

FIG. 25-16   Partly submerged slice.

where γ_d = unit weight of soil above the uppermost flow line, and
$\gamma_{\text{subm}} = (1 - n)(G - 1)\gamma_w$ = unit weight of the submerged soil,
n = porosity of soil,
G = specific gravity of soil particles, and
γ_w = unit weight of water.

Therefore the terms $\sum N$ and $\sum T$ in the η-equation should be formed according to these partially submerged conditions of soil.

The resisting moment is then generally indicated as

$$M_R = \left[\sum_1^s (c_1 L_1) + \sum_1^d (c_2 L_2) + \right.$$

$$\left. + \tan \phi_1 \sum_1^s (w_1 + w_2)_s \cos \alpha_s + \tan \phi_2 \sum_1^d (w_2)_d \cos \alpha_d \right] R.\qquad (25\text{-}51)$$

The driving moment:

$$M_D = \left[\sum_1^s (w_1 + w_2)\sin \alpha + \sum_1^d w_2 \sin \alpha \right] R + \left(\sum_1^s D \right) r,\qquad (25\text{-}52)$$

where s = number of submerged slices;
    d = number of dry slices, unsubmerged;
    $w_1 + w_2$ = submerged plus dry weight of one slice, respectively.

Factor of safety:

$$\eta = M_R/M_D.$$

The stability of slopes of an earth dam must be evaluated for both the upstream and the downstream sides of the dam.

Fields and Wells[21] describe a modified circular arc method applied in the analysis of the Pendleton Levee failure, where the ruptured soil mass was of an irregular shape differing from those shapes discussed in this book.

25-20. Seismic Forces. In regions of seismic activity the stability calculations of slopes of a dam should also include the seismic forces, because they reduce the margin of safety, or may even bring about the collapse of a structure. Seismic forces are applied at the center of gravity of the body, or at the center of gravity of the section of the body above any horizontal plane passed through the structure. Both horizontal and vertical seismic forces must be considered. The magnitude of a horizontal seismic force, F, is calculated as

$$F = \frac{W}{g}\, a = ma, \tag{25-53}$$

where m = mass of structural body above the horizontal plane being studied,

g = acceleration of gravity, and

a = seismic acceleration, such as the acceleration of the earthquake wave.

In the United States, the value of the seismic factor for a is taken as 0.75, or $a = (0.75)g$ for rock foundations and $a = (0.10)g$ on sand and other soil foundations, where g is the acceleration due to gravity. If the dam is constructed near a live, or active fault, or, if it is founded on loose soil material, higher values of horizontal acceleration are in order.

After studying all the available data on the effect of earthquakes on structures, American engineers have arrived at the following opinion:[23,24] the maximum acceleration, a, of a foundation soil at earthquakes in Japan probably attained a value of 0.5-fold of the acceleration of gravity, i.e., $a = (0.5)g$, where g = acceleration of gravity = 981 cm/sec^2 = 32.2 ft/sec^2. For example, the very severe Japanese earthquake of September 1, 1923, had an acceleration of $a = (0.33)g$. According to Briske,[25,26] the Tokyo Bridge Building Code requires a vertical acceleration of $(\frac{1}{6})g$ coupled with a horizontal acceleration of $(\frac{1}{3})g$. In California the horizontal acceleration, a, is calculated with a seismic factor of 0.25, i.e., $a = (0.25)g$. It is interesting to note that structures which in Japan were designed for $a = (0.10)g$, have survived the most severe earthquakes.[27]

For the design of the San-Francisco-Oakland bridge, the engineers reckoned on a horizontal acceleration of the soil of $a = (0.10)g$ with a period of oscillation of 1.5 sec, corresponding to an oscillation of 56 mm.

The area of a contemplated dam should be subjected to very careful geologic examination, particularly in respect to fault zones. With reference to a possible vibration of the dam induced by earthquakes, or other tremors and shocks, in no instance should a dam be constructed across live faults or in the immediate vicinity of such faults.

Although usually vertical acceleration on structures due to earthquakes is neglected in stability analyses of structures, and regardless of the casual figures for seismic effects here cited, it is imperative that in regions of seismic activity the design of any structure should meet all of the seismic requirements prescribed by the corresponding building codes.[28,29,30]

25-21. Friction-Circle Method. The friction-circle method of stability analysis of slopes is particularly applicable to (ϕ-c) soils. However, the method applies to slopes which are just at equilibrium ($\eta = 1.0$).

The stability analysis by the ϕ-circle method can be performed in two ways, namely: 1) use a known cohesion of soil, c, and find the necessary angle of friction, ϕ_{nec}, for maintaining equilibrium, or, 2) use a known angle of friction of soil, ϕ, and determine the necessary amount of cohesion, c_{nec}, for maintaining equilibrium.

The factor of safety, η_ϕ, relative to friction, in the first case is then expressed as the ratio of the actual angle of friction, ϕ, to the necessary angle of friction, ϕ_{nec}:

$$\eta_\phi = \phi/\phi_{nec}. \tag{25-54}$$

In the second case the factor of safety, η_c, is expressed relative to cohesion as the ratio of the actually available cohesion of the soil to the amount of cohesion, c_{nec}, necessary for maintaining equilibrium:

$$\eta_c = c/c_{nec}. \tag{25-55}$$

The working of the ϕ-circle method, again, is by trial and error, whereby one tries to find for the same slope the most dangerous rupture surface. The principal reasoning in this method is that for a definite ϕ-value (viz., c-value) that rupture surface is the most dangerous one which requires for equilibrium the greatest c-value (viz., ϕ-value).

With reference to Fig. 25-17, the forces of reaction, F, at point N, for example, are directed against the direction of motion of the sliding soil wedge, $ABCNA$. In such a case, it is assumed, based on statics principles, that at the instant of the impending rupture all reactive forces, F, along the circular rupture surface, $\overset{\frown}{AC}$, form with the normal, n-n (point N), to that rupture surface an angle, ϕ, which is the angle of internal friction of the slope-forming soil. Therefore, in the case of a circular-cylindrical rupture surface, all reactions (from under each of the slices) would touch (tangent) a circle, the so-called friction or ϕ-circle, the radius of which is $R_\phi = R \sin \phi$. The ϕ-circle is concentric with the rupture circle of radius R. When $\phi = 0$, there is no ϕ-circle.

In the ϕ-circle system, with a known ϕ, for example, the following quantities are known:

1) magnitude of weight of sliding wedge and its direction of action;
2) direction of reaction, F (under the known angle ϕ with the normal of the rupture surface), though the magnitude of F is not yet known;
3) the direction of the total cohesion, $c\overset{\frown}{L}$ (along the rupture surface, viz., parallel to the chord, $\bar{L} = \overline{AC}$); its magnitude is not yet known.

To find the above-mentioned unknown quantities at equilibrium, the force triangle, viz., force polygon, is used, from which the magnitudes of reactions, F, and the necessary cohesion, c_{nec}, for equilibrium can be determined. In the case of equilibrium, the force triangle must close. From the magnitude of $c_{nec}\widehat{L}$, one determines the necessary cohesion for equilibrium, and compares it with the available cohesive strength of the soil in question:

$$\eta_c = c_{nec}/c_{avail}. \tag{25-56}$$

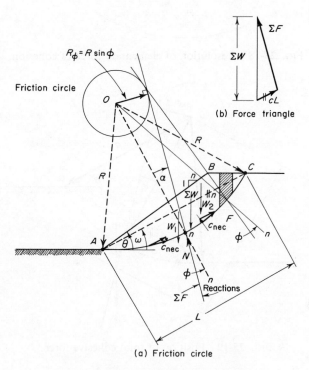

(b) Force triangle

(a) Friction circle

FIG. 25-17   Friction-circle system.

The direction and point of application of the total resultant, necessary cohesive force, $c_{nec}\widehat{L}$, acting along the circular sliding surface, $\widehat{AC}$, is found as follows: assuming a uniform distribution of cohesion over the entire sliding surface, the sum of the components of c_{nec}, of elementary cohesive forces parallel to $\overline{AC} = \overline{L}$, form a total moment, M_c, about point O (Fig. 25-18):

$$M_c = c_{nec}\overline{L}r_c, \tag{25-57}$$

where r_c = arm of the cohesive moment.
The c_{nec}-components perpendicularly to $\overline{AC} = \overline{L}$ are oppositely directed (Fig. 25-19), and do not contribute any moment.

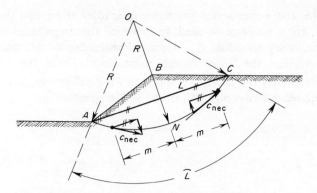

FIG. 25-18   Resolution of elementary force of cohesion.

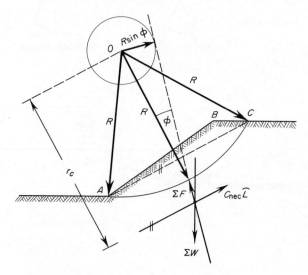

FIG. 25-19   Position of total cohesive force.

This moment, M_c, is, therefore, also equal to the general expression of

$$M_c = c_{nec}\widehat{L}R \qquad (25\text{-}58)$$

or

$$c_{nec}\overline{L}r_c = c_{nec}\widehat{L}R, \qquad (25\text{-}59)$$

or the moment arm, r_c, of the cohesive force is

$$r_c = \frac{\widehat{L}}{\overline{L}}R \qquad (25\text{-}60)$$

Because $\widehat{L} > \overline{L}$ by geometry, then $r_c > R$. Hence, the direction of the total cohesive force, $c\widehat{L}$, to use in the force triangle or polygon, whichever the case is, is parallel to the direction of the chord, AC.

The position of the total cohesive force, cL, in the slope-friction angle system can now be determined by means of r_c, and the direction of $c\widehat{L}$. The point of application, M, of $c\widehat{L}$, is the point of intersection of $c\widehat{L}$ with $\sum W$, through which point, M, the third force, $\sum F$, the reaction, passes so that $\sum F$ is tangent to the friction-circle.

25-22. Remedial Work Against Failures of Slopes. The scope of remedial work against the failures of earthwork slopes comprehends a variety of practices. Some such remedial means are:

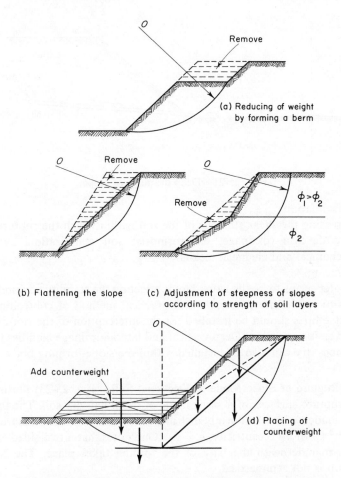

(a) Reducing of weight by forming a berm

(b) Flattening the slope

(c) Adjustment of steepness of slopes according to strength of soil layers

(d) Placing of counterweight

FIG. 25-20   Some means or remedy against rupture of slopes.

1) removing some weight of the slope-forming soil material which tends to cause failure, thus reducing the slope angle and weight of the slope-forming earthwork body as well (see Fig. 25-20). This will reduce the driving moment, thus increasing the calculated factor of safety;

2) providing some external support to hold back the toe of the slope by sheet piling, retaining wall, or counterweight at the toe (Fig. 25-20d), for example;

3) protection against undercutting of the slope;

4) providing a good and appropriate drainage system, thus preventing the water from entering the earthworks. Deep drainage of slope (Fig. 25-21), under some conditions, may be very effective;

5) practicing good maintenance concerning slopes (Fig. 25-22), repair activities, water and snow;

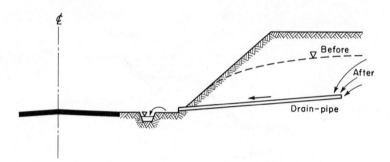

FIG. 25-21   Deep drainage of slope.

6) consolidation;

7) increasing the shear strength of the soil within which the rupture surface may develop (drainage, electrosmosis, soil stabilization by various mechanical and chemical means);

8) surfacing.

Since water seems to be the worst factor affecting the stability of slopes, drainage seems to be the most effective and practical method of controlling slides. Drainage facilities should be installed for the interception of the run-off waters and for diversion of water. Deep vertical and lateral drainage facilities for keeping the slopes dry can also be installed within the slope-forming body of earthworks.

25-23. Rupture of Slope Made of Frictional Soil. (Fig. 25-23) illustrates the shape of rupture surfaces of a slope made of frictional, dry soil. The top of the slope was loaded with a uniformly distributed ultimate contact pressure of $\sigma_o = 2.45$ kg/cm^2 (with no eccentricity, $e = 0$). One notes that a two-sided expulsion of soil from underneath the base of the footing takes place. The two-sided deformation is not symmetrical.

25-24. Summary of the Circular Rupture Surface Method

1) It is assumed that failure of a slope, upon the exhaustion of the shear strength of soil, takes place in shear suddenly along the whole curved rupture surface.

2) The shape of the curved rupture surface is an assumed one, namely that of the circular cylinder.

3) The circularly shaped rupture surface agrees approximately with the real one as observed in practice.

4) The approximate position, or coordinates, of the center of the circular rupture surface is an assumed one determined by the method of trial and error.

5) The average shear is assumed to be distributed uniformly along the predetermined rupture surface.

6) The rupture surface can conveniently be drawn by means of a compass.

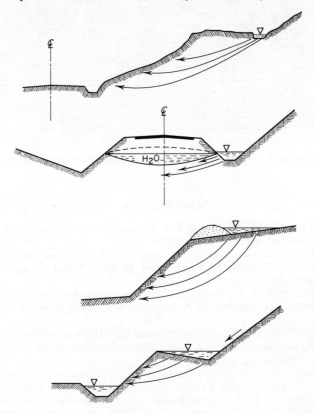

FIG. 25-22   Illustrating some maintenance problems of slopes relative to drainage.

7) The method of trial and error for finding the most dangerous rupture surface is somewhat cumbersome and time-consuming.

8) The calculated factor of safety against the rupture of slopes is not absolute.

9) The interaction of forces between neighboring slices may be neglected.

10) The method of slices is very useful for analyzing the stability of slopes of pure cohesive soils consisting of differing shear strengths. This applies particularly to slopes which are submerged, or if the slope-forming cross section is an irregular one.

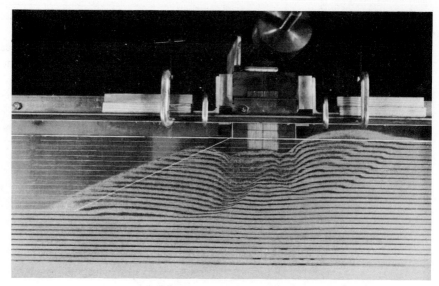

FIG. 25-23   Deformation of slope made of dry sand and brought about by a surcharge
load.

REFERENCES

1. D. F. MacDonald, *Outline of Canal Zone Geology*, Trans. International Engineering Congress, San Francisco, 1915, pp. 67-83.
2. *Memoirs of the National Academy of Sciences*, vol. 18, Report of the Committee of the National Academy of Sciences on Panama Canal Slides, Government Printing Office, Washington, D.C., 1924.
3. W. V. Binger and T. F. Thomson, "Excavation Slopes", *Panama Canal—The Sea-Level Project*, A Symposium. *Proceedings*, ASCE, vol. 74, no. 4, April, 1948.
4. See Ref. 2.
5. W. V. Binger, "Analytical Studies of Panama Canal Slides", *Proceedings*, 2d International Conference on Soil Mechanics and Foundation Engineering, Rotterdam, June 21-30, 1948, vol. 2, p. 54.
6. C. A. Coulomb, *Essai sur une application des règles de maximis et minimis à quelques problèmes de statique relatifs à l'architecture.* Mèmoires de la mathématique et de physique, présentés à l'Académie Royale des Sciences, par divers savans, et lûs dans sés Assemblées, vol. 7, Année 1773. De L'Imprimerie Royale, Paris, 1766.
7. J. Résal, *Poussée des terres*, vol. 2, *Theorie des terres cohérentes.* Béranger, Paris, 1910.
8. J. F. Français, "Recherches sur la poussée des terres sur la forme et le dimensions des revêtements et sur les talus d'excavations", *Memoires de l'Officier de Génie*, Paris, vol. 4, pp. 157-193, 1820.
9. A. Collin, *Landslides in Clays*, Translated by W. R. Schriever. University of Toronto Press, 1956.
10. M. Frontard, Cycloides de Glissement des Terres, Comptes Rendues Hebdomadaires, Academie des Sciences, Paris, pp. 526-529, 1922.
11. K. E. Petterson, "Kajraset i Göteborg den 5te mars 1916". *Teknisk tidscrift*, Stockholm, 1916, nos. 30 and 31; pp. 281-287, and 289-291, respectively.
12. K. E. Petterson, "The Early History of Circular Sliding Surfaces", *Geotechnique*, London, The Institution of Civil Engineers, 1955, vol. 5, pp. 275-296.

13. S. Hultin, "Grusfyllningar för kajbyggnader". *Teknisk Tidscrift*, Stockholm, 1916, no. 31, pp. 292-294.
14. W. Fellenius, "Kaj- och jordrasen i Göteborg", Stockholm, 1918, no. 2, pp. 17-19.
15. W. Fellenius, "Calculation of Stability of Earth Dams". *Transactions*, 2d Congress on Large Dams, held in Washington, D.C., 1936, U.S. Government Printing Office, Washington, D.C., 1938, vol. 4, pp. 445-462, p. 447.
16. Statens Järnvägars Geotekniska Kommision: Slutbetänkande. Stockholm, 1922, p. 57.
17. W. Fellenius, *Erdstatische Berechnungen mit Reibung und Kohäsion (Adhäsion) und unter Annahme kreiszylindrischer Gleitflächen*, Berlin, Wilhelm Ernst und Sohn, 1947, pp. 7-29.
18. J. Ehrenberg, "Standsicherheitsberechnungen von Staudämmen", *Transactions*, 2d Congress on Large Dams, held in Washington, D.C., U.S. Government Printing Office, Washington, D.C., 1938, vol. 4, pp. 331-389, pp. 356-357.
19. H. D. Krey, *Erddruck, Erdwiderstand und Tragfähigkeit des Baugrundes*, Berlin, Wilhelm Ernst und Sohn, 1936 (Table between pp. 172 and 173).
20. D. W. Taylor, "Stability of Earth Slopes", *Journal of the Boston Society of Civil Engineers*, Boston, Mass., July 7, 1937, vol. 24, no. 3.
21. K. E. Fields and W. L. Wells (with discussions by R. Peck, K. Terzaghi, T. A. Middlebrooks, D. P. Krynine and K. E. Fields and W. L. Wells), "Pendleton Levee Failure", *Transactions* ASCE, New York, 1944, vol. 109, p. 1400.
22. L. C. Urquhart, *Civil Engineering Handbook*, New York, McGraw-Hill Book Company, Inc., 1940, p. 800.
23. N. C. Raab and H. C. Wood, "Earthquake Stresses in the San Francisco-Oakland Bay Bridge", *Transactions*, ASCE, New York, 1941, vol. 106, pp. 1363-1384.
24. N. C. Raab and H. C. Wood, *Proceedings*, ASCE, October, 1940, p. 1447.
25. R. Briske, *Die Erdbebensicherheit von Bauwerken*, Berlin, Wilhelm Ernst und Sohn, 1927.
26. Discussion on "The Relationship between Earthquakes and Engineering Substructures", *Proceedings*, ASCE, New York, 1929, vol. 55, pp. 219-227.
27. N. H. Heck, *Earthquakes*, Princeton, N.J., Princeton University Press, 1936, p. 202.
28. J. E. Rinne, "Building Code Provisions for Aseismic Design", *Proceedings*, Symposium on Earthquake and Blast Effects on Structures, held at Los Angeles June 26-28, 1952, Earthquake Engineering Research Institute and University of California, Berkeley, California, 1952, pp. 291-308.
29. H. W. Bolni, "The Field Act of the State of California", *Proceedings*, Symposium on Earthquake and Blast Effects on Structures, held at Los Angeles June 26-28, 1952, Earthquake Engineering Research Institute and University of California, Berkeley, California, 1952, pp. 309-313.
30. F. M. Andrus, "Earthquake Design Requirements of the Uniform Building Code", *Proceedings*, Symposium on Earthquake and Blast Effects on Structures, held at Los Angeles June 26-28, 1952, Earthquake Research Institute and University of California, Berkeley, California, 1952, pp. 314-316.

PROBLEMS

25-1. The slope of a firm, inclined geologic formation is $i = 1 : 10$. Upon this inclined layer rests a mass of unconsolidated soil material, forming a slope angle with the horizontal of $\theta = 45°$. The ground surface, AC, of this soil mass is horizontal ($\delta = 0$). If the unit weight of the (ϕ-c) soil is $\gamma = 110$ lb/ft^3, the angle of internal friction is $\phi = 25°$, the cohesion is $c = 500$ lb/ft^2, and the height of the slope is $H = 15.0$ ft, calculate the factor of safety, η, of this slope.

25-2. If in the above problem the required factor of safety of the slope is $\eta = 1.5$; calculate the height, H, of the slope.

25-3. Given a pure cohesive soil, unit weight of soil, γ, slope angle θ = constant by construction, and height of slope, H. The upper ground surface above the slope is horizontal. Determine algebraically the maximum amount of cohesion in the plane rupture surface for a factor of safety of $\eta = 1.0$, and $\eta = 1.5$.

Also, find the angle, ω, of the most dangerous rupture surface. Express in terms of c, γ, and θ the maximum height, H, to which the slope will stand for $\eta = 1.0$ and for $\eta = 1.5$.

$$\left[c = (\tfrac{1}{2})\gamma H \tan \frac{\theta}{2}; \qquad \omega = \frac{\theta}{2}; \qquad H = \frac{4c}{\gamma} \cot \frac{\theta}{2} \right]$$

25-4. If in Fig. 25-5, $\theta = 40°$, $\delta = 40°$, $H = 15.0$ ft, $\gamma = 110$ lb/ft³, $\phi = 20°$ and $c = 700$ lb/ft², calculate

a) for a $(\phi\text{-}c)$-soil the critical angle, ω, the necessary cohesion to maintain the given slope at a 15.0-foot height, and the factor of safety of such a slope against rupture.

b) Calculate the factor of safety for a ϕ-soil.

c) Calculate the critical slope angle and the necessary cohesion for a pure c-soil to hold the slope at a 15-foot height. Find factor of safety, η.

If the factor of safety in the above solutions are less than 1.5, then calculate the heights of slopes for a factor of safety of $\eta = 1.5$.

d) What should the slope angle θ be for a c-soil for $\eta = 1.5$, and $H = 15.0$ ft?

25-5. The shear strength of a slope (1 : 1.5) of a cut in a cohesive soil is 0.4 tons per square foot. The weight of a circular sliding mass of soil with a slip circle through the toe of the cut is 50,000 pounds per unit depth perpendicular to drawing plane. The radius of the rupture surface is 32 ft. The length of the arc of rupture is 55 ft.

a) Compute the factor of safety against sliding. The length of the rotational moment-arm, a, of the mass of sliding soil wedge with respect to the center of rotation is 11.0 ft.

b) If the factor of safety against sliding were $\eta < 1.5$, propose and sketch remedial measures so as to increase $\eta > 1.5$.

c) Prepare an analytical expression for factor of safety, η, if on the bank of the slope there is a concentrated load, P, distant, d, from the center of rotation, and located within the boundaries of the circular sliding surface. (Assume all necessary reasonable engineering values not given in this problem.)

25-6. Perform stability analysis of the downstream slope of the earth dam as shown in Fig. Problem 25-6. Especially,

a) Show all forces partaking in the system, as well as their magnitudes, points of application, and directions of action;

b) Report and indicate on a drawing the most dangerous rupture surface, as well as the minimum factor of safety obtained in the analysis.

c) Is the slope safe? If not, what remedial works would you recommend in order to increase the safety of the downstream slope?

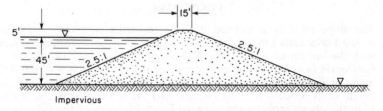

FIG. Problem 25-6.

Given: Unit weight of saturated soil mass, $\gamma_{sat} = 120$ lb/ft³; unit weight of water, $\gamma_w = 62.4$ lb/ft³; specific gravity of soil particles, $G = 2.66$; porosity of soil, $n = 40\%$; angle of internal friction of soil, $\phi = 15\%$; cohesion, $c = 250$ lb/ft².

25- 7. In the problem 25-6, determine the stability of the upstream slope after a rapid draw-down of water.

25- 8. In the Example 25-18, calculate the factor of safety, η, for the most dangerous rupture surface if $\phi = 7°$ and the shear strength of this soil material is $c = 600$ lb/ft² instead of 1200 lb/ft².

25- 9. Write algebraically a formula for the factor of safety, η, for the slope system as shown in Fig. Problem 25-9.

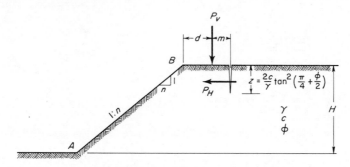

FIG. Problem 25-9 (Stability problem with a tension crack)

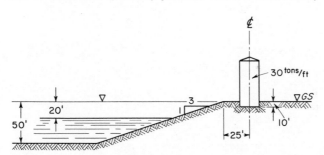

FIG. Problem 25-10 (Stability problem).

25-10. The total height of the slope is 50 ft, and the submerged part of the slope is 30 ft. The slope of the bank is 1 : 3. At the top of the bank a grain elevator is constructed at a center line 25 ft from the edge and exerting a load of 60 tons per linear foot along the shore line of the bank. The soil is a homogeneous clay with a cohesive strength of 700 lb/ft². It has a specific gravity of $G = 2.67$ and a void ratio of $e = 0.57$.

    a) Check the stability and design a safe slope of the partially submerged embankment shown in Fig. Problem 25-10.

    b) Calculate factor of safety, η, if the depth of the water in the basin is 50 ft.

    c) Compute factor of safety if the basin is empty.

    d) Calculate factor of safety if the slope is to be made in a noncohesive soil the angle of internal friction of which is $\phi = 30°$. The specific gravity is $G = 2.65$, and the void ratio is $e = 0.25$.

    e) Calculate factor of safety if the slope is to be made in a cohesive soil the characteristics of which are $\phi = 6°$, $c = 700$ lb/ft², and $G = 2.67$.

f) Calculate factor of safety for the condition of a rapid draw-down of the water level to the bottom of the basin (empty basin).

g) Evaluate stability when the entire slope is covered with an impervious layer (unsaturated embankment).

25-11. The total load on a 4-foot-wide strip foundation is 5 tons per one foot of run of foundation. The footing is founded at a depth of 4 ft in a clay, the shear strength of which is 600 lb/ft^2, and the unit weight is $\gamma = 115$ lb/ft^3.

Assuming that rupture takes place along a circular sliding surface, calculate the factor of safety against shear failure of the soil mass underneath the base of the foundation. Assume that the soil has shrunk away from one side of the footing, and there is no adhesion between the soil on this side of the footing.

Soil Exploration

PART VI

Soil Exploration

Chapter 26

SOIL EXPLORATION

26-1. Introduction. Soil exploration here means technical investigation before any preliminary design is drawn or final plans prepared, by which the necessary information is obtained about geological, hydrological, and soil conditions; geotechnical properties of soil at the prospective building site, and the performance of the various soil types encountered when acted upon by structural and applied loads, water, and temperature. This information is necessary as a background upon which to base the design of a structure, and to decide upon construction methods to be applied.

An engineering structure, however carefully designed, is no better than its foundation-supporting soil. Insufficient or inadequate information with respect to the character and bearing capacity of the underlying soil may result in serious structural damage, or even collapse of the structure.

Soil exploration at a proposed building site is to be considered similar in purpose to the material survey, because soils are construction materials in, or on which, or by means of which civil engineers build structures. This would seem to be so apparent that there would be no extra need to emphasize the importance of soil exploration. However, practice demonstrates that adequate soil exploration is frequently disregarded and even omitted. Lack of time, insufficient funds, or both, are often given as excuses. Cases are known where, due to improper economy or to an attempt to save funds or time, the final cost of the structure exceeded every reasonable limit. The result may even be the failure of the structure itself, thus causing great troubles both to the builder and to the owner. This emphasizes the fact that it is the task of every civil engineer designing any construction work always to give first preference to the factor "safety". The factor "economy" should follow, but after safety. In the light of safety, economic considerations should be regarded as secondary matter. This rule, however, does not exclude the postulate of economical and safe structure.

Besides, timely and intelligently made soil explorations are relatively cheap as compared with the total cost of the structure, or even as compared with the expenditures required merely for the revision of the project and redesigning of the structure to fit the real soil conditions in order to avoid serious trouble.

Efficient, safe, economical design and construction can be achieved only through thorough evaluation of soil conditions under and adjacent to a proposed structure. This, in turn, requires that adequate soil exploration at a proposed site should be made before any design of the foundations of a structure is started, or the purchase of the lot is made. It is best to pay attention to the bearing capacity and other geotechnical properties of soil prior to the purchase of the lot.

26-2. Purpose of Soil Exploration. In general, the exploration of soil at a proposed building site, road, or airfield site has for its purpose:

1) to provide the civil engineer with reliable specific and detailed information as to the locally existing soil and groundwater conditions (under atmospheric pressure, or artesian water) at and near the site in order to enable him to determine, technically, the most efficient and economical type of foundation to use;

2) to provide the builder with accurate information on existing soil conditions, so that the most economical construction method and efficient equipment for building the foundation may be planned and used.

If the groundwater does not affect the design of a structure directly, it may sometimes greatly influence the construction method of the foundation, or earthwork. Therefore, in exploration work the engineer should never neglect to pay attention to the opponent water, that is, to the surface water regime and to groundwater.

By surface water regime is understood the highest flood level, drainage conditions of the area, erosion and washing out of soil and other conditions.

The site exploration should furnish information on groundwater carrying layers, their numbers, depth; position of the groundwater table and its fluctuation; groundwater flow (direction and velocity), and aggressiveness with regard to soil and foundation materials.

The fluctuation of the groundwater table may cause settlements of structures. Also, such fluctuations are very dangerous to foundations constructed on timber piles, especially to their upper sections, and timber rafts. They decay due to variations in the groundwater level. Such a condition is illustrated in Fig. 26-1, showing the foundation of the Boston Public Library. The situation was remedied by methods unaffected by the fluctuation of the groundwater table.

Also, the owner, the engineer, and the builder should be interested in the amount of compression of the soil, viz., the amount of settlement of the structure to be anticipated. The stability of loaded soil against shear failure is likewise important.

For evaluation of these problems, undisturbed soil samples in their natural state should be taken for laboratory treatment.

SOIL EXPLORATION METHODS

26-3. Groups. Soil exploration can be grouped into two parts, namely: 1) preliminary explorations and 2) detailed exploration.

Besides, one distinguishes between a) shallow soil exploration, and b) deep soil exploration.

The shallow soil exploration includes probings, auger borings, test trenches and test pits, shafts, or wells. Deep soil exploration includes test tunnels and deep borings.

26-4. Probings. Probings or soundings are made with the so-called probing or test rod, a steel rod 6 to 13 ft long, $\frac{3}{4}$ to 1 in. in diameter, which is forced into the soil by driving and churning. The sounding rod consists of sections, connected by couplings, the end section of which is pointed and the top section fitting into a driving cap.

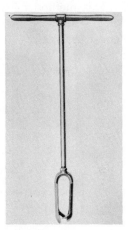

FIG. 26-1 Decayed tops of timber piles caused by fluctuating groundwater table. (Courtesy of the Trustees of the Boston Public Library).

FIG. 26-2 S. and H. Ivan type post-hole auger. (Courtesy of Sprague and Henwood, Inc., Scranton, Pa).

In using such a test rod, the type of soil and some of its properties may be inferred from the resistance felt as the rod is being driven, from the attendant noises, and from the particles of soil adhering to the rod when the latter is pulled up. The information obtained about the soil characteristics using a test rod is very meager and uncertain. Soil exploration by means of a test rod is practiced only for preliminary and shallow explorations. This kind of exploration does not disclose the type of soil through which the test rod penetrates. In order to obtain some sort of soil samples with a test rod, the rod is provided with so-called pockets or grooves which are spaced approximately 12 inches apart along the length of the test rod. Resistance to driving and penetration does not necessarily indicate that rock has been reached. A boulder may be mistaken for bedrock.

Soil exploration by means of a test rod is of limited value. This method, however, is used as a secondary source of information to supplement the information on soil conditions obtained from borings.

26-5. Auger Borings. Auger borings are classified as a shallow soil exploration method. These are made in cohesive soil or in non-cohesive soils above the groundwater table. The post-hole auger, Fig. 26-2, is rotated until filled with soil and then taken up to the ground surface. The soil samples so obtained by auger borings are badly disturbed. However, the auger may also be used for advancing the hole down to the point where undisturbed soil samples are to be taken. The auger is then removed, a sharp-edged soil sampler lowered and forced into the soil, given a half twist, and the undisturbed soil sample withdrawn, conserved, labeled, and provided with identification numbers and other marks of information. In cohesive soils, bore holes without casings may be advanced to a depth of about 30 ft. For greater depth, casing is used for lining the hole. This method of exploration is fairly satisfactory for highway soil exploration at shallow depths, and for exploring borrow pits for locating material for road construction.

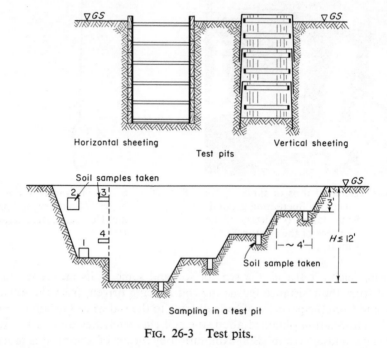

Horizontal sheeting   Vertical sheeting

Test pits

Sampling in a test pit

FIG. 26-3   Test pits.

Auger sample borings may be used for preliminary soil exploration of shallow depths only, and to supplement information on soil conditions obtained from borings. For deep soil exploration borings, shafts and tunnels are used.

26-6. Test Trenches, Pits, Shafts, Tunnels. Test trenches, test pits, Fig. 26-3, test shafts, and test tunnels permit a direct inspection of the soil and its stratification in place, and the taking of adequate disturbed and accurate undisturbed soil samples. Which one of the soil exploration methods is used depends upon the local conditions, design of the type of foundation, and the depth to which the exploration is to be made. Test pits and shafts are excavated to such a size that a man can easily work in them. It will generally be necessary to use timber or steel sheeting to protect the walls of the pits from caving in, and to save the pits for possible future use for additional soil exploration. The soil exploration results must be recorded on a log sheet. An accurate description of the place where the sample was taken must be given in each case.

The size of small test trenches is about 2 to 3 ft in width. Test tunnels have a cross section of about 7 ft × 7 ft, and test pits or shafts, a cross section of about 15 to 20 sq. ft.

Test pits are the most satisfactory method for disclosing the soil strata conditions. Disturbed as well as undisturbed soil samples can be readily obtained. Also, it is possible to take sand samples in their undisturbed state. The cost of test pits increases rapidly with depth; they are uneconomical beyond a depth of about 12 ft. They are particularly impractical when groundwater is to be handled.

All of these explorations are made for the purpose of taking disturbed and mainly undisturbed soil samples for laboratory investigations to determine the geotechnical characteristics of the construction material-soil.

Shallow soil exploration is applied in the case of highways, airfields, and for small and light structures. The shallow exploration methods permit a direct inspection of the soil and its stratification, and the dip of the layers in place. Also, the securing of soil samples is convenient. One of the important tasks in any soil exploration is to attempt to ascertain the position of the groundwater table and its fluctuation, often indirectly indicated by soil color.

26-7. Soil Borings. Soil exploration below the groundwater table is usually very difficult to perform by means of test trenches, pits, and auger-holes. These methods, therefore, are replaced by borings.

Boring is considered a method of deep soil exploration, in fact the most accepted reliable method for this purpose. The boring is put down into the soil mainly for the purpose of obtaining suitable soil samples for performing tests for foundation engineering purposes.

A boring in soil exploration is understood to be a cylindrical hole of a relatively small diameter. Its diameter usually varies from 2 to 8 in.

There are two principal types of equipment for making borings: the cable-tool drilling rig, and the rotary drill. A cable-tool boring rig is shown schematically in Fig. 26-4. The bore-hole in soil is lined with a pipe to prevent the walls of the hole from caving in. The pipe or casing is driven in with a drop weight. The hole is advanced by a chopping bit. The motive power for boring the hole is machine, or man power. The bit is screwed to a hollow drill rod supported on a tripod by a rope or steel cable over a pulley. The drill rod and the bit are hollow, and a stream of water under pressure is forced through the tools downward into the hole. Upon entering the bore-hole at its lower end, the stream of pressure water, or wash water forces up to the surface loosened soil and/or rock particles and other debris in suspension and jets them out of the boring, thus cleaning the bore-hole.

26-8. Wash Borings. The soil suspension from the bore-hole is discharged in a tub, Fig. 26-4. If the tub is shallow or small in volume, the soil-water mixture with the fine particles in suspension goes over the overflow and the fine particles are washed away. The coarser soil particles settle down in the tub. The soil in the tub can be examined, but such an examination, if recorded and logged, gives a wrong impression about the composite soil and its texture because the fine particles such as clays and silts, which contribute to settlement and other negative properties of the soil, are washed away. The type of boring by which the soil samples are recovered from the wash water is generally called a "wash boring". The soil samples obtained from wash borings are disturbed. The soil material recovered from the tub is an inevitable mixture of the coarse soil particles from every layer the bit or drill passed through, and from this mixture it is

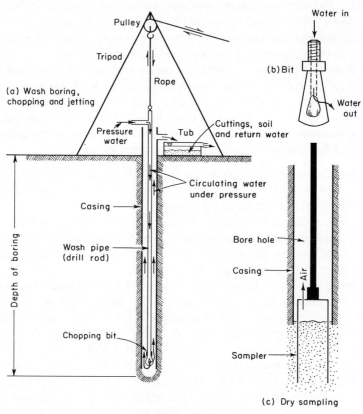

FIG. 26-4 Boring.

almost impossible to interpret intelligently the geotechnical characteristics of a soil obtained by means of so-called "washboring". Therefore, wash boring and soil samples from such borings should not be used for foundation engineering purposes. Soil samples procured from wash water by the method of "wash borings" are unreliable for design purposes.

Warning should be given that soil exploration borings should never be made in the excavation of the foundation at points where the footings would rest where there is an artesian groundwater present because of the danger of over-flooding the pit. A good many construction sites have had to be abandoned for this reason.

26-9. Dry-Sample Boring. The advancement of a dry-sample boring is the same as described under wash borings. When, upon drilling the hole, a change in soil layers is felt, the drill rod is lifted off the bottom of the bore-hole, and washing of the hole continued until the wash water in the casing becomes clean. The chopping bit, or the drill, whichever the case is, is then removed and a cylindrical soil sampling spoon or a seamless, stainless steel sampling cylinder is attached to the drill rod. The sampling spoon or tube is forced into the virgin soil, a 90° twist is made to shear the soil sample off the soil mass, the rod with the soil sample in the sampler is raised out of the hole up to the ground surface, and a "dry soil sample" is obtained. The advancement of the bore-hole is then continued in the usual way until a new "dry soil sample" is taken. Soil samples are taken where a change in soil formations occurs, or, if the soil deposit is thick, soil samples are taken at predetermined intervals.

As the boring operations continue, the soil samples are subjected to visual examination, identified, classified roughly, sealed to prevent moisture loss, and shipped to the soil mechanics laboratory.

In this method, as well as when soil samples are taken by means of a sampling spoon below the groundwater table, the soil samples are not truly dry in the real sense of the word. One remembers that the voids of the soil usually are filled to a certain degree with water. In practice the term "dry soil sample" in this kind of boring is merely a trade designation. However, the soil samples obtained by the "dry" method are not churned up, nor are the soil particles dispersed in a suspension.

Although forcing the soil sampler into the soil causes some disturbance in the soil about the periphery of the sampler, the soil sample thus recovered contains all of its textural contents because practically nothing has been washed away. This is the principal advantage of a dry-sample boring. Dry undisturbed soil samples from deep borings can be obtained with relative ease from cohesive soils. Sands are almost impossible to sample from deep borings in their undisturbed state. The soil exploration method by means of dry-sample borings is one of the most satisfactory methods used today for engineering purposes.

In the course of boring and sampling operations, the number of blows of a 140 lb rammer falling 30″ on a 2″ diameter sampler or spoon to penetrate the sampler 12 inches through a soil is recorded. This test is called the standard penetration test, and gives one a clue as to the strength or bearing capacity of the soil thus tested.

26-10. Mechanical Rotary Soil Drilling Unit. A mobile, mechanical drilling unit, modified after the drilling rigs used in oil drilling operations, has a hydraulic drilling rig mounted on a power truck. It consists essentially of a boom; a drilling mechanism to rotate the soil bit; bit, or diamond core drill; a hydraulic jack to force the sampling tubes into the soil; water supply and pump; a settling tub to contain the recirculating "drilling mud" for coating the inside walls of the boring with an impervious skin of clay, thus preventing water from seeping in and out of the bore-hole and caving it in; a winch to hoist the sampling tubes, and a rammer for performing standard penetration tests into soil with the tube or sampling spoon.

As auxiliary equipment, a pick-up truck is used to carry light soil exploration devices and soil samples, and the water necessary for the drilling operation. The rotary drilling machines have the advantage of getting through rock much faster than other type of machines.

The boring operation starts by ramming a casing 5 ft long down into the soil. After the casing has been driven down, a rotary drill is set to start the hole, with the cuttings (soil and/or rock) being washed out by the drilling mud. The drilling mud is a mixture of bentonite clay and water. The use of the drilling mud is unique in that a casing need not be driven down the entire depth of the bore-hole.

If a compression test is to be performed on a soil sample, the soil sampling devices are forced down into the soil hydraulically in order to obtain an undisturbed soil sample. Small rotary rigs obtain samples by driving.

When rock core samples are necessary, a long tube with a diamond bit is rotated, forcing the rock core up into the tube. Soil or rock samples are taken whenever the soil engineer deems it necessary, or when specified intervals are called for by the designer.

The extruded soil and/or rock samples are examined for color, structure, and other identifying characteristics. Particular attention must be paid to areas where changes in soil layers and soil types occur. The sample is logged on a boring log, the samples are preserved, labeled, and then shipped to the laboratory.

26-11. Soil Samplers. A soil sampler known as the *Shelby tube*, Fig. 26-5, is a thin-walled tube with a sharp cutting edge. This tube is attached to a ball check head. The ball check prevents washing out of the soil sample while being hoisted from the hole. The sampler is used for sampling undisturbed cohesive silts and soft clay. This sampler is to be forced into the soil by pressing or jacking under a steady pressure. After sampling, the sampling tube containing the sampler is detached, its ends sealed and capped, and the unit shipped to the soil mechanics laboratory for further treatment.

The *split-tube sampler* is a tube split longitudinally and held together by a ball check head and a hardened shoe, Fig. 26-6. When the sample is lifted up, and the ball check head and the shoe unscrewed, the sampler opens like a book. Some types of split-tube sampler have a liner in them. Such a sampler is good for plastic soils.

The *stationary-type sampler* resembles a suction pump. Upon pulling the inner plunger rod up, the soil sample is drawn into the sampling tube by holding the piston rod firmly in place and pressing the tube past the piston into the soil. The piston-created vacuum aids in the sampling of "hard-to-hold" fine silts. The piston-type soil sampler is illustrated in Fig. 26-7.

The *solid tube sampler*, Fig. 26-8, is intended for hard driving. It has a ball check, and interchangeable hardened shoe for various soil conditions.

Rather elaborate sampling devices have been devised for obtaining soil samples containing great amounts of water, or having very plastic properties. Such soil samples are "hard to hold" and slide out of the ordinary sampling tube back into the bore-hole.

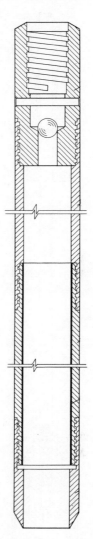

FIG. 26-5 Thin-walled Shelby tube sampler. (Courtesy of Sprague and Henwood, Inc.)

FIG. 26-6 Split tube sampler with liner. (Courtesy of Sprague and Henwood, Inc.)

SOIL SAMPLES

In soil exploration two kinds of soil samples are taken, namely: 1) disturbed samples and 2) undisturbed samples.

26-12. Disturbed Soil Samples. A disturbed soil sample is one whose natural conditions such as structure, texture, density, natural moisture content, and stress conditions, are disturbed.

Disturbed soil samples are sampled by means of a shovel, or obtained from auger borings and deep borings. In disturbed soil sampling, where the sampler

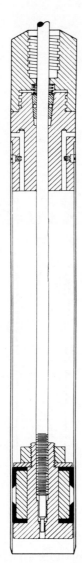

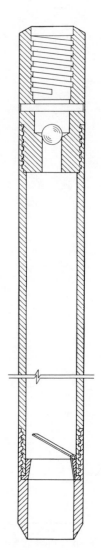

FIG. 26-7 Stationary piston type sampler.   FIG. 26-8 Solid tube sampler. (Courtesy
(Courtesy of Sprague and Henwood, Inc.)   of Sprague and Henwood, Inc.)

penetrates the various soil layers, the different types of soil may become mixed
up, or may lose a comparatively great percent of their moisture content. Also,
the soil texture may be altered by washing away the fine particle fractions.
This can happen when sandy soils are sampled and brought up to the ground
surface through the medium of groundwater. When improperly preserved, and
kept for a long period of time, the soil sample may lose its original color.

Preservation and storing of soil samples in cardboard boxes, match boxes,
loosely covered cans, cigarette boxes, open wood boxes and the like, are not

considered to be good practice; exposed, the soil samples dry out, change their natural color and, in the case of cohesive soils, they often crack. Hence, such soils do not represent the natural prototype soil correctly.

The soil samples should be placed for further study or storage in sealed sampling tubes, paraffined and sealed in wooden boxes, in wide-necked jars, or other containers provided with air-tight lids to protect the sample from evaporation and hardening. In highway engineering practice, for certain soil tests the soils are sampled in bags.

26-13. Undisturbed Soil Samples. An undisturbed soil sample is understood to be one which is removed from the soil in its natural condition without disturbing its structure and the packing of the soil particles. Such a soil sample should retain upon and after sampling all of its original natural physical and mechanical properties such as its structure, density, porosity, moisture content, and the stress condition of the soil. Unfortunately, the term "undisturbed" is only a relative one. This is because physically it is impossible to obtain a soil sample, to transport it, to handle and prepare it for tests in the course of laboratory investigation without disturbing it to some degree. The removal of any sample from its original environment is certain to disturb the sample to some extent. Undisturbed soil samples, therefore, should be sampled and handled with great care. The guiding principle in soil sampling work is to obtain samples which would reflect the soil prototype as nearly as possible.

Undisturbed soil samples, as already mentioned under Dry-Sample Borings, are obtained by forcing a thin-walled, seamless, stainless steel sampling cylinder into the soil at the bottom of the bore-hole, or at the bottom of a test pit, and/or shaft, or in their walls, or in the walls of a soil exploration tunnel. The forcing is accomplished by jacking, or a continuous push.

Undisturbed soil samples are used for testing the shear or compressive strength of the soil, for performing settlement analysis, and for determining the coefficient of permeability of a soil. Undisturbed as well as disturbed soil samples are used for determining the particle size analysis, the consistency limits of the soil, its compaction, and other properties.

26-14. Shallow Sampling. Shallow undisturbed sampling from open test trenches and test pits in cohesive and non-cohesive soils is not difficult to do. In the case of cohesive soils, undisturbed soil samples are cut out and trimmed to the shape of cubes, or obtained by means of a sharp-edged stainless steel cylinder forced into the soil. The cylinder containing the soil is then freed from the surrounding soil mass at the sides. The top of the cylinder is then marked. This is important, particularly when performing permeability tests on these samples, because the permeability of a cohesive soil in a horizontal direction may be different from the permeability in a vertical direction.

The upper end of the cylinder containing the soil is leveled off by means of a straight-edge, and the upper end is covered with a tightly fitted copper or plastic cover cap. Then the soil sample, still in contact with the soil mass at the bottom of the sampling tube, is cut off from underneath by means of a trowel, lifted up, turned upside down, the bottom end (now up) leveled off, and also covered with a cap as the top was covered.

This method is good also for taking non-cohesive samples, sands for example. It is unsatisfactory, however, for sampling gravelly soils because it is difficult to force the sampling device into the coarse-particled soil without disturbing the core seriously.

After securing the soil samples in the cylinders, the joints of the caps are sealed with a waterproof adhesive tape. In case of lack of caps, the ends of the cylinder containing the soil sample may be double-coated with paraffin. The second coat is applied by dipping the ends of the cylinder into liquid paraffin. Then the soil samples are properly labeled and shipped to the soil mechanics laboratory for analyses. Between preserving and labeling the samples and shipping, the samples should not be left lying around in direct sun, or rain, or in freezing weather.

Undisturbed cube samples are coated first with paraffin, then wrapped in gauze, paraffinized, and put in wooden boxes in moist sawdust. The boxes are sealed (they should not be nailed because of vibrations; screws are preferable), labeled, and shipped to the laboratory.

The labels of the soil samples, as well as the sampling log should contain the following information:

1) Date of sampling
2) Locality
3) Number of test pit or bore-hole
4) Number of sample
5) Sampling depth
6) Ground elevation
7) Thickness of soil layer
8) Designation of soil
9) Indication which end of the sample is "up"
10) Method of sampling (disturbed or undisturbed)
11) Sampling tool used
12) Position of groundwater table
13) Atmospheric conditions during sampling time
14) Sampling performed by . . .

26-15. Deep Sampling. This topic has already been discussed under "Samplers" for deep sampling. It can only be added here that generally undisturbed soil samples of cohesive soils from great depths are obtained from boring holes, and normally with fairly satisfactory results. However, the problem of sampling of non-cohesive soils from borings, especially from deep borings at the present time has not yet been solved satisfactorily.

26-16. Boring Log. The results of a soil boring should be documented in a boring log, Fig. 26-9. A boring log contains, for example, the following information:

1) Depth below ground surface
2) Elevation of soil layers and groundwater table

3) Thickness of layers

4) Graphical symbol of the soil type

5) Description of soil

6) Position where soil sample is taken; whether disturbed or undisturbed

7) Sample number

8) Natural moisture content, in percent of dry weight of soil

9) Number of blows of a 140 lb or 300 lb hammer falling 30″ to penetrate a 2″ diameter sampling device or a casing one foot into soil, and

10) Notes indicating position of groundwater table, encountered tree roots, or other pertinent facts.

The boring log should also indicate the title of the project, job and/or contract number, location of the project, the boring number, surface elevation of the boring, date, and the name of the foreman in charge of drilling.

26-17. Boring Report. A boring report should contain

1) Situation plan of construction site drawn to scale and oriented with respect to north.

2) Location plan of borings indicating their coordinates from a reference axis, as well as the elevation of the ground surface at each boring with reference to a permanent surveyor's bench mark.

3) Description of the terrain.

4) Surface drainage conditions.

5) Probable source of free water.

6) Groundwater conditions.

7) The boring log, drawn to a stated scale, and containing information of soil types and thicknesses encountered.

8) Information on eventual difficulties and obstructions encountered in boring operations (sand in "quick" condition, boulders, for example).

9) Soil identification and classification test results.

NEED AND IMPORTANCE OF BORINGS

26-18. Examples of Importance of Borings. The need for borings may be illustrated by the following examples.

1) An excavation 18 ft deep was made in a stiff clay where no borings had been made prior to the work being started. After the excavation reached the indicated depth, a boring was made from the bottom of the excavation. The boring disclosed that 3 ft below the bottom of the pit there was a 30 ft thick layer of soft clay. Under the soft clay layer a firm layer of dense gravel was detected.

The lesson of the condition in this problem is:

a) Had the boring not been made, the foundation would have suffered a comparatively large settlement because of the soft clay, or it might even have broken through the 3 ft thick, stiff clay layer into the soft clay.

b) A timely soil exploration had suggested the use of long piles to transmit the load from the structure to the dense layer of gravel.

c) It would have been possible to use a foundation of a raft type in the layer of stiff clay, excavating the pit so that its bottom would be as close as the

Method of boring: washing
Method of sampling: shelby piston and spoon
Total depth of hole: 59 ft
Size of casing: 4" BX
I.D. of shelby tubes: 2.8 in.
Size of spoon: 2 in.
Surface elevation: + 205 ft.

Hammer: on casing: 300 lb; 30" drop
on spoon: 300 lb; 18" drop
Time of boring operations: from January 10
to January 14, 1961
Date of Log: April 20, 1961
Prepared by A. R. J.

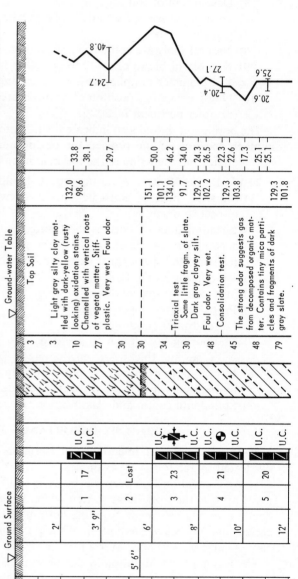

1 Scale of depth below ground surface in feet	2 Depth to layer in feet	3 Depth to bottom of sampling tube in feet	4 Sample tube and Sample Nos.	5 Recovery in.	6 Recovery, Jar sample	7 Soil tests	8 Nos. of blows per foot	9 Symbol	10 Number of blows per foot on casing	11 Description	12 Wet and dry unit weights in lb/ft³	13 Moisture content by dry weight in %	14 Moisture distribution diagram
0.0 ▽ Ground Surface													
1									3	Top Soil			
2		2'	1	17		U.C. U.C.			3	Light gray silty clay mottled with dark-yellow (rusty looking) oxidation stains. Channelled with vertical roots of vegetal matter. Stiff. plastic. Very wet. Foul odor	132.0 98.6	33.8 38.1	24.7
3		3' 9"							10				40.8
4			2	Lost					27			29.7	
5	5' 6"								30	▽ Ground-water Table			
6		6'				U.C.			30		151.1 101.1	50.0	20.4
7			3	23		U.C.			34	Triaxial test	134.0	46.2	
8		8'				U.C.			30	Some little fragm. of slate. Dark gray clayey silt.	91.7	34.0	27.1
9			4	21		U.C.			48	Foul odor. Very wet. Consolidation test.	129.2 102.2	24.3 26.5	
10		10'				U.C.			45	The strong odor suggests gas from decomposed organic matter. Contains tiny mica particles and fragments of dark gray slate.	129.3 103.8	22.3 22.6	20.6
11			5	20		U.C.			48			17.3	
12		12'				U.C.			79		129.3 101.8	25.1 25.1	25.6

Moisture distribution diagram axis: 0   10   20   30   40   50%   P.L. — P.I. — L.L.

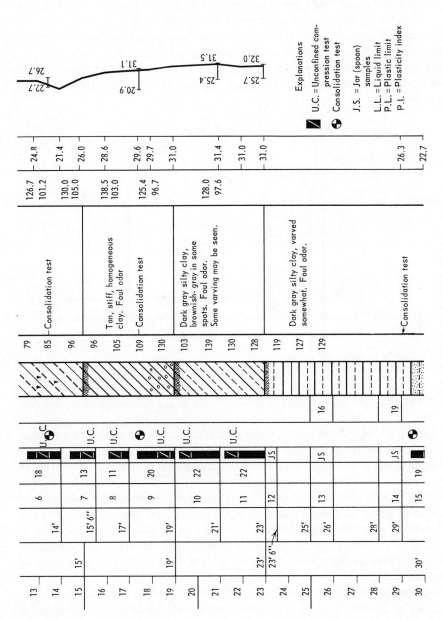

FIG. 26-9 Boring log (D-9).

ground surface as the building code permits (below the frost line). The stiff clay would spread out the pressure of the foundation and would also serve as a protection against squeezing out of the soft clay. Of course, the tolerable settlement should be taken into account.

Much of this reasoning, of course, depends upon the magnitude of the pressure transmitted on the soft clay and the safe bearing capacity of the latter.

Such an analysis would have been possible had the borings been made prior to the start of the excavation work, which would have allowed greater latitude in final decisions.

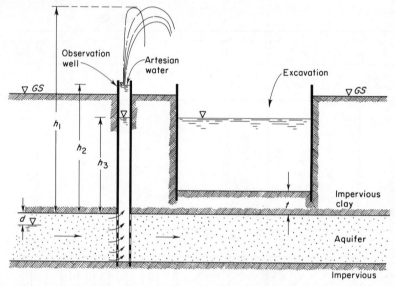

FIG. 26-10   Effect of artesian water on the stability of the bottom of the excavation.

2) Figure 26-10 indicates the possible destruction of a foundation pit excavated in a soil where an artesian groundwater condition prevails. If the impermeable soil layer below the foundation is of insufficient thickness, t, the artesian water pressure may break through the bottom of the pit, inundate it, or even destroy it totally. The various possible heights, h_1, h_2, h_3 above the ceiling of the aquifer (and depth, d, below the ceiling of the aquifer) are sketched in the figure.

If the borings are made prior to the beginning of the excavation work (preferably outside of the perimeter of the proposed excavation), it is possible to evaluate the type of foundation and the method of construction procedure to the best advantage.

If the groundwater in the pervious stratum is not under pressure (note symbol, d, in Fig. 26-10), the level in the observation well would practically coincide with the groundwater table in the pervious stratum.

3) A navigational canal in a heterogeneous, cohesive soil was widened and deepened to permit the passage of vessels of deeper draft. A relatively short time after the earthworks were completed, the newly formed slope of the bank of the

canal ruptured. Borings made prior to the improvement works of the canal did not disclose the thin seam of a fine sand. This layer of fine sand was undercut by the deepening excavation. Groundwater washed the fine sand into the canal and caused the slumping down of the slope of the canal. This phenomenon caused a real concern to the authorities in charge of the canal relative to the maintenance of the slope and the canal at that spot.

AMOUNT OF SOIL EXPLORATION

26-19. Spacing of Borings. The spacing of borings cannot be determined with absolute exactness. They depend upon many factors, for example, the nature and conditions of soil; the shape and extent of the structure, load, and other factors. Therefore, it is difficult to define rules.

However, borings should be so spaced as to detect the various soil layers in sequence, number as well as in type, to determine their extent, course, and dip as precisely as possible in order to disclose variations in these conditions over the entire building site. They should be made in sufficient number to include all the soil layers likely to have a bearing on the construction problem. Where irregularities in soil conditions can be expected, borings are spaced closer. With a uniform course of soil layers a wider spacing is satisfactory.

Furthermore, the spacing of borings should conform to the importance, size, and system of the structure, i.e., whether statically determined or statically indeterminate structures are considered. In case the soil conditions are unknown one usually starts purposely with a network of widely spaced borings, which are called *primary* or *informatory* borings. They are deep borings, and serve to disclose the nature and stratification of the soil and to detect the position of a satisfactory firm soil layer below the active zone. Core borings should be made into rock (if present) deeper than the required design depth. Also, these borings may give a clue as to what method and procedure to use for combating the opponent water in foundation works if groundwater is present. Depending upon the results obtained by means of the informatory borings it may be that the need for more detailed and extensive soil exploration becomes evident. Therefore a second set, called *main* borings, within the network of informatory borings is made at certain points or anywhere necessary, narrowing the network of the first set of borings. These main borings are made for the purpose of following the course, extent, and dip of the various soil layers; and for observation of the groundwater table at equilibrium, its fluctuation, and the draw-down at pumping tests. Usually this set of borings is not as deep as the first set.

To plot accurately the position and extent of the several soil strata and soil pockets in clay beds or clay pockets in sand, and to secure additional soil samples, a third intermediate or supplementary set of borings or test pits is made.

A clue to the spacing of borings is usually obtained from the dimensions of the structure. If its plan is rectangular, borings are made at the four corners.

If the structure is long, intermediate borings are made. Also, soil and water conditions permitting, additional borings are made at the intersections of the diagonals of the plan. When groundwater or artesian water is present, it is advisable not to make the borings in the foundation pit itself or directly underneath the foundation because of the danger of the quicksand phenomenon which may set in, in which case the whole pit may be damaged by the opponent water flowing upward from below under pressure. Fig. 26-11 illustrates some layouts of the different kinds of borings.

If the terrain is totally unknown, one would space borings in quadrants of approximately 120 ft to a maximum of about 300 ft apart. When great changes and variations in the soil pattern are anticipated the spacing of the borings must be such as to comprehend all the changes. In such cases a spacing of the order of 30 to 60 ft is practiced.

For foundations of large engineering constructions, important industrial structures, towers, chimeys, radio towers, one boring should be made at each corner of the structure, and as many more as are required to get a complete characterization of the soil conditions. For such structures borings are spaced not over 50 ft center to center. The depth of the informatory borings should be at least 1.5 times the width of the foundation contact area (refer to sections on Depth of Borings and Pressure Bulb). When particularly heavy, concentrated loads are anticipated, the depth of the borings must be greater.

For bridges and dams, in general, two sets of borings are made. The first set of borings, the informatory ones, is located on the center line of the bridge (Fig. 26-12) or dam. The purpose of these borings is to find out whether the site of the proposed location of the structure furnishes favorable soil conditions for supporting the bridge. If the results are positive, these borings aid in determining the proper position of the abutments and piers of the bridge. The first set of borings is spaced as needed, and carried down well below into the rock if present, to be sure it is not confused with large boulders, or well below into a firm soil layer. One or more of these borings should be drilled at least 20 ft deep into the bedrock; one or more of these borings should be drilled at least 50 ft deep into bedrock at each pier.

After the first set of borings is spaced, the second set of borings—the main borings—is spaced at each abutment and pier. They are located on the longitudinal axes of the piers—upstream and downstream—and on the longitudinal axis of the abutments.

After these, additional or supplementary borings are made at the abutments and piers, as needed, and sometimes some more intermediate borings may be necessary, for example, to ascertain silt pockets in clay beds.

For highways, borings (usually 4-in. or 6-in. post auger borings) are spaced at certain intervals, for example, at 100-ft stations, along the proposed alignment and distance from the center lines at the edges of pavements and edges of shoulders of a new road.

To ascertain the subsurface conditions of the soil thickness of layers, color, structure, consistency, compactness or density, and cementation, borings are made generally 3 to 6 to 12 ft deep either below the bottom of the pavement of the road or below the finished grade in cut sections, or, when very little grading

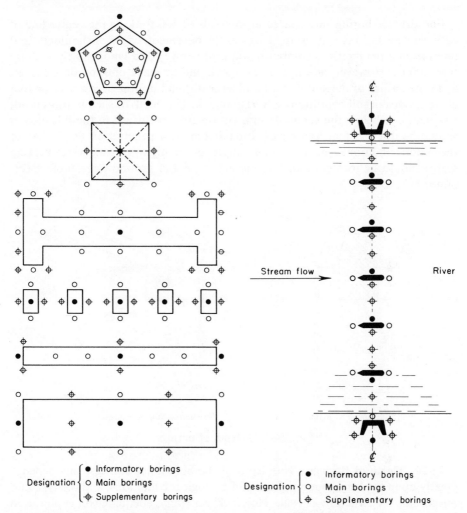

Designation	⬤ Informatory borings
	○ Main borings
	⊕ Supplementary borings

FIG. 26-11 Layout of different sets of borings.

Designation	⬤ Informatory borings
	○ Main borings
	⊕ Supplementary borings

FIG. 26-12 Layout of borings for a bridge.

is required, the borings should be made 6 to 12 ft below the existing natural ground surface, as the case may be.

If the soil is such that these boring tools cannot be operated successfully, it may be necessary to dig test pits. However, the depth of the test pit or boring should be not less than the regional frost penetration depth.

When free water or groundwater is encountered, the borings should be carried through the water-bearing layer, and the groundwater elevation and the direction of flow determined.

Additionally spaced borings may be necessary at culverts, bridges, ramps, weak zones, at transition points from one type of soil to another, wide cuts and fills, in swamps, muck and peat deposits, and borrow pits.

For airfields borings are spaced at intervals of 100 ft along the center line of each runway and taxiway, at the edges of the pavement, edges of shoulders, and intermediate points if the combined width of runway and landing strip is more than 200 ft. However, additional borings should be made until no doubt is left as to the nature of the soil material underneath, and until it becomes clear that all variations in soil conditions can be mapped. The depth of such borings is not less than 6 ft below the subgrade in a cut or ground surface in the fill; also, it should be not less than the regional maximum frost penetration depth. As to the water conditions, the same hints apply as for highways: all water-bearing seams should be located, and the fluctuation of the groundwater table ascertained.

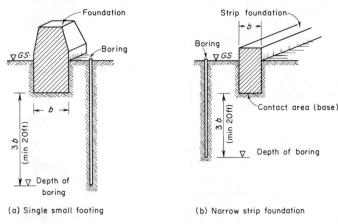

(a) Single small footing   (b) Narrow strip foundation

FIG. 26-13   Depth of borings.

26-20. Depth of Borings. The depth of the bore-holes and test pits depends greatly upon the local topographical and geological conditions, and the type and purpose of the structure as well. However, generally, adequate soil exploration should extend to a considerable depth below the proposed elevation of the base of the footing, or tips of piles. It should include all stressed zones of soil involved in the foundation-soil system. Borings should cover at least all layers of soil which affect the settlement of the structure within the so-called zone or seat of settlement of the soil underneath the foundation. In some cases a few deep borings (primary or informatory borings) are made if by this means a position of a satisfactory firm and continuous layer of soil is detected. From the other set of borings (secondary or main borings), and from a third set of borings (supplementary borings), soil samples are taken. In general, borings should be made down to rock (if in reasonable proximity or depth) or so deep as to leave no doubt as to the character of the soil below.

Usually the depth of the borings is approximately estimated dependent upon the width and load of the foundation (this method, in its turn, is based upon the depth of the stressed zone. For example, for separate, or single footings, or for relatively narrow strip foundation, borings are carried down three times the width of the foundation below the contact area or base of the footing, but not less than about 20 ft below the contact area, Fig. 26-13.

For group foundations consisting of several separate or single foundations, whose influence in pressure distribution overlaps in the deeper strata, and for raft and mat foundations, the depth of preliminary borings is estimated to be one and one half the width of the foundation (or combined width of the foundation in case of a group of footings) below the base of the footings or mats.

According to European practice, the depth to which primary borings are carried down is predetermined considering the average pressure and the least width of the area covered by the structure. By average pressure is here understood the stress, in kg/cm^2, which is obtained by dividing the total load of the structure (dead weight and useful load) over the entire area covered by the structure. Thus, the depth of the borings for narrow and long strip foundations at an average stress up to

1 kg/cm^2 should be one-fold,

up to 2 kg/cm^2 should be two-fold,

up to 3 kg/cm^2 and more should be three-fold

of the least width of the area covered by the structure.[1]

For structures, the side ratio of which is less than 2:1, the depth of borings is according to Ref. 1:

0.8 fold at 1 kg/cm^2 of average pressure,

1.6 fold at 2 kg/cm^2 of average pressure,

2.5 fold at 3 kg/cm^2 and more of average pressure.

For wide-spanned structures, for example, bridges; certain harbor and factory installations, such as portal cranes; or for wide frames or arches as in the case

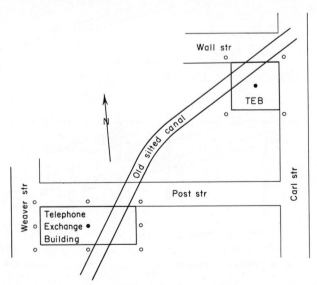

Fig. 26-14   Old silted city canal is not disclosed by borings.

of hangars, market halls, locomotive depot halls or workshops, where the spacing of the foundations is large, the depth of the borings is directed not in accordance with the area covered by the structure but by taking into consideration the actual dimensions of the foundations and the load transmitted by them. However, the depth of such borings should be not less than 30 ft.

Under certain special conditions borings should be carried down deeper. These would include areas where holes or cavities may be expected, as in mining regions when subsidence occurs; when there are yielding, highly compressible layers of materials, such as peat; when the load concentration is heavy, or when special geological and technical conditions obtain.

For pile foundations, the depth of borings is measured below the points of the piles. Here the depth of the borings is sometimes reduced by one-third as compared with and applied to other types of foundations.

26-21. Effect of the Spacing and Depth of Borings on Disclosing Soil Conditions. The effect of the spacing and depth of the borings on the design and performance of soil and structure can be perceived from the following illustrative examples.

1) In a city block two telephone exchange buildings were designed. The structures are located as shown in Fig. 26-14. Borings were spaced in accordance with all the golden rules as shown. Based on the information obtained from these borings, designs were made. However, during the course of excavations it was revealed that both construction sites were traversed by an old, forgotten, silted

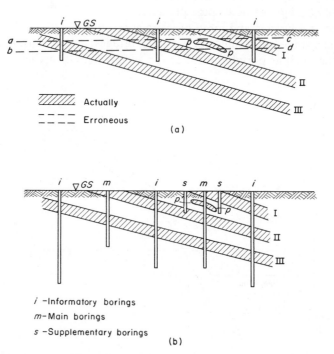

i –Informatory borings
m– Main borings
s –Supplementary borings

(b)

FIG. 26-15   Effect of spacing and depth of borings on disclosure of soil conditions.

city canal, the existence of which was not disclosed by the borings as indicated. The foundations had to be redesigned in favor of piles.

2) Fig. 26-15 illustrates that if borings are not spaced in sufficient numbers and deep enough, the soil profile, constructed according to such data, may be very erroneous. The three informatory borings, i, Fig. 26-15a, if spaced far apart, may give the incorrect impression that there is only one soil layer (a-b-c-) running almost parallel to the ground surface, instead of three dipped layers (I, II, III) of the same material. The pocket or lens, (p-p), is not disclosed at all. Additional borings (m), Fig. 26-15b, would disclose the actual conditions of the stratification. All the borings should be made deeper than shown in Fig. 26-15a.

3) Another effect of the spacing of borings may be demonstrated in connection with clayey soils containing lenses or thin, narrow belts of permeable sand (Fig. 26-16). The profile is erratic, but the interpretation is erroneous. Interpretation

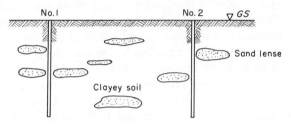

FIG. 26-16 Too wide spacing of borings does not disclose sand lenses in clayey soil.

serves as a basis for design and may result in a great disaster, particularly with sheet piling work. Sheet piling may be driven in clay in the belief it will form an impervious medium for water-holding purposes, whereas if the lower ends of the sheet piling happen to be driven in an undisclosed permeable sand pocket, water may undermine the sheet piling, enter the foundation pit enclosed by sheet piling, fill it with water, and wash out and collapse the sheet piling.

26-22. Cost of Soil Exploration and Soil Testing. Nothing else impresses a civil engineer in charge more deeply than the stubborn conviction of the owner of the structure that soil investigations are unnecessary, or that additional borings are unnecessary, or that they increase the cost of the structure, or that they delay the construction work.

However, if the soil investigation plan is set up intelligently, borings and laboratory soil tests never increase the cost of the project. Rather they decrease it (too often one learns the lesson of a bad soil condition only after failure has occured). Experiences indicate conclusively that in most cases the cost of soil exploration, compared with the total cost of engineering projects, is very small. The relatively small cost involved in soil investigation in a great many instances varies from 1% to 2%, sometimes 3% of the total construction cost. In many instances the cost of exploration of big jobs, depending upon geological and soil conditions, drops even below 1%. For example, Legget,[2] writes that the cost of preliminary work, including geological and geophysical surveys and test drilling of the Bridge River Tunnel, B.C., Canada, was 0.3% of the cost of the tunnel, and that the cost of trial holes and boreholes made for the Battersea Power Station in London was 0.2% of the total cost and 1.5% of the cost of the main building foundations alone.

Soil investigation is of great value in that it furnishes a clear picture of the soil, its behavior under loads and under the influence of water, and the mutual interaction of soil and structure. Money and effort spent for soil investigation are never wasted. It is the cheapest insurance against expensive failures.

ENGINEERING SOIL SURVEY

26-23. Purpose. The purpose of an engineering soil survey is to provide the engineer with a soil materials inventory showing the extent and distribution of the various soil types in relation to other prominent physical and cultural features of the earth's surface. The survey is documented in the form of engineering soil maps and the technical information is embodied in the form of descriptive bulletins, following the principle that one has first to know what types of soil are available in an area. Such an engineering soil survey has been made for the state of New Jersey. The area of New Jersey is of particular engineering signifi- cance because through it all of the major interstate highways radiate out of and into New York, carrying the world's largest traffic volume. In this respect, New Jersey may be considered a heavily traveled corridor state.

In 1955, at the time of the completion of this survey, New Jersey was the first state in the Union to have a complete state-wide engineering survey of the con- tents it represents.

The objective of a soil survey is to identify, classify systematically, correlate, and describe the soil. The bulletins describe the location, distribution, quantity and quality, as well as some geotechnical properties of soils related to locating and relocating road alignments, and finding of suitable road construction material. The ultimate purpose of the survey is to help the engineer dealing with soils and highways to make important decisions in his work in order to facilitate design and construction of good roads.

It is very difficult to give definite instructions for performing an engineering soil survey. The techniques are learned best through contact or serving an apprenticeship with an experienced research group. However, the basic principles underlying an engineering soil survey are sketched in the following paragraphs.

26-24. Soil Maps. In the field reconnaissance work it is very difficult to trace the scope of a soil deposit because of man's inability to see great distances. Therefore the soil mapping was based to a considerable extent on engineering interpretation of aerial photographs. The evaluation of soil patterns and the interpretation of various factors discerned on the aerial photograph is an exer- cise in deductive reasoning. Where the geology and soil patterns and their changes on the aerial photograph revealed to be complex, field work was carried out to clarify the condition. In field reconnaissance work, soil samples were taken and shipped to Rutgers University's Soil Mechanics and Foundation Engineering Laboratory for testing.

The engineering soil survey and the soil test results were described and compiled in appropriate soil bulletins. The soil survey bulletins describe the geologic area, drainage conditions, and discuss from an engineering point of view the performance of the soil in highway work (pumping of joints, possible slides, damage to roads by frost action, suitability of the material for fill, ease and/or difficulty of alignment problems, the size of cuts and fills), and list the engineering test values of the delineated soil types. In other words, emphasis was put on materials which are essential to highway construction.

The resulting engineering soil survey may be considered as something unique, useful, and new in the field of soil exploration and highway technology.[3,4,5,6]

A part of an engineering soil map showing an esker (GE), a kame (GK), glacial lake beds (GL), stratified drift (GS), ground moraine (GM), swamps (Z)

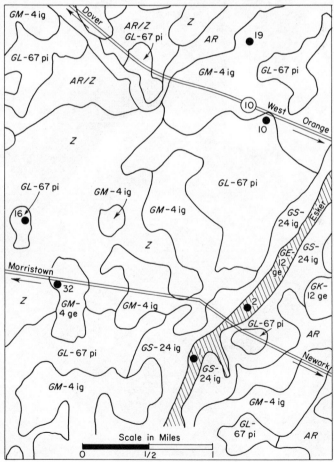

FIG. 26-17 Part of an engineering soil map. Glacial soils. By permission of Rutgers University Press.

and some highways is shown in Fig. 26-17. Black dots on this map indicate points from which soil samples were taken.

26-25. Aerial Photographs. The aerial photographs, mentioned previously in connection with soil exploration and the engineering soil survey, can be combined in a mosaic or photo map (note that the aerial photograph by itself is not a map), such as illustrated in Fig. 26-18 and used successfully as an effective aid in solving certain engineering problems. This figure represents the Round Valley, encompassed by Cushetunk Mountain, in Hunterdon County, N. J., a proposed site of a reservoir. The horseshoe-like geologic feature is a diabase ridge. The dark areas are the shadows the ridges cast. The diabase was intruded into the Piedmont shale, sandstone, and conglomerate where it cooled and solidified beneath

FIG. 26-18 Uncontrolled mosaic of Round Valley, New Jersey. By permission of Aero Service Corp.

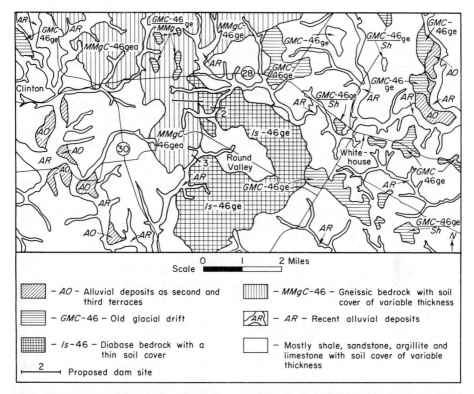

FIG. 26-19   Part of the engineering soil map of the Round Valley area. By permission of Rutgers University Press.

the surface. To keep the reservoir closed, three dams, 1, 2, and 3, Fig. 26-18, and Fig. 26-19, must be built. These three proposed dam sites all lie across the fault zones. The two short dams, represented on the photos as bars, lie across the narrow, deep valleys through which the streams leave Round Valley. The long bar represents the site of a proposed earth dam across a higher, shallow, divided valley.

Water would be obtained from accumulation within the valley, probably augmented by pumping from the south branch of the Raritan River. The New Jersey Department of Conservation and Development explored the nature of the faults at the dam sites to learn whether the fault zones across which the dams are to be built would endanger the dams, or would cause loss of water from the reservoir through the fault zones underneath the dams, and to learn how to cope with these faults for the benefit of the project.

A part of the engineering soil map of the Round Valley area, prepared from aerial photographs, geologic, agronomic and highway base maps, field reconnaissance, soil sampling and testing is shown in Fig. 26-19. Note the horseshoe-like Cushetunk Mountain, the three proposed dam sites, the network of roads (solid lines), and the delineated soil and non-soil areas.

REFERENCES

1. *Directives for Structural Soil Investigation*, 3rd Ed., German Committee for Soil Research, Berlin, Beuth-Vertieb, 1941.
2. R. F. Legget, *Geology and Engineering*, New York, McGraw-Hill Book Co., Inc., 1939, p. 88.
3. A. R. Jumikis, *Engineering Aspects of Glacial Soils of the Newark Metropolitan Area of New Jersey*. Engineering Research Bulletin No. 42, Bureau of Engineering Research, Rutgers—The State University, New Brunswick, New Jersey, 1959.
4. W. W. Holman, R. K. McCormack, J. P. Minard, and A. R. Jumikis, *Practical Applications of Engineering Soil Maps* (Engineering Soil Survey of New Jersey), Report No. 22, Rutgers University Press, New Brunswick, New Jersey, 1957.
5. A. R. Jumikis, W. W. Holman, and J. R. Schuyler, *The Engineering Soil Survey and its Relation to Engineering Problems*, Highway Research Board Bulletin, no. 213, Washington, D.C., 1958.
6. A. R. Jumikis, "Geology and Soils of the Newark (N.J.) Metropolitan Area", *Journal of the Soil Mechanics and Foundation Division*, *Proceedings* of the ASCE, Paper no. 1646, May, 1958, New York.

Other Useful Volumes

7. M. J. Hvorslev, Papers and reports prepared for the Committee on Sampling and Testing, American Society of Civil Engineers: a) March, 1940, b) July, 1940, c) January, 1942, and d) 1943.
8. M. J. Hvorslev, *Subsurface Exploration and Sampling of Soils for Civil Engineering Purposes*, Waterways Experiment Station, Vicksburg, Mississippi, November, 1949.
9. H. A. Mohr, *Exploration of Soil Conditions and Sampling Operations*, Soil Mechanics Series, 21, November, 1943, Graduate School of Engineering, no. 376, Harvard University, Cambridge, Mass.
10. American Society of Photogrammetry, *Manual of Photogrammetry*, 2d ed., Menasha, Wis., George Banta Publishing Company, 1952.
11. D. S. Jenkins, *et al.*, *The Origin, Distribution, and Airphoto Identification of U.S. Soils*, Washington, D.C., Civil Aeronautics Administration publication, 1946.

QUESTIONS AND PROBLEMS

26- 1. What is the most rational method of obtaining soil samples for foundation engineering purposes?

26- 2. Of what value to the engineer is the information on soil conditions obtained by way of sounding with a test rod?

26- 3. Distinguish between a wash sample of soil and so-called dry soil sample. How do they differ fundamentally?

26- 4. What kind of soil samples are sampled for foundation engineering purposes?

26- 5. How deep should borings be planned?

26- 6. List and discuss briefly the various soil exploration methods.

26- 7. What is the purpose of engineering soil surveys?

26- 8. Present a general soil exploration program for a bridge supported by two abutments and three piers spaced 250 ft center to center.

26- 9. If a structure is 40 ft by 100 ft in plan, how deep below the base of the footing of the structure should soil borings be made?

26-10. What are primary and secondary borings?

26-11. What is "drilling mud"? What is its purpose?

26-12. What is a test trench? A test pit? A test tunnel?

26-13. Distinguish between deep and shallow sampling of soils, and between disturbed and undisturbed soil sampling.

APPENDICES

Appendix I

GREEK ALPHABET

A α	Alpha		N ν	Nu
B β	Beta		Ξ ξ	Xi
Γ γ	Gamma		O o	Omicron
Δ δ	Delta		Π π	Pi
E ε	Epsilon		P ρ	Rho
Z ζ	Zeta		Σ σ ς	Sigma
H η	Eta		T τ	Tau
Θ θ	Theta		Υ υ	Upsilon
I ι	Iota		Φ φ	Phi
K κ	Kappa		X χ	Chi
Λ λ	Lambda		Ψ ψ	Psi
M μ	Mu		Ω ω	Omega

KEY TO SIGNS AND NOTATIONS

Symbol	Description
A	Area; shear area; stressed area; specific surface. Also, a coefficient in an equation. Fraction of soil by dry weight
A'	Point on a graph
Å	Angstrom; 1 Å $= 1.10^{-4}\mu = 1.10^{-1}$ mm
A_e; A_{eff}	Effective areas
A_{av}; A_m; A_o; A_t	Areas
ASCE	American Society of Civil Engineers
ASTM	American Society for Testing Materials
AASHO	American Association of State Highway Officials
a	Coefficient; length; acceleration; fraction weight of soil, in percent, retained on a sieve
a_1	Same as above but passing
a_r	Air void ratio
B	Coefficient; constant; fraction of soil; cylindrical surface buoyant force of a liquid
BPR	Bureau of Public Roads
b	A coefficient; length; fraction weight of soil, in percent, retained on a sieve
b_1	Same as before but passing that sieve

749

C	A constant; a constant of integration; a temperature range on the Centigrade scale; a fraction of soil
°C	Degree centigrade
$\mathbb{C}_L$	Center line
CBR	California Bearing Ratio
C_v	Coefficient of compressibility, or compression index
C_s	Expansion index
c	A coefficient; a constant; cohesion of soil; specific heat
c_1	Fraction weight of soil, in percent, retained on sieve. Same passing that sieve
cm	centimeter
const	Constant
cot	cotangent
c_v	Coefficient of consolidation
c_s	Coefficient of expansion
D	Diameter; relative density of sand; dielectric constant; unit seepage pressure; fraction of soil
D_s	Total seepage pressure
DIN	Deutsche Industrie Normen (German Industrial Norms)
d	Differential; a coefficient, diameter; thickness
d_1	Fraction weight of soil, in percent, retained on a sieve; same passing through that sieve
$d_{10}; d_e$	Effective size of soil particle, or 10% diameter
d_{60}	60% diameter of soil particle
dA	Differential of A; differential area
$de = d(e)$	Differential of e (void ratio)
$dH; dh$	Differential of H; differential of h
dm	Length of side of a rectangle in a flow net
dn	Length of side of a rectangle in a flow net
dp	Differential of p; differential of pressure
$dQ; dq$	Differential of Q; differential of q
ds	Differential of s; differential of length of arc
dT	Differential of T; differential of temperature
dt	Differential of t; differential of time
du	Differential of u; differential of neutral stress
dv	Differential of v
dx	Differential of x
dy	Differential of y
dz	Differential of z
$d\xi$	Differential of ξ
∂h	Partial differential of h
∂p	Partial differential of p
∂Q	Partial differential of Q
∂T	Partial differential of T

∂t	Partial differential of t
∂u	Partial differential of u
∂v	Partial differential of v
∂x	Partial differential of x
∂y	Partial differential of y
∂z	Partial differential of z
dT/dt; dT/dx	First derivatives
$\partial T/\partial t$; $\partial T/\partial x$	First partial derivatives
d^2T/dt^2; d^2T/dx^2	Second derivatives
$\partial^2T/\partial t^2$; $\partial^2T/\partial x^2$	Second partial derivatives

E	Modulus of elasticity; soil fraction; earth pressure
E_a	Active earth pressure
E_p	Passive earth pressure (earth resistance)
E_s	Streaming potential
E.L.	Elastic limit
e	Base of natural logarithmic system (2.7182 . . .). Also, void ratio; length; fraction weight of soil, in percent, retained on a sieve
e_1	Fraction of soil, in percent by dry weight, passing a sieve
e_{av}; e_{ave}	Average void ratio
e_f	Final void ratio
e_i	Initial void ratio
e_{max}	Maximum void ratio
e_{min}	Minimum void ratio
e_o	Void ratio at time $t = 0$

F	A function of. Also, force: shear force; gravitational force; seismic force; also, fluidity; also, a temperature range (or number of degrees) on the Fahrenheit temperature scale
°F	Degrees Fahrenheit
$F(x)$	A function of x
f	A function of. Also, coefficient of friction; also, length
ft	Feet
$f(x)$	Function of x

G	Specific gravity of soil particles; also, a symbol for gravelly soil
GK	Glacial kame
GL	Glacial lake bed; also, gelation limit of soil
GM	Ground moraine
GMM	Glacial marginal (terminal) moraine
GO	Glacial outwash
GP	Poorly graded gravel
GS	Glacial stratified drift

G.S.	Ground surface
G_s	Specific gravity of soil particles
G_{T_1}	Specific gravity of soil particles at temperature T_1
G_{T_2}	Specific gravity of soil particles at temperature T_2
GW	Well graded gravel
G.W.T.	Groundwater table
G_w	Specific gravity of water
$G_{w4°}$	Specific gravity of water at 4°C
$G_{w20°}$	Specific gravity of water at 20°C
$G_{4°}$	Specific gravity of soil at 4°C
$G_{30°}$	Specific gravity of soil at 20°C
g	Acceleration of gravity $= 981$ cm/sec^2 $= 32.2$ ft/sec^2; also, gram; also, dry weight of a soil fraction
H	Height; depth; thickness; capillary height; also, a horizontal force; also, a fraction of soil
Hg	Mercury
HRB	Highway Research Board
h	Height; depth; thickness; capillary height; height of outcrop of the uppermost seepage line. Also, fraction weight of dry soil, in percent, retained on a sieve. Also, pressure head.
h_1	Fraction of a soil, in percent, passing a sieve.
h_c	Capillary height
h_o	A particular height
h_{max}	Maximum height
h_{min}	Minimum height
h, h_1, h_2	Height of triangles. Also, thickness of layers of soil
hr	Hour
I	Moment of inertia. Also, electric current
i	Hydraulic gradient
in.	Inches
i_u	Hydraulic pressure gradient
J	Fraction of soil
j	Fraction weight of soil, in percent, retained on a sieve
j_1	Same as above, but passing a sieve
K	Coefficient. A temperature range on the Kelvin scale. Coefficient of heat transmission. Coefficient of Boussinesq's stress distribution in a homogeneous medium.
°K	Degree Kelvin
K_a	Trigonometric earth pressure coefficient for the active case
K_p	Trigonometric earth pressure coefficient for the passive case
K_η	Viscosity correction factor for water

k	Coefficient. Coefficient of permeability of soil
k_{ave}	Average coefficient of permeability. Also, geometric mean permeability
k_{aw}	Permeability when voids are filled with air and water
k_1, k_2, k_3	Coefficients of permeability
$k_{1\perp}$	Perpendicular permeability
$k_{1\parallel}$	Coefficient of parallel permeability
k_h	Coefficient of horizontal permeability
k_v	Coefficient of vertical permeability
km	Kilometer
L	Length or linear dimension. Also, heat of latent fusion
L_o	Length
L.L.	Liquid limit
l	Liter $= 1000$ cm^3
log	Common (Brigg's) logarithm to the base 10
ln	Natural logarithm of, or logarithm to the base of e $= 2.7182$
M	Mass. Also, moment; bending moment. Number of flow channels
$M_2, M_s, M_b{}^s$	Static moments
M_D	Driving moment
M_f	Moment of certain value
M_R	Resisting moment
M_v	Compression modulus
MIT	Massachusetts Institute of Technology
m	Meter. Also, mass
max; max max	Maximum. Maximum maximorum.
min	Minimum
min min	Minimum minimorum
mm	Millimeter
mv	Millivolts
N	An integer. Normal force. Also, number of squares between two adjacent equipotential lines. Also, a variable.
n	Any number. Number of blows. Number of cubes. Porosity of soil. Geometric mean: $n = \sqrt{ab}$. Also, number of equal drops in pressure head.
n_a	Relative volume of air voids
n_s	Relative volume of solid particles
n_w	Relative volume of water in soil
O	Origin of coordinates; a geometric point. Center. Also, zero.
$_o$	Index to various quantities
^{o}	Degree (of temperature or angle).

P	Force; load
P.I.	Plasticity index of soil
P.L.	Plastic limit of soil. Also, plastic limit of steel
PRA	Public Roads Administration
p	Half-parameter of parabola. Total stress. Uniformly distributed load.
p_c	Capillary pressure
p_e	Effective stress
p_i	Initial stress
$p_\circ$	Initial stress. Also, surcharge
p_p	Stress at proportional limit
p_{pr}	Preconsolidation load
p_y	Stress at yield point
p_1, p_2	Pressure
Q, Q_1, Q_2	Discharge; yield
Q.E.D.	*quod erat demonstrandum* (which was to be proved, or shown)
q	Discharge
q_u	Ultimate bearing capacity of soil
R	Radius of influence. Resultant force. Resistance of soil to penetration, or ultimate bearing capacity of pile. Also, relative consistency index (relative plasticity index)
R_{sat}	Relative plasticity index at full saturation
R_w	Relative plasticity index at moisture content w
R_1, R_2, R_3	Reactions
r	Radius
$r_\circ$	Radius of well
r_1	Radius of curvature. Also, inside radius
r_2	Outside radius
S	Degree of saturation. Surface tension. Sandy soil
S.L.	Shrinkage limit of soil
SP	Poorly graded sand
SW	Well graded sand
S_a, S_b	Surface tension forces
S_c, S_t	Surface tension forces
S_d	Saturation deficit
S_r	Degree of shrinkage
s	Specific surface of soil particles. Sensitivity of clay. Settlement of soil. Settlement of structure. Length of base of Feret triangle.
s, s_1, s_2, s_3	Settlements in relative density determinations of sand
s_1, s_t	Settlement
s, s_1, s_2, s_{max}	Draw-down; maximum draw-down

T	Temperature. Variable. Shearing force (tangential force)
T_f	Freezing temperature $= 0°C = 32°F$
T_1, T_2	Temperatures.
t, t_1, t_s, t_t	Time; time intervals.
tan	Tangent of . . .
tan ϕ	Coefficient of internal friction of soil
U	Coefficient of uniformity of soil; also, perimeter
U.S.	Ultimate strength
U.S.C.	Unified soil classification
u, u_t	Neutral stress
u_{h_2}	Neutral stress at depth $(h_1 + h_2)$
u_i	Initial pore water (neutral) pressure
u_o	Pore water (neutral) pressure at time $t = 0$
u_z	Neutral stress at depth $(h_1 + h_2)$
V	Volume; total volume of soil. Volts
V_a	Volume of air
V_f	Final volume of soil sample after drying
V_i	Initial volume of soil sample before drying
V_L	Volume of liquid
V_n	Volume of voids
V_s	Volume of solid particles
V_w	Volume of water
V_1	Volume of cylinder
V_2	Volume of cylinder
V_3	Vibrated volume of sand
v_v, v_{v_1}, v_{v_2}	Specific loss of pore water
W	Weight of soil
W_d	Dry weight. Dry density in soil compaction
W_r	Weight of hammer
W_s	Weight of solids
W_v	Weight of water occupying all voids (saturation)
W_w	Weight of water
w	Moisture content, in percent. Weight of pile
w_G	Moisture content at gelation limit
w_i	Initial moisture content
$w_{L.L.}$	Moiture content at liquid limit
$w_{P.L.}$	Moisture content at plastic limit
w_{sat}	Moisture content at saturation of soil
$w_{S.L.}$	Moisture content at shrinkage limit
w_1, w_2	Moisture contents
x	An unknown quantity. Abscissa. A coordinate
x_1	A coordinate

Y.P.	Yield point
y	A coordinate
z	A coordinate. A variable. Depth of tension crack in cohesive soil.
∇	Symbol to indicate a particular surface, for example ground-water table, or road surface, or ground surface, or any elevation on soil profiles
α (alpha)	A constant. Angle of rupture. Angle of wetting. Slope angle of a line. Angle of discharge face of a dam. Angle of batter. Coefficient of thermal diffusivity $= K/c\rho = K/C = \alpha$
β (beta)	A constant. Angle. Angle of slope of a line
γ (gamma)	Gamma rays. Unit weight
γ_c	Unit weight of concrete
γ_d	Dry unit weight of soil
γ_{Hg}	Unit weight of mercury
γ_s	Unit weight of soil
γ_{sat}	Unit weight of saturated soil
γ_{sub}	Submerged unit weight of soil
γ_w	Unit weight of water $= 62.4 \text{ lb/ft}^3 = 1 \text{ g/cm}^3 = 1000 \text{ kg/m}^3$
Δ (delta)	A symbol for a triangle. Difference. Increment. Decrement
Δe	Amount of compression. Change in void ratio
Δh	Compression. Change in thickness. Frost heave
Δh_1	Deformation
ΔL	Length increment, decrement
Δp	Pressure increment
Δt	Time increment
Δv	Velocity increment. Loss of moisture upon drying. Decrease of moisture
$\Delta x, \Delta y, \Delta z$	Coordinate increments (decrements)
δ (delta)	Angle in theory of relative density of soil. Also, angle of slope of ground surface
$\delta, \delta_b, \delta_c$	Deflection of beam
ε (epsilon)	Strain. Central half-angle
ζ (zeta)	Electrokinetic (zeta) potential
η (eta)	Dynamic viscosity of water. Also, factor of safety; efficiency; frost danger
θ (theta)	Angle of slope with horizontal

λ (lambda)	A coefficient. Ratio. Specific conductivity of water
μ (mu)	A coefficient. Micron: 1 micron $= 1\mu = 1 \times 10^{-4}$ cm $=$ $= 1 \times 10^{-3}$ mm. Also, degree of consolidation Coefficient of internal friction of soil: $\mu = \tan \phi$. Millimicron: $1\mu\mu = 1 \times 10^{-7}$ cm $= 1 \times 10^{-6}$ mm
ξ (xi)	Frost penetration depth
π (pi)	Geometric ratio of circumference of a circle to its diameter $=$ $= 3.14159 \ldots$
ρ (rho)	Radius of curvature. Angle of rupture. Density
$\sum$ (sigma)	Summation of.
$\sum_1^n$	Summation of . . . from 1 to n
σ (sigma)	Stress. Normal stress. Also, surface tension, in dynes/cm
σ_{adm}	Allowable (safe) bearing capacity of soil
σ_a, σ_b	Surface tension stresses
σ_{ave}	Average stress.
σ_e	Effective stress
σ_{max}	Maximum stress
σ_{min}	Minimum stress
$\sigma_{n_{eff}}$	Normal effective stress
$\sigma_\circ$	Surface tension. Contact pressure on soil
σ_R	Radial stress in space (Boussinesq's theory)
σ_r	Horizontal radial stress. Also resultant stress
σ_T	Surface tension at T°C
σ_t	Tangential stress in Boussinesq's theory
σ_{tot}	Total stress
σ_u	Ultimate stress; ultimate bearing capacity of soil
σ_v	Vertical stress
$\sigma_x, \sigma_y, \sigma_z$	Stresses
σ_z	Vertical stress in Boussinesq's theory
σ_1	Major principal stress
σ_2	Intermediate principal stress
σ_3	Minor principal stress
σ_{11}, σ_{12}	Principal stresses in first and second tests
σ_{31}, σ_{32}	
σ^*	Surface tension, in g/cm
τ (tau)	Shear stress. Shear strength. Time factor
τ_1, τ_2	Slope angles of tangents
τ_{max}	Maximum shear stress
τ_r	Remolded shear stress of clay

τ_u Ultimate shear strength of clay

$\tau_{xy}, \tau_{yz}, \tau_{zx}$ Shear stresses

Φ (phi)   Function of. Equipotential line. Angle

ϕ (phi)   Function of. Angle of internal friction of soil. Angle of friction between backfill material and wall. Angle

ψ (psi)   Angle. Designation of a flow line

Ω (Omega)   Angle

ω (omega)   Angle, Amplitude

DYNAMIC VISCOSITY TABLES FOR WATER
DYNAMIC VISCOSITY CORRECTION FACTOR TABLES FOR WATER

Prepared by A. R. Jumikis

In analyzing soil freezing experiment data there is a need for dynamic viscosity values of water in the freezing range of temperatures, as well as for values of viscosity for whole degrees and for every decimal of degrees of temperature in the freezing range as well as in the temperature range above freezing.

The viscosity values found in various publications usually are not given for such close temperatures. Therefore, it was expedient to prepare such viscosity tables, which would be useful for work in connection with studies on freezing soil systems and on soil moisture migration. The viscosity and the viscosity correction tables were calculated and prepared based on N. E. Dorsey's data found in his book entitled *Properties of Ordinary Water-Substance* (New York, Reinhold Publishing Corporation, 1940), the viscosity values for most part of which are based on *International Critical Tables for Numerical Data, Physics, Chemistry and Technology*, published for the U.S. National Research Council by the McGraw-Hill Book Co., Inc., New York, 1929, vol. 5, p. 10.

The published viscosity values were plotted to a large scale on millimeter paper, the viscosity ordinates were connected by a curve, and the viscosity values for each decimal of a degree of temperature were scaled on such a curve and tabulated. The work on freezing soil systems is sponsored by the National Science Foundation, Washington, D.C., and performed in the Soil Mechanics and Foundation Engineering Laboratory of the Department of Civil Engineering at Rutgers. The State University, New Brunswick, New Jersey.

APPENDIX II
DYNAMIC VISCOSITY OF WATER, $\eta[\text{g}/(\text{cm sec})]$ TABLE

$T°C$	0	0.1	0.2	0.3	0.4	0.5	0.6	0.7	0.8	0.9
−10	0.0260	—	—	—	—	—	—	—	—	—
−9	250	0.0251	0.0252	0.0253	0.0254	0.0255	0.0256	0.0257	0.0258	0.0259
−8	240	241	242	243	244	245	246	247	248	249
−7	230	231	232	233	234	235	236	237	238	239
−6	220	221	222	223	224	225	226	227	228	229
−5	0.02140	0.02142	0.02146	0.02151	0.02156	0.02162	0.02168	0.02175	0.02183	0.02191
−4	2050	2060	2067	2075	2083	2092	2100	2110	2120	2130
−3	1979	1980	1987	2000	2007	2015	2022	2030	2036	2044
−2	1910	1915	1922	1930	1935	1943	1950	1956	1965	1972
−1	1840	1847	1853	1860	1866	1873	1880	1887	1895	1902
0	0.01790	0.01795	0.01799	0.01803	0.01808	0.01813	0.01818	0.01824	0.01830	0.01835
0	0.01790	0.01785	0.01778	0.01773	0.01766	0.01760	0.01754	0.01748	0.01742	0.01736
1	0.01730	0.01724	0.01718	0.01712	0.01706	0.01700	0.01694	0.01687	0.01682	0.01675
2	1670	1663	1657	1651	1647	1640	1635	1629	1623	1617
3	1610	1605	1600	1594	1588	1583	1578	1573	1568	1564
4	1560	1555	1551	1546	1543	1539	1535	1531	1528	1524
5	1520	1515	1510	1505	1501	1493	1487	1484	1478	1475

DYNAMIC VISCOSITY OF WATER, $\eta[g/(cm\ sec)]$ TABLE (*continued*)

T°C	0	0.1	0.2	0.3	0.4	0.5	0.6	0.7	0.8	0.9
6	0.01470	0.01466	0.01463	0.01458	0.01454	0.01450	0.01446	0.01442	0.01438	0.01434
7	1430	1426	1422	1418	1414	1410	1406	1402	1398	1394
8	1390	1387	1382	1377	1373	1370	1365	1361	1357	1353
9	1350	1345	1342	1338	1334	1330	1326	1322	1318	1313
10	1308	1305	1301	1298	1293	1290	1285	1282	1278	1275
11	0.01271	0.01268	0.01264	0.01261	0.01258	0.01254	0.01350	0.01246	0.01243	0.01240
12	1236	1233	1229	1226	1222	1218	1215	1212	1208	1205
13	1202	1199	1196	1193	1190	1186	1183	1180	1176	1173
14	1171	1166	1164	1161	1157	1154	1151	1148	1145	1143
15	1140	1136	1133	1131	1128	1125	1122	1119	1116	1113
16	0.01111	0.01107	0.01104	0.01101	0.01098	0.01095	0.01093	0.01090	0.01087	0.01084
17	1082	1078	1076	1073	1070	1068	1065	1062	1059	1056
18	1055	1051	1048	1046	1043	1040	1038	1035	1033	1030
19	1029	1025	1022	1020	1016	1014	1012	1009	1007	1006
20	1005	1003	1000	0998	0995	0993	0991	0988	0986	0983

DYNAMIC VISCOSITY OF WATER, η[g/(cm sec)] TABLE (continued)

$T°C$	0	0.1	0.2	0.3	0.4	0.5	0.6	0.7	0.8	0.9
21	0.00981	0.00979	0.00976	0.00974	0.00972	0.00969	0.00967	0.00965	0.00962	0.00960
22	958	956	953	951	949	947	945	942	940	938
23	936	933	931	929	927	925	922	920	918	916
24	914	912	910	908	906	904	902	900	898	896
25	894	892	890	888	886	884	882	880	788	786
26	0.00874	0.00872	0.00870	0.00868	0.00866	0.00864	0.00862	0.00860	0.00858	0.00856
27	854	852	850	848	846	845	843	841	839	837
28	836	834	832	830	828	826	824	823	821	819
29	818	816	814	812	811	809	807	806	804	802
30	801	799	798	796	794	792	791	788	787	785
31	0.00784	0.00782	0.00781	0.00779	0.00777	0.00776	0.00774	0.00772	0.00771	0.00769
32	768	766	764	763	761	760	758	757	755	754
33	752	751	749	748	746	745	743	742	740	739
34	737	736	734	733	731	730	728	726	725	724
35	722	720	719	718	716	715	714	712	711	709
36	0.00708	0.00707	0.00705	0.00704	0.00703	0.00701	0.00700	0.00699	0.00697	0.00696
37	695	693	692	691	689	688	687	685	684	683
38	681	680	679	677	676	675	673	672	670	669
39	668	667	666	665	663	662	661	660	658	657
40	656	—	—	—	—	—	—	—	—	—

APPENDIX III

DYNAMIC VISCOSITY CORRECTION FACTORS, η_T/η_{20} FOR WATER

Calculated and prepared by A. R Jumikis

$T°C$	0.0	0.1	0.2	0.3	0.4	0.5	0.6	0.7	0.8	0.9
−10	2.58706	—	—	—	—	—	—	—	—	—
−9	2.48756	2.49751	2.50746	2.51741	2.52736	2.53731	2.54726	2.55721	2.56716	2.57711
−8	2.38805	2.40796	2.40796	2.41791	2.42786	2.43781	2.44776	2.45771	2.46766	2.47761
−7	2.28855	2.30845	2.30845	2.31840	2.32835	2.33830	2.34825	2.35820	2.36815	2.37810
−6	2.18905	2.19900	2.20895	2.21890	2.22885	2.23880	2.24875	2.25870	2.26865	2.27860
−5	2.12935	2.13134	2.13532	2.14029	2.14527	2.15124	2.15721	2.16417	2.17213	2.18009
−4	2.03980	2.04975	2.05671	2.06467	2.07263	2.08159	2.08955	2.09950	2.10945	2.11940
−3	1.96915	1.97014	1.97711	1.99004	1.99701	2.00497	2.01194	2.01990	2.02587	2.03383
−2	1.90049	1.90547	1.91243	1.92039	1.92537	1.93333	1.94029	1.94626	1.95522	1.96218
−1	1.83084	1.83781	1.84378	1.85074	1.85671	1.86368	1.87064	1.87761	1.88557	1.89253
0	1.78109	1.78606	1.79004	1.79402	1.79900	1.80398	1.80895	1.81492	1.82089	1.82587
0	1.78109	1.77611	1.76915	1.76417	1.75721	1.75124	1.74527	1.73930	1.73333	1.72736

DYNAMIC VISCOSITY CORRECTION FACTORS, η_T/η_{20} FOR WATER (continued)

$T°C$	0.0	0.1	0.2	0.3	0.4	0.5	0.6	0.7	0.8	0.9
1	1.72139	1.71542	1.70945	1.70348	1.69751	1.69154	1.68557	1.67860	1.67363	1.66666
2	1.66169	1.65472	1.64875	1.64278	1.63880	1.63184	1.62686	1.62089	1.61492	1.60895
3	1.60199	1.59701	1.59203	1.58606	1.58009	1.57512	1.57014	1.56517	1.56019	1.55621
4	1.55223	1.54328	1.54328	1.53830	1.53532	1.53134	1.52736	1.52338	1.52039	1.51641
5	1.51243	1.50746	1.50248	1.49751	1.49353	1.48557	1.47960	1.47661	1.47064	1.46766
6	1.46268	1.45870	1.45572	1.45074	1.44676	1.44278	1.43880	1.43482	1.42084	1.42686
7	1.42288	1.41890	1.41492	1.41094	1.40696	1.40298	1.39900	1.39502	1.39104	1.38706
8	1.38308	1.38009	1.37512	1.37014	1.36616	1.36318	1.35820	1.35422	1.35024	1.34626
9	1.34328	1.33830	1.33532	1.33134	1.32736	1.32338	1.31940	1.31542	1.31094	1.30646
10	1.30149	1.29850	1.29452	1.29104	1.28656	1.28358	1.27860	1.27562	1.27164	1.26865
11	1.26467	1.26169	1.25771	1.25472	1.25174	1.24776	1.24378	1.23980	1.23681	1.23383
12	1.22985	1.22686	1.22288	1.21990	1.21592	1.21194	1.20895	1.20597	1.20199	1.19900
13	1.19601	1.19303	1.19004	1.18706	1.18407	1.18009	1.17711	1.17412	1.17014	1.16716
14	1.16507	1.16019	1.15820	1.15522	1.15124	1.14825	1.14527	1.14228	1.13930	1.13731
15	1.13432	1.13034	1.12736	1.12537	1.12238	1.11940	1.11641	1.11343	1.11044	1.10746

DYNAMIC VISCOSITY CORRECTION FACTORS, η_T/η_{20} FOR WATER (continued)

T°C	0.0	0.1	0.2	0.3	0.4	0.5	0.6	0.7	0.8	0.9
16	1.10547	1.10149	1.09850	1.09552	1.09253	1.08955	1.08756	1.08457	1.08159	1.07860
17	1.07661	1.07263	1.07064	1.06766	1.06467	1.06268	1.05970	1.05671	1.05373	1.05074
18	1.04975	1.04577	1.04278	1.04079	1.03781	1.03482	1.03283	1.02985	1.02787	1.02487
19	1.02388	1.01990	1.01691	1.01492	1.01094	1.00895	1.00696	1.00399	1.00199	1.00099
20	1.00000	0.99761	0.99502	0.99303	0.99034	0.98805	0.98587	0.98328	0.98109	0.97810
21	0.97611	0.97363	0.97114	0.96915	0.96716	0.96437	0.96218	0.96019	0.95721	0.95522
22	0.95323	0.95124	0.95124	0.94626	0.94427	0.94228	0.94029	0.93731	0.93532	0.93333
23	0.93134	0.92835	0.92636	0.92437	0.92238	0.92039	0.91741	0.91542	0.91343	0.91144
24	0.90945	0.90746	0.90547	0.90348	0.90149	0.89950	0.89751	0.89552	0.89353	0.89154
25	0.88955	0.88756	0.88756	0.88358	0.88159	0.87960	0.87761	0.87562	0.87363	0.87164
26	0.86965	0.86766	0.86567	0.86368	0.86169	0.85970	0.85771	0.85572	0.85373	0.85174
27	0.84975	0.84776	0.84577	0.84378	0.84179	0.84079	0.83880	0.83681	0.83482	0.83283
28	0.83184	0.82985	0.82786	0.82587	0.82388	0.82189	0.81990	0.81890	0.81691	0.81492
29	0.81393	0.81194	0.80995	0.80796	0.80696	0.80497	0.80298	0.80199	0.80000	0.79800
30	0.79701	0.79502	0.79402	0.79203	0.79004	0.78805	0.78706	0.78407	0.78308	0.78208

DYNAMIC VISCOSITY CORRECTION FACTORS, η_T/η_{20} FOR WATER (*continued*)

$T°C$	0.0	0.1	0.2	0.3	0.4	0.5	0.6	0.7	0.8	0.9
31	0.78009	0.77810	0.77711	0.77512	0.77313	0.77213	0.77014	0.76815	0.76716	0.76517
32	0.76517	0.76218	0.76019	0.75920	0.75721	0.75621	0.75422	0.75323	0.75124	0.75024
33	0.74825	0.74526	0.74527	0.74427	0.74228	0.74129	0.73930	0.73830	0.73631	0.73532
34	0.73333	0.73233	0.73034	0.72935	0.72736	0.72636	0.72437	0.72238	0.72139	0.72039
35	0.71840	0.71641	0.71542	0.71442	0.71243	0.71144	0.71044	0.70845	0.70746	0.70547
36	0.70447	0.70348	0.70149	0.70049	0.69950	0.69751	0.69651	0.69552	0.69353	0.69253
37	0.69154	0.68955	0.68855	0.68756	0.68557	0.68457	0.68358	0.68159	0.68059	0.67960
38	0.67761	0.67661	0.67562	0.67363	0.67263	0.67164	0.66965	0.66865	0.66666	0.66567
39	0.66467	0.66368	0.66268	0.66169	0.65970	0.65870	0.65771	0.65671	0.65472	0.65373
40	0.65273	—	—	—	—	—	—	—	—	—

SUBJECT INDEX

AUTHOR INDEX